YALE UNIVERSITY

MRS. HEPSA ELY SILLIMAN

MEMORIAL LECTURES

EVOLUTION AND ENVIRONMENT

*A Symposium Presented on the Occasion of
the One Hundredth Anniversary of the
Foundation of Peabody Museum of Natural History
at Yale University*

Edited by Ellen T. Drake

New Haven and London, Yale University Press, 1968

Foreword

by A. W. Crompton, Director

The Peabody Museum of Natural History, Yale University, celebrated its centennial during 1966 and in commemorating this event we attempted to look forward into the future rather than dwell on the past history of this institution. The boundaries of the typical concept of a museum are rapidly changing; perhaps not rapidly enough. I feel that the future of natural history museums is assured only if they are willing to break down classic barriers and definitions and to become involved in and adapt themselves to current science. It is essential that museum research develop a broader base than the classic systematics and descriptive sciences which have dominated the intellectual efforts of natural history museums up to the present time. The papers published in this volume are several of the invited contributions that were read at the symposium held at Yale University on October 26, 27, and 28, 1966, and are examples of the type of exciting and stimulating research work that we wish to see undertaken within or associated with museums of earth and life sciences in future years. A major frontier for science in the immediate future will be the application of the recently acquired techniques and spectacular results of modern experimental biology to the broader scene of organic diversity in all its aspects and interrelationships. It is here that museum-based research can perhaps make its greatest contribution.

A tradition has become established for Yale and the Peabody Museum to award the Verrill Medal to distinguished naturalists and sponsors of natural history. Five medals were presented at the banquet terminating the Centennial celebrations in 1966. In choosing the recipients, we searched for persons who had furthered areas and disciplines that we felt should be the main concern of natural history museums now and in future years. We chose to do this rather than to honor persons who had devoted their lives to the more traditional pursuits of natural history museums. Medals were presented to Theodosius Dobzhansky for his work on the nature of species and mechanisms of adaptation, to Richard Stockton MacNeish for his important work on the origin of New World agriculture, to Ernst Mayr for his work on evolution and natural selection, to Norman Dennis Newell for his pioneering work in the field of paleoecology, and to George Gaylord Simpson for his magnificent achievements in the field of vertebrate paleontology and for his clarification of the process of evolution.

It was my original intention to place the articles in this volume in the order of presentation by the contributors within the five half-day sessions of the Peabody Museum Centennial Symposium, October 26–28, 1966. The sessions of the original program were: I, Symposium on Ethnobotany; II, Symposium on Evolutionary Processes at the Population Level; III, Symposium on the Evolution of Physiological Adaptation; IV, Symposium on Paleoecology; V, Symposium on the Origin of Major Groups. A few of the papers that were read are being published elsewhere. The wide diversity of subject matter covered in the sixteen articles in this volume is obvious, but one can perceive among the seemingly autonomous disciplines a general feeling of continuity and interdependence which was the essence of the spirit of the Centennial Celebrations. The papers have been rearranged in an almost reverse order from the program, but chronologically in the history of life on earth—starting with the concepts of the origin of life itself and ecological considerations past and present, through the evolutionary processes in the light of recent research advances, and ending with man's control of his environment. *Evolution and Environment* thus is an integration of diverse and far-reaching ideas.

I wish to acknowledge with gratitude the guidance and counsel provided by A. W. Crompton, Director of Peabody Museum, throughout the preparation of the entire volume; the kind help from the chairmen of the five sessions, Professors H. C. Conklin, C. L. Remington, T. L. Poulson, A. L. McAlester, and A. W. Crompton, with whom many technical problems were discussed and solved; the generous assistance of Mrs. Nancy Ahlstrom whose aid in handling numerous problems was invaluable; the artistic skill of Ward Whittington who retouched or redrew many of the illustrations for reproduction; and finally the cordial and prompt cooperation I received, without exception, from each of the contributors.

Corvallis, Oregon   Ellen T. Drake
May 1967

Contributors

Harlan P. Banks, Department of Botany, Cornell University, Ithaca, New York

Stanley D. Beck, Department of Entomology, University of Wisconsin, Madison

Harold C. Brookfield, The Research School of Pacific Studies, The Australian National University, Canberra

William G. Chaloner, Department of Botany, University College London, England

Bryan C. Clarke, Department of Zoology, University of Edinburgh, Scotland

Preston E. Cloud, Jr., Department of Geology, University of California, Los Angeles

H. Barraclough Fell, Museum of Comparative Zoology, Harvard University, Cambridge, Massachusetts

James E. Heath, Department of Physiology and Biophysics, University of Illinois, Urbana

Walter G. Kühne, Lehrstuhl für Paläontologie, Freie Universität, Berlin, Germany

Léo F. Laporte, Department of Geological Sciences, Brown University, Providence, Rhode Island

Richard Levins, Committee on Mathematical Biology, University of Chicago, Illinois

Kenneth S. Norris, Department of Zoology, University of California, Los Angeles

J. M. Rendel, Division of Animal Genetics, Commonwealth Scientific and Industrial Research Organization, Epping, New South Wales, Australia

Francis G. Stehli, Department of Geology, Western Reserve University, Cleveland, Ohio

Frank C. Vasek, Department of Life Sciences, University of California, Riverside

Douglas E. Yen, Bernice P. Bishop Museum, Honolulu, Hawaii

In addition to the formal papers, various informal talks were given at the Symposium by the following invited discussants. Space does not allow for the publication of their remarks, some of which were almost of article length. However, they have contributed no less to the significance of this volume, since in many cases the discussions affected the revisions of the papers.

ETHNOBOTANY
Hugh C. Cutler
David J. Rogers
J. E. Spencer
William C. Sturtevant

EVOLUTIONARY PROCESSES AT THE POPU-
LATION LEVEL
Paul R. Ehrlich
C. S. Holling
David Lack
Richard C. Lewontin

EVOLUTION OF PHYSIOLOGICAL ADAPTATION
W. D. Billings
W. Frank Blair
William R. Dawson
Donald S. Farner
Malcolm S. Gordon

PALEOECOLOGY
Elso S. Barghoorn
Alfred G. Fischer
John Imbrie
John W. Wells
Ralph G. Johnson

ORIGIN OF MAJOR GROUPS
G. Evelyn Hutchinson
K. A. Kermack
Everett C. Olson
Theodore Delevoryas
Elwyn L. Simons
John R. Napier

Contents

Preston E. Cloud, Jr.

1. PRE-METAZOAN EVOLUTION AND THE ORIGINS OF THE METAZOA[1]

Nothing perishes in this great universe, but all varies, and changes its figure. I think that nothing endures long under the same appearance. What was solid earth has become sea and solid ground has issued from the bosom of the waters.

Ovid, Metamorphoses

My first task in preparing a discussion of the origins of the Metazoa was to ascertain what I might add that had not already been said by Steinböck (1937), Hyman (1940, p. 248–53), Hardy (1953), Hadži (1953, 1963), de Beer (1954), and Kerkut (1960, p. 36–49). In considering this, it became apparent that opportunity for a contribution by me lay in assessment of the geological and paleontological events that had to take place before the Metazoa could arise.

My mission, therefore, is not to present a solution but to try to place a problem in perspective. Hence many lines of evidence must be explored. What kinds of ancestral organisms would be consistent with what is known of the anatomy, embryology, and physiology of existing and fossil Metazoa? How closely can we identify the times and order of appearance of different metazoans in the fossil record? What were the environmental conditions and changes at and preceding the first appearance of fossil Metazoa? What sorts of organisms were available for metazoan ancestors when the Metazoa arose? In short, what would be a credible and testable model of biospheric, hydrologic, and atmospheric conditions and

1. Research from which this paper is an outgrowth was supported from 1949–61 by the U.S. Geological Survey, from 1961–63 by grants from the Graduate School of the University of Minnesota, during 1964 and 1965 by National Science Foundation Grant GP–1807, and from October 1965 by the University of California at Los Angeles. For criticisms and suggestions useful in revision of an early draft, I am especially indebted to G. E. Hutchinson, I. R. Kaplan, H. L. James, Lynn Sagan Margulis and A. R. Palmer. This paper is dedicated to the late Professor Charles Schuchert, who made it possible for me to do my graduate work at Yale by employing me there; to Professor Emeritus Carl O. Dunbar, who supervised my work there; and to Dr. G. A. Cooper, who pointed me that way.

See Appendix B for definitions of technical terms and abbreviations.

evolution extending from pre-Metazoan or Cryptozoic time into the Phanerozoic Eon and Paleozoic Era?

In attempting to construct such a model it is necessary to make two assumptions. The first and self-evident assumption is that there was a necessary and close relationship among the separate evolutions of biosphere, atmosphere, hydrosphere, and crustal lithosphere—a principle of evolutionary interaction if you like. The second, not demonstrable but essential to a scientific treatment of geologic problems, is that the fundamental laws of nature have operated in essentially the same manner as today throughout geologic time—in effect the concept most modern geologists hold of the principle of uniformitarianism, not to be confused with gradualism.

I am keenly aware of the pitfalls that await the person who attempts to coordinate in short space the evidence from the diverse fields of scientific effort which relate to the questions here discussed, or who is so timid in his presentation that he leaves no clear framework for further construction or target for attack. Indeed it is possible to examine the problem in the space available only because (in addition to references mentioned) of the appearance during 1966 of important reviews by Miller and Horowitz, Mazia, Abelson, and Glaessner; of a slightly earlier summary of chemical evolution by Calvin (1965); and of the compilation by my former colleague A. R. Palmer, especially for this paper, of the records of first appearances of Metazoa in the western United States. With apologies, then, only for the inevitable deficiencies and oversights, and with the necessary acknowledgment that almost the only original thing about this story is the way it is put together, let me get on with it.

BASIS FOR CONSTRUCTIVE DISCUSSION

To begin with, what is meant by a metazoan? The term as used here does not denote simply a many-celled animal, as metaphyte is used informally to designate a many-celled plant. In that case there would be no difference between a colonial protozoan and a metazoan. The crux of the matter is that, whereas both the metaphytes and their protistan predecessors absorb nutrient and essential gases over a large part of their external surfaces, so that a complete gradation from singlecelled to relatively complex multicelled plants is seen repeatedly or easily visualized, the change from protist to metazoan involves a fundamental revision of feeding methods, oxygen transfer, and related anatomy. In order to capitalize on the metabolic advantage of larger size combined with heterotrophic oxidative metabolism, a metazoan characteristically requires a mouth and digestive system, a circulatory system for oxygen distribution, and a nervous system to control these and related processes. Such characteristics define the Metazoa in a strict sense. Exceptions to the rule involve special circumstances of adaptation, environment, or, probably, evolutionary transition.

In a much broader but less discriminating sense we may define a metazoan as a multicelled animal in which there is more than one kind of somatic cell. Such a definition includes all animals not Protozoa—that is the Metazoa in a strict sense, or Eumetazoa, plus the sponges, or Parazoa, an entirely aberrant and independent group, which, like the Protozoa, derive their oxygen directly from the surrounding water by diffusion instead of by means of special oxygen-carrying and circulating body fluids like those of the Eumetazoa. I believe that it leads to more interesting questions to think of the animal kingdom as consisting of three subkingdoms; the Protozoa (or animal Protista), the Parazoa (sponges), and the Metazoa (Eumetazoa)—plus perhaps a fourth, the parasitic Mesozoa. Even under a restricted definition, however, I hope it will become clear that a polyphyletic origin for the Metazoa cannot be excluded. We should be prepared to entertain the possibility that their appearance in the geologic record may represent the more or less simultaneous attainment of a metazoan grade of organization from different preexisting protistan or even metaphytic stocks.

Discussion of metazoan origins has usually been limited by a very widespread assumption for which there is no unequivocal evidence. This restrictive assumption is that a large fraction of geologic time must have been involved in traveling a monophyletic route from some ancestral protist to recognizable and fossilizable metazoans. The Metazoa, in this view, must extend far down into the Precambrian or Cryptozoic record, and argument has centered on the nature of the ancestral protist, the first metazoan, and the steps by which other Metazoa arose from this ur-metazoan. Whether or not the central assumption of previous models eventually proves to be true, however, it has not as yet led to conspicuously clarifying insights. It is worth exploring, therefore, what kind of a model can be constructed from only the evidence actually available now—not from that we may expect to find someday.

My explorations of this possibility and examinations of evidences for Precambrian life, beginning in 1948, indicate that a model different from those previously advanced is, in fact, possible, if not necessary. It incorporates many aspects of previous models but differs from them in requiring neither a very long (hundreds of millions of years) and as yet uncertain record of preskeletal metazoan evolution nor a monophyletic origin. It is also consistent with the record of lithospheric evolution and with deductions drawn from this and other lines of evidence.

In thus suggesting alternatives to widely accepted views my aim is to keep the discussion open and to focus and heighten the search for new and more critical evidence.

PRE-METAZOAN EVOLUTION

In considering the origin of the Metazoa under any definition and assumptions, of course, it is necessary to have some idea of what came before, in terms both of organisms and environmental conditions. I propose to go clear back to the origin of the earth, and of life. Such a viewpoint is germane, among other reasons, because it matters whether the life that preceded metazoan life had a single or a multiple origin.

Unless life has always existed or has been specially created, neither of which is an acceptable hypothesis so long as there is an alternative with verifiable corollaries, it has arisen spontaneously on the earth or elsewhere and been brought here. In either case it is of interest to see how far back the record of life on earth can be taken, and to consider what the conditions on earth might have been at that time. Would they have been conducive to the spontaneous origin of life, or, if viable transport through irradiated space is assumed, to its persistence after arrival?

Atmosphere and Hydrosphere of the Primitive Earth

Of critical concern is the nature of the early atmosphere and hydrosphere. Life could not arise or persist in the presence of either free O_2 or of DNA-inactivating ultraviolet radiation in the range of 2,500–2,600 Å unless it arose or arrived fully equipped with oxygen and peroxide-reducing enzymes, resistance to radiation, and the capacity for chemosynthetic or photosynthetic manufacture of its own food. As early as 1897, T. C. Chamberlin was arguing that the earth resulted from the aggregation of cold particles and that gravitational heating of this aggregate caused the atmosphere to be generated from occluded gases within. This gave rise to the view, articulated by Kelvin (1899), Clarke (1924), and Eskola (1932), that the source of the persisting atmosphere and hydrosphere should be sought in volcanic gases, which included N_2, CO_2, H_2O, and H_2, but no free O_2, these being the gases that are found in crystalline occlusions in igneous rocks. This concept was reinforced by Russell and Menzel in 1933, who first pointed out that gross deficiencies of the noble gases in the terrestrial atmosphere, when compared to cosmic ratios, require that, *if* there was a primary atmosphere it escaped the earth's gravity field during an early episode of high temperatures (5,000 to 8,000° K).

Such views, and the facts on which they are based, have since been elaborated and refined by many (e.g. Poole, 1941, 1951; Rubey, 1951, 1955; Brown, 1952; Urey, 1952a-c, 1957; Hutchinson, 1954; Poldervaart, 1955; Grundland, 1959; Holland, 1962; Sagan, 1965; Abelson, 1957, 1966). Among these, the writings of Rubey, Brown, and Hutchinson have had the most far-reaching influence. All agree, however, that there was no source of free oxygen in the primitive atmosphere except from photolytic dissociation of H_2O (or CO_2, Abelson 1957). Some consider, from postulated equilibrium reactions or from analogy with the larger planets, that CH_4 and NH_3 were major gases (e.g. Brown, Urey, Hutchinson, Grundland). Others take the view, from other equilibria or geologic evidence, that methane and ammonia were unlikely major constituents, and that some mix of CO_2, H_2O, N_2, H_2, and CO was more likely (e.g. Poole, Rubey, Abelson).

The rarity of carbonate rocks and abundance of cherts among the oldest sedimentary rocks testify to a pH too low to be consistent with more than trivial amounts of free ammonia in either atmosphere or hydrosphere as early as about 3.4 billion years (BY) ago. Also, as Abelson (1966) emphasizes, if either methane or ammonia had been common constituents of an initial atmosphere, they would have been lost along with the xenon, krypton, and neon. Moreover, an episode of heating sufficient to bring about the loss of all but a fraction of any initial atmosphere that may have existed would have eliminated any forms of life that might have arisen (or arrived) before that time. And, in advance of gravity stratification with formation of a core and magnetic field, the solar wind would probably have swept the surface of the earth, tending to denude it of atmospheric gases of whatever source and rendering it uninhabitable. Hence we may use as a starting atmosphere for biogenesis only one which may conceivably arise from volcanic sources.

Abelson (1966), drawing on concepts summarized by Sillén (1961), suggests that the buffering effect of weathered silicates would maintain the pH of ocean waters somewhere between about 8 and 9 from the onset of outgassing. Even if the pH were somewhat less than this, it would limit the amount of free CO_2 in hydrosphere and atmosphere. Most of the outgassed H_2O would condense and precipitate, and the atmosphere from somewhere around 3.5 BY (or earlier) onward would most likely consist in the main of CO, N_2, H_2, H_2O comparable to that of the present atmosphere, and probably somewhat more CO_2 than now. This would be an anoxygenous or "reducing" atmosphere, in which such free O_2 as was produced by photolytic dissociation and circulated to the surface of the earth would be rapidly consumed in the oxidation of reduced materials then abundant at the earth's surface.

Chemical Evolution and the Origin(s) of Life

The abiogenic origin of many organic molecules from simple starting materials under anoxygenic conditions has now been accomplished, with a variety of energy sources used to produce the combining reactions. The first reported synthesis of an amino acid was that of alanine by A. Strecker in 1850 (Meister, 1965, p. 5–6), who produced it by treating acetaldehyde-ammonia with HCN and HCl. This is the so-called Strecker synthesis, whereby a synthetic aminonitrile goes, on hydrolysis, to the corresponding amino acid. The origin of life was not a problem at that time, however, except to a few people like Charles Darwin (Fox, 1960; Ponnamperuma, 1965), and the matter went no farther until W. Loeb, in 1913 (Grundland, 1959), produced glycine by electric discharge through a mixture of CO_2, NH_3, and H_2O. Again the synthesis excited little interest. A great problem was demanding attention, but the minds of those who might have taken it up were dominated by a simplistic interpretation of Pasteur's results—"life only from life" (which Pasteur never claimed).

It remained for J. B. S. Haldane in 1929 (Haldane, 1954, p. 15) and again in 1932 to point out, with credit to the (unpublished?) work of Baly and associates at Liverpool, that UV irradiation of a credible starting atmosphere devoid of O_2 would produce "a vast variety of organic substances" (Haldane, 1932, p. 155)—his now famous, but no longer hot, "hot dilute soup." Haldane, it might also be mentioned, appears to have been among the first of many to state unambiguously the obvious conclusion that initial life generated under such conditions would not only be anaerobic, or better, anoxygenic, but almost certainly also heterotrophic (preceded by Loeb, 1913, per Grundland, 1959). For neither life (before oxygen defenses) nor its predecessor molecules could arise or persist in the presence of free O_2, and to consider that first life was capable of manufacturing its own building materials (autotrophic) would be to postulate the miraculous.

The stage was now set. A new era of conceptual and experimental investigation into the nature of first life was being launched, and Oparin's great book, *The Origin of Life* (1953, original 1936), was to be its *Golden Bough*. The end of the wartime scientific lull is identified by the publication of N. H. Horowitz's insights on the evolution of biochemical syntheses (1945), and by further consideration of primitive energy sources by Haldane (1944) and Giese (1945).

The first modern experimental work, utilizing radioactive tracers resulting from the same war, was done by Garrison and others in Calvin's laboratory (1951), on a CO_2-rich atmosphere, and by Miller in Urey's laboratory (1953) on a methane-ammonia atmosphere. And a now-classic volume (no. 16) of the Penguin Books' New Biology Series, appearing in 1954, summarized the views to that time of Haldane, Bernal, Pirie, and Pringle on what Pirie likes to call biopoiesis. Subsequent developments are now common knowledge. Hundreds of experiments with various energy sources and assumed atmospheric compositions have been performed in a dozen or more laboratories; and a geological component has been introduced into the discussion as a result of small interdisciplinary conferences (Woodring, 1954; Cloud and Abelson, 1961) and a book by Rutten (1962). The results of these experiments are summarized by Miller and Horowitz (1966), along with a good bibliography of modern investigations. And Abelson (1966) has presented additional results obtained with high-energy UV and geologically probable starting atmospheric conditions.

One result of these investigations seems particularly significant. Under a variety of possible (and some unlikely) anoxygenous starting compositions, acted upon by a variety of energy sources (electric discharge, 2,400–2,900 Å UV, heat, and X-irradiation), three important molecules are prevalent: hydrogen cyanide (HCN), formate (COOH), and formaldehyde (HCHO). And from these can be made, in an aqueous anoxygenous environment, under other reasonable primitive earth conditions, a variety of amino acids, purines, sugars, lipids, and even peptides and polypeptides (Ponnamperuma and Peterson, 1965).

Reported syntheses of the pyrimidine uracil (Fox and Harada, 1961; Oró, 1963) do not meet defensibly primitive earth conditions, nor do reported syntheses of nucleotides, ATP or other high-energy phosphate combinations, or porphines (see Miller and Horowitz, 1966; Szutka, 1965). Synthesis of polynucleotides, nucleic acids, and enzymes from starting materials of nonvital origin has not yet been achieved, but their production in cell-extract systems as reported by several researchers (Nirenberg and Matthaei, 1961; Pollard, 1965; Lehman et al., 1958; Kornberg, 1961; Speyer et al., 1962) begins to suggest how this might be brought about. Moreover, Granick (1953) and Calvin (1956, 1959a,b, 1961) have shown how naturally occurring and mainly ferruginous catalysts in the physical environment and primitive prevital systems could perform, albeit inefficiently, critical functions such as electron transfer, now assisted by a variety of enzymes.

We are, to be sure, a very long way from producing in the laboratory a self-replicating, entropy-retarding, mutating, morphologically defined entity that might be considered living (Mazia, 1966), and even after this has been done we will have no assurance as to what route or routes nature took in doing the same thing. But we do see rather clearly now that life could have arisen spontaneously under primitive earth conditions, and we can even see some ways in which this might have happened.

Fox (1965, p. 339) expresses the present viewpoint well when he says: "Any remaining discontinuity between non-life and life should . . . be regarded as not yet understood rather than as hopelessly incomprehensible."

Was the Origin of Life on Earth a Unique Event?

Let us now consider whether earthly life itself might have had only one or more than one origin.

As Kerkut (1960, p. 6–17) and Cohen (1963) have stressed, the notion of the unity of biochemistry is usually presented in oversimplified form. It is commonplace to read, for instance, that the same twenty or so amino acids are used by all forms of life, that only L-amino acids occur naturally, and that all organisms obtain their metabolic energy through either the glycolysis (Embden-Meyerhof) or tricarboxylic acid (Krebs) cycle. On the contrary, more than 170 different naturally occurring amino acids had been identified to 1965, and new ones were being discovered at the rate of about ten a year (Meister, 1965, p. 2). Also, at least a few D-amino acids exist in nature, not only among bacteria but even in animals as advanced as earthworms and insects (Camien, 1952; Stevens et al., 1955; Kerkut, 1960, p. 11; Cohen, 1963; Meister, 1965, p. 113–17) and, it is reported (Fox et al., 1956) that some microorganisms are rich in D- rather than L-amino acids. In addition, six main pathways for glucose synthesis have been identified (Cohen, 1955). Finally, certain plant viruses can carry out both nucleic acid replication and protein synthesis in the host cells, although they contain only the nucleic acid RNA and no DNA of their own (Cohen, 1963).

A strong element of biochemical unity is, nevertheless, suggested by the following (also Mazia, 1966, p. 35–38):

1. Despite the variety of amino acids now known, only 23 occur frequently, and no new major amino acids have been reported since the recognition of threonine in 1935 (Meister, 1965, p. 3). Figure 1, from Young and Ponnamperuma (1964) suggests the degree to which the common L-amino acids approach ubiquity among living things.

2. A large degree of consistency is seen in the detailed amino acid sequences of proteins. For example, of the 104 positions of amino acids in cytochrome C from yeast and the horse, 64 are identical (Eck and Dayhoff, 1966).

3. Only two nucleic acids are known in nature, comprising only five nucleic acid bases, and both of these nucleic acids are found in all organisms investigated,

except for some viruses and perhaps bacteriophages which may have only RNA (Kerkut, 1965, p. 19–20).

4. Similarly, with the same exceptions, all nuclear and other hereditary material (the genome) seems to consist exclusively of DNA.

5. Adenosine triphosphate appears to be the energy-storing molecule in all organisms (Stumpf, 1953; Mazia, 1966, p. 34–35) and ferredoxin the usual mediator of the phosphorylation of ADP to yield ATP, at least in plants (Arnon, 1965; Arnon et al., 1965).

We must also recognize that first life, short of highly improbable coincidence, would be heterotrophic and therefore dependent on the preceding or continuing nonvital production of organic materials for nutrients. The great likelihood is that it would also be aquatic, because water is the most likely UV shield. Subsequent arrivals in the same water body of organisms newly emerged from chemical evo-

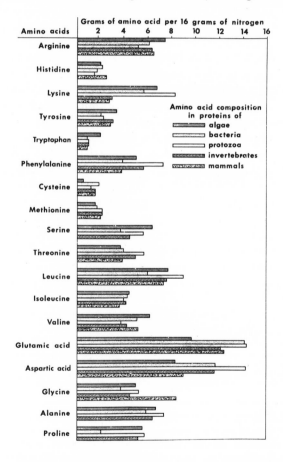

Fig. 1. Common occurrence of major amino acids in phylogenetically distant groups of organisms (after Young and Ponnamperuma, 1964, p. 14; by permission of the Biological Sciences Curriculum Study, AIBS).

lution, unless they appeared simultaneously in great numbers, would probably be ingested as nutrients by preexisting organisms.

For any given origin of life to be successful over the long pull, however, it would eventually have to give rise to an autotroph. It is conceivable that there was more than one unsuccessful start before an autotroph arose. It is also possible that there may have been more than one successful start in separate water bodies beneath the primitive atmosphere during the time it remained anoxygenic, and before the hydrosphere became unified into a single world ocean.

In the latter event the degree of biochemical unity observed needs an explanation. Why, under a polyphyletic origin, are there not separate main lines of L- and D-amino acid evolution, and why has only ATP been singled out from the various compounds suitable for energy storage (Mazia, 1966, p. 34–35)? The occasional D-amino acid in higher organisms, and other deviations from complete unity at the molecular level, might, to be sure, merely be a consequence of eliminative competition between separate origins in later united water bodies. One can visualize how the "losing" D-amino acid competitors, in temporarily becoming part of the surviving food chains, might give rise to Horowitz-type syntheses, leading to retention of D-amino acids as trace molecules in some organisms.

If life were monophyletic, however, why are some microorganisms still rich in D-amino acids? And how would we differentiate, improbable though it may be, between lineages that arose separately and survived habitat union, but which happened to use similar protein building blocks? Would the observed departures from molecular unity seem less glaring if the observed unity were explained by the likely prevalence of HCN, COOH, and HCHO as starting materials in all initial water bodies, and by the fact that the common amino acids seem to be easier to synthesize than others—that is, by prevital and subsequent biologic selection instead of by monophyly? Is ATP the universal energy-storing molecule today simply because it is the best? Does the separate evolution among procaryotic organisms of different types of autotrophy (including three different types of photosynthesis, using three different forms of chlorophyll) imply anything about initial independence of the lineages in which these developments took place?

At this stage of knowledge, three special cases of the general theory of spontaneous generation appear defensible:

1. Life had a monophyletic origin—this can be supported, but not established, by the observed degree of unity at the molecular level, in combination with the probabilities of survival on the primitive earth.

2. Life is diphyletic—the existence of L-amino acid–rich and D-amino acid rich categories of organisms, although greatly disparate, supports this view.

3. Life is polyphyletic—in support of this view may be offered the existence of both D- and L-amino acid–rich organisms, plus the likelihood that the initial hydrosphere consisted of discrete major parts and the difficulty of recognizing independent origins within D- or L-amino acid lineages, after convergence of habitat and biochemical evolution.

I see no compelling objective grounds for choosing among these alternatives at this time. The bacteria and blue-green algae, representing the morphologically simplest and earliest forms of life, include distinct major groups that have as their only common character the procaryotic nature of their cells (Stanier and van Niel, 1962, p. 33). The suggestion (Stanier et al., 1963, p. 95) that the common features of the eucaryotic cell demand a unique origin for *it* would explain the level of identity observed.

Record Between About 3.5 and 1.8 Billion Years Ago

On theoretical grounds, therefore, it is to be expected that there existed, at a very early stage in earth history, an assemblage of single-celled, anoxybiotic, aquatic heterotrophs. Where should we expect to find such entities, and what may they have been like?

Now that Young (1965) has made things like Fox's "proteinoid" microspheres (e.g. Fox, 1964) at likely temperatures (by cooling down from 25° C), such objects offer promise as a feasible prototype. Indeed objects seemingly only a little more advanced than these have been reported from the Figtree Series of eastern South Africa (>3 BY old) by Barghoorn and Schopf (1966, Figs. 7–9) and by Pflug (1966). Next to the Figtree objects, the oldest record of something perhaps once living is that of possible bacteria or blue-green algae from pyrite of the Soudan Iron Formation (+2.7 BY old) of Minnesota (Cloud et al., 1965). Prospects for pushing the record back still farther are limited—the Figtree sediments are older than granites giving a "tentative" Rb/Sr age of 3.4 + 0.3 BY (Allsopp et al., 1962), the oldest rocks yet acceptably dated on earth are approximately 3.6 BY old (Catanzaro, 1963; A. I. Tugarinov, oral communication, 1965), and the age of the earth from meteoritic and lead isotope evidence appears to be no more than about 4.8 BY (Tilton and Steiger, 1965; Brown, 1957; Patterson, 1956). Carbon-containing cherts from rocks still older than the Figtree (the Onverwacht Series at the base of the Swaziland System) have been investigated by myself and associates without as yet finding anything of biological interest.

So, although there are reasonably convincing suggestions of life in almost the oldest sedimentary rocks on earth, the oldest completely unequivocal and abundant, structurally preserved organisms are those of the Gunflint microflora, considered to be about 2 BY old (Tyler and Barghoorn, 1954; Barghoorn and Tyler, 1965; Cloud, 1965; Cloud and Hagen, 1965; Schopf et al., 1965).[2] This assemblage includes organisms that are morphologically comparable to living blue-green algae, others that resemble living bacteria, and still others that could just

2. I do not wish to leave the impression that the reports by Gruner (1923, 1924) of possible algae from the supposedly pre-Soudan Ogishke Conglomerate and from cherts at the base of the Pokegama Quartzite are unworthy of attention. These records, however, are puzzling and less than completely convincing to me, especially after seeing the works by Leduc, 1914, and Hawley, 1926, describing the artificial production of fungiform filaments by chemical diffusion.

I should also comment that C. F. Davidson (carbon copy of letter of 4 October 1965 to Lloyd Berkner) disagrees with the conclusion of Hurley et al., 1962, that the dated minerals of the Gunflint are unaffected by metamorphism, and considers that the 1.9± 0.2 BY age given by them is a metamorphic date and therefore a minimum age. Davidson logically suggests that the Gunflint can be dated on geological grounds only as younger than the Kenoran orogeny at

as well be either myxophycean algae or bacteria. Some of the separate tubules in this assemblage show structures that resemble heterocysts and some of the coccoid forms show division (or union?), suggestive of vegetative reproductive processes. The possible fungal hyphae earlier suggested both by myself and by Barghoorn and Tyler, however, if not aberrancies of degradation or preservation, could be procaryotic (nonmitosing) fungal analogs and not true fungi.

There are also well-authenticated stromatolitic structures of presumed blue-green algal origin in limestones, dolomites, and cherts from more than 2 BY onward (Witwatersrand System). However, those reported from the Figtree (Pretorius, 1963, p. 22; Davidson, 1964, p. 2) are not convincing, and those from the Bulawayan rocks of Rhodesia are neither completely convincing morphologically nor unequivocally dated. Carbon isotope studies by Hoering (1961) support an algal component in the Bulawayo Limestone, but the Bikita Pegmatites, which have been taken to give a minimum age of some 2.7 BY for it, are over 300 km to the east and a good deal farther than that by way of the discontinuous and complicated geological trends. "Protozoans" reported by Madison (1957) from Keewatin cherts west of Schreiber, Ontario, are unverifiable from his drawings, and, if organisms, are almost surely not eucaryotes, as his identifications imply.

Unsatisfactory though this early record is, nevertheless it is sufficiently substantial to illuminate several significant convergences: (1) believable biologic structures of this age range probably all represent the work of nonmitosing or procaryotic cells;[3] (2) they are all intimately bound with chert, limestone, or pyrite; and (3) they are all associated either directly with sedimentary iron formations or with episodes of sedimentary iron deposition. Such characteristics can be interpreted as follows.

1. The procaryotic cell (Stanier and van Niel, 1962, p. 20–21; Stanier et al., 1963, p. 66–85), with hereditary material not surrounded by a nuclear membrane or organized into cytologically well-defined chromosomes and with cytoplasm lacking organelles, is relatively more resistant to radiation than the eucaryotes (Giese, 1945, p. 245; Witkin, 1966) and hence less likely to be adversely affected by radiation-induced mutations.

2. The close association with sediments, involving in particular the binding or inclusion within originally gelatinous silica and mucilaginously entrapped calcium carbonate, provides a means by which essentially nonbenthic microorganisms can remain anchored below a UV-shielding layer of water, as well as a degree of radiation shielding by the enveloping or encrusting sediments upon exposure to the atmosphere. It is presumably more than coincidence that throughout geologic

---

about 2.5 BY and perhaps contemporary with the type Huronian, supposedly dated as older than about 2.15 BY by the intrusive Nipissing Diabase (Van Schmus, 1965). On a combination of geological and geochronological grounds, therefore, the Gunflint appears to be between about 2 and 2.5 BY old. Until more convincing evidence to the contrary is forthcoming, 2 BY remains a reasonable round number.

3. I thank Dr. Lynn Sagan Margulis for first bringing my attention to this (letter, 19 April 1965).

time until the present the sediment-binding and precipitating, stromatolite-building, blue-green algae have been conspicuously successful inhabitants of the highly insolated, very shallow waters within and just below the intertidal zone.

3. The general abundance of iron in solution in the anoxygenous waters of the primitive earth solves the problem of metabolic catalysis in early, aqueous, anoxygenic, living systems, inasmuch as iron by itself can effect, albeit inefficiently, all principal types of catalysis that are carried out in oxidative metabolism by the four general kinds of heme enzymes (Granick, 1953; Calvin, 1959b) and ferredoxin (Arnon, 1965; Arnon et al., 1965). Its principal function in early organisms could reasonably have been the transport of electrons. And iron would have been the most probable element to be selected for this purpose, in the absence of a sufficient supply of gaseous H_2, first because it is a more abundant and probably more efficient electron carrier than, for example, chromium, titanium, or copper, and later because of its capacity for oxygen and peroxide reduction.

We can say, then, with some support from the geologic record, that a reasonably diversified, anoxygenic, aquatic, procaryotic microbiota, probably dependent on iron in solution for its metabolism, and on UV shielding by water and sediment, was in existence at least 2 BY and perhaps as much as 3.5 BY ago. This biota contained credible antecedents for, and presumably representatives of, the blue-green algae and bacteria, and, through them, for advanced protists, metaphytes, sponges, and metazoans.

But I have agreed with Haldane and others that first life was heterotrophic. Where do the autotrophs come in to keep the sequence going? That is not easy to say. The procaryotes include, in addition to a variety of biochemically complex (and aerobic) chemoautotrophs, at least three distinct kinds of photoautotrophs— the purple bacteria, the green bacteria, and the blue-green algae. All these photoautotrophs can use light energy in order to obtain H_2 from the water molecule as an electron carrier (I. R. Kaplan, oral communication), but only the blue-greens actually release free O_2 in the process; the photosynthetic (and anaerobic) bacteria depend for survival on reduced components such as sulfur compounds or alcohols, which combine with any nascent oxygen so that free O_2 never appears in the system. Different forms of autotrophy probably arose independently, but similarity to living blue-green algae and photosynthetic thread bacteria on the part of the septate tubules in the Gunflint microbiota implies that photosynthetic organisms of some sort had arisen by Gunflint time.

I have suggested elsewhere (Cloud, 1965) that, since free O_2 is a universal poison, the first organisms to produce it would be unable to survive without an oxygen acceptor of some kind to remove it and to reduce any coincident H_2O_2. Perhaps, then, we find a clue to the time of origin of photosynthesis in the siliceous banded iron formations, or BIF, that are so characteristic of the Precambrian sequence between perhaps 3.4 and 1.8 to 2 BY ago, and especially at about 1.8 to 2 and 2.5 to 2.7 BY ago (Goldich et al., 1961; Lepp and Goldich, 1964; James, 1966, p. 34), but which are rare in or absent from younger rocks. These iron deposits consist in great part of alternating bands of cryptocrystalline chert and siliceous ferric oxide, are often thick and extensive, and, unlike younger sedimentary iron deposits of comparable dimensions, appear to have originated as primary precipitates from ordinary open-water bodies and not in environments unusual for their time, or by diagenetic or later replacement from interstitial fluids. The iron comprising the BIF could have been transported only in the ferrous state but required the addition of oxygen to bring about precipitation as ferric oxides or hydroxides. The ferrous ion then abundant thus would provide an excellent oxygen acceptor and "sink," while the ferrous–ferric system could in addition (or sooner) have taken over as an electron-transfer mechanism whenever and wherever gaseous H_2 or other preceding electron sources were no longer available or suitable.

Hence we might expect to find a long-term balance between primitive metabolism and different types of Precambrian iron sedimentation—BIF, ferrosulfides, ferrocarbonates, or ferrosilicates. This would be terminated when more efficient oxygen and peroxide-mediating molecules such as the cytochromes and catalases arose, permitting biologically generated O_2 to sweep the hydrosphere of iron, accumulate, and begin to evade to the atmosphere.

Such events should put an end to the deposition of BIF as a common sedimentary rock, and, because O_2 would accumulate first in the lower layers of the atmosphere, chemically very reactive UV-generated ozone and atomic oxygen would also be present at the earth's surface. Hence there should result, concurrently with or after the tapering off of BIF deposition, a widespread retention of insoluble ferric iron in the weathering profile and the deposition of the world's first extensive detrital red beds—ferric-oxide coated sediments of subaerial origin which may accumulate either as terrestrial or marginal marine deposits. The thickest and most extensive deposition of BIF would, in theory, have been a somewhat earlier event. The type and proportions of iron formation produced in any given sedimentary sequence during the prevalence of BIF is best visualized as a function of the availability and diffusion of biologically generated O_2 and the type of locally present bacterial metabolism.

When I first proposed such a model in 1965 I was puzzled by the fact that there seemed to be a gap of about 0.6 BY between the youngest BIF of the Lake Superior type at about 1.8 BY[4] and the oldest widespread and thick red beds at about 1.2 BY. This mystery has now been cleared up by correspondence and published reports drawing attention to older red beds, some very recently dated, in many regions of Precambrian outcrop.

In the Northwest Territories of Canada the Dubawnt Group contains a thick and extensive sequence of red beds associated with contemporaneous volcanic rocks whose K/Ar ages cluster around 1.7 BY (Donaldson, 1965). The oldest South African red beds are those of the Waterberg System, unconformably underlain by the Loskop System which appears to have a minimum age of about 1.3 BY, and

---

4. I am aware that younger banded iron formation has been reported (e.g. James, 1966, p. 30–31; Gross, 1965, p. 115–20), but those instances of significant volume in which the dating has not already proved to be in error should be reexamined very carefully, both as to age and nature, to see if they are indeed proper exceptions to the suggested generalization.

which overlies rocks associated with the Bushveldt Complex dated at around 1.95 BY (Nicolaysen, 1962, p. 580). "Jotnian" red beds in the eastern Baltic Shield and Karelia are intruded by gabbroic and diabase dikes whose micas give K/Ar ages of 1.6 to 1.8 BY (oral communications from M. A. Semikhatov, 2 April 1965, and E. K. Gerling, 12 April 1965). A. I. Tugarinov (oral communication, 9 April 1965) suggests an age possibly as great as 1.9 to 2.0 BY for Karelian red bed sedimentation. Red beds of the Siberian platform have K/Ar ages of 1.5 to 1.6 BY (Davidson, 1965). In South America the oldest well-dated and apparently authentic, thick, and extensive red beds are those in the upper part of the Roraima Formation (Gansser, 1954). These are intruded by dolerite sills which give K/Ar ages clustering around 1.7 BY and unconformably underlain by granites having ages of around 2 BY (Snelling, 1963; Cannon, 1965). Still older Canadian "red beds" mentioned by Davidson (1965) and by Frarey and McLaren (1963) may be in part a premonitory occurrence of limited extent and in part not truly red beds. These are pink-to-red sediments of the Huronian Lorrain Formation in Ontario, apparently older than about 2.1 BY (Van Schmus, 1965). It appears in the field that the color of some of these sediments may be due mainly to their inclusion of abundant pink-to-red feldspar. Others should be restudied to ascertain if the color could result from redeposition of iron formation materials. To the extent that neither of these explanations is applicable, the possibility remains, until extensive and thick correlatives of established age are found, that we are dealing here with an early phase in the transition from conditions suitable for the deposition of BIF to those favoring the formation of red beds.

It has also been suggested from very roundabout reasoning that the "pink" Muruwa Formation, which "appears" but is not known "to underlie" the Roraima Formation, may be more than 2.6 BY old (Cannon, 1965). The latter figure is sufficiently insecure and sufficiently discrepant with other evidence as to need reinvestigation. If such an age is substantiated we must be assured that the coloration of any Muruwa "red beds" is due to ferric oxide coatings and not to included red or pink feldspars.

Taken together, these records strongly suggest a clustering of the oldest red beds at around 1.8 to perhaps 2 BY ago, during or immediately after the tapering off of the deposition of BIF. This is roughly consistent with the conclusion reached by Jolliffe (1964) that valency changes in Fe and Mn compounds in an ancient and now vertical weathering profile constituting the iron ores at Steep Rock Lake, Ontario (Jolliffe, 1955), imply a change from an anoxygenous to an oxygenous atmosphere about 2 BY ago, although Gruner (1956) gives substantial reasons for questioning that interpretation of the evidence. Briggs (1959) also proposes a date of about 2 BY for this transition. The range from 2 BY to the 1.8 BY suggested here is within the resolving power of geochronology this far back in geologic time. Also, inasmuch as there may have been an interval of transition when red beds were beginning to form on land while BIF was still sedimenting out of the sea, we may well be unable to define the transition much more closely than about 1.8 to 2 BY.

It further deserves emphasis that these banded iron formations are primary basinal deposits that originated in large, probably marine, water bodies (James, 1954, 1960, 1966, p. 50). Large oxygenous water bodies of the present day contain only infinitesimally small amounts of iron in solution. It is hard to see how the source ions of BIF could be transported except in anoxygenous solutions that would permit their carriage in the ferrous state, or precipitated except through metabolic processes or as a result of local conversion to the ferric state. Nothing forbids the occurrence of other types of iron deposits in the older rocks, but it is difficult to visualize a supply and transport mechanism whereby BIF could form in large volume as a primary precipitate from oxygenated waters of the indicated pH and alkalinity under an oxygenous atmosphere such as apparently prevailed from about 1.8 BY onward.

Other geochemical evidence supporting the concept of an anoxygenous atmosphere up to around 2 BY ago is given by Geijer (1956) or referred to in Holland (1962, p. 467)—especially as related to the local abundance in sediments that young of easily oxidized but probably detrital pyrite and uraninite. Davidson (1964, 1965) doubts the detrital nature of these minerals, but his conclusions are not supported by the geologists who have studied the deposits in question most intensively (e.g. Roscoe and Steacy, 1958; Roscoe, 1960; Ramdohr, 1958).

Record from About 1.8 to 0.65 Billion Years Ago

So it appears that by about 1.8 BY ago, free oxygen was prevalent at presumably very low partial pressures in a perhaps by-then interconnected hydrosphere, and beginning to accumulate in the atmosphere.

Because of self-limitation (Urey, 1959) of photolytic O_2 and its reduction in surface oxidations, the only thing that could have made this possible was the addition of photosynthetic O_2, resulting from the evolution of oxygen and peroxide-mediating biological molecules, of which the cytochromes and catalases are today the most prevalent. Thus one may suggest that such molecules or their precursors appeared in the structure of organisms at about this time.

For a while after this, O_2 and its derivatives would accumulate slowly, because they would be taken up by reduced substances in solution and at the earth's surface. Eventually, however, oxygen would begin to build up, ozone would start to accumulate, and some screening out of high-energy UV radiation would take place. But it would not yet be possible for photosynthesizing organisms to take up a truly planktonic existence that would carry the risk of extended exposure to DNA-inactivating UV radiation (Deering, 1962) in the 2,400–2,900 (and especially the 2,600) Å wavelengths that still penetrated the surface layers of water. Therefore life would presumably remain restricted to shielded habitats and O_2 would accumulate only slowly.

As ozone did build up, however, a degree of radiation shielding would follow, and a better system of genetic recombination could be selected for. Presumably some time after about 1.8 BY, therefore, the mitosing or eucaryotic cell arose, as a result of the packaging of chromatin into chromosomes, their enclosure within a nuclear membrane, and the origin of various functional organelles. As such a cell is adapted primarily to an oxidative type of metabolism (even though many eucaryotes are also anaerobes) it could probably not have evolved much sooner.

It was stressed by Stanier and van Niel (1962, p. 20) and by Stanier et al. (1963, p. 85) that the evolutionary discontinuity between procaryotic and eucaryotic organisms is profound. Stanier et al. (p. 95) conclude that the common features of the eucaryotic cell are so numerous that it probably had a unique origin. If that is true, it is likely that blue-green algae were the ancestors, unless, as Echlin (1966) and Margulis (in press)[5] have been the most recent to suggest, they became merely captive chloroplasts. For blue-green algae alone among procaryotes possess chlorophyll-*a*, a universal attribute of the photosynthesizing higher protists and the metaphytes.

Again we would like to know when the eucaryotic cell arose, and there are encouraging prospects that we may some day have that knowledge. Algal filaments and spheroidal aggregates from the Bitter Springs Formation of central Australia are convincingly identified as green algae and therefore eucaryotes by Barghoorn and Schopf (1965). These, however, appear to be relatively young Precambrian. Nothing as yet has been reported between this and the much older Gunflint chert that warrants a confident identification of specific nature, although a possible occurrence of filamentous algae reported by Walcott (1914, p. 103, Pl. 20, Fig. 4) from the lower Newland Limestone in the Belt Series should be reinvestigated. All we can say with reasonable assurance at present is that the eucaryotic cell had evolved by late Precambrian time and maybe earlier.

Meanwhile O_2 was slowly accumulating in the atmosphere, probably with fluctuations relating to the following: the prevalence, size, and efficiency of photosynthesizing populations; the availability of CO_2 from volcanic sources; and the demands of exposed reduced materials. The ratios in sedimentary rocks of Fe_2O_3/FeO, K/Na, Ca/Mg, and carbonate to clastic rocks were increasing (Engel, 1963; Engel and Engel, 1964, p. 33). Red beds became common rocks and carbonate rocks much commoner than they had been before. The great episodes of volcanism that characterize this part of the geological column accelerated the process by supplying CO_2 which, in combination with H_2O, gave rise to additional gaseous oxygen and carbonate ion. The earth was being prepared for an innovation so conspicuous that its subsequent records would come to be classified primarily in terms of elaborations on that innovation. I refer to the appearance of the Metazoa.

Prelude to the Metazoa

The Metazoa, of course, could not arise directly from procaryotic origins, or in the absence of an adequately oxygenous atmosphere. Although the basic energy-liberating process itself appears to be anaerobic in all organisms (Borradaile et al.,

5. Margulis' report was published under the name of Lynn Sagan, 1967. On the origin of mitosing cells. *J. Theoretic. Biol.*, *14*: 225–74.

1958, p. 137), and although there are Metazoa that can tolerate very low O_2 pressures and even total deprivation of O_2 for short intervals (von Brand, 1934) or within aerobic hosts, it seems that all Metazoa depend on a relatively effective oxidative metabolism. No known Metazoa can permanently tolerate truly anoxygenic conditions (Baldwin, 1949, p. 77–78, 1953, p. 366; Abelson, 1959, p. 83). We are justified, then, in assuming that candidates for metazoan ancestry were organisms made of one or more mitosing eucaryotic cells, with a nuclear membrane and a well-differentiated cytoplasm, but with only one kind of somatic cell. Furthermore, such organisms either already were obligatory aerobes or had the imminent capacity to become such. If these and previously expressed conclusions are true, moreover, they eliminate from consideration reports such as those of Edgell (1964) and Bain (1965) of Metazoa from BIF and other rocks more than about 1.8 to 2 BY old—reports which can also be eliminated on morphological grounds.

Before the Metazoa can make their entrance, therefore, we want a population of eucaryotic progenitors, preadapted to or already carrying out a respiratory type of metabolism. Many eucaryotic protists and algae, other than those that are obligate anaerobes, have extremely low O_2 requirements, and their O_2 intake does not require complicated respiratory mechanisms but can occur by diffusion, water exchange, and protoplasmic streaming (Jahn, 1964, esp. p. 386–87). Many also, as among the yeasts, can metabolize alternatively by fermentation or respiration, depending on the lack or supply of O_2. Such ancestors, therefore (and perhaps sponges as well), could survive and evolve under partial pressures of oxygen too low to support a metazoan type of metabolism—possibly but not necessarily in close dependence on local sources of O_2 such as Fischer (1965) has so imaginatively postulated.

As Nursall first observed in 1959, what was needed to bring about the attainment of a truly metazoan level of evolution, by one or more of the available protistan or metaphytic ancestors, was an increase in the general *level* of gaseous and dissolved O_2 to one permanently capable of supporting metazoan respiratory metabolism. What this level was we cannot say for sure, but we have some clues, not only as to what it was but when it happened.

It is known that when the partial pressure of oxygen becomes high enough to carry out oxidative phosphorylation, hydrogenase and similar anaerobic catalytic mechanisms are oxidized into inactivity (except in the case of the hydrogen bacteria), and ADP and inorganic phosphate are rapidly converted to ATP. In consequence, fermentation is suppressed, biosynthesis becomes much more efficient, and production of toxic products is reduced (Gaffron, 1957; Stanier et al., 1963, p. 282). This was observed by Pasteur (although he did not describe it in those terms), who also observed that at such O_2 levels organisms change from fermentative to respiratory metabolism or die. Berkner and Marshall (1964, 1965) refer to this level of O_2 concentration as the "Pasteur point," and observe that it seems to be about 1 per cent of the present atmospheric level (PAL) of O_2 for many living organisms which are adaptable to such alternative metabolic pathways. They draw attention, also (their Fig. 9, present Fig. 2) to the fact that at about this con-

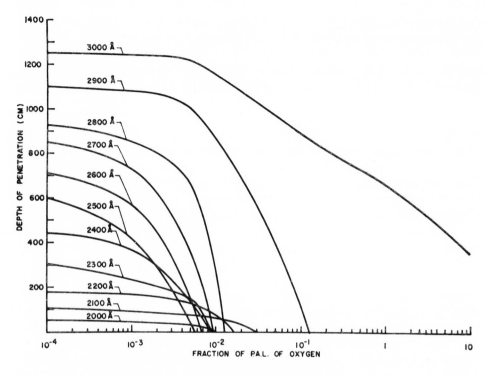

Fig. 2. Penetration of different wavelengths of ultraviolet light in liquid water at different percentages of O_2 compared to atmospheric level (biologically most damaging radiation peaks near 2,600 Å), (after Berkner and Marshall, 1965, Fig. 9).

centration of O_2, lethal UV radiation no longer penetrates the water column, opening up the surface waters of the hydrosphere to colonization by planktonic photosynthesizers.

It is not important for purposes of the model being developed whether this level is precisely 1 per cent PAL or somewhat greater. In fact, it might have been as high as 10 per cent PAL, which would eliminate the 2,900 Å UV radiation as well as shorter and more damaging wavelengths (Fig. 2). What is important, as Berkner and Marshall have so perceptively argued, is that biologically damaging radiation is abruptly reduced or excluded from penetration to the earth's surface, hence of H_2O, at some O_2 concentration between 1 and 10 per cent PAL. Once this level was exceeded, they point out, phytoplankton could spread throughout the surface layers of the ocean, and the rate of O_2 buildup could be expected to undergo a large increase, for photosynthesizers would no longer be dependent on the sediment shields or attachments that protected their ancestors or retarded their circulation into UV-irradiated surface waters, thus limiting their existence mainly to bottoms within the photic zone.[6]

6. Nothing here is opposed to the principle of uniformitarianism as I believe most modern geologists understand it, and this interpretation as well as a gradualistic one is possible from

A premium would concurrently be placed on the ability to carry out respiratory metabolism and to evolve organized systems that would maximize and control the process. Heterotrophic systems of this nature, with mouth, digestive tract, and specific O_2-distributing mechanisms would be Metazoa; and it does not tax the imagination unduly to visualize either a wave of multicellularization affecting the then existing protistan stocks, or adaptive radiation within the new grade of organization once it was attained (Cloud, 1948, p. 346–48). This may have occurred at about 3 per cent PAL of O_2, which (Berkner and Marshall, letter of 10 Jan. 1967) appears to be about that required for the metabolism of Metazoa with relatively low oxygen requirements.

In keeping with the principle of evolutionary interaction, geochemical and lithologic evidence is consistent with the suggested changes in atmosphere and biosphere. The slow increase in O_2 after 1.8 to 2 BY is accompanied by an increase in the prevalence of limestone and dolomite, indicative of increasing carbonate ion as atmospheric CO_2 decreased. The suggested large increase in O_2 as Precambrian time drew to a close may be reflected in widespread glacial deposits, brought on by reduction in temperature as a result of accompanying large decrease of CO_2. The rarity in the Precambrian of the mineral glauconite, a potassium iron silicate (ferric/ferrous ratio about 7/1) of only slightly reducing environments, suggests paucity of oxygen during the Precambrian at sites where it may have been deposited. More significantly, the great rarity in the Precambrian of sedimentary calcium sulfate deposits (gypsum and anhydrite), as contrasted with their abundance in younger sediments, indicates limited supply of the oxygen needed to make sulfate ion from reduced states of sulfur during that time (Hutchinson, 1954; Abelson, 1966).

To be sure, sand casts of gypsum crystals and crystal clusters are fairly common in some Precambrian littoral deposits, where they are sometimes taken for fossils, but only in the 1.2 + - BY - old Grenville rocks (Silver, 1963) and in rocks right at the top of the Precambrian in Arctic Canada and the late Precambrian of central Australia do we find plausible candidates for substantial deposits of sedimentary gypsum and anhydrite. Caution must be urged about the interpretation of these deposits, however. The Grenville deposit (Brown and Engel, 1956, p. 1607) *may* replace a marble body (A. E. J. Engel, letter of 5 Oct. 1966 to Cloud), and the Precambrian age of the Arctic deposits (Thorsteinsson and Tozer, 1962) is not completely certain. Although these beds are separated by regional unconformity from overlying Middle Cambrian and younger beds, they are also underlain by rocks whose intercalated diabase sills give K/Ar whole-rock

---

Hutton's and Lyell's exposition of the principle. "The present is the key to the past" in the sense that we must assume the validity of the basic laws of matter and energy throughout geologic time in order to deal with geologic problems at all, not in the sense that we can analogize only with existing processes or gradual changes. Continental glaciation, for instance, could have been deduced from the properties of H_2O and geologic evidence without benefit of existing glaciation as a reference model (although it would have called for different and more difficult insights than those arising from the analogies that did give rise to this theory).

ages of 635–640 million years (MY) ago (Leech et al., 1963, p. 55). The evidence available thus does not discriminate between a Paleozoic or very young Precambrian age for these Arctic sulfate deposits. The gypsum reported from the Bitter Springs Formation of young Precambrian age at two places in central Australia is most comprehensively described in unpublished reports of the Australian Bureau of Mineral Resources. One of these occurrences is merely a 15-meter purple gypsiferous siltstone in the lower Bitter Springs beds, seen at the surface near Limbla Homestead; and the other is a body of unknown source that penetrates the lower Bitter Springs diapirically in a structurally complex area near Ringwood Homestead (A. J. Stewart, letter of 24 Jan. 1967). Such sulfates, to be sure, are soluble and might be expected to be increasingly rare in the older rocks. Indirect evidence of their presence should be sought in features such as collapse breccia deposits associated with red beds or dolomites. Until better evidence than now in hand is found, however, the record of Precambrian sedimentary sulfates must be considered both slim and moot.

THE OLDEST METAZOAN FOSSILS

Main Aspects of the Record to Date

What does the fossil record of the early Metazoa tell us about their origins? That is a longish story, and one about which there is disagreement.

It is well known, of course, that rocks containing a well-documented metazoan fauna are assigned to the Paleozoic and younger geologic eras, or, collectively, to the Phanerozoic Eon; and that beneath these there is a catch-all called the Precambrian, or Cryptozoic, which lumps together the records of the first seven eighths of earth history, in which Metazoa are absent or rare. The term Precambrian is an anachronism, stemming from the time when geologists held no hope of subdividing these rocks and no clear concept of the length of time they represented; and the term Cryptozoic applies logically only to the younger Precambrian. We might better abandon Precambrian and use the terms Archean for rocks older than about 2.5 BY and Proterozoic for rocks about 2.5 to 0.65 BY old, as is widely done; but it is convenient to have a single word for pre-Paleozoic rocks and time, and Precambrian is the term in current use.[7] It is also useful to be able to refer to the two great divisions of geologic time by means of the contrasting terms Phanerozoic and Cryptozoic (Cloud and Nelson, 1966).

Now there is no standard reference section for the Precambrian, any more than for the Paleozoic; and, there has been no worldwide consensus as to where the base of the Cambrian, or the coincident or lower base of the Paleozoic and Phanerozoic, should be placed operationally. Nevertheless, on various grounds, different geologists have arrived at the notion that the Paleozoic–Precambrian boundary is probably somewhere near the 600-million-year mark (Davidson, 1959,

---

7. In reports prepared since this one I have preferred the term Pre-Paleozoic as being less ambiguous and avoiding semantic confusion between pre-Cambrian and Precambrian.

1960; Kulp, 1961; Stockwell, 1964a,b). Mayne et al. (1959) have even suggested that the *Upper* Cambrian might be as much as 650 MY to 800 MY old; but both Davidson and Kulp give reasons for rejecting that conclusion, and Davidson shows that even some estimates that converge on the 600-MY mark are based on faulty data. Perhaps the best number we have that is close to the base of the Paleozoic is a K^{40}/Ca^{40} determination on sylvite from the Lower Cambrian potash deposits of the Irkutsk region, which gives the age of 620 ± 20 MY that Davidson (1959, 1960) accepts for the base of the Cambrian. So, until a better determination is forthcoming, 600 to 650 MY is a good round number to talk about, provided we bear in mind that geologic time is punctuated by events and not numbers (Barrell, 1917, suggested a range of 550 to 700 MY—which still covers the likely limits).

One of the most striking things that is known geologically and needs to be explained about the origin of the Metazoa is that a number of different phyla of Metazoa first appeared over a relatively short interval in early Paleozoic time. This is illustrated by Figure 3, compiled for this publication from files of the U.S. Geological Survey through the great kindness of A. R. Palmer. Certainly, continued study can be expected to reveal a greater scatter of first records than is here indicated, but this tabulation does show that most of the metazoan phyla that are characterized by preservable hard parts, or are readily represented by tracks or burrows, are already present in the lower half of the Lower Cambrian (although the diversity within major groups is as yet not great). They are preceded by a few earlier records that reach down into rocks whose assignment to Paleozoic or Precambrian is not agreed upon. Palmer has also called my attention to the interesting fact that the main flood of first recorded appearances in both the U.S.S.R. (for which he has made a similar tabulation) and the U.S. is in limestones and calcareous shales of the Aldan and Poleta beds. Since similar rock types were available in the preceding Precambrian, this may simply mean that the new metazoan faunas first appear abundantly in any given section in the oldest favorable facies following their origin.

Of special interest, also, is the occurrence (summarized by Glaessner, 1966, p. 43) in the Ediacara Hills of South Australia, the Charnwood Forest of England, the Nama System of Southwest Africa, northern Russia and Siberia, and perhaps in California (Cloud and Nelson, 1966), of elements of a very ancient and mainly soft-bodied metazoan fauna that may have had a worldwide distribution at or near the beginning of the Paleozoic. Some investigators have considered this aptly designated Ediacaran assemblage to be late Precambrian (Ford, 1958; Glaessner, 1958b, 1959, 1961–1966; Glaessner and Daily, 1959; Meneisy and Miller, 1963). Others have considered it most probably Cambrian (Sprigg, 1947, 1949; Glaessner, 1958a; Haughton, 1960; geologic maps of South and Southwest Africa, 1958, 1963). And still others have considered it to be so close to the Paleozoic–Precambrian boundary that a Paleozoic age cannot be excluded (Sdzuy, 1960; Cloud, 1965). But more of this anon.

This is the end of the well-documented early metazoan record, leaving out

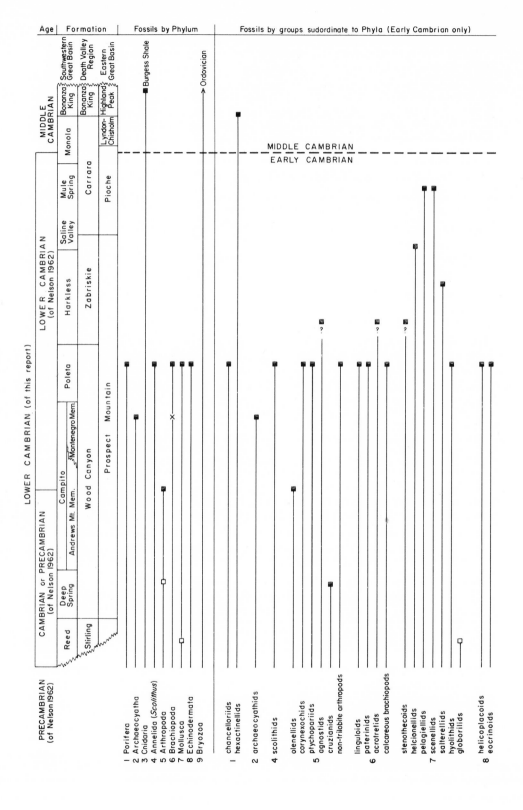

Fig. 3. First known Metazoa and Parazoa in western North America (compiled for this paper by A. R. Palmer).

■ An established record (where queried, the exact level and not the record is in doubt).
☐ A record less reliable as to precise assignment because of preservation.
X As yet undocumented record.

The following notes are by A. R. Palmer (unless followed by the initials PEC; ARP & PEC means revised by Cloud).

Records by phylum

1. Porifera: based on my records of *Chancelloria* spicules from residues of limestones within the Poleta.
2. Archaeocyatha: Nelson, 1962, p. 139–44. These first appear in the Montenegro in small biohermal masses according to W. Durham (oral comm.).
3. Cnidaria: no western Lower Cambrian forms known; the earliest record that seems acceptable for western North America is from the Burgess shale.
4. Annelida: *Scolithus* was recorded in the Poleta by Nelson, 1962.
5. Arthropoda: lower record (open block) based on tracks from the Deep Spring that Cloud, Seilacher, and Daily have examined and indicated are probably arthropodan, referable to *Cruziana* or *Rusophycus* (ARP & PEC).
6. Brachiopoda: the earliest records I have are of *Kutorgina*-like forms from the Poleta. W. Durham says he thinks he has some phosphatic brachiopods in a Montenegro collection, but this has to be confirmed.
7. Mollusca: based on W. Durham's verbal report of hyolithids in the Poleta. I have seen *Hyolithellus*-like forms (slender cones with rounded cross sections) in these beds also.
8. Echinodermata: Durham and Caster (1963). Durham reports (oral comm.) a greater diversity of unpublished kinds in the Poleta than the chart shows (ARP & PEC).
9. Bryozoa: excluding *Cambrotrypa montanensis* Fritz & Howell, which is a fossil but more likely algal than bryozoan; there is no known Cambrian record for this phylum.

Records by groups subordinate to phyla

Chancelloriids: these calcareous spicules often turn up in residues, and we have some from the Poleta.

Hexactinellids: this is the most surprising result of the compilation. Despite considerable acid dissolution of limestones of all ages, there is only one locality in the Great Basin that has yielded hexactinellids older than the *Bolaspidella* zone of the upper Middle Cambrian. This is an occurrence in beds correlated with the *Glosspleura* zone near Currant, Nev. that I have assigned to the outer detrital belt of my regional facies scheme. Hexactinellids are very common in most younger collections from beds that I assign to the outer detrital belt. Thus it looks as if these may be potentially good indicators of some kind of special environment.

Archaeocyathids: Nelson, 1962.

Scolithids: Nelson, 1962, from the Poleta.

Olenellids: Nelson, 1962, reference to olenellids in the Andrews Mountain.

Corynexochids: based on my identification of an *Ogygopsis*-like trilobite in one of Nelson's Poleta collections.

Fig. 3 *(cont.)*

Ptychopariids: based on my identification of material from one of Nelson's Poleta collections.

Agnostids: the earliest Great Basin record is in the *Albertella* zone of the early Middle Cambrian. Rasetti records a *Pagetia*-like form from the Mount Whyte in Canada, which is a Carrara equivalent. The record shown here is based on one of the Alaskan collections that includes an unusual new genus also known from the Tah limestone in British Columbia. The Tah is part of the Gog Group which includes beds with *Nevadella*-like trilobites and is thus early Lower Cambrian. Our Great Basin nevadiids are in the Poleta or older beds, and William Fritz of the Geological Survey of Canada tells me that the new genus is in beds slightly above *Nevadella*. Thus, if the correlation stands up, agnostids (in this case eodiscids), stenothecoides-like forms, and acrotretids occur this far back in the record.

Cruzianids: trails from the Deep Spring referred to under Arthropoda above.

Nontrilobite arthropods—based on USGS collections from the Poleta with small bivalved conchostracan-like forms.

Calcareous brachiopods: Walcott (1912b) records *Kutorgina,* and also linguloid and paterinid brachiopods from the upper Wood Canyon with *"Nevadella" gracile.* These beds are correlative with the Poleta. The acrotretid reference is based on roundabout correlation with Alaska. In the Great Basin, the oldest acrotretids I have seen are in the latest Early Cambrian beds.

Stenothecoidids: the earliest Great Basin record is from the top of the Lower Cambrian by Walcott (1884). However, I have excellent specimens in the Alaskan collections from the beds correlated as a little younger than the Poleta, including one that shows the beast to be bivalved.

Helcionellids: this record is based on our collections with *Wanneria* in western Nevada that come from beds in the lower Saline Valley.

Pelagiellids: I have small specimens in residues from the Mule Spring equivalent in the Death Valley region.

Scenellids: we have specimens collected from Mule Spring equivalents in Esmeralda County, Nev.

Salterellids: all the western *Salterella* material seems to be from the Harkless as far as the USGS collections are concerned. I know of no older published records in western North America.

Hyolithids: my earliest record is from the lower Carrara, but W. Durham says he has specimens in collections from the Poleta.

Globorilids: Taylor, 1966 (PEC).

Helicoplacoids and eocrinoids: This is the published breakdown so far of the Poleta echinoderms by W. Durham. Additional material is being worked on.

details of Cambrian occurrences in other parts of the world. In addition, however, there are literally scores of references to supposed Precambrian Metazoa that are either doubtfully Precambrian, doubtfully metazoan, or simply unverifiable.

Beginning in 1948 I have studied such of these records as I could get at, as well as various hypotheses that have been advanced to explain the absence or rarity of metazoan fossils from the Precambrian. My conclusions from this study to date are as follows. (1) There is no good reason why we should not expect to find records of Precambrian Metazoa if they were present. Authentic, well-preserved, and little-metamorphosed young Precambrian sediments of a wide range of depositional environments, many preserving delicate physical structures, do in fact exist and, moreover, have been searched with care for metazoan fossils, their tracks or imprints. (2) There are as yet no records of unequivocal Metazoa in rocks of undoubted Precambrian age—neither fossils themselves, nor their tracks, burrows, or after-death imprints.

This second conclusion is too sweeping to stand undocumented, and, at the same time, there is no need for another detailed review of the generally ambiguous to downright groundless history of reported Precambrian Metazoa. Those who want such detail can find it at a number of places (e.g. Raymond, 1935; Whittard, 1953; Schindewolf, 1956; Seilacher, 1956; Sdzuy, 1960; Glaessner, 1962, 1966). And those who are interested in the hypotheses that have been offered to explain the absence or paucity of Precambrian Metazoa will also find them discussed elsewhere (e.g. Brooks, 1894; Daly, 1907; Sederholm, 1912; Raymond, 1935; Cloud, 1948; Axelrod, 1958; and Glaessner, 1962).

To such hypotheses I will comment only that (1) the availability or lack of $CaCO_3$ is not the explanation for distributions of fossils observed; carbonate rocks are abundant, both above and below the Paleozoic–Precambrian boundary. (2) The "Lipalian" gap does not exist; sequences of sedimentary rock transitional from Precambrian into Cambrian appear to be present in Australia, the southern Great Basin, perhaps British Columbia, perhaps Arctic Canada, the Appalachian region, the eastern Baltic, Siberia, and possibly Africa. (3) An explanation that calls on the absence of Precambrian littoral and intertidal sediments is invalid; such deposits, as well as deeper water sediments, are well represented in the Precambrian, although their proportions vary. (4) Metamorphism and loss of fine structure in the Precambrian does not provide an acceptable general explanation; delicate sedimentary structures are preserved in Precambrian sediments of a variety of ages and depths of deposition with a degree of fidelity that would assure the preservation somewhere of tracks, trails, burrows, or after-death impressions of pelagic metazoan organisms if they had been present. (5) A very long interval of preskeletal metazoan evolution seems unlikely, although 50 to 100 MY of mainly preskeletal development represented by the Ediacaran and approximate equivalents is not out of question. One should expect to find after-death imprints of such organisms even if not tracks or burrows, and some organisms, such as brachiopods, could hardly exist except in context with a shell (Cloud, 1948). (6) Insufficient search is an increasingly unlikely explanation, although always a possible one; exhaustive searches have been made in favorable sediments. To this last point I may mention the heroic labors of Walcott through years of search by himself and employed collectors, and the phenomenal industry reported by David and Tillyard (1936) who had some fifty-five tons of hard quartzite quarried free and seven tons of selected blocks carefully split into thin slabs at one site. I myself, and others, in recent years have also searched, so far in vain, for unequivocal metazoan fossils through thousands of feet of sediments at scores of selected localities.

Luck may yet give us a record of Precambrian Metazoa, but hope is not admissible evidence, and I conclude that so far as a substantial record of Precambrian life is concerned, we have mostly been looking for the wrong things, in the wrong rocks, with the wrong techniques, and that our best hope for positive results lies in the application of ultramicroscopic techniques to the fine-grained sediments.

Let us, however, get on with the Metazoa.

Reported Precambrian Metazoa of Dubious Age or Nature

My grounds for skepticism about Precambrian Metazoa can be illustrated sufficiently by reviewing a representative selection of records that have been widely accepted as authentic, and which illustrate well the problems involved. A more comprehensive sample of doubtful records not considered to warrant further discussion at this time is also listed in Appendix A.

We can begin with *Xenusion*, a fossil somewhat suggestive of an onychophoran, that has found its way into textbooks and treatises (e.g. Dechaseaux, 1953) as a genuine Precambrian metazoan, despite the fact that Pompeckj, who described it, specifically stated that it was represented by a single specimen from a glacial pebble of "Algonkian or old Cambrian quartzite." Very serious doubt about the possible Precambrian age of *Xenusion* has now been raised by Anders Martinsson (oral communication),[8] who believes that he may have traced its source to the Cambrian Kalmarsund Sandstone of southern Sweden. Here then is an example of a genuine metazoan fossil, but one that is simply of unknown age and most likely Cambrian.

Next let us take the case of the Grand Canyon and other "jellyfish." Objects so designated have been described, among others, by Alf (1959), Bassler (1941), and Dunnet (1965). Alf described two kinds, of which a sample of the most abundant and impressive is illustrated in Figure 4, B and C, adjacent to a similar imprint of known origin (Fig. 4A) reproduced at the same scale. The imprints of known origin were produced experimentally by Nathorst in 1880, by allowing drops of water to fall on setting plaster of Paris covered by a thin film of water. Figure 4D, from the frontispiece of D'Arcy Thompson's great book, *On Growth and Form* (1945), an early Edgerton instantaneous photograph, shows how this

8. Martinsson's work has now been published—Hermann Jaeger and Anders Martinsson, 1966. Remarks on the problematic fossil *Xenusion auerswaldae*. Geol. Föreningens Stockholm Förhandlingar, 88: 435–52.

happens. The shock wave from the impacting main drop produces the "umbrella"; the radiate structure is made by an array of secondarily generated droplets. The objects illustrated by Alf do indeed resemble small jellyfish (or perhaps gelatinous myxophycean sheaths, as suggested by Glaessner, 1966, p. 41), but, because very similar structures can be produced by the means described, we cannot exclude the possibility that all we have evidence of here is a Precambrian rain.

To be sure, the objects described by Alf do show features, such as pairs and triplets surrounded by marginal lines (Fig. 4B), which we do not discern in the made imprints of Figure 4A. This, however, may be an accident of replication—I have been unable, for instance, to reproduce structures exactly like those made by Nathorst in 1880, despite scores of experiments varying consistency of sediment, thickness of overlying water layer, and height of fall of the impacting drops. The variety of medusoid-like features that might be produced by the mechanism of impacting drops in circumstances favorable for preservation is suggested by illustrations in Worthington (1908).

The other object described as jellyfish-like by Alf and the one described by Bassler as *Brooksella canyonensis* resemble structures that have been produced by gas-evasion from sediments or by compaction around compressible or soluble objects such as gas domes or crystals (which, if salt or gypsum, might then be dissolved away). Gerald Webers and I spent several days in 1962 scouring the site at which Van Gundy obtained the interesting object illustrated and named by Bassler but found only one other specimen that was definitely of the same sort. This specimen (Fig. 4, E and F) shows that the marginal lobation is a result of small-scale jointing, probably due to compaction of fine sands deposited over a compressible but otherwise unidentifiable subcircular structure, possibly a small gas blister (Cloud, 1960, p. 43). The curious but imperfect resemblance between this structure and one of the Ediacaran medusoids (Glaessner, 1962, p. 479, Pl. 1, Figs. 1, 2) is, in my judgment, fortuitous.

As for Dunnet's "possible jellyfish," which he suggested might be compared with the Ediacaran medusae, specimens from the same site are illustrated in Figure 4, G–I, where they are seen to resemble a radiating planar crystal growth of comparable dimensions (Fig. 4K) and, even more strikingly, a constrained crystal growth of much smaller size produced in the laboratory (Fig. 4J).

Then there is *"Obolella" montana* Fenton and Fenton (Fig. 5, B and C). Anyone familiar with the characteristic patterns of brachiopod growth lines can only be astonished, on examining this material closely, that it was ever taken for a brachiopod, even with reservation. Despite the suggestively sphenoidal shape of the holotype (Fig. 5C), the accretion lines do not swing around subparallel to the posterolateral margins and converge on the beak or hinge line as they do in true *Obolella* and other brachiopods (Fig. 5, A and D). Rather they directly abut the sides. Moreover, the manner in which these accretion lines are brought out by weathering reveals that their structure is present at depth in the rock and is not a purely surface feature. Finally, the array of more irregular paratypes in the block illustrated in Figue 5B shows a gross morphological pattern and orientation at a

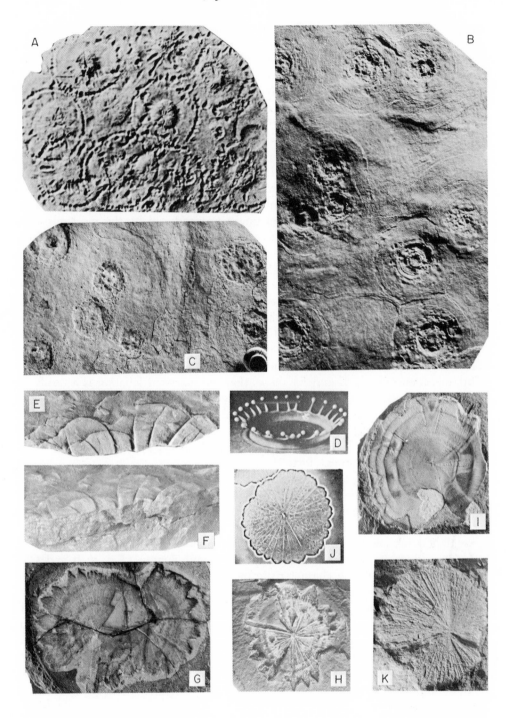

high angle to a probable bedding-parallel stylolite passing through the middle of the block. This indicates that we are in fact dealing with an aggregate of small, sphenoidal, algal stromatolites on a weathered joint face perpendicular to the stratification and not with brachiopods at all.

To interpret these fossils as brachiopods would require either that they be in growth position with beak down, in which case the presence of only one valve would have to be explained, or that they have achieved the preferred orientation and selective elimination of brachial valves (on a probably unreal bedding surface) as a result of currents which had no discernible visual, microscopic, or radiographic sorting effect on the associated sedimentary particles of this remarkably homogeneous rock. I concluded, therefore, some years ago, from study of the type specimens loaned by B. F. Howell, that here is a record of Precambrian life all right, only not a metazoan but a sedimentary structure of algal origin.

One of the most puzzling examples of alleged Precambrian Metazoa involves the *Manchuriophycus* problem, which has been discussed by many since these structures were first described and attributed to algae by Endo (1933). Such curious sinusoidal sand strings and depressions and arcuately spindle-shaped sand wedges occur in association with incomplete contraction-crack patterns in ripple-marked sandstones and quartzites of various ages. Like the characteristically arcuate contraction cracks of such sediments (Fig. 6B), they show a marked preference for the ripple troughs as well as a high degree of coincidence with recognizable contraction cracks. They are most frequently recorded from the Precambrian,

---

Fig. 4. Pseudo-medusae of different ages.

A. Imprints (about ×⅔) made by drops of water falling on soft plaster-of-paris covered by a thin film of water (after Nathorst, 1880, Pl. 11. Fig. 4).

B, C. "Jellyfish-like" structures (×⅞ and about ×⅔) from Precambrian, Unkar Group, Bass Formation, Grand Canyon south of Bright Angel Creek, Ariz. (photographs courtesy of R. M. Alf).

D. Instantaneous photograph of a splash produced by a falling drop, by H. E. Edgerton in Thompson, 1945 (frontispiece).

E, F. "*Brooksella*" *canyonensis* Bassler (×⅔). Specimen found by Gerald Webers at "holotype" locality (Cloud's loc. 2 of 20 June 1963) above Basalt Cliffs in southeastern part of Grand Canyon National Park, Ariz. Note in F how lobation is related to contemporaneous compaction jointing of sediments that offsets only lower and not upper bedding laminae. Imprint is on under surface of bed.

G–I. Specimens (×⅔) from young Precambrian (?) Ord Group, Ranford Formation, at top of Mt. Brooking, Kimberley Region, Western Australia. This is the locality and bed from which similar material was described by Dunnet (1965) as *Cyclomedusa*-like (cf. Fig. 7E) and considered "similar to the Ediacara Fauna" (specimens from coll. R 1859 of Geological Survey of Western Australia, Eugene Driscoll, collector).

J. Constrained growth of a hexagonal crystal of isotactic polystyrene (greatly enlarged; after Tiller, 1964, Fig. 5).

K. Imprints (×⅔) of radiating marcasite(?) growths parallel to surface of beds of Upper Cretaceous (Laramie) age, 150 feet east of Douglas (Lehigh) Coal Mine, Sedalia, Colo. (U.S. Geological Survey coll. 3582, R. W. Brown collector).

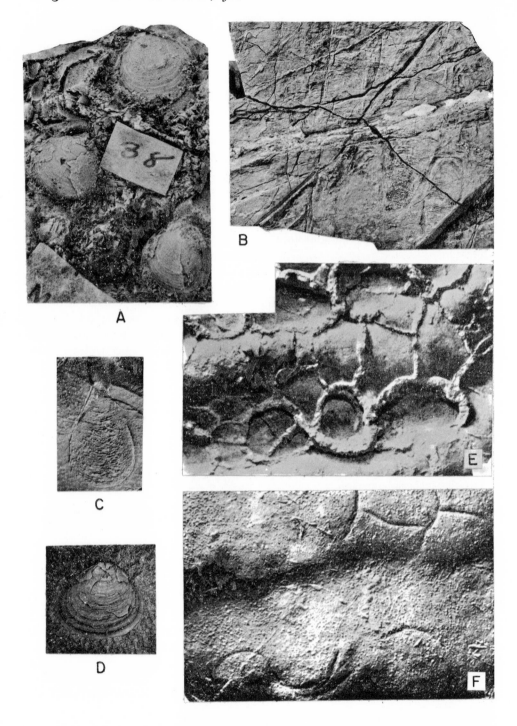

where they are often reported as "worm tracks"; but there are records of similar structures from Cambrian, Carboniferous, perhaps Permian, and Triassic sandstones (summarized in Häntzschel, 1949; also Schindewolf, 1956, Pl. 31, reproduced in Fig. 5, E and F of the present report). Häntzschel (1949), and Wheeler and Quinlan (1951) have interpreted such markings as of nonbiologic origin, and Barnes and Smith (1964) have given a clear exposition of the mechanics by which some similar markings may be produced nonbiologically.

Nevertheless the notion that these things might not only be fossils but Metazoa has persisted, and Frarey and McLaren (1963), and Frarey et al. (1963), have recently given very persuasive arguments in favor of such an interpretation for an occurrence in the ripple troughs of arkosic quartzites of the Huronian Lorrain Formation northeast of Desbarats, Ontario (Fig. 6A). Subsequently discovered similar structures in quartzites (also ripple-marked) of younger Huronian age about 15 miles north of Elliot Lake, Ontario, include even more convincingly lifelike forms. Like some of the forms illustrated at the upper left of Figure 6A, they are bilaterally symmetrical, doubly tapering spindles, with a central axis and lateral corrugations suggesting segmentation. Photographs of selected material from this new occurrence sent to me by McLaren were so persuasive that I was willing to concede a biologic origin until a visit to the field locality in October 1966, under the guidance of Frarey and Hans Hofmann, who is preparing a report on the material.[9] On outcrop, however, the association with a pattern of contraction cracking is so persistent, the superposition of doubly tapering arcuate spindles on similarly tapering arcs of sinusoidal contraction cracks that follow the ripple troughs so usual, and divergences from this pattern so consistent with observed deviations of recent contraction-cracked, ripple-marked sediments (Fig. 6B), that it strains credulity to accept the corrugated spindles as truly the sand casts of organisms.

9. Hofmann's report was published in *Science, 156* (1967), 500–04.

Fig. 5. *"Obolella" montana* compared with early brachiopods. Triassic pseudo-annelids.
A. *Obolella chromatica* Billings (×3½). Lower Cambrian, Strait of Belle Isle, Newfoundland (photograph courtesy of U.S. National Museum).
B, C. *"Obolella" montana* Fenton and Fenton (×1), Precambrian, Belt Series, Newland Limestone, 8 miles west of White Sulphur Springs, Mont. B is of paratypes, weathered out on joint surface. C is the holotype from Fenton & Fenton (1936, Pl. 3, Fig. 5). Compare abutment of accretion lines against margins with the growth lines of *Obolella* in A and *Obolus* in D, which converge on beak of shell.
D. *Obolus* sp. (×2), Ordovician (Whiterock), Upper Table Head Series, Port-au-Port, Newfoundland.
E, F. Triassic pseudo-annelids for comparison with Fig. 6A. Both specimens are of ripple-marked and contraction-cracked Keuper sandstones (after Schindewolf, 1956, Pl. 31). Specimen E (×⅓) is an upper surface from a locality near Tübingen, and F (×¼) is a lower surface from near Gaildorf, Germany.

Unsolved problems include how corrugated symmetrical structures of this nature could form by purely physical processes and how sandy sediments happen to undergo contraction cracking. I am unable to suggest how the spindles could have formed abiologically, any more than I can suggest how they could have lived where found, or, if they are the sand fillings of exhumed and redeposited chaetopterid or other metazoan tubes, why such structures should repeatedly be arrayed in great abundance in interconnected strings in exact superposition on or mimicry of a contraction-crack pattern and hardly anywhere else! Perhaps they result from injection under load or squeezing up of the fillings of contraction cracks. Experiments need to be made, but my unsuccessful efforts to replicate exactly Nathorst's imprints (Fig. 5A) illustrate how large an element of chance is involved. Why contraction cracks should form in sand is equally a mystery, but Figure 6B shows that they do. Failing a high clay content, it is possible that salt precipitated from interstitial waters would provide enough cohesion to favor such a pattern. Sand casts of halite concentrated in some ripple troughs suggest such a possibility. Or perhaps cracks starting in clay fillings in the ripple troughs were propagated laterally and downward. Such an origin would be consistent with the fact that many of the spindles observed show a partial clay sheath—particularly those that also show corrugations. Indeed it is possible that the clay sheaths have something to do with the origin of the corrugations.

As a last example of why I am skeptical about reported Precambrian Metazoa, I want to consider how some Metazoa may come to be called Precambrian by inversion of usual biostratigraphic reasoning: instead of dating the rocks by the fossils found in them, the supposed age of the rocks is used to date the fossils. Such is the report by A. H. McNair of supposedly Precambrian fossils from northern Canadian rocks, said to be intruded by gabbroic sills and containing glauconite at first reported, respectively, to yield K/Ar ages of about 650 and 720 MY (McNair, 1965a,b). Photographs of these fossils were kindly sent to me by McNair on 14 September 1965 and also displayed by him on presentation of his paper announcing their occurrence on 4 November 1965 (McNair, 1965a). Among these fossils are unusually large species (10-14 mm wide) of the distinctive Early and Middle Cambrian brachiopod genera *Paterina* and *Dictyonina*, not to mention a probable genal spine of a trilobite and a wealth of trace fossils. This is clearly a Cambrian fauna, and most likely Middle Cambrian. The only legitimate question that was ever involved here was whether the base of the Cambrian was older than had previously been thought, or whether the radiometric ages or supposed associations were in error. As it turned out, McNair (1965c) subsequently announced that discovery of a computational error had reduced the reported "minimum" age to 445 MY, but there are other peculiarities about these outcrops and their associations that leave as the only certain conclusion on evidence now available that the rocks containing the fossils are, in fact, of Cambrian age.

Let me conclude this discussion by commenting that I do not happen to know of a convincing occurrence of Precambrian sponges or sponge spicules either (Appendix A). Sponges, however, being little more than benthic colonial protists whose low oxygen requirements are satisfied by diffusion, would not be complete anomalies in the Precambrian, before Metazoa in the strict sense arose. Records of sponges even as far back as 1.8 to 2 BY, although unlikely, would not invalidate the model here suggested.

The Ediacaran Assemblage

Where then are the records of Precambrian life more advanced than such as the stromatolite-building algae and the Gunflint (Barghoorn and Tyler, 1965; Cloud, 1965) and Bitter Springs (Barghoorn and Schopf, 1965) microbiotas? One that has been proposed is an authentic and very early metazoan assemblage of great interest, for the knowledge of which we are particularly indebted to the prolific pen of M. F. Glaessner. I refer, naturally, to the fossils from the Pound Quartzite at Ediacara, whose remarkable preservation in South Australia and wide representation on other continents has already been mentioned.

Let us consider first the possible age and stratigraphic significance of this fauna and then its biological affinities.

Relation of the Ediacaran fauna to the base of the Paleozoic. Sprigg (1947), the discoverer of the Ediacara assemblage, originally suggested a middle Early Cambrian age for it, although with a query. By 1949 the query had apparently been removed in Sprigg's mind, and in 1958 additional fossils from the same beds were assigned, without reservation, to the basal Cambrian by Glaessner (1958a). In the same year, however, impressed by the differences between the Ediacaran assemblage and known Cambrian faunas, and following an earlier suggestion by Noakes (1956), Glaessner (1958b) adopted a Precambrian age. Coincidentally, a paper by Ford (1958), describing supposed Precambrian fossils from England that were to prove generically close to Ediacaran forms, appeared in the same year. These fossils, *Charnia* and *Charniodiscus*, from the Charnwood Forest, in Leicestershire, came from beds which had long been considered Precambrian because of their great structural deformation as compared with overlying Triassic and Carboniferous rocks. This seemed to provide timely confirmation of the suggestion by Noakes (1956) and Glaessner (1958) that the Paleozoic–Precambrian boundary be placed at the top instead of, as previously, beneath the Pound Quartzite, which contains the Ediacaran fossils. That is, it did until Haughton (1960) described a supposed archaeocyathid from the Kuibis Quartzite, at the base of the Nama System in Southwest Africa. These happen to be the same beds that produced the pennatulid-like genus *Rangea*, which also occurs at Ediacara, is apparently closely related to *Charnia*, and which Richter (1955) had concluded could not possibly be older than Cambrian.

Since then, both Glaessner (1963) and I have independently reexamined the Kuibis "archaeocyathids" and concur in the view that, striking though the superficial resemblance is, they are not archaeocyathids but the tracks of a burrowing soft-bodied organism. In the same paper, though, Glaessner refers to a 590-MY age determination on a granite older than the Nama beds, which would appear to place them and the Kuibis fossils firmly in the Cambrian.

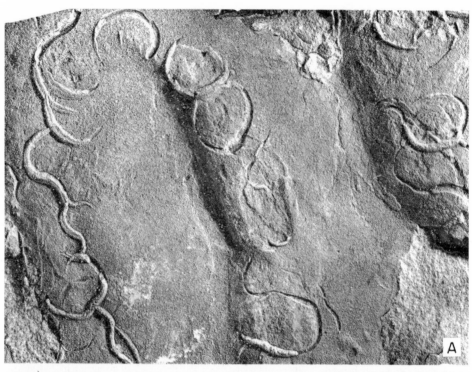

However, I have since been unable to obtain a confirmation from anyone in South or Southwest Africa either of this age or of the fact that a granite suitable for providing such an age exists. Therefore I assume that it is not accepted as established.[10]

Meanwhile, in the same year that Glaessner's paper gave an age of less than 590 MY for the Nama beds, there appeared a paper by Meneisy and Miller (1963) dealing with the geochronometry of the Charnian rocks. They obtained, from K/Ar determinations on whole-rock samples from porphyroids intrusive into the Charnian, ages of 574 ± 26 MY, and 684 ± 29 MY and concluded from this (p. 516) that the age of intrusion of the porphyroids was > 684 ± 29 MY, and the intruded sediments, consequently, older than this. If we choose to believe this particular number, which has been reported elsewhere, incidentally, as about 1 BY (Anderson, 1965, p. 98) or > 1 BY (Ford, 1962), and if we decide flatly that the base of the Paleozoic is no older than 620 ± 20 MY, the age of the Ediacaran fauna would be settled as late Precambrian. The issue, however, is not that clear.

Although the relation of the dated porphyroids to the fossiliferous outcrops is not particularized, it does seem likely that the porphyroids are younger, although probably not much younger, than the Charnian sediments. What seems to me to be not as yet firmly established is the age of the porphyroids on the one hand, and of the base of the Paleozoic on the other. Although it is generally assumed that K/Ar ages are minimal values, because of the possibility of argon loss, it is now also well known that pyroxene and perhaps other minerals can absorb

10. While this paper was in press, Glaessner (oral communication, June 1967) informed me that he was quoting information now known to be in error. No currently known radiometric dates serve to fix an age or close age limits for the Nama Series.

Fig. 6. Spindle-shaped sand bodies and linear depressions of Precambrian age compared with ripple-marked and contraction-cracked Recent sediments.

A. Markings (×½) on *under surface* of ripple-marked Precambrian Lorrain Formation, Algoma District, Ontario. Like 6B and 5E-F, these markings are concentrated in but not limited to the troughs of the ripples. Illustrated by Frarey and McLaren (1963) as "possible metazoans"; compared by Frarey, Ginsburg, and McLaren (1963) with *Chaetopterus* tubes (photograph courtesy Geological Survey of Canada).

B. Contraction-cracked Recent ripple-marked sandy sediments in bed of dry Badlands creek 1 mile east northeast of Scenic, N.D., 22 Sept. 1964. Although the pattern is on the top and not the bottom of the bed, and is by no means identical with above (especially in absence of corrugated, bilaterally symmetrical fillings) there are similarities that would be consistent with a similar origin. The cracks are concentrated in the ripple troughs, but they also branch and run into, and occasionally at right angles across, the ripple crests. Some loop around in near circles (lower center and left, both sides of hammer) and others intersect so that later compressed fillings or injected material might appear to overlap.

argon on heating and therefore give spuriously high ages (by as much as several orders of magnitude). Inasmuch as satisfactory basis has not yet been established for evaluation of K/Ar ages on whole-rock systems, any numbers proposed contain the possibility of bias for excessive as well as minimal age, as do either whole-rock or single-mineral age determinations on detrital sediments (e.g. Wermund et al., 1966; Dasch et al., 1966). The age given by Meneisy and Miller for the Charnian sediments cannot, therefore, at this time be considered firmly established.

If it were established, it would not as yet be proof of a Precambrian age for the Charnian, Ediacaran, etc., because the age taken by Davidson as best tying down the base of the Cambrian at 620 + 20 MY is based on sediments reported as being *within* the Lower Cambrian (Davidson, 1959). Meanwhile, new evidence has appeared of the occurrence of something like the genus *Pteridinium,* common to the Nama and Ediacaran assemblages, in beds only slightly below fossils of definitely Cambrian age in eastern California (Cloud and Nelson, 1966). If these beds are correlated with the Ediacaran it would seem that the transitions between Phanerozoic–Cryptozoic, Paleozoic–Precambrian, and Cambrian–Precambrian are not far apart.

What conclusions can we draw, then, about the relation of the Ediacaran assemblage to the base of the Paleozoic? I suggest the following.

1. The Ediacaran fauna is a primarily planktonic or pelagic association whose representatives in various parts of the world probably comprise an approximately correlatable and essentially contemporaneous ancestral metazoan assemblage—the oldest unequivocal metazoan fossils so far known.

2. As age assignments are now made, this assemblage is very near the base of the Paleozoic, either just above or just below; and it certainly belongs within the Phanerozoic Eon.

3. To place it in the Precambrian in no way eases the problem of seemingly abrupt metazoan origins.

4. It would be consistent with the model here elaborated of atmospheric evolution and its probable relations to biospheric and lithospheric evolution, and would also be operationally practical, to consider the base of the Paleozoic as coincident with the base of the Phanerozoic and to place the Paleozoic–Precambrian boundary below the level of the Ediacaran fauna, as the Termiers suggested in 1960.

5. If that were done, we might wish, on practical as well as theoretical grounds, to take the boundary as low as the top or bottom of the tillites that are reported to be so widespread in the young Precambrian, and which, if a reality, presumably represent climatic conditions that could have affected the timing of the initial metazoan radiations (e.g. Harland, 1964; Rudwick, 1964; Harland and Rudwick, 1964). Winsnes (1965, p. 7), for instance, uses the upper boundary of a tillite zone below Cambrian fossils in Svalbard to delimit the top of the Precambrian there. There is, however, nothing compelling about the relation, nor is it an essential part of the model here suggested.

6. For the time being, I prefer a testable definition of the Paleozoic–Precambrian boundary as the base of the range zone of Metazoa, and the top of the range zone of the conical stromatolite *Conophyton* s.s. (Korolyuk, 1960; Cloud, 1961, 1965).[11] This definition is operationally more universal than a simplistic one based on *Olenellus* or the olenellids, and at the same time philosophically more satisfying in that it is itself disprovable and reflects a model of the earth that has testable corollaries.

7. The definition proposed would include in the Paleozoic the Pound Quartzite and perhaps underlying rocks of the Adelaide System down to recognizable tillites, the Charnian, the Nama System, and probably the Vendian of the U.S.S.R. The Vendian is reported to contain extensive tillites as well as elements of the Ediacaran fauna and is considered to have a basal age of about 650 ± 50 MY (Semikhatov, 1966). Some, but not all, of the so-called Eocambrian or Infracambrian rocks of other areas, such as the upper beds of the Scandinavian Sparagmite Group, the Sinian above tillites, and part of the rocks called Vindhyan in India (e.g. Sokolov 1958, p. 121), may also belong here, as well as some Great Basin and Sonoran rocks, but apparently no part of the Belt. This is not a novel notion. Although not previously stated in exactly these terms, the idea has often been approached, most closely by the Termiers in 1960.

8. If it were to become apparent that this interval of geologic time could not properly be included in a manageable Cambrian Period, a different period name should be given to it. Nama and Adelaide are both available as systemic names, but it is time we broke with the tradition that bases Period and System on the same sequence. Let Nama, Vendian, Charnian, and other names be used as regional rock units up to the magnitude of systems if need be, but the name of the time unit, be it Period or smaller, should be Ediacaran (or Ediacarian) from the best development of the fauna, as the Termiers proposed in 1960.

9. Finally, let me add that I do not conclude that a Paleozoic age has been demonstrated for the Ediacaran, but only, as will appear from consideration of the fossils themselves, that no great gulf exists between the Ediacaran and younger rocks, and that a Precambrian age has also not been demonstrated. By my criteria, if accepted, the Ediacaran would be Paleozoic (perhaps pre-Cambrian, but not Precambrian and certainly not Cryptozoic). A final resolution, however, cannot be achieved until general agreement has been reached on what criteria shall prevail. I would only urge that the criteria employed have a time–stratigraphic sig-

11. The term *Conophyton* has been applied to a variety of conical and subconical stromatolites, and the nomenclature needs restudy. I use it here to refer only to multiconical structures in which the depositional laminae are continuous across the interspaces and the upwardly directed cones are sharply peaked. The interspace laminae are also conical and point downward, but the conical tips are slightly U-shaped rather than V-shaped. Size of individual cones may range from that of a candle to that of a man. Similar forms in which the laminae do not cross the interspaces may also be Precambrian. Bluntly conical, subcylindrical stromatolites with laminae not crossing the interspaces are found both in Precambrian and Paleozoic strata. They are best referred to *Collenia* until the nomenclature can be brought up to date.

nificance and be self-testing to the extent that they define what *is* Precambrian as well as what is *not* Paleozoic; and I submit that no extant definition other than the one proposed in item 6 above meets this condition. I also submit that the principle of evolutionary interaction predicts that the origin of the Metazoa be nearly coincident with other major events in geologic history—hence a good place for an era boundary (or, better, transition).

Biological affinities of the Ediacaran fossils. As for the Ediacaran fauna itself, as elaborated in various papers by Sprigg, Glaessner, and Glaessner and Daily, it consisted at last count (Glaessner, 1966) of perhaps a thousand specimens, representing some twenty-five species in fifteen genera and three phyla—all Metazoa. This includes seven designated genera of medusoids, three genera considered to be pennatulids, and two genera considered to be closely similar to living annelids. Not a very impressive fauna by biological standards, but thoroughly engrossing for its geological position.

Although Glaessner has emphasized its divergence from known Early Cambrian faunas, it is not really remarkable that this mainly soft-bodied pelagic assemblage should be different from the mainly benthonic shelly assemblages available for comparison. There are, moreover, as one would expect, some rather interesting similarities not only between Ediacaran and known Cambrian fossils, but between Ediacaran and much younger Metazoa. Indeed, it is because of such similarities that this striking early assemblage is biologically meaningful.

Many of the Ediacaran medusoids provide little to come to grips with (although Harrington and Moore, 1956, assigned some of them to the scyphomedusid Scyphozoa and the trachylinid Hydrozoa), and in this respect they are not dissimilar to reported Paleozoic occurrences. Stasinska (1960), however, has described as similar to *Ediacaria* (Sprigg, 1949) a medusoid, *Velumbrella czarnockii* (Fig. 7, A–C), which occurs with *Protolenus* and above a level rich in trilobites in the Lower Cambrian of Poland. To my eye *Velumbrella* is even more suggestive of Sprigg's *Cyclomedusa radiata* (Fig. 7E) and *Tateana inflata* (Fig. 7D).

Dickinsonia (Fig. 8, B and C), compared by Glaessner with the living amphinomorphid polychaete *Spinther* (Fig. 8A; see also Hartman, 1948, p. 10, 15–18) is similar in gross morphology and segmentation to the imprinted soft parts of shelly cambridiid or stenothecoid mollusks like *Cambridium* (Fig. 8, D and E) and *Bagenovia* (Horný, 1956) of the Lower Cambrian of eastern Siberia.

Fig. 7. Early Cambrian and Ediacaran medusae.

A–C. *Velumbrella czarnockii* Stasińska ($\times 1$, $\times 1$, $\times \frac{2}{3}$) from trilobite-bearing Lower Cambrian beds at Brzechów, Holy Cross Mts., Poland, after Stasińska 1960, Pl. 3, Fig. 1; Pl. 2, Fig. 1; Pl. 1, Fig. 1).

D. *Tateana inflata* Sprigg (ca. $\times 1$), Pound Sandstone, Ediacara, South Australia (after Sprigg, 1949, Pl. 11, Fig. 1).

E. *Cyclomedusa radiata* Sprigg (ca. $\times 1$), Pound Sandstone, Ediacara, South Australia (after Sprigg, 1949, Pl. 15, Fig. 1).

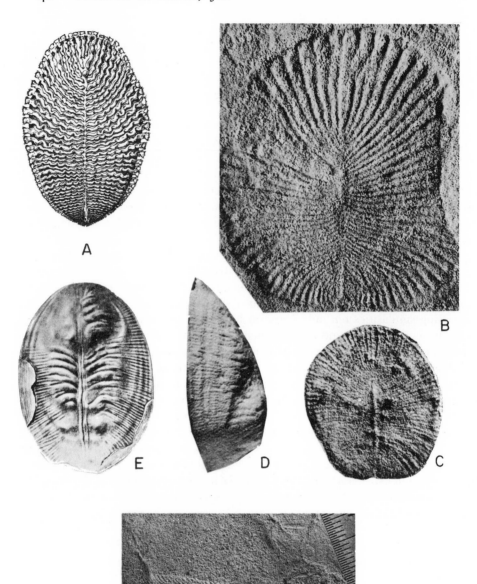

A

B

E

D

C

F

The other annelid, *Spriggina* (Fig. 8F), is related by Glaessner to the living errant and pelagic polychaete *Tomopteris* (family Tomopteridae) and considered to resemble possible ancestors of the Middle Cambrian Burgess Shale genus *Marrella* (Fig. 9B; see also Walcott, 1931, p. 28–37; and Ruedemann, 1931, p. 9–16, Pls. 3, 6, 7), which suggests affinities with branchiopods and trilobites.

These are grounds for arguing that, when one takes the differences of preservation into account, there is no great gulf between the Ediacaran fauna and fossils from younger rocks.

But there are more Ediacaran fossils. They include the curious anchor-shaped *Parvancorina* and the three-rayed *Tribrachidium* of as yet unfathomed affinities, possibly representing, respectively, another annelid and a filter-feeding organism perhaps ancestral to the echinoderms. There are also the arborescent and spicular fossils *Rangea* and *Charnia*, as well as *Pteridinium* (Gürich, 1930, 1933; Richter, 1955), an organism of some rigidity and dubious affinities somewhat reminiscent of the Conularida. Although there are differences in the manner of branching and the lack of evidence for the zooidal dimorphism that is ubiquitous among living Pennatulacea (Hyman, 1940, p. 559), Glaessner has given reasonably persuasive grounds for considering *Rangea* and *Charnia*, at least provisionally, to be pennatulids. They are not very convincing gorgonaceans, despite the careful and comprehensive study of Richter (1955), nor very convincing algae, as Ford (1958) tentatively proposed.

A curious thing about these pennatulid-like organisms, however, is their apparent association with medusoid floats of some kind. *Charnia* appears to be attached to *Charniodiscus* (Ford, 1958, 1962). Also a number of the medusoids at Ediacara seem to show pieces of central stems about the diameter of *Rangea* stems, or places where stems may have broken off; and these stranded medusoids show a preferred orientation with the "stem" side up. This goes with wide distribution and associated pelagic elements to suggest that *Rangea* and *Charnia*, rather than being "rooted" pennatulids, may have been pelagic Anthozoa that hung beneath medusoid floats. On stranding, such floats could have been turned convex side down as their pennatuliform appendages dragged out and became detached.

Fig. 8. *Dickinsonia, Spinther, Cambridium, Spriggina.*
A. *Spinther alaskensis* Hartman (×2.8). Recent, from 25 to 40 fathoms in Canoe Bay, Alaska (after Hartman, 1948, Fig. 1a).
B. *Dickinsonia costata* Sprigg (ca. ×2), Pound Sandstone, Ediacara, South Australia (after Glaessner, 1964).
C. *Dickinsonia minima* Sprigg (×½), Pound Sandstone, Ediacara, South Australia (after Sprigg, 1949, Pl. 21, Fig. 2 [sic = Fig. 3]).
D, E. *Cambridium nikiforovae* Horný (×3), upper Lower Cambrium (Cm₁), Yelanka, East Siberia, U.S.S.R. (after Horný, 1956, Pl. 1, Fig. 2; Pl. 4, Fig. 1).
F. *Spriggina floundersi* Glaessner (×1.2), Pound Sandstone, Ediacara, South Australia (print supplied by M. F. Glaessner).

ORIGINS OF THE METAZOA

Now we can discuss the origin of the Metazoa from the viewpoint of what some early Metazoa were like as well as in terms of possible cause and time of origin. As the discussion proceeds from this point, reference should be made to the suggested phyletic model in Figure 10. Since we have already considered pre-eucaryote evolution, and since details of plant evolution are not germane, the ensuing discussion will focus on the upper right and center of this plan.

Beginning with Haeckel (1866, 1872; see also Rádl, 1930, p. 138–40), whose monophyletic gastraea hypothesis prevailed as ruling theory for over half a century, this problem has mainly occupied zoologists, with surprisingly little constructive input from paleontology. Indeed, except for the work of Franz (1924), it is only in recent years that there has been any really serious consideration of hypotheses alternative to Haeckel's by people such as Steinböck (1937), Hyman (1940, p. 248–53), Carter (1946, p. 140–41), Baker (1948), Hardy (1953), Hadži (1953, 1963), de Beer (1954, presenting an earlier version of Hadži's work), and Kerkut (1965, p. 36–49). Kerkut's account also gives a convenient summary of the characteristics of likely ancestral types.

In considering metazoan origins, all conceivable choices, other than special creation or new arrival from another planet (which it would not be fruitful to consider farther), fall in one or another of four categories: (1) Metazoa arose directly from single-celled Protista; (2) They arose by differentiation of colonial protists (in effect Haeckel's gastraea hypothesis); (3) they arose as a result of the development of cell boundaries in and differentiation of multinucleate syncytial or plasmodial protists (e.g. Steinböck, 1937; Hadži, 1953, 1963); (4) they arose from metaphytes (e.g. Hardy, 1953).

Of these alternatives, the first is perhaps less likely than the others, simply because it seems easier to get a metazoan if one already has something multicelled to begin with.

The sponges (Parazoa) might logically be derived via the second route, from colonial choanoflagellates (e.g. Hyman, 1940, p. 107; but not from "Proterospongia," Kerkut, 1960, p. 59), with little more than an increase in number and slight specialization of cells, and improvement of organization and axial symmetry. Haeckel (1872, v. 111, Pl. 1, Fig. 8) already knew that the choanocyte cells of sponges could change from collared to amoeboid as they wandered through the mesoglea. Hyman (1940, p. 293) observes that the various types of sponge cells appear to be modifications of an undifferentiated amoeboid cell. And Willmer (1956) describes the optional dimorphism from amoeboid to flagellate of the amoeboid protist *Naegleria gruberi*, as well as the habit of isolated sponge choanocytes of changing to creeping amoeboids, only to reacquire their collar and sometimes their flagellum. It is consistent with all we know, therefore, and probably as close as we will come to approximating the origin of a multicelled animal, to judge that sponges very likely did arise from colonial choanoflagellates early in Paleozoic time, if not in the Precambrian. Indeed, it is not impossible that sponges arose from choanoflagellate ancestors more than once! The extinct and short-lived Archaeocyatha may be a sterile offshoot from the Porifera proper, or an independent origin that was only temporarily successful. We cannot do better at this time because we do not have the necessary information about archaeocyathid cytology.

But the origin of the relatively uncoordinated and poorly integrated Parazoa is not the origin of the Metazoa. It seems less likely although not impossible, as we shall see, that the Metazoa, strictly speaking, would have originated directly from a colony of fully independent protistan cells. Let us first consider, then, how a metazoan might arise from a multinucleate syncytial or plasmodial state by cellularization, as Steinböck (1937) and Hadži (1963) would have it, or from a multicelled plant as Hardy (1953) proposes.

Hardy does not develop his proposal in detail. He only asks why not a metazoan from a metaphyte at least once, and suggests the Anthozoa as a possible candidate. Perhaps the anthozoan zooxanthellae hark back to such an ancestor. And perhaps Ford's difficulty in deciding whether *Charnia* was an "algal frond" or a "primitive coelenterate of unknown affinities" (Ford, 1958) should cause us to reconsider whether the pennatulid-like structures from various Ediacaran equivalents might conceivably have had metaphytic ancestors. The possibility bears further exploration.

Hadži (1963 and earlier) develops the notion of metazoan origins from multinucleate ciliates at great length, mercifully condensed by de Beer (1954), who first presented his views in English. His basic theme, to risk oversimplification, is that bilateria and not the radiata are truly primitive, and that, structurally and histologically, all true metazoans (excluding sponges) are derivable via the turbellarian platyhelminths, of which the most primitive, the Acoela, arose directly from syncytial ciliates.

Hadži, having devoted a long career to this matter, is able to offer an impressive body of evidence in support of his views. Certain multinucleate ciliates already have a well-established symmetry; an anterior-posterior axis; practice sexual conjugation; show a differentiation into inner, middle, and outer body material and organelles; and possess trichocysts which are similar to turbellarian sagittocysts and cnidarian nematocysts. In effect, all that is needed to convert such a protist to an acoelous turbellarian, which has neither gut nor complete cellularization, is partial cellularization and a primitive nerve net. A hollow gut comes later.

Hadži next derives the rhabdocoelid and polyclad Turbellaria from them and gets the Cnidaria from the rhabdocoelids and the Ctenophora by paedomorphosis ("neoteny") from something like the larval polyclad known as Müller's larva. The similarity of ctenophorans to Müller's larva has, of course, been long known, but Hadži reverses the previously suggested order. He has no trouble accounting for the characteristically cnidarian nematocysts, because they find their precursors in the turbellarian sagittocysts. Hadži also reverses the usual model of cnidarian evolution and derives the Hydrozoa from the Scyphozoa, which in turn arise from the Anthozoa.

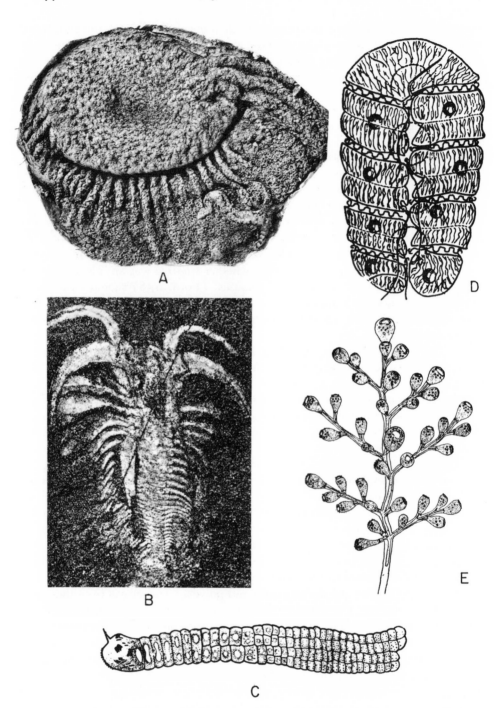

A

B

C

D

E

This model, be it noted, is not contradicted by the paleontological record. The annelids *Spriggina* (Fig. 8F) and *Dickinsonia* (Fig. 8, B and C) could reasonably have arisen from preceding or contemporary platyhelminths. And, since organisms representing probable Anthozoa (*Rangea, Charnia*), possible Hydrozoa (*Protodipleurosoma*), and certainly Scyphozoa (*Cyclomedusa, Tateana,* Fig. 7, D and E) are all present among the earliest metazoans known, any one of these classes could have been the first cnidarian. Or they might have arisen nearly simultaneously.

It seems to me, however, that we are not restricted to deriving all Metazoa (excluding Parazoa) from a single ancestor or group of ancestors. Alternative routes to the Cnidaria and Ctenophora are suggested by dashed lines in Figure 10. A simple cnidarian or ctenophoran for instance, might have arisen *directly* from a syncytial ciliate, armed with trichocysts as nematocyst or colloblast precursors, or a ctenophoran from a protozoan like Müller's larva. Nor does it seem too remote a conjecture to derive these phyla from colonial dinoflagellates similar, say, to the family Polykrikidae (Fig. 9D; also Kerkut, 1965, p. 40), which possess a marked anterior–posterior axis, interconnected cytoplasm, and cnidocysts that are made inside the cell and used for catching prey in a manner analogous to the nematocysts of cnidaria and colloblasts of ctenophorans. Something like the colonial ciliate *Zoöthamnium* (Fig. 9E), with its interconnected cytoplasm and differentiation into feeding and reproductive zooids, would seem also to require little change to give rise to a hydrozoan.

Finally, if a colonial dinoflagellate can develop a structure superficially as similar to a naked machaerid as is the parasitic but interconnected and differentiated *Haplozoon* (Fig. 9C; also Grassé, 1952), it is not inconceivable that the Echinodermata may have arisen from a similar armored pyrophyte, perhaps via the Machaerida themselves or something like the Early Cambrian medusaform genus *Camptostroma* (Fig. 9A), recently recognized by Durham (1966) as a primitive pelagic echinoderm.

That an ample microbiota was available at the right time is well established by the investigations of Timofeev (1959) and others who have described many

---

Fig. 9. *Camptostroma, Marrella,* multicelled protists.
A. *Camptostroma roddyi* Ruedemann (×1.5), Kinzers Formation, Lower Cambrian, Lancaster, Pa., U.S. Nat. Mus. no. 85181 (print supplied by J. Wyatt Durham).
B. *Marrella splendens* Walcott (×3), Middle Cambrian, Burgess Shale, 1 mile northeast of Burgess Pass, near Field, British Columbia; showing similarities to *Spriggina,* brachiopods, and trilobites (after Ruedemann, 1931, Pl. 6, Fig. 3).
C. *Haplozoon* (greatly enlarged, a living syncytial dinoflagellate (after Grassé, 1952).
D. *Pheopolykrikos* (greatly enlarged), a living colonial dinoflagellate of the family Polykrikidae (after Chatton, 1952).
E. *Zoöthamnium* (greatly enlarged), a living colonial ciliate (after Hyman, 1940, Fig. 66B).

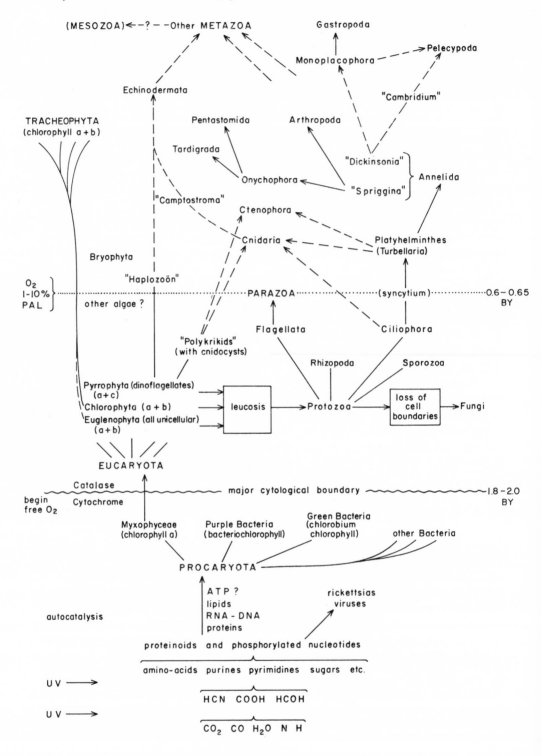

presumably microplanktonic forms, some suggesting dinoflagellates, from the late Precambrian and early Paleozoic.

Recall, now, the resemblances between *Spriggina* and the arthropods, as well as the former's obvious polychaete affinities and the possibility of getting these from Turbellarian platyhelminths. Added to the preceding, means can be suggested of accounting for all so-far reported early Cambrian metazoan phyla, in either a narrow or a broad sense, except the Mollusca.

On grounds of the already mentioned gross morphological similarity between another possible polychaete, *Dickinsonia,* from the Ediacaran, and the shelly *Cambridium* from the Early Cambrian of Siberia (Horný, 1957), I further suggest that morphology and geologic distribution are consistent with an origin of the cambridiid mollusks, the Amphineura-Monoplacophora, and, via these, more advanced molluscan types from something like *Dickinsonia.* McAlester (1965) has shown elsewhere how the pelecypods might be derived from the Monoplacophora through something like the Ordovician lucinoid *Babinka,* and the cambridiids are another possible ancestral or intermediate form. Of course, it is no great step from a monoplacophoran to a gastropod. Pteropods and cephalopods are more difficult to account for; but I suppose that if we have a "basic mollusk" to start with, these things can be achieved within the time observed.

It is, of course, hardly necessary to say that all of this must remain highly conjectural until better intermediates are found and a much more refined biostratigraphy and geologic history worked out.

With this caveat, the preceding sketch could account for the Metazoa that were known by the end of Early Cambrian time, although in doing so it suggests as many as four possible independent metazoan origins from reasonable premetazoan ancestors, not counting a fifth independent origin for the Parazoa from colonial choanoflagellates. If we follow Hardy in considering a metaphytic origin for the cnidaria, we change the pattern but do not necessarily increase the number of main channels. There may, of course, have been parallel secondary routes within the main channels.

Clearly, the value of such a model, if any, lies in the extent to which it assists in focusing the large amount of work that needs yet to be done in paleontology, zoology, and geology before we can begin to think of this or any other model as if it were a theory. However, I do propose, as a working hypothesis, that the Metazoa are broadly polyphyletic in origin, in consequence of more or less simultaneous attainment of a metazoan grade of organization by different pre-metazoan stocks. This may have been brought on, as Nursall (1959) and Berkner and Marshall (1964, 1965) have suggested, by increase in atmospheric oxygen to levels consistent with metazoan oxidative metabolism (about 3 per cent PAL) near the beginning of Paleozoic time. I add to this my earlier suggestion (Cloud, 1948, p.

Fig. 10. Capsule phylogeny from biogenesis to Metazoa (quotation marks suggest gross morphology, not specific taxon named).

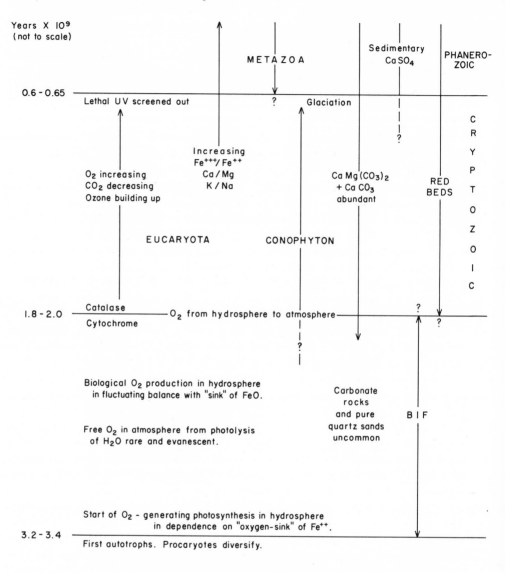

Years X 10^9
(not to scale)

METAZOA

Sedimentary
$CaSO_4$

PHANERO-
ZOIC

0.6 - 0.65   Lethal UV screened out   ?   Glaciation

P
H
A
N
E
R
O

Increasing
Fe^{+++}/Fe^{++}
Ca / Mg
K / Na

O_2 increasing
CO_2 decreasing
Ozone building up

$CaMg(CO_3)_2$
$+ CaCO_3$
abundant

RED
BEDS

C
R
Y
P
T
O
Z
O
I
C

EUCARYOTA   CONOPHYTON

1.8 - 2.0   Catalase
Cytochrome O_2 from hydrosphere to atmosphere   ?   ?

?

Biological O_2 production in hydrosphere
in fluctuating balance with "sink" of FeO.

Free O_2 in atmosphere from photolysis
of H_2O rare and evanescent.

Carbonate
rocks
and pure
quartz sands
uncommon

BIF

Start of O_2 - generating photosynthesis in hydrosphere
in dependence on "oxygen-sink" of Fe^{++}.

3.2 - 3.4

First autotrophs. Procaryotes diversify.

Simple heterotrophic PROCARYOTA arise

3.5 - 3.8   Biogenesis

2000-2900Å UV at surface, chemical evolution, prebiological synthesis.

Atmosphere of CO_2, CO, H_2O, N_2, H_2. Sedimentation begins.

Melting, degassing, beginning of atmosphere and hydrosphere.

Gravitational heating, segregation, core formation, magnetic field.

No magnetic field, no atmosphere, solar wind sweeps surface.

4.7 - 4.8   Accumulation of the earth completed.

346–48) that the attainment of a metazoan grade of evolution not only was nearly coincident with the base of the Paleozoic, but was surely followed by rapid diversification of new morphological types, inasmuch as all ecological niches occupiable by metazoans would then be unoccupied. Thus, a proliferation of metazoan forms equivalent to what we see in the first 50 to 100 million years or so of Paleozoic time can be accounted for.

The argument as to which was primitive, radiata or bilateria, is probably meaningless. The earliest metazoan fossils and their hypothetical predecessors include both radially and bilaterally symmetrical forms. Probably both symmetries existed from the beginning, although this is not to say that in the course of evolution either may not have converged on the other.

SUMMARY AND MODEL OF THE EARLY EARTH

We have now covered a large territory, and the parts may not adhere as tightly as one would like. Let me close, then, by laying out in abbreviated and unqualified form a general working model of the early earth leading to the origin of the Metazoa.

There is a necessary relationship between the evolution of the biosphere and that of atmosphere, hydrosphere, and lithosphere that allows us to draw on evidence from all these subjects in reaching conclusions about any one of them. This also requires conclusions about one to be consistent with evidence and conclusions from the others. For instance, and crucial to the question of metazoan origins, the evolution of both the eucaryotic cell and a sufficient level of free O_2 in atmosphere and hydrosphere are necessary, if not sufficient, preconditions for the origin of the Metazoa. There are no permanently anaerobic nonparasitic Metazoa, and the potential of metazoan evolution as we know it can be realized only when the oxidative energy rates of respiratory metabolism are generally available. This limits conjecture concerning metazoan origins and suggests events in geologic history sufficiently important to mark a major time boundary.

To begin at the beginning, and at the bottom of Figure 11, the great depletion in the terrestrial atmosphere of the noble gases, as compared with their cosmic abundance, implies that, when the accumulation of the earth was completed about 4.7 to 4.8 billion years ago, it was essentially without an atmosphere.

Accumulation of the earth was accompanied and followed by gravitational heating and segregation, leading eventually to formation of a core, a magnetic field to shield the surface from the solar wind, and the commencement of volcanism and outgassing, as a result of which atmosphere and hydrosphere began to build up. With their appearance sedimentation commenced.

Ultraviolet irradiation of an O_2-free secondary atmosphere of internal origin consisting of CO_2, CO, H_2O, N_2, and H gave rise to chemical evolution of a variety of prebiological compounds. From these, mediated by autocatalysis

---

Fig. 11. Simplified model of the early earth.

involving H_2 and metal oxides, there eventually arose energy-storing and transferring, self-replicating, mutating structures comprising the first heterotrophic
and nonmitosing or procaryotic organisms.

Eventually, perhaps after one or more unsuccessful starts, autotrophs evolved
and the system became self-sustaining. Diversification of the procaryotes ensued,
including the appearance of three different types of photoautotrophs, one of
which produces free O_2. In the absence of an efficient oxygen and peroxide reduc-
tant, however, photosynthetically generated O_2 had to be disposed of.

Ferrous iron was an abundant solute in the primitive hydrosphere. It comprised a ready-made "oxygen sink." Addition of biogenic oxygen would convert
it to ferric oxides or hydroxides, which would then be precipitated along with
silica, some of the latter in biologically associated gelatinous form. Such precipitates were the parent materials of banded iron formation (BIF). The origin of
BIF as thick and extensive cyclic chemical precipitates from open-water bodies is
thus interpreted as having been biologically mediated (a condition of fluctuating
balance being suggested by the cyclic banding of iron-rich and iron-poor
silica). Adequate source ions could be transported only in the ferrous state, hence
only beneath an essentially anoxygenous atmosphere; the oxygen for precipitation of ferric oxides or hydroxides is best visualized as having a microbiologic
source, and suitable microorganisms are known to have been present. In adjacent
local environments, under variant conditions, perhaps in association with other
procaryotic microautotrophs, iron was deposited as ferrosulfides, ferrocarbonates,
or ferrosilicates.

Precambrian rocks characterized by BIF have an established age range from
more than 3 BY to about 1.8 to 2 BY and are not known to overlap the deposition
of important terrestrial red beds in younger sediments. This may represent a long
interval of fluctuating balance between O_2 production by organisms, dependent
on an oxygen acceptor to remove that poisonous by-product, and the supply of
dissolved ferrous iron. Oxygen resulting from photolysis of water vapor in the
atmosphere did not accumulate (1) because the process is limited and self-
regulating (Urey, 1959), and (2) because the small quantities of O_2 so produced
would, wherever circulated to the earth's surface, immediately be consumed in
the oxidation of reduced substances there abundant.

In time, however, O_2 and H_2O_2 reduction by iron itself was superseded by
the evolution of cytochromes and catalases or other more efficient oxygen and
peroxide reductants, and it became possible for organisms to survive in the presence of free O_2 and eventually even to use it in their metabolism.

At this point, green-plant photosynthesis could expand beyond a narrow dependence on a local oxygen acceptor, the seas would be swept of iron in solution
in a last surge of deposition of BIF, and O_2 could begin to accumulate and evade
from hydrosphere to atmosphere. Ultraviolet irradiation would result in the production of ozone and atomic oxygen in contact with the earth's surface, and the
transport of iron in surface waters in the ferrous state would decrease toward a
vanishing point. Ferric iron would be retained in the weathering profile, and the
formation of continental and marginal marine red beds of subaerially oxidized

source materials would result. The appearance of thick and widespread red beds just as the BIF drops out of the geological sequence about 1.8 BY ago is in keeping with such an interpretation.

After about 1.8 to perhaps 2 BY ago, therefore, it would be possible for restricted, low-demand, oxidative metabolism to commence, and for the mainly oxygen-employing, nucleated, and mitosing eucaryote cell to arise. Between then and about 600 to 650 MY ago, oxygen built up slowly in the hydrosphere—slowly because, until the accumulation of a sufficient ozone screen for UV shielding, the habitats occupiable by photosynthesizers would be limited to that part of the aquatic photic zone in which they could be shielded either by a layer of water or by agglutinated sediments. The land and the surface waters of the open sea would remain unoccupied until O_2 had reached somewhere upward of 1 per cent of present atmospheric level, permitting ozone to accumulate to levels such that UV radiation in the DNA-inactivating range of 2,500–2,600 Å would be effectively screened out.

Occupation of the open sea by phytoplankton at this time would likely be followed by a quantum increase in hydrospheric and atmospheric O_2. Such an increase of O_2, say to about the 3 per cent PAL sufficient for Metazoa of low oxygen requirements, could have led to the more or less simultaneous attainment of a metazoan grade of organization from several different premetazoan stocks, in turn followed by bursts of adaptive radiation into a host of then unoccupied and geographically isolated ecologic niches. As suggested by Nursall (1959) and effectively elaborated by Berkner and Marshall (1964, 1965), this would account for the seemingly abrupt appearance of the Metazoa at or near the opening of the Paleozoic Era. It is possible, also, that the same relatively abrupt increase in O_2 was brought about at the expense of a comparable decrease of CO_2, and therefore temperature, sufficient to bring on or trigger the reportedly great epoch of glaciation that somewhat preceded the appearance of a well-documented metazoan record. In that event, the tillites resulting from this glaciation could identify the dawn of the Paleozoic Era and Phanerozoic Eon. Subsequent climatic amelioration, plus increased availability of $CaCO_3$ in the warming seas, could have played a catalytic part in bringing this about.

It is consistent with these interpretations that thick and extensive deposits of sedimentary calcium sulfate, whose source of sulfate depends on oxidation of sulfides or other reduced sulfur molecules (Hutchinson, 1954; Abelson, 1966), are rare in or absent from the Precambrian but abundant from early Paleozoic onward.

Until such time, therefore, as a convincing record of Precambrian Metazoa may be established, any candidate for this distinction must survive three questions. Is it surely a fossil or the work of an organism? Does it represent an authentic metazoan? And is it surely endemic to rocks whose stratigraphic position is such that they cannot reasonably be included in the Paleozoic? For bold though we may be in building hypotheses in context with the framework of knowledge available, that framework itself may be extended beyond known limits only by demonstrable facts.

Appendix A. Some Reported Precambrian Metazoa and Parazoa of Dubious Age or Nature

Asterisk indicates items discussed in text; daggar indicates items most likely to be or to include Precambrian Metazoa, and hence needing further study or restudy.

Object in question	Reported by	Why queried	Present interpretation
1. Referred to brachiopods			
*Brachiopods and other fossils	McNair, 1965a, b, c	Presence of Cambrian brachiopods as displayed by specimens and photographs	Cambrian
*Obolella montana	Fenton & Fenton, 1937	Accretion lines abut margins instead of converging on apex; structural relations (Fig. 5 B, C)	Algal stromatolites
Chuaria circularis	Walcott, 1899	Tiny discoid specimens show complex crinkling as from compression of hollow sphere	Alga
Chuaria wimani	Wiman, 1894; Brotzen, 1941	Comparison to above of abundant round dark bodies, 2.5 mm diameter	Alga
Fermoria etc.	Chapman, 1936	Sahni, 1936; Sahni & Shrivastava, 1954	Possibly algal, but need restudy
†Protobolella	Chapman, 1936	Same	Pl. 2, Fig. 1, of *P. jonesi* (Chapman, 1936), a specimen unfortunately reported lost; could represent a fairly advanced inarticulate brachiopod; more specimens comparable to this and a radiometric age from

Taxon	Reference	Remarks	Interpretation
Linqulella and *Obolella*	Chapman, 1929	Grossly retouched photographs of Figs. 4–5 unrecognizable: Figs. 1–3 possibly pebbles or shale-blebs	Nonvital
2. Referred to arthropods			
*Xenusion auerswaldae	Pompeckj, 1928	Represented by only one specimen from a glacial erratic; probably from Cambrian Kalmarsund ss. (pers. comm. Anders Martinson)	Cambrian
Protoadelaidea, Reynella, Beaumontia, Beaumontella	David & Tillyard, 1936; David, 1928	Resemblance to mudflakes formed in ss. of many ages; see Seilacher, 1956, p. 79; Glaessner, 1958b, 1962 p. 159	Mud flakes in ss.
Beltina	Walcott, 1899	Irregular carbonaceous films	Nonvital or algal
3. Referred to "Coelenterata"			
cf. Coelenterata	Barghoorn & Tyler, 1963	Minute size; subsequently referred to soil bacteria and named *Kakabekia umbellata*, Barghoorn & Tyler, 1965	Bacterium
4. Referred to medusoids			
Medusoids	Haughton, 1962	Resemblance to concretionary structures	Concretions
*Jellyfish-like	Alf, 1959, Fig. 2	Nathorst, 1880, p. 79, Pls. 2, 11; D'Arcy Thompson, 1945, frontispiece; Worthington, 1908; see also Fig. 4 A–C	Made by raindrops splashing on water-veneered sediments
*Jellyfish-like	Alf, 1959, Fig. 1	Resemblance to forms produced by gas evasion, concretions, and compaction around solid objects	Nonvital
Medusoids?	Edgell, 1964, Pl. 3, Figs. 2, 7	Resemblance to other structures considered by Edgell as pseudofossils, and to structures made by concretions, diffusion, crystallization, etc.	Nonvital

Object in question	Reported by	Why queried	Present interpretation
"Jellyfish"	Dunnet, 1965	Similarity to radiating crystalline structures; mineralogical difference between weathered material of pseudofossil "impressions" and surrounding matrix; Tiller, 1964 (esp. Fig. 5); see also present Fig. 4 G–K.	Radiating crystal growths constrained parallel to bedding
*Brooksella canyonensis	Bassler, 1941	Irregularity, small-scale jointing delineating lobation, and possible origin by sand casting of collapsed gas dome (Fig. 5 E, F)	Nonvital
Protoniobia	Sprigg, 1949, Fig. 1	Examination of specimen	Imprint of a concretion
Carelozoon jatulicum	Metzger, 1924, Figs. 26, 27, Pl. 1	Seilacher, 1956, p. 158	Concretionary structure
5. Referred to "annelidan" and other trace fossils			
Sabellidites of Yanishovski	Dragunov, 1958	Previously known only from and used as index fossil to Cambrian	Probably Cambrian
*†Metazoan(?) tubes in troughs of rippled sediments	Frarey & McLaren, 1963; Frarey et al., 1963	Häntzschel, 1949; Wheeler & Quinlan, 1951; Schindewolf, 1956, p. 459–60, Pl. 31; Barnes & Smith, 1964	Injection or load phenomena related to incomplete contraction cracks
Worm tracks in Heavitree Quartzite	Glaessner, 1962, p. 480; 1966, p. 40	Not illustrated; compared with sinuous markings whose vital origin questioned by Häntzschel, 1949, and Barnes & Smith, 1964; also samples	Same as above
Worm tracks	Peach, Horne, et al., 1907, p. 301	Field examination in company of Scott Johnstone	Small clastic dikes

Scolithus	Various authors	Reliably reported occurrences not far below accepted Cambrian fossils	Best referred to Paleozoic where identification is sure
Skolithos	McDougall et al., 1965, p. 80	Not illustrated	Uncertain
Grabspuren kleiner Artikulaten (?)	Seilacher, 1956	Minute, divided welt along crack on mottled surface	Probably nonvital
6. Miscellaneous			
Corycium	Sederholm, 1912	van Straaten, 1949	Slump balls or pseudonodules
Aspidella Billings	Walcott, 1899	Morphology; homogeneous nature of containing mudstones	Compaction and spall marks
Telemarkites	Dons, 1959	Glaessner, 1962, p. 471	Concretion?
Umbrella-shaped fossils (?)	Robertson, 1962	Similarity to spring mounds and forms produced by expulsion of water from setting concrete; sorting pattern of component grains; also Gill & Kuenen, 1957	Nonvital
Planolites	Walcott, 1899, 1914	Inspection	Algal?
†Spiral impressions	Beer, 1919	Collected from talus slope	Probably imprint or track of an organism; possibly metazoan; age not established
Helminthoidichnites	Walcott, 1899, 1914	Featureless spiral films	Probably algal

Object in question	Reported by	Why queried	Present interpretation
Objects called worm burrows, worm tracks, fucoidal markings, jellyfish, sponges, sponge spicules, arthropod segments, brachiopods, echinodermal remains, *Eophyton*, *Ctenichnites*, *Taonichnites*, etc.; cited by various authors without illustration & often without locality or description	Various authors	Where possible to relocate such occurrences they are attributable to incomplete mud cracks, small clastic dikes or other injection features, shrinkage or expansion ruptures, cracks or joints in the rock, volcanic shards, impact or evasion marks, tracks of water or gas expulsion, clay flakes or galls, pebbles, pseudomorphs of gypsum or salt (often partially redissolved or impacted), crystals or crystal boundaries, clusters or rosettes of crystals (along mud cracks or bedding surfaces), colloidal structures (in chert or limestone), concretions, or nodules	Dubious

7. Porifera

triact spicules	Dunn, 1964	Absence of central canal, matrix possibly a silicified tuff	Possibly remnants of volcanic shards
Sponge?	Alf, 1959	Morphology and association	Silica nodule
"Spicules"	Moorhouse & Beales, 1962, Fig. 3, b, c	Parallelism of individual "spicules" and their relation to crystal boundaries and cleavage	Possibly inorganic
Sponge?	Moorhouse & Beales, 1962, Fig. 3d	Morphology	Possibly algal
Sponge spicules	Cayeux, 1895	Illustrations; Seilacher, 1956, p. 157; but de Laubenfels, 1955, accepts as sponges, proposing name *Eospicula cayeuxi*	Crystals?

Neantia	Lebesconte, 1886	Illustrations; also Seilacher, 1956, p. 167; †other objects reported by Lebesconte 1886 appear of vital origin, but affinities and age very uncertain—material should be restudied and age established	Ripple marks
Cyathospongia (?) *eozoica*	Matthew, 1890	Criss-crossing rectilinearity shown by illustrations	Probably crystals
Halichondrites graphitiferus	Same	Same	Same
Atikokania	Walcott, 1912a	Morphology and geologic associations	Replacement structure
Other records	Various authors	de Laubenfels, 1955, p. 53	Doubtful

Appendix B. Glossary of Technical Terms and Abbreviations

Å: Ångstrom unit, 1/10,000 of a micron.

Aerobic: Characterized by or operating in the presence of free oxygen.

ADP: Adenosine diphosphate. An ester of adenosine and pyrophosphoric acid that transfers energy during carbon assimilation.

Amino acid: Organic molecules containing amino and carboxyl groups; the building-blocks of the protein molecule.

Anaerobic: Characterized by or operating in the absence of free oxygen.

Atomic oxygen: O, consisting of single atoms of oxygen; a highly reactive form, resulting from absorption of light by O_2 in the far UV region (1,600–1,800 Å).

ATP: Adenosine triphosphate; an ester of adenosine and triphosphoric acid formed by the reaction of ADP and an orthophosphate, or by the interaction of ADP and phosphocreatine or certain other substrates; the universal energy source for biological reactions.

Autotroph: An organism capable of creating its cell components from carbon dioxide and an external source of energy. According to whether the energy source is light quanta or chemical, autotrophs are classed as photoautotrophs and chemoautotrophs. Green-plant photosynthesis is the most familiar type of autotrophy.

BIF: Banded iron formation; sedimentary iron deposits consisting of alternating thin layers of siliceous iron-rich rock and nearly pure silica; they are often thick and extensive, and are interpreted to represent rhythmic chemical deposition from open-water bodies. Although many such deposits are iron ores, having a commercially minable content of iron is not part of the definition. Characteristically developed at the margins of ancient shield areas in rocks from 1.8 to $> 3 \times 10^9$ years old. Dissimilar to the characteristic iron formations of younger rocks, which are ordinarily oölitic, earthy, nodular, granular, or replacement bodies. The younger types of iron formation, however, may extend downward into the range of banded iron formations.

BY: Billion years; used in connection with a preceding number to refer to the age of a rock $\times 10^9$. Often written $1,000 \times 10^6$m.yr.

Catalase: Any of several complex enzymes with molecular weights of 100,000 or more, which in organisms bring about the decomposition of peroxides.

Chromatin: Cell material rich in nucleic acids, concentrated in the nucleus if there is one, and in chromatin granules within the cytoplasm; so called because of its staining properties.

Cytochrome: Any of various pigments found in all cells capable of aerobic metabolism and which, on catalysis, absorb free O_2.

Cytoplasm: Cell contents excluding the nucleus.

Diagenesis: Those changes that affect a sediment during its consolidation to form a rock.

D-Amino acid: A dextro or right-handedly asymmetrical amino acid.

DNA: Deoxyribonucleic acid; a nucleic acid that contains deoxyribose—the genetic coding and replicating molecule; also serves as template for the manufacture of RNA from suitable nucleotide molecules.

Enzyme: A protein that catalyzes biological reactions.

Eucaryote: An organism consisting of eucaryotic cells, having a nucleus enclosed within a nuclear membrane and capable of mitotic cell division by which the genetic coding material is successively parceled out among the different cells and descendants of the organism.

Fermentation: Anaerobic metabolism in which sugars are converted to alcohols with liberation of energy, for example:

$$C_6H_{12}O_6 \rightarrow 2CH_3CH_2OH + 2CO_2 + 50 \text{ Cal/mole}$$
(ethyl alcohol)

See also glycolysis, oxidative metabolism, photosynthesis.

Ferredoxin: An iron-containing protein important in catalyzing phosphorylation of ADP to ATP through electron transfer in plants (and some animals?).

Glycolysis: Anaerobic metabolism in which sugars are converted to lactic acid with liberation of energy, in simplified manner as follows:

$$C_6H_{12}O_6 \rightarrow 2CH_3CH(OH)COOH + 36 \text{ Cal/mole}$$
(lactic acid)

See also fermentation, oxidative metabolism, photosynthesis.

Heterotroph: An organism depending on ready-made foodstuffs to grow and reproduce. Early heterotrophs, also anaerobes, presumably depended on a supply of abiogenically produced organic compounds; later they became dependent on autotrophs as a source of food.

H_2O_2: Hydrogen peroxide; hydrogen in combination with oxygen having a negative valence of one; highly reactive and destructive to organic matter.

°K: Degrees Kelvin; referring to an absolute scale of temperature in which degree intervals equal those of the Celsius (centigrade) scale, but in which zero °K equals $-273.16°C$.

K/Ar: Radiometric dating method utilizing ratio between potassium-40 and daughter product argon-40. Validity of results depends on accuracy of knowledge of rate of decay of K^{40} to Ar^{40} (a process taking place by electron capture) and on geologic factors such as argon loss and absorption of argon by pyroxenes.

K^{40}/Ca^{40}: Radiometric dating method utilizing the ratio between potassium-40 and its daughter product calcium-40. Validity of results depends on accuracy of knowledge of the rate of decay of K^{40} to Ca^{40} (a process that takes place by emission of a beta-ray) and on geologic factors.

L-Amino acid: A left-handedly asymmetrical amino acid.

Micron: 1/1000 of a millimeter (μ).

Molecular oxygen: O_2, made up of atom pairs; the usual and least reactive allotroph of oxygen.

MY: Million years; Used in connection with a preceding number to refer to the age of a rock $\times 10^6$; often written m. yr.,

Nucleic acid: Organic acids characteristic of the cell nucleus, e.g. deoxyribonucleic acid (DNA) and ribonucleic acid (RNA).

Nucleotide: The basic unit building block of nucleic acids; it is the nucleotide base plus sugar and PO_4.

Nucleotide base: The basic ring structures or "side chains" from which nucleotides are built; nucleotide bases include the purines adenine and guanine, and the pyrimidines thymine, cytosine, and uracil. These, on combination with sugar and PO_4, yield the nucleotides adenylic acid, guanylic acid, thyminic acid, cytidilic acid, and uridylic acid.

Nucleus: That part of the cell in which the DNA or genetic coding material is concentrated.

O_2: Molecular oxygen.

Oxidative metabolism: Aerobic metabolism, in which sugars are converted to carbon dioxide with liberation of energy, in simplified manner as follows:

$$C_6H_{12}O_6 + 6O_2 \rightarrow 6CO_2 + 6H_2O + 686 \text{ Cal/mole}$$

Ozone: O_3, each molecule consisting of three atoms of oxygen; a highly reactive and unstable allotroph of oxygen, owing to its very high energy content (the decomposition of 1 gram of ozone to oxygen is accompanied by the liberation of 675 calories of energy). Formed by absorption of light in the far UV region (1,600–1,800 Å) by O_2, yielding $2O$, and subsequent thermal reaction between O and O_2. Its concentration in a layer about 15 miles above the earth's surface serves as shield from UV radiation in the range of 2,400–3,000 Å, owing to absorption of these wavelengths by ozone.

Paedomorphosis: Evolution involving phylogenetic additions to an ontogenetically early stage of development as a result of reproduction while somatically immature (neoteny).

PAL: Present atmospheric level (of oxygen).

Peptide: Relatively small polymers of amino acids, the subunits of proteins.

Peroxide: A compound containing the peroxide ion, O_2^{--}; here refers to hydrogen peroxide, H_2O_2, highly reactive and destructive to organic matter.

Photosynthesis: The light-energized assimilation of CO_2; in green plants this involves water as a source of electrons for energy, thus splitting the water molecule and yielding free oxygen. Green-plant photosynthesis can be described in oversimplified manner as:

$$6CO_2 + 6H_2O + 686 \text{ cal/mole} \rightarrow C_6H_{12}O_6 + 6O_2$$

Polynucleotide: A chain of connected nucleotides; where nucleotides are arranged in prescribed manner the polynucleotide is the nucleic acid DNA or RNA. Polynucleotides may also consist of a single nucleotide (such as uridylic acid) repeated over and over again; Such polynucleotides have been synthesized in the laboratory from uridylic acid starting materials.

Polypeptide: A sequence of peptides linked together.

Porphyrin: An oxygen-transporting ring-structured molecule, involving various metal ions in a central location, such as Mg^{++} in chlorophyll, and Fe^{++} in heme.

Procaryote: An organism consisting of procaryotic cells, lacking a nuclear wall and incapable of mitotic cell division.

Purine: The basic ring structure of adenine and guanine, two of the nucleotide bases.

Pyrimidine: The basic ring structure of uracil, thymine, and cytosine, three of the nucleotide bases.

Rb/Sr: Radiometric dating method utilizing ratio between rubidium-87 and daughter product strontium-87. Validity of results depends on accuracy of knowledge of half-life of Rb^{87}, on identification of nonradiogenic Sr^{87}, and on geologic factors; often written Rb-Sr.

Red beds: Sediments whose red color is due to the coating of constituent particles (grains) with ferric oxides in an oxygenous weathering profile, such particles being subsequently moved to and deposited in depressions on continents or in marginal marine environments. Preservation depends on protection from subsequent reduction, as by continued exposure to a richly oxygenous milieu or rapid burial beneath the reach of percolating reducing fluids.

RNA: Ribonucleic acid; a nucleic acid containing ribose. Replicated by using DNA as a template (within the nucleus in eucaryotes), then serves in turn as templating mechanism in assembling amino acids into proteins within the cytoplasm.

Solar wind: Pressure of radiation from the sun, deflected from the earth by its magnetic field.

Stromatolite: A thinly laminated, usually basally attached (unattached forms are called oncolites), and morphologically distinctive buildup of sedimentary material, usually $CaCO_3$ but sometimes SiO_2. Formed under metabolic and sediment binding influences of various associations of microorganisms, most characteristically blue-green algae.

Stylolite: Pressure-solution zone in a rock (characteristically limestone or dolomite), usually sharply denticulate and marked by a concentration of insoluble residues; characteristically but not invariably parallel to, or at a low angle to, the stratification of the rock.

UV: Ultraviolet; beyond violet light in the electromagnetic radiation spectrum as far as X rays; corresponding to wavelengths from 100 to 4,000 Å.

REFERENCES

Abelson, P. H., 1957. Effects of ultraviolet light on the "primitive environment." Carnegie Inst. Washington, *Yearbook* 56: p. 179–85.

———, 1959. Geochemistry of organic substances. In *Researches in Geochemistry*, P. H. Abelson, ed. Wiley, New York, p. 79–103.

———, 1966. Chemical events on the primitive earth. *Proc. Nat. Acad. Sci. U.S.A.*, 55: p. 1365–72.

Alf, R. M., 1959. Possible fossils from the early Proterozoic Bass formation, Grand Canyon, Arizona. *Plateau*, Northern Arizona Soc. Sci. Art, *31* (3): 60–63.

Allsopp, H. L., H. R. Roberts, and G. D. L. Schreiner, 1962. Rb–Sr age measurements on various Swaziland granites. *J. Geophys. Res.*, 67: 5307–13.

Anderson, J. G. C., 1965. The Precambrian of the British Isles. *In The Precambrian*, v. 2, Kalervo Rankama, ed. New York, Interscience (Wiley), New York, p. 25–111.

Arnon, D. I., 1965. Ferrodoxin and photosynthesis. *Science, 149:* 1460–69.

Arnon, D. I., H. Y. Tsujimoto, and B. D. McSwain, 1965. Photosynthetic phosphorylation and electron transport. *Nature, 207:* 1367–72.

Axelrod, D. I., 1958. Early Cambrian marine fauna. *Science, 128:* 7–9.

Bain, G. W., 1965. Precambrian fossils and their distribution. *Geol. Soc. Am., Program, 1965 Annual Meetings, Abstracts*, p. 8.

Baker, J. R., 1948. The status of the Protozoa. *Nature, 161:* 548–51, 587–89.

Baldwin, Ernest, 1949. *An Introduction to Comparative Biochemistry*. Cambridge Univ. Press, 164 p.

———, 1953. *Dynamic Aspects of Biochemistry*, 2d ed. Cambridge Univ. Press, 544 p.

Barghoorn, E. S., and S. A. Tyler, 1963. Fossil organisms from Precambrian sediments. *Ann. N.Y. Acad. Sci., 108:* 451–52.

———, 1965. Microorganisms from the Gunflint chert. *Science 147:* 563–77.

Barghoorn, E. S., and J. W. Schopf, 1965. Microorganisms from the late Precambrian of central Australia. *Science 150:* 337–39.

———, 1966. Microorganisms three billion years old from the Precambrian of South Africa. *Science, 152:* 758–63.

Barnes, A. G., and A. G. Smith, 1964. Some markings associated with ripple-marks from the Proterozoic of North America. *Nature, 201:* 1018–19.

Barrell, J., 1917. Rhythms and the measurement of geologic time. *Geol. Soc. Am. Bull., 28:* 745-904.

Bassler, R. S., 1941. A supposed jellyfish from the Pre-Cambrian of the Grand Canyon. *Proc. U.S. Nat. Mus., 89:* 519–22.

Beer, E. J., 1919. Note on a spiral impression on Lower Vindhyan Limestone. *Rec. Geol. Surv. India, 50:* 139.

de Beer, G. 1954. *The Evolution of Metazoa.* In *Evolution as a Process,* J. Huxley, A. C. Hardy, and E. B. Ford, eds. Allen & Unwin, London, p. 24–33.

Berkner, L. V., and L. C. Marshall, 1964. The history of oxygenic concentration in the earth's atmosphere. *Disc. Faraday Soc., 37:* 122–41.

———, 1965. History of major atmospheric components. *Proc. Nat. Acad. Sci. U.S.A., 53* (6): 1215–25.

Borradaile, L. A., F. A. Potts, L. E. S. Easthan, J. T. Saunders, and G. A. Kerkut, 1958. *The Invertebrata,* 3d ed. Cambridge Univ. Press, 795 p.

von Brand, Theodor, 1934. Das Leben ohne Sauerstoff bei wirbellosen Tieren. *Ergebn. Biol., 10:* 37–100.

Briggs, M. H., 1959. Dating the origin of life on earth. *Evolution, 13*(3): 416–18.

Brooks, W. K., 1894. The origin of the oldest fossils and the discovery of the bottom of the ocean. *J. Geol. 2*(pt. 2): 455–79.

Brotzen, F., 1941. Några bidrag till visingsö formationes stratigrafi och tektonik. *Geol. Frening, Stockholm Förh., 63:* 245–61.

Brown, Harrison, 1952. Rare gases and the formation of the earth's atmosphere. In *The Atmospheres of the Earth and Planets,* 2d ed., G. P. Kuiper, ed. Univ. Chicago Press, p. 258–66.

———, 1957. The age of the solar system. *Sci. American,* April, 11 p.

Brown, J. S., and A. E. J. Engel, 1956. Revision of Grenville stratigraphy and structure in the Balmat-Edwards district, Northwest Adirondacks, New York. *Geol. Soc. Am. Bull., 67:* 1599–22.

Calvin, Melvin, 1956. Chemical evolution and the origin of life. *Am. Scientist, 44:* 248–63.

———, 1959a. Round trip from space. *Evolution 13*(3): 362–77.

———, 1959b. Evolution of enzymes and the photosynthetic apparatus. *Science, 130:* 1170–74.

———, 1961. *Chemical Evolution.* Condon Lectures, Oregon State System of Higher Education, Eugene, 41 p.

———, 1965. *Chemical Evolution.* The Bakerian Lecture, 1965. *Proc. Roy. Soc. A, 288:* 441–66.

Camien, M. N., 1952. Antagonisms in the utilization of D-amino acids by lactic acid bacteria. *J. Biol. Chem., 197*(2): 587–693.

Cannon, R. T., 1965. Age of transition in the Pre-Cambrian atmosphere. *Nature, 205:* 586.

Carter, G. S., 1946. A General Zoology of the Invertebrates, 2d ed. Sidgwick & Jackson, London, 507 p.

Catanzaro, E. J., 1963. Zircon ages in southwestern Minnesota. *J. Geophys. Res.*, 68(7): 2045–48.

Cayeux, L., 1895. De l'existence de nombreux débris de Spongiares dans le Précambrian de Bretagne. *Ann. Soc. Géol. Nord*, 23: 52–65.

Chamberlin, T. C., 1897. A group of hypotheses bearing on climatic changes. *J. Geol.*, 5: 653–83.

Chapman, Frederick, 1929. Some fossil remains from the Adelaide Series of South Australia. *Trans. Roy. Soc. South Australia*, 53: 5–6.

——, 1936. Primitive fossils, possibly atrematous and neotrematous Brachiopoda, from the Vindhyans of India. *Rec. Geol. Sur. India*, 69: 109–20.

Clarke, F. W., 1924. The data of geochemistry. *U.S. Geol. Surv. Bull.*, 770, 5th ed., 841 p.

Cloud, P. E., Jr., 1948. Some problems and patterns of evolution exemplified by fossil invertebrates. *Evolution*, 2(4): 322–50.

——, 1960. Gas as a sedimentary and diagenetic agent. *Am. J. Sci.*, *Bradley Volume* (258A): p. 35–45.

——, 1961. Pre-Metazoan evolution. *Geol. Soc. Am.*, *Program, 1961 Annual Meetings, Abstracts*, p. 28A–29A.

——, 1965. Significance of the Gunflint (Precambrian) microflora. *Science, 148:* 27–35.

Cloud, P. E., Jr., and P. H. Abelson, 1961. Woodring conference on major biologic innovations and the geologic record. *Proc. Nat. Acad. Sci. U.S.A.*, 47(11): 1705–12.

Cloud, P. E., Jr., J. W. Gruner, and Hannelore Hagen, 1965. Carbonaceous rocks of the Soudan Iron Formation (Early Precambrian). *Science, 148:* 1713–16.

Cloud, P. E., Jr., and Hannelore Hagen, 1965. Electron microscopy of the Gunflint microflora: Preliminary results. *Proc. Nat. Acad. Sci. U.S.A.*, 54: 1–8.

Cloud, P. E., Jr., and C. A. Nelson, 1966. Phanerozoic–Cryptozoic and related transitions —New evidence. *Science, 154:* 766–70.

Cohen, S. S., 1955. Other pathways of carbohydrate metabolism, In *Chemical Pathways in Metabolism*, v. 1, D. M. Greenberg, ed. Academic Press, New York, p. 173–233.

——, 1963. On biochemical variability and innovation. *Science, 139:* 1017–26.

Daly, R. A., 1907. The limeless ocean of pre-Cambrian time. *Am. J. Sci.*, 23(4): 93–115.

Dasch, E. J., F. A. Hills, and K. K. Turekian, 1966. Strontium isotopes in deep-sea sediments. *Science, 153:* 295–97.

David, T. W. E., 1928. Notes on newly-discovered fossils in the Adelaide Series (Lipalian?) South Australia. *Trans. Roy. Soc. South Australia*, 52: 191–209.

David, T. W. E., and R. J. Tillyard, 1936. *Memoir on Fossils of the Late Pre-Cambrian (Newer Proterozoic) from the Adelaide Series, South Australia.* Angus & Robertson, Sidney, 122 p.

Davidson, C. F., 1959. How old is the Cambrian System? *Nature, 183:* 768–69.

——, 1960. Age of the Cambrian System. *Nature, 187:* 1020–21.

——, 1964. Uniformitarianism and ore genesis. *Mining Mag.*, March-April, 11 p.

——, 1965. Geochemical aspects of atmospheric evolution. *Proc. Nat. Acad. Sci. U.S.A.*, 53(6): 1194–1205.

Dechaseaux, Colette, 1953. Onychophores. In *Traité de Paléontologie*, v. 3, Jean Piveteau, ed., p. 3–7.

Deering, R. A., 1962, Ultraviolet radiation and nucleic acid, *Sci. American*, December, 8 p.

Donaldson, J. A., 1965. The Dubawnt Group, districts of Keewatin and Mackenzie. *Geol. Surv. Canada*, Paper 64–20, 11 p.

Dons, J. A., 1959. Fossils(?) of Precambrian age from Telemark, Southern Norway. *Norsk Geol. Tidsskr., 39:* 249–62.

Dragunov, V. I., 1958. A find of *Sabellidites* in the Sinian of the western margin of the Tungus syncline. *Dokl. Akad. Nauk SSR, 122:* 685–86 (in Russian), p. 781–82 of Consultants Bur. translation.

Dunn, P. R., 1964. Triact spicules in Proterozoic rocks of the Northern Territory of Australia. *J. Geol. Soc. Australia, 11*(2): 195–97.

Dunnet, Douglas, 1965. A new occurrence of Proterozoic "jellyfish" from the Kimberly region, Western Australia. Commonwealth of Australia, Dept. Nat. Devel., Bur. Mineral Resources, Geol. and Geophys., Rec. 1965/134, 5 p.

Durham, J. W., 1966. *Camptostroma*, an Early Cambrian supposed scyphozoan, referable to Echinodermata. *J. Paleont. 40*(5): 1216–20.

Durham, J. W. and K. E. Caster, 1963. Helicoplacoidea: A new class of echinoderms. *Science, 140* (3568): 820–22.

Echlin, Patrick, 1966. Origins of photosynthesis. *Sci. J.*, April, p. 2–7.

Eck, R. V., and M. O. Dayhoff, 1966. Evolution of the structure of ferredoxin based on living relics of primitive amino acid sequences. *Science, 152:* 363–66.

Edgell, H. S., 1964. Precambrian fossils from the Hamersley Range, Western Australia, and their use in stratigraphic correlation. *J. Geol. Soc. Australia, 11*(2): 235–61.

Endo, Riuji, 1933. *Manchuriophycus*, nov. gen., from a Sinian formation of South Manchuria. *Japan J. Geol. Geog., 11:* 43–48, Pls. 6–8.

Engel, A. E. J., 1963. Geologic evolution of North America. *Science, 140:* 143–52.

Engel, A. E. J., and C. G. Engel, 1964. Continental accretion and the evolution of North America. In *Advancing Frontiers in Geology and Geophysics*, A. P. Subramaniam and S. Balakrisha, eds. Indian Geophys. Union, p. 18–37e.

Eskola, Pentti, 1932. Conditions during the earliest geological times as indicated by the Archaean rocks. *Ann. Acad. Sci. Fennicae, A, 36*(4): 74 p.

Fenton, C. L., and M. A. Fenton, 1936. Walcott's "Pre-Cambrian Algonkian Algal Flora" and associated animals. *Geol. Soc. Am. Bull., 47:* 609–20.

———, 1937. Belt Series of the north; Stratigraphy, sedimentation, paleontology. *Geol. Soc. Am. Bull., 48*(12): 1873–1969.

Fischer, A. G., 1965. Fossils, early life, and atmospheric history. *Proc. Nat. Acad. Sci. U.S.A., 53*(6): 1205–15.

Ford, T. D., 1958. Pre-Cambrian fossils from Charnwood Forest. *Proc. Yorkshire Geol. Soc., 31:* 211–17.

———, 1962. The oldest fossils. *New Scientist, 15*(297): 191–94.

Fox, S. W., 1956. Evolution of protein molecules and thermal synthesis of biochemical substances. *Am. Scientist, 44:* 347–62.

———, 1960. How did life begin? *Science, 132:* 200–08.

———, 1964. Experiments in molecular evolution and criteria of extraterrestrial life. *Bio-Science, 14*(12): 13–21.

——, 1965. A theory of macromolecular and cellular origins. *Nature, 205:* 328–40.

Fox, S. W., J. E. Johnson and Allen Vegotsky, 1956. On biochemical origins and optical activity. *Science, 124:* 923–25.

Fox, S. W., and Kaoru Harada, 1961. Synthesis of uracil under conditions of a thermal model of prebiological chemistry. *Science, 133:* 1923–24.

Franz, Victor, 1924. *Geschichte der Organismen.* Fischer, Jena, 949 p.

Frarey, M. J., and D. J. McLaren, 1963. Possible metazoans from the Early Proterozoic of the Canadian Shield. *Nature, 200:* 461–62.

Frarey, M. J., R. N. Ginsburg, and D. J. McLaren, 1963. Metazoan tubes from the type Huronian, Ontario, Canada. *Geol. Soc. Am., Program, 1963 Annual Meetings, Abstracts,* p. 63A.

Gaffron, Hans, 1957. Photosynthesis and the origin of life. In *Rhythmic and Synthetic Processes in Growth,* Dorothea Rudnick, ed. Princeton Univ. Press, p. 127–54.

Gansser, August, 1954. The Guiana shield (S. America). *Eklogae. Geol. Helv., 47:* 77–112.

Garrison, W. M., J. G. Hamilton, D. C. Morrison, A. A. Benson, and Melvin Calvin, 1951. Reduction of carbon dioxide in aqueous solutions by ionizing radiations. *Science, 114:* 416–18.

Geijer, Per, 1956. Pre-Cambrian atmosphere: Evidence from the Pre-Cambrian of Sweden. *Geochim. Cosmochim. Acta, 10:* 304–10.

Giese, A. G., 1945. Ultraviolet radiations and life. *Physiological Zool., 18* (3): 233–50.

Gill, W. D., and P. H. Kuenen, 1957. Sand volcanoes on slumps in the Carboniferous of County Clare, Ireland. *Quart. J. Geol. Soc. London, 113:* 441–64.

Glaessner, M. F., 1958a. New fossils from the base of the Cambrian in South Australia. *Trans. Roy. Soc. South Australia, 81:* 185–88.

——, 1958b. The oldest fossil faunas of South Australia. *Geol. Rundschau. 47* (Pt. 2): 522–31.

——, 1959. Precambrian coelenterata from Australia, Africa and England. *Nature, 183:* 1472–73.

——, 1961. Pre-Cambrian animals. *Sci. American, 204:* 72–78.

——, 1962. Precambrian fossils. *Biol. Rev. Cambridge Phil. Soc., 37* (4): 467–94.

——, 1963. Zur Kenntnis der Nama-Fossilien Sudwest-Afrikas. *Ann. Naturhist. Mus. Wien, 66:* 113–20.

——, 1964. Pre-cambrian fossils. In *Australian Natural History, 14* (9): 4 p.

——, 1965. Pre-Cambrian life—Problems and perspectives. *Geol. Soc. London, Proc.* 1626: 165–69.

——, 1966. Precambrian paleontology. In *Earth-Science Reviews,* v. 1. Elsevier, Amsterdam, p. 29–50.

Glaessner, M. F., and Brian Daily, 1959. The geology and late Precambrian fauna of the Ediacara fossil reserve. *South Australian Mus. Rec., 13* (3): 369–401.

Goldich, S. S., A. O. Nier, H. Badsgaard, J. H. Hoffman, and H. W. Kreuger, 1961. The Precambrian geology and geochronology of Minnesota. *Minnesota Geol. Surv. Bull.* 41, 193 p.

Granick, Sam, 1953. Inventions in iron metabolism. *Am. Naturalist, 87:* 65–75.

Grassé, P. P., 1952. *Traité de Zoologie,* v. 1. *Généralités.* Masson, Paris, p. 43.

Gross, G. A., 1965. *Geology of Iron Deposits in Canada,* v. 1, *General Geology and Evaluation of Ore Deposits.* Geol. Surv. Canada, Econ. Geol. Rept. 22, 181 p.

Grundland, I., 1959. Origines de la vie. *Experientia, 15*(6): 239–44.

Gruner, J. W., 1923. Algae, believed to be Archean. *J. Geol., 31:* 146–48.

——, 1924. Contributions to the geology of the Mesabi Range. *Minnesota Geol. Surv. Bull. 19:* 1–67.

——, 1956. Geology and iron ores of Steep Rock Lake. *Econ. Geol., 51:* 98–99.

Gürich, G., 1930. Über den Kuibis Quarzit in Südwestafrika. *Deut. geol. Ges. Z., 82:* 637.

——, 1933. Die Kuibis-Fossilien der Nama Formation von Südwestafrika. *Paleont. Z., 15:* 137–54.

Hadži, Jovan, 1953. An attempt to reconstruct the system of animal classification. *Systemat. Zool., 2:* 145–54.

——, 1963. *The Evolution of the Metazoa.* Macmillan, New York, 499 p.

Haeckel, Ernst, 1866. *Generelle Morphologie der Organismen,* v. 2, *Allgemeine Entwickelungsgeschichte der Organismen.* Reimer, Berlin, 461 p.

——, 1872. *Die Kalkschwämme.* I. *Biologie der Kalkschwämme,* 484 p.; II. *System der Kalkschwämme,* 418 p.; III. *Atlas der Kalkschwämme,* 60 Pls.

Haldane, J. B. S., 1932. *The Inequality of Man and Other Essays.* Chatto & Windus, London, 295 p.

——, 1944. Radioactivity and the origin of life in Milne's cosmology. *Nature, 153:* 555.

——, 1954. The origins of life. *New Biol. 16:* 12–27.

Häntzschel, Walter, 1949. Zur Deutung von *Manchuriophycus* Endo und ähnlichen Problematika. *Geol. Staatsinst. Hamburg, Mitt. 19:* 77–84.

Harada, Kaoru, and S. W. Fox, 1964. Thermal synthesis of natural amino-acids from a postulated primitive terrestrial atmosphere. *Nature, 201:* 335–36.

Hardy, A. C., 1953. On the origin of the Metazoa. *Quart. J. Microscop. Sci., 94:* 441–43.

Harland, W. B., 1964. Evidence of late Precambrian glaciation and its significance. In *Problems in Palaeoclimatology,* A. E. M. Nairn, ed. Interscience (Wiley) New York, p. 119–49.

Harland, W. B., and M. J. S. Rudwick, 1964. The great infra-Cambrian ice age. *Sci. American, 211*(2): 28–36.

Harrington, A. J., and R. C. Moore, 1956. Scyphomedusae and Trachylinida. In F. M. Bayer et al., *Coelenterata,* pt. F, *Treatise on Invertebrate Paleontology.* Geol. Soc. Am. and Univ. Kansas Press, p. F38–53, F68–76.

Hartman, Olga, 1948. The polychaetous annelids of Alaska. *Pacific Sci., 2*(1): 3–58.

Haughton, S. H., 1960. An archaeocyathid from the Nama system. *Trans. Roy. Soc. South Africa, 36*(pt. 1): 57–59.

——, 1962. Two problematic fossils from the Transvaal system. *Ann. Geol. Surv. South Africa (1964), 1:* 257–62.

Hawley, J. E., 1926. An evaluation of the evidence of life in the Archean. *J. Geol., 34:* 441–61.

Hoering, T. C., 1961. The stable isotopes of carbon in the carbonate and reduced carbon of Precambrian sediments. Carnegie Inst. Washington, *Yearbook* 61: p. 190–91.

Holland, H. D., 1962. Model for the evolution of the earth's atmosphere. In *Petrologic Studies,* A. E. J. Engel, H. L. James, and B. F. Leonard, eds. Geol. Soc. Am., New York, p. 447–77.

Horný, Radvan, 1956 (=1957). Problematic molluscs (?Amphineura) from the lower

Cambrian of south and east Siberia (U.S.S.R.). *Sborník Ustředního Ustavu Geologického 1956, 23:* 397–432 (English summary p. 423–32).

Horowitz, N. H., 1945. On the evolution of biochemical syntheses. *Proc. Nat. Acad. Sci. U.S.A., 31:* 153–57.

Hurley, P. M., H. W. Fairbain, and W. H. Pinson, Jr., 1962. Unmetamorphosed minerals in the Gunflint formation used to test the age of the Animikie. *J. Geol., 70*(4): 489–92.

Hutchinson, G. E., 1954. The biochemistry of the terrestrial atmosphere. In *The Earth as a Planet*, G. P. Kuiper, ed. Univ. Chicago Press, p. 371–433.

Hyman, L. H., 1940. *The Invertebrates,* v. I, *Protozoa Through Ctenophora.* McGraw-Hill, New York, 726 p.

Jahn, T. L., 1964. Respiratory metabolism. In *Protozoa in Biological Research*, G. N. Calkins and F. M. Summers, eds. Hafner, New York, p. 352–403.

James, H. L., 1954. Sedimentary facies of iron formation. *Econ. Geol., 49:* 235–93.

———, 1960. Problems of stratigraphy and correlation of Precambrian rocks with particular reference to the Lake Superior region. *Am. J. Sci., Bradley Volume, 258A:* p. 104–14.

———, 1966. Geochemistry of the iron-rich sedimentary rocks. U.S. Geol. Surv., Prof. Paper 440-W, *Data of Geochemistry*, 6th ed., 61 p.

Jolliffe, A. W., 1955. Geology and iron ores of Steep Rock Lake. *Econ. Geol., 50:* 373–98.

———, 1964. Stratigrapny of the Steep Rock Group, Steep Rock Lake, Ontario, and evidence for evolution of the Precambrian atmosphere. *Abstracts of Papers*, Am. Assoc. Petroleum Geologists, Toronto, May 18–21: p. 533–34.

Kelvin, Lord (Wm. Thomson), 1899. The age of the earth as an abode fitted for life. *Phil. Mag.,* 5th ser., *47:* 66–90.

Kerkut, G. A., 1960. *Implications of Evolution.* Pergamon Press, Oxford, 174 p.

Kornberg, Arthur, 1961 (= 1962). *Enzymatic Synthesis of DNA* (CIBA Lectures in Microbiol. Biochem.). Wiley, New York, 103 p.

Korolyuk, I. K., 1960. Cambrian and Precambrian subdivision of eastern Siberia on the basis of the stromatolites. In *Stratigraphy of Late Precambrian and Cambrian*, Internat. Geol. Cong., 21st sess., Problem 8, p. 118–23, (in Russian).

Kulp, J. L., 1961. Geologic time scale. *Science, 133:* 1105–14.

de Laubenfels, M. W., 1955, Porifera. In *Treatise on Invertebrate Paleontology*, v. E, R. C. Moore, ed. Univ. Kansas Press, p. 21–122.

Lebesconte, P., 1886. Constitution générale du massif breton comparée à celle du Finistèrre. *Bull. Soc. Geol. France,* ser. 3, *14:* 776–820.

Leduc, Stephane, 1914. *The Mechanism of Life.* Rebman, New York, 172 p. (trans. by W. D. Butcher).

Leech, G. B., J. A. Lowdon, C. H. Stockwell, and R. K. Wanless, 1963. *Age Determinations and Geologic Studies.* Geol. Surv. Canada, Paper 63–17, 140 p.

Lehman, I. R., S. B. Zimmerman, Julius Adler, M. J. Bessman, E. S. Simms, and Arthur Kornberg, 1958. Enzymatic synthesis of deoxyribonucleic acid. V. Chemical composition of enzymatically synthesized deoxyribonucleic acid. *Proc. Nat. Acad. Sci. U.S.A., 44:* 1191–96.

Lepp, H., and S. S. Goldich, 1964. Origin of Precambrian iron formations. *Econ. Geol., 59:* 1025–60.

McAlester, A. L., 1965. Systematics, affinities, and life habits of *Babinka*, a transitional Ordovician lucinoid bivalve. *Palaeontology*, 8(pt. 2): 213–46.

McDougall, I., P. R. Dunn, W. Compston, A. W. Webb, J. R. Richards, and V. M. Bofinger, 1965. Isotopic age determinations on Precambrian rocks of the Carpentaria Region, Northern Territory, Australia. *J. Geol. Soc. Australia*, 12(1): p. 67–90.

McNair, A. H., 1965a. Precambrian metazoan fossils from the Shaler Group, Victoria Island, Canadian archipelago. *Geol. Soc. Am., Program, 1965 Annual Meetings, Abstracts*, p. 105.

——, 1965b. Reported in *Time*, Nov. 12, p. 100.

——, 1965c. How old the fossils? *Time*, Nov. 19, p. 29 (letter to ed.).

Madison, K. M., 1957. Fossil protozoans from the Keewatin sediments. *Illinois State Acad. Sci., Trans.*, 50: 287–90.

Matthew, G. F., 1890. On the occurrence of sponges in Laurentian rocks at St. John, New Brunswick. *Bull. Nat. Hist. Soc. New Brunswick*, 9: 42–45.

Mayne, K. I., R. St. J. Lambert, and D. York, 1959. The geological time scale. *Nature*, 183: 212–14.

Mazia, Daniel, 1966. What is life? In *Biology and the Exploration of Mars*, C. S. Pittendrigh, Wolf Vishniac, and J. P. T. Pearman, eds. Nat. Acad. Sci.–Nat. Res. Council, Publ. 1296, p. 25–40.

Meister, Alton, 1965. *Biochemistry of the Amino Acids*, 2d ed., v. I. Academic Press, New York, London, 119 p.

Meneisy, M. Y., and J. A. Miller, 1963. A geochronological study of the crystalline rocks of Charnwood Forest, England. *Geol. Mag.*, 100(6): 507–23.

Metzger, A. A. T., 1924. *Die jatulischen Bildungen von Soujärvi*. Bull. Comm. Geol. Finlande, v. 64, 86 p.

Miller, S. L., 1953. A production of amino acids under possible primitive earth conditions. *Science*, 117: 528–29.

Miller, S. L. and N. H. Horowitz, 1966. The origin of life. In *Biology and the Exploration of Mars* (cited above), p. 41–69.

Moorhouse, W. W., and F. W. Beales, 1962. Fossils from the Animikie, Port Arthur, Ontario. *Trans. Roy. Soc. Canada*, 56, ser. 3, sec. 3: 97–110.

Nathorst, A. G., 1880. Mémoire sur quelques traces d'animaux sans vertèbres etc. et de leur portée paléontologique. *Kungl. Svenska Vetenskapsakad. Handl.*, 18(7): 61–109.

Nelson, C. A., 1962. Lower Cambrian–Precambrian succession, White-Inyo Mountains, California. *Geol. Soc. Am. Bull.*, 73: 139–44.

Nelson, C. A. and Pierre Hupé, 1964. Sur l'existence de *Fallotaspis* et *Daguinaspis*, trilobites marocains, dans le Cambrien inférieur de Californie, et ses conséquences. *Compt. Rend.* 258: 621–23.

Nicolaysen, L. O., 1962. Stratigraphic interpretation of age measurements in Southern Africa. In *Petrologic Studies*, A. E. J. Engel, H. L. James, and B. F. Leonard, eds. Geol. Soc. Am., p. 569–98.

Nirenberg, M. W., and J. H. Matthaei, 1961. The dependence of cell-free protein synthesis in *E. coli* upon naturally occurring or synthetic polyribonucleotides. *Proc. Nat. Acad. Sci. U.S.A.*, 47: 1588.

Noakes, L. C., 1956. Upper Proterozoic and sub-Cambrian rocks in Australia. XX Congreso Geol. Internat., *El Sistema Cambrico, Su Paleogeografia y el Problema de su Base*, pt. II, *Australia, America*, p. 213–38.

Nursall, J. R., 1959. Oxygen as a prerequisite to the origin of the Metazoa. *Nature, 183:* 1170–72.

Oparin, A. I., 1953. *The Origin of Life*. 2d ed. of a translation by S. Morgulis from the 1936 Russian edition. Dover, New York, 270 p.

Oró, A., 1963. Non-enzymatic formation of purines and pyrimidines. *Federation Proc., 22:* 681.

Patterson, Claire, 1956. Age of meteorites and the earth. *Geochim. Cosmochim. Acta, 10:* 230–37.

Peach, B. N., John Horne, W. Gunn, C. T. Clough, and L. W. Hinxman, 1907. *The Geological Structure of the North-West Highlands of Scotland*. Memoir, Geol. Survey Great Britain, 668 p.

Pflug, H. D., 1966. Structured organic remains from the Fig Tree Series of the Barberton Mountain Land. *Econ. Geol. Research Unit, Inf. Circ.*, Univ. Witwatersrand Johannesburg, No. 28, 14 p.

Poldervaart, Arie, 1955. Chemistry of the earth's crust. In *Crust of the Earth* (a symposium), A. Poldervaart, ed. Geol. Soc. Am. Spec. Paper 62, p. 119–44.

Pollard, E. C., 1965. The fine structure of the bacterial cell and the possibility of its artificial synthesis. *Am. Scientist, 53*(4): 437–63.

Pompeckj, J. F., 1928. Ein neues Zeugnis uralten Lebens. *Paläont. Z., 9:* 287–313.

Ponnamperuma, Cyril, 1965. The chemical origin of life. *Sci. J.*, May, p. 39–45.

Ponnamperuma, Cyril, and Etta Peterson, 1965. Peptide synthesis from amino acids in aqueous solution. *Science, 147:* 1572–74.

Poole, J. H. J., 1941. The evolution of the atmosphere. *Sci. Proc. Roy. Soc. Dublin, 22* (36) (n.s.): 345–65.

——, 1951. The evolution of the earth's atmosphere. *Sci. Proc. Roy. Soc. Dublin, 25* (16) (n.s.): 201–24.

Pretorius, D. A., 1963. *Fourth Ann. Report* [for 1962] *of Econ. Geol. Research Unit*, Univ. Witwatersrand, Johannesburg, 31 p.

Rádl, Emanuel, 1930. *The History of Biological Theories*. Oxford Univ. Press, London, 408 p. (trans. by E. J. Hatfield).

Ramdohr, P., 1958. Die Uran- und Goldlagerstätten Witwatersrand—Blind River District—Dominion Reef—Serra de Jacobina: Erzmikroskopische Untersuchungen und ein geologischer Vergleich. *Deutsche Akad. Wiss. Berlin Abh., Klasse für Chemie, Geologie, und Biologie*, no. 3, 35 p.

Raymond, P. E., 1935. Pre-Cambrian life. *Geol. Soc. Am. Bull., 46:* 375–92.

Richter, Rudolph, 1955. Die ältesten Fossilien Süd-Afrikas. *Senckenbergiana Lethea, 36:* 243–89.

Robertson, W. A., 1962. Umbrella-shaped fossils (?) from the Lower Proterozoic of the Northern Territory of Australia. *J. Geol. Soc. Australia, 9:* 87–90.

Roscoe, S. M., 1960. Huronian uraniferous conglomerates. *Econ. Geol., 55*(2): 410–14.

Roscoe, S. M., and H. R. Steacy, 1958. On the geology and radioactive deposits of Blind River Region. Proc. 2d U.N. Internat. Conf. *The Peaceful Uses of Atomic Energy*, v. 2, *Survey of Raw Material Resources*, Geneva, p. 375–83.

Rubey, W. W., 1951. Geologic history of sea water. *Geol. Soc. Am. Bull., 62:* 1111–48.

————, 1955. Development of the hydrosphere and atmosphere with special reference to probable composition of the early atmosphere. *Geol. Soc. Am. Spec. Paper 62*, p. 631–50.

Rudwick, M. J. S., 1964. The infra-Cambrian glaciation and the origin of the Cambrian fauna. In *Problems in Paleoclimatology*, A. E. M. Nairn, ed., Interscience (Wiley), New York, p. 119–49.

Ruedemann, Rudolf, 1931. Some new Middle Cambrian fossils from British Columbia. *Proc. U.S. Nat. Mus., 79* (art. 27): 1–18.

Russell, H. N., and D. H. Menzel, 1933. The terrestrial abundance of the permanent gases. *Nat. Acad. Sci. Proc. U.S.A., 19:* 997–1001.

Rutten, M. G., 1962. *The Geological Aspects of the Origin of Life on Earth.* Elsevier, Amsterdam, New York, 146 p.

Sagan, Carl, 1965. Origins of the atmospheres of the earth and planets. In *Origin of the Earth, International Dictionary of Geophysics*, S. K. Runcorn and H. C. Urey, eds. Pergamon Press, London.

Sahni, M. R., 1936. *Fermoria minima*—A revised classification of the organic remains from the Vindhyans of India. *Rec. Geol. Surv. India. 69:* 458–68.

Sahni, M. R., and R. N. Shrivastava, 1954. New organic remains from the Vindhyan System and the probable systematic position of *Fermoria*, Chapman. *Current Sci., 23:* 39–41.

Schindewolf, O. H., 1956. *Über Präkambrische Fossilien.* Deutsch. Geol. Gesell., Stuttgart, p. 455–79.

Schopf, J. W., Elso Barghoorn, M. D. Maser, and R. O. Gordon, 1965. Electron microscopy of fossil bacteria two billion years old. *Science, 149:* 1365–67.

Sdzuy, Klaus, 1960. Zur Wende Präkambrium/Kambrium. *Paläont. Z. 34:* 154–60.

Sederholm, J. J., 1912. Sur les vestiges de la vie dans les formations progonozoiques. *11th Internat. Geol. Cong.* (Stockholm 1910), *Compt. Rend., 1:* 515–23.

Seilacher, A., 1956. Der Beginn des Kambriums als biologische Wende. *Neues Jahrb. Geol. Paläont. Abh., 103:* 155–80.

Semikhatov, M. A., 1966. The suggested stratigraphic scheme for the Precambrian. *Izv. Akad. Nauk SSSR*, Ser. Geol., *4:* 70–84. (in Russian).

Sillén, L. G., 1961. The physical chemistry of sea water. *Am. Assoc. Adv. Sci. Publ. 67*, p. 549–81.

Silver, L. T., 1963. Isotope investigations of zircons in Precambrian igneous rocks of the Adirondack Mountains, New York. *Geol. Soc. Am., Program, 1963 Annual Meetings, Abstracts:* p. 150A–151A.

Snelling, N. J., 1963. Age of the Roraima Formation, British Guiana. *Nature, 198:* 1079–80.

Sokolov, B. S., 1958. Le problème de la limite inférieure du Paléozoique et les dépots les plus anciens sur les plates-formes antésiniennes de l'Eurasie. *Centre National de la Recherche Scientifique, Colloques Internat., 76:* 103–28.

Speyer, J. F., P. Lengyel, C. Basilio, and Ochoa Severa, 1962. Synthetic polynucleotides and the amino acid code, IV. *Proc. Nat. Acad. Sci. U.S.A., 48:* 441.

Sprigg, R. C., 1947. Early Cambrian (?) jellyfishes from the Flinders Ranges, South Australia. *Trans. Roy. Soc. South Africa, 71* (pt. 2): 212–24.

————, 1949. Early Cambrian "jellyfishes" of Ediacara, South Australia and Mount John,

Kimberley District, Western Australia. *Trans. Roy. Soc. South Australia,* 73(1): 72–99.

Stanier, R. Y., and C. B. van Niel, 1962. The concept of a bacterium. *Arch. Mikrobiol.,* 42: 17–35.

Stanier, R. Y., Michael Doudoroff, and E. A. Adelberg, 1963. *The Microbial World,* 2d ed. Prentice-Hall, Englewood Cliffs, N.J., 753 p.

Stasinska, Anna, 1960. *Velumbrella czarnockii* n. gen., n. sp.—méduse du Cambrian Inférieur des Monts de Sainte-Croix. *Acta Palaeont. Polonica,* 5(3): 337–46.

Steinböck, Otto, 1937. Eine Theorie über den plasmodialen Ursprung der Vielzeller (Metazoa). *Arch. exp. Zellforsch.,* 19(2/4): 343.

Stevens, C. M., R. P. Gigger, and S. W. Bowne, Jr., 1955. The cellular D-amino acids of *Bacillus brevis. J. Biol. Chem.,* 212(1): 461–67.

Stockwell, C. H., 1964a. Fourth report on structural provinces, orogenies, and time-classification of rocks of the Canadian Precambrian Shield. *Geol. Surv. Canada,* Paper 64–17 pt. II Geol. Studies, p. 1–21.

———, 1964b. Principles of time-stratigraphic classification in the Precambrian. In *Geochronology in Canada.* Roy. Soc. Canada Spec. Publ. 8, p. 52–60.

van Straaten, L. M. J. U., 1949. Occurrence in Finland of structures due to subaqueous sliding of sediments. *Bull. Comm. Geol. Finlande,* 25(144): 9–18.

Stumpf, P. K., 1953. ATP. *Sci. American,* April, 6 p.

Szutka, Anton, 1965. Probable synthesis of porphine-like substances during chemical evolution. In *The Origins of Prebiological Systems and of Their Molecular Matrices,* Academic Press, New York, p. 243–54.

Termier, Henri, and Geneviève Termier, 1960. L'Ediacarien, premier étage paléontologique. *Rev. Gén. Sci. et Bull. Assoc. Franç. Avan. Sci.,* 67 (3–4): 79–87.

Thompson, D'Arcy W., 1945. *On Growth and Form.* Cambridge Univ. Press, 1116 p.

Thorsteinsson, R., and E. L. Tozer, 1962. Banks, Victoria, and Stefansson Islands, Arctic Archipelago. *Mem. Geol. Surv. Canada,* 330, 85 p.

Tiller, W. A., 1964. Dendrites. *Science,* 146: 871–97.

Tilton, G. R., and R. H. Steiger, 1965. Lead isotopes and the age of the earth. *Science,* 150: 1805–08.

Timofeev, B. V., 1959 Ancient flora of the Baltic area and its stratigraphic significance: *Trudy Inst. for the All-Union Sci. Invest. and Prospecting of Petroleum,* no. 129, 320 p. (in Russian).

Tyler, S. A., and E. S. Barghoorn, 1954. Occurrence of structurally preserved plants in pre-Cambrian rocks of the Canadian shield. *Science,* 119: 606–08.

Urey, H. C., 1952a. On the early chemical history of the earth and the origin of life. *Proc. Nat. Acad. Sci. U.S.A.,* 38(4): 351–63.

———, 1952b. *The Planets—Their Origin and Development.* Yale Univ. Press, New Haven, 245 p.

———, 1952c. The origin of the earth. *Sci. American,* Oct., 8 p.

———, 1957. *Primitive Planetary Atmospheres and the Origin of Life.* Proc. First Internat. Symposium on the Origin of Life on the Earth, Moscow, Internat. Union of Biochem. Ser., v. 1: Pergamon Press, Oxford, p. 16–22.

———, 1959. The atmospheres of the planets. In *Handbuch der Physik,* v. 52, Astrophysik III, Das Sonnensystem, Springer, Berlin-Gottingen-Heidelberg, p. 363–418

Van Schmus, Randall, 1965. The geochronology of the Blind River–Bruce Mines Area, Ontario, Canada. *J. Geol., 73*(5): 755–80.

Vologdin, A. G., and A. B. Maslov, 1960. A new group of fossil organisms from the bottom of the Yudoma Series of the Siberian Platform. *Dokl. Akad. Nauk SSSR, 134* (1–6): 691–93 (in Russian), English trans. by A. G. I., Sept. 1961, p. 1031–34).

Walcott, C. D., 1884. *Paleontology of the Eureka District.* U.S. Geol. Sur., Monog. 8, 298 p.

——, 1895. Algonkian rocks of the Grand Canyon of the Colorado. *J. Geol., 3:* 312–30.

——, 1899. Pre-Cambrian fossiliferous formations. *Geol. Soc. Am. Bull., 10:* 199–244.

——, 1912a. Notes on fossils from limestone of Steeprock Lake, Ontario. Reprint of Appendix, Mem. *Geol. Surv. Canada, 28,* 6 p.

——, 1912b. *Cambrian Brachiopoda.* U.S. Geol. Surv., Monog. 51, v. 1, 872 p.; v. 2, 104 pls.

——, 1914. Cambrian geology and paleontology III, no. 2. Precambrian Algonkian algal flora. *Smithson. Misc. Coll., 64*(2): 77–156.

——, 1931. Addenda to descriptions of Burgess Shale fossils. *Smithson. Misc. Coll., 85* (3): 46 p., 23 pls.

Wermund, E. G., W. H. Burke, Jr., and G. S. Kenny, 1966. K–Ar ages of detrital muscovite in the Meridian sand of Alabama and Mississippi. *Geol. Soc. Am. Bull., 77:* 319–22.

Wheeler, H. E., and J. J. Quinlan, 1951. Pre-Cambrian sinuous mud cracks from Idaho and Montana. *J. Sed. Petrol., 21*(3): 141–46.

Whittard, W. F., 1953. The enigma of the earliest fossils. *Bristol Naturalists Soc. Proc., 28*(pt. 4): 289–304.

Willmer, E. N., 1956. Factors which influence the acquisition of flagella by the amoeba, *Naegleria gruberi. J. Exp. Biol., 33:* 583–603.

Wiman, Carl, 1894. Ein Präkambrisches Fossil. *Geol. Inst. Uppsala, Bull., 2:* 109–17.

Winsnes, T. S., 1965. The Precambrian of Spitsbergen and Bjørnøya. In *The Precambrian,* v. 2, Kalervo Rankama, ed. Interscience (J. Wiley), New York, p. 1–24.

Witkin, E. M., 1966. Radiation-induced mutations and their repair. *Science, 152:* 1345–53.

Woodring, W. P., 1954. Conference on biochemistry, paleoecology, and evolution. *Proc. Nat. Acad. Sci. U.S.A., 40*(3): 219–24.

Worthington, A. M., 1908. *A study of splashes.* Longmans, Green, New York, 129 p.

Young, R. S., 1965. Morphology and chemistry of microspheres from proteinoid. In *The Origins of Prebiological Systems and of Their Molecular Matrices.* Academic Press New York, p. 347–457.

Young, R. S., and Cyril Ponnamperuma, 1964. *Early Evolution of Life.* Biological Sci. Curriculum Study Pamph. 11. Heath, Boston, 30 p.

Harlan P. Banks

2. THE EARLY HISTORY OF LAND PLANTS

Our predecessors painted successfully a broad and exciting picture of the origin and early evolution of land plants. Bower of Glasgow (1935), Zimmermann at Tübingen (1949), and Eames of Cornell (1936), to name but three, treated the Devonian psilophyte flora as a starting point in the comparative morphology of vascular plants. They made the evolution of psilophytes such an attractive concept that it is included in many introductory textbooks. Their achievements are remarkable because what few data were available to them were imprecise. Current research is filling in many gaps, correcting many misimpressions, and evolving new generalizations. My intent is to document some of the gaps in our knowledge, some means of filling them, some current data being obtained, and some of the fertile fields for future research.

Stratigraphy. The most serious drawback to accurate studies of evolution among the first land plants has been the lack of adequate data on the stratigraphic occurrence of the plants under consideration. Simply to label a plant as Devonian puts it in a time span of 60 million years (Table 1). If the data are more precise, Lower Devonian for example, the plant is included somewhere in a time span of 15 million years. Even in a general discussion, however, we can no longer rely solely on the words Lower, Middle, and Upper Devonian. In Table 2 the Devonian period is subdivided into six series. Even these are insufficient. Wherever possible

Table 1. Geologic Periods Involved in Origin of Land Plants

From Kulp, 1961.

Period		Time period began	Duration of period (millions)
Mississippian		345	
Devonian	Upper	365	20
	Middle	390	25
	Lower	405	15
Silurian	Middle	415	10
	Lower	425	10

Fig. 1. Rhyniophytina. A, *Rhynia*. B, *Cooksonia*. C, *Eogaspesiea*. D, *Hostimella*. E, *Hicklingia*. F, *Taeniocrada*. G, *Yarravia*. H, *Hedeia*. (A, After Kidston and Lang, 1921; B, from Andrews, 1959; C, after Daber, 1960; D, from a specimen; E, based on Kidston and Lang, 1923; F, from Kräusel and Weyland, 1930; G, from Andrews, 1959; H, from Andrews, 1959.)

one must pinpoint a lesser subdivision from which a given taxon is derived. It must be recognized also that for a variety of good reasons precise boundaries between certain horizons cannot always be drawn by stratigraphers. Thus such an assertion as "an abundance of vascular plants appears in Lower Devonian strata" must be challenged. Are the strata proved to be Lower Devonian? If true, exactly where in Lower Devonian time? These and other questions must be asked and re-asked as new data pour in.

The more precise stratigraphic approach changes some earlier impressions. We shall assume here without discussion that nearly all reports of pre-Devonian plants are ill-founded either because the plants have not been proved to be vascular or because the strata have been determined incorrectly. For example, the well-known *Baragwanathia* flora of Australia which was regarded as of Silurian age is now interpreted as Devonian (Jaeger, 1962). The one Upper Silurian plant

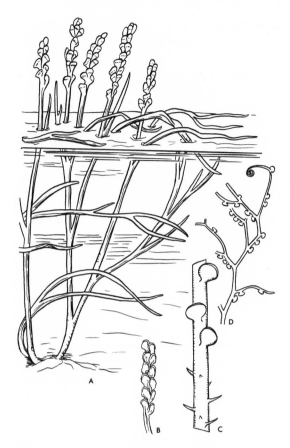

Fig. 2. Zosterophyllophytina. A, *Zosterophyllum*. B, *Bucheria*. C, *Psilophyton ornatum*. D, *Gosslingia*. (A, From Kräusel and Weyland, 1936; B, from Dorf, 1934; C, from Hueber, 1964; D, from Andrews, 1959.)

that seems to be indisputable is *Cooksonia* (Obrhel, 1962). At the moment it appears to be the oldest known vascular plant. More important, *Cooksonia* (Fig. 1B) is a simple plant in the original sense of a naked, dichotomizing axis bearing terminal sporangia. It was in this sense that *Rhynia* (Fig. 1A) was considered a starting point in the evolution of land plants.

After this late Silurian appearance, *Cooksonia* occurs again in the basal Lower Devonian Downtonian (Gedinnian) of Wales where it is represented by two species (Lang, 1937). There it is accompanied by another plant, *Zosterophyllum* (Fig. 2A), with naked stems on which sporangia are borne laterally rather than terminally. These two genera may be the extent of the flora of Gedinnian time. The next strata in which plants are found are either clearly Siegenian or are continental strata whose position with respect to the Gedinnian–Siegenian boundary is still in doubt. Several new taxa appear. Some of them (Figs. 1, 2, 4, 5) are *Taeniocrada*,

Psilophyton, Gosslingia, Hedeia, and *Yarravia* in the psilophytes; *Drepanophycus, Protolepidodendron,* and *Baragwanathia* among the lycopods; and *Dawsonites,* a pre-fern.

In brief there is probably only one taxon that can be called a Silurian vascular plant, and there are but two in the early part of Gedinnian time. These are psilophytes. By Upper Gedinnian or Lower Siegenian time several additional taxa appear, and the psilophytes are joined by lycopods and possibly pre-coenopterids. This amount of change occurred in the span of 15 million years (Table 1) and it is the kind of change envisioned by Bower, Zimmermann, and Eames but is based entirely on data accumulated since they wrote.

Time and space do not permit a continued elaboration of stratigraphic data throughout the Devonian period, but without this much or more detail many generalizations about the Devonian flora are essentially meaningless. Of particular interest here is the parallelism between the evidence that is emerging from palynological studies and that presented above for macrofossils. Richardson (1964 and personal communication) reports that simple spores with trilete marks appear in Wenlockian time (Table 2) and become more numerous in Ludlovian and Gedinnian time. By Siegenian time the spore flora is considerably more diverse. Of course it is possible that some of these earliest spores represent bryophytes or algae, but the agreement between studies of micro- and macrofossils supports the concept that land plants may have arisen in uppermost Silurian or lowermost Devonian time after all. It does not support the hypothesis of a long antecedent history (e.g. Axelrod, 1959; Leclercq, 1956) for vascular plants. We seem to be back where we were in 1940, believing that simple land plants evolved into more complex land plants during Devonian time. Now, however, we have more evidence to support the hypothesis.

PSILOPHYTALES. Much has been said in the last decade about the use of this order as a catchall for plants whose affinities are unknown. However, current discoveries are refining our knowledge of individual taxa (Banks, 1965) and are adding intriguing new taxa. I venture therefore a reclassification of the psilophytes (Table 3) solely to emphasize the new information and to postulate some evolutionary developments that result. It will be noted that some categories included among the psilophytes—for example Psilophytidae, Asteroxylidae, and Pseudosporochnidae of Pichi-Sermolli (1958)—are now excluded for reasons given below.

Tentatively I propose two new subdivisions, Rhyniophytina and Zosterophyllophytina (Figs. 1, 2; Table 3). RHYNIOPHYTINA *subdiv. nov.* Type: *Rhynia* Kidston and Lang 1917, includes those genera whose sporangia are terminal in the sense employed originally by Kidston and Lang (1917) when they proposed the new category Psilophytales. Their stems are naked and, as pointed out by Hueber (1964), their sporangia are usually fusiform and may dehisce longitudinally. Sporangia of *Cooksonia* are globose. Therefore *Cooksonia* is maintained in a family by itself. In *Rhynia* and *Horneophyton* the xylem strand is terete in cross section and the protoxylem is central (Fig. 3A). I have recently found (1966) a similar strand in the form genus *Hostimella* (Fig. 1D), a genus for naked axes that dichoto-

Table 2. Subdivisions of Devonian Time and the First Appearance of Some Vascular Plants.

Period	Series	Stage	First occurrences
Mississippian	Tournaisian		
Devonian	Famennian		
	Frasnian		
	Givetian		*Colpodexylon, Archaeosigillaria,* other lycopods
	Eifelian (or Emsian)		*Asteroxylon, Rhynia, Horneophyton*
	Coblencian	Emsian	*Trimerophyton, Eogaspesiea*
		Siegenian	*Protolepidodendron, Cooksonia Taeniocrada* spp., *Gosslingia Psilophyton ornatum, Hedeia, Zosterophyllum, Dawsonites Drepanophycus, Baragwanathia, Yarravia*
	Gedinnian		cf. *Zosterophyllum myretonianum Cooksonia hemisphaerica Cooksonia pertonii*
Silurian	Ludlovian	Upper	*Cooksonia* sp.
		Middle	*Taeniocrada* sp. *Cooksonia* cf. *hemisphaerica C.* sp.
		Lower	
	Wenlockian		
	Llandovery		

Table 3. Reclassification of Psilophytes

Rhyniophytina (psilophytes)
  Rhyniales
    Rhyniaceae
      Rhynia
      Horneophyton
      Hicklingia
      Eogaspesiea
      Taeniocrada
      Hedeia
      Yarravia
      Hostimella

    Cooksoniaceae
      Cooksonia

Zosterophyllophytina (not psilophytes)
  Zosterophyllales
    Zosterophyllaceae
      Zosterophyllum
      Bucheria
    Gosslingiaceae
      Gosslingia
      Psilophyton (non-Dawson, new name required)
      "*Serrulacaulis*"
      New genus of Lyon

Table 4. Classification Used in this Paper, with New Proposals

Division	Tracheophyta
Subdivision	Rhyniophytina
	Type *Rhynia* Kidston and Lang 1917
Order	Rhyniales
Family	Rhyniaceae
	Type: *Rhynia* Kidston and Lang
Family	Cooksoniaceae
	Type: *Cooksonia* Lang 1937
Subdivision	
subdiv. nov.	Zosterophyllophytina
	Type: *Zosterophyllum* Penhallow 1892
Order	Zosterophyllales
Family	Zosterophyllaceae
	Type: *Zosterophyllum* Penhallow 1892
	Gosslingiaceae
	Type: *Gosslingia* Heard 1927
Subdivision	Psilophytina–Psilotales
	Lycophytina
	Sphenophytina
Subdivision	
subdiv. nov.	Trimerophytina
	Type: *Trimerophyton* Hopping 1956
Subdivision	Pterophytina
Class	Cladoxylopsida
Class	Coenopteridopsida
Class	Filicopsida
Class	Progymnospermopsida
Class	Cycadopsida
Class	Coniferopsida
Class	Gnetopsida
Class	Angiospermopsida

mize. In the remaining Rhyniales the shape of the xylem strand is unknown. The genera here included in Rhyniaceae are fairly well established despite the paucity of good specimens and of morphological detail for several of them. Until these deficiencies are corrected, I am inclined to retain them in one family. Within this family the tendency toward more frequent branching and toward an aggregation of sporangia is clear (Fig. 1).

Cronquist et al. (1966) have proposed the divisional name Rhyniophyta with *Rhynia* as the type. I agree in all respects with their argument but am retaining the divisional name Tracheophyta (Table 4) and the recommended subdivisional ending -phytina for the *Rhynia*-type plants. I am going farther than they by removing those former psilophytes whose sporangia are lateral. They are no longer to be considered psilophytes.

The second subdivision proposed, Zosterophyllophytina, is more diverse and is distinct from the original concept of Psilophytales. ZOSTEROPHYLLOPHYTINA *subdiv. nov.* Type: *Zosterophyllum* Penhallow 1892, includes those taxa (Fig. 2) whose sporangia are borne laterally, are globose or reniform in shape, and dehisce along the distal edge (Hueber, 1964). Where the xylem has been petrified (Fig. 3B) it appears in cross section as an elliptical, exarch strand (Heard, 1927; Hueber, work in progress). It is a relatively massive strand, at least as compared to those psilophytes whose anatomy is known. So far we do not know whether the sporangia are supplied by vascular traces. If they were, one would interpret them as terminal on short branches as in Psilotales. The question remains open pending the discovery of better-preserved axes.

Diversity in Zosterophyllophytina (Fig. 2) is apparent both between the two families (Table 3) and within each. Zosterophyllaceae have naked stems; Gosslingiaceae have naked, spiny, or toothed stems. In Zosterophyllaceae, *Zosterophyllum* and *Bucheria* have sporangia aggregated into spikes whereas in Gosslingiaceae they are scattered along the axis. In Gosslingiaceae, *Psilophyton* (non Dawson, new name required) (Hueber, 1964) has multicellular spines and Lyon (personal communication) has found a new taxon in the Rhynie chert that bears lateral, reniform, or globose sporangia and unicellular spines. *Gosslingia* and *Nothia* are naked. "*Serrulacaulis*" (Hueber, 1961) has teeth along the stem. All genera have sporangia scattered variously along the stem.

Certain genera (cf. Andrews, 1961) sometimes included among the psilophytes are omitted here. For example I now treat *Asteroxylon* as a lycopod. Other genera are omitted because they do not fit naturally into the present redefinition of psilophytes and do not contribute to the evolutionary series proposed here.

LYCOPHYTINA. Zosterophyllophytina appear first in rocks of late Gedinnian age (Table 2) followed soon by several Lycophytina such as *Drepanophycus* and *Baragwanathia*. Characters common to the two groups are lateral sporangia, exarch protostele (Fig. 3C,D,E), and small appendages. Lyon's (1964) discovery that *Asteroxylon* bore lateral sporangia strengthens the argument that it is a lycopod, not a psilophyte. In addition, its stelar anatomy agrees with that of several Devonian lycopods (Grierson and Banks, 1963). I have studied Lyon's preparations at Cardiff and am convinced that he has the true fertile region of *Asteroxylon* with its typical stele and leaves. If, as some geologists suspect, the Rhynie chert is Lower Devonian (Siegenian or Emsian) the possibility that *Asteroxylon* represents an intermediate stage in evolution of lycopods is markedly increased (Fig. 4). Its leaf traces extend only to the base of its leaves, but they are typical leaf traces and, morphogenetically, the stimulus to cause differentiation of vascular tissue in the leaves need be only slight. By contrast, the outgrowths on stems of Gosslingiaceae are clearly only multicellular (or unicellular) emergences.

It has been suggested that the three-forked leaves of *Colpodexylon* and bifid leaves of *Protolepidodendron* originated from a branch system. We do not have fossil evidence for branching systems that might have been reduced to produce

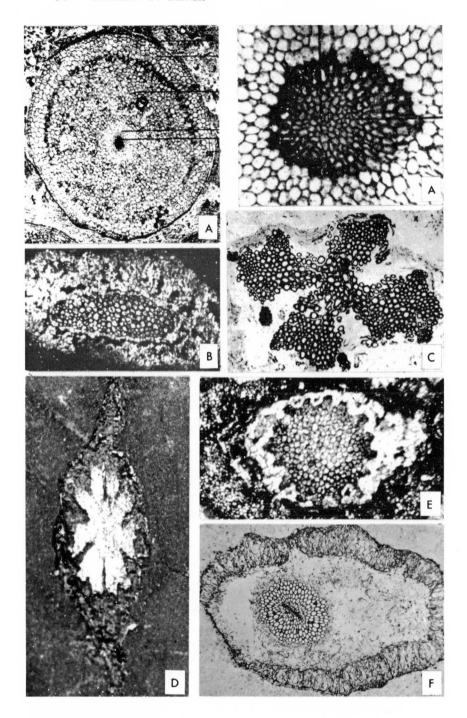

the abundance of leaves found characteristically on lycopod stems. On the contrary, the fossil evidence that we do have reveals axes liberally supplied with outgrowths (enations). Modern experimental studies demonstrate morphogenetic relationships between outgrowths and stems. I find it more in keeping with these studies to believe that the enations observed on stems that bear lateral sporangia might evolve into leaves interspersed between sporangia (*Asteroxylon* level) and then into leaves with axillary or adaxial sporangia (*Baragwanathia–Protolepidodendron*). This hypothesis (Table 5), starting with sporangia that are already lateral, also avoids the necessity of reducing terminal fertile telomes to produce the adaxial sporangia (Zimmermann, 1949, p. 70). Thus I am inclined toward the view that lycopod leaves arose as enations rather than as modified branch systems.

Again we are led back to the early ideas of Bower. We can speculate that he would be impressed by the new fossil evidence that supports more firmly his concept of origin of small leaves from enations than did the evidence available to him. We need not be disturbed by the appearance of *Baragwanathia, Protolepidodendron,* and *Drepanophycus* in the fossil record slightly earlier than *Asteroxylon,* for many reasons. Chief among these are the possibility that the Rhynie chert may ultimately be proved to be Lower Devonian or that *Asteroxylon* may have existed elsewhere in Lower Devonian time without being preserved in a form we can recognize. Hence, although stratigraphic data must be sought with care and with vigor, they must be used as guidelines rather than hindrances.

TRIMEROPHYTINA. In the Senni beds of early Siegenian age in Wales (Table 2) Croft and Lang (1942) found *Zosterophyllum, Psilophyton* (non Dawson, new name required) with lateral sporangia, and *Gosslingia.* Along with these genera they obtained a few small specimens of *Dawsonites* (Fig. 5A). This is the genus to which Halle assigned Dawson's supposed terminal sporangia of *Psilophyton* (Hueber, 1964). *Dawsonites* is abundant in strata of Emsian age at Gaspé, James Bay, and in Belgium. I am suggesting that it and *Trimerophyton* Hopping (1956), also from the Emsian, be included in a new subdivision for which I propose the name TRIMEROPHYTINA *subdiv. nov.* Type: *Trimerophyton* Hopping 1956. This subdivision includes plants with a main axis that branches pseudomonopodially. Each lateral branches a number of times, either trichotomously or dichotomously and finally terminates in a mass of fusiform sporangia (Fig. 5, A and B). Anatomy is known only for *Dawsonites* (Hueber, 1964; Banks, 1964; Fig. 3F). Its vascular strand is massive in comparison to that of *Rhynia.* These genera, branching freely and producing large sporangial trusses, seem a natural outgrowth of Rhyniophytina and simultaneously foreshadow the still more complex branching pattern

---

Fig. 3. Anatomy of some early Devonian plants, from specimens. A, *Rhynia* with small central, centrarch protostele. To the right, xylem enlarged. B, *Gosslingia* with large, exarch, elliptic protostele; cortical area of thick-walled cells. C, *Asteroxylon* with lobed protostele and leaf traces (small circles). D, *Colpodexylon* with lobed protostele. E, *Protolepidodendron* with ridged, exarch protostele. F, *Dawsonites.*

Fig. 4. *Asteroxylon* and the lycopods. A, *Asteroxylon* with leaf trace, appendages, and one lateral sporangium. B, *Baragwanathia* with sporangia (black) either cauline or axillary. C, *Colpodexylon,* one three-forked leaf with adaxial sporangium. D, *Protolepidodendron,* bifurcate leaves and adaxial sporangia. (A, Based on Lyon, 1964; B, based on Lang and Cookson, 1935; C, based on specimen; D, modified from Kräusel and Weyland, 1932.)

found among Cladoxylopsida, Coenopteridopsida and Progymnospermopsida toward which I suggest they evolved (Table 6).

My suggested new subdivision Trimerophytina was actually foreseen many years ago by Halle (1916) when he described a Lower Devonian flora from Röragen in Norway. It included *Hostimella, Aphyllopteris, Drepanophycus* (*Arthrostigma*), *Psilophyton, Sporogonites, Pachytheca,* and groups of sporangia that he considered similar to those Dawson had assigned to *Psilophyton.* Halle pointed out that neither Dawson nor any subsequent author had found these paired, terminal sporangia attached to *Psilophyton.* He gave them a new name, *Dawsonites arcuatus,* to emphasize this point. I have studied Halle's types in Stockholm and find them similar to those from Gaspé being studied by Hueber, Leclercq, and me (Fig. 5A). Halle's comments on morphology (1916, p. 39) are significant here. He referred to *D. arcuatus* as the "best evidence of the beginnings of the filicinean phylum in the Older Devonian." He further stated that "the sporangia of *Dawsonites* recall those of certain Upper Devonian and Carboniferous ferns generally considered to be primitive as for instance *Dimeripteris* and perhaps *Stauropteris.*" Clearly Halle felt that the lateral, fertile branch systems of *Dawsonites* could become planated and ultimately webbed to make fronds such as those characteristic of Carboniferous strata.

Andrews (1961) has made the point in another way. He discusses the psilo-phytes in one chapter and then, in order to show the "broad stream of evolution with many specialized side branches," discusses in successive chapters the "pre-ferns," the true ferns, and finally seed-ferns. Among the pre-ferns he includes the plants I refer to Cladoxylopsida, Coenopteridopsida, and Progymnospermopsida. In separate chapters he writes later about lyocopods and horsetails as distinct groups that pursued paths independent of the "main stream." It is also noteworthy that Andrews treats *Trimerophyton* as a plant included in the psilophytes only with doubt. I have simply gone farther in separating it and *Dawsonites* taxonomi-cally from other psilophytes.

CLADOXYLOPSIDA. Devonian Cladoxylopsida, once rare, are proving to be more abundant than was expected. Genera whose stratigraphic position is based on reli-able evidence appear in Givetian time and continue into the Frasnian (Table 6). Only *Cladoxylon* (Fig. 5C,H) is known from younger rocks, and the group as a whole lasts only through Carboniferous time. *Schizopodium* (Fig. 5G) and *Xeno-cladia* (Fig. 5F) are known only from petrifactions. The former was first reported by Harris (1929) from the Middle Devonian of Australia. Subsequently it has been found in the Middle Devonian (Read, 1938) and Upper Devonian (Hueber, 1959) of New York. One of its major features is the radially seriated tracheids that surround the apices of the xylem arms. The problem is whether to call them secondary xylem or simply radially seriated primary xylem. *Xenocladia* was first reported from the Middle Devonian by Arnold in 1940 and by him again in 1952 on the basis of better material. I have found it in rocks of Upper Devonian age (Banks, 1961). It compares favorably with the Carboniferous plants assigned to Cladoxy-lales by Bertrand (1935).

Pseudosporochnus (Fig. 5D,E) has long been held to be a bushy psilophyte. Leclercq and Banks (1962) showed that it had a typical cladoxylalean stele and

Table 5. *Relationship of Devonian Lycopods to Zosterophyllophytina*

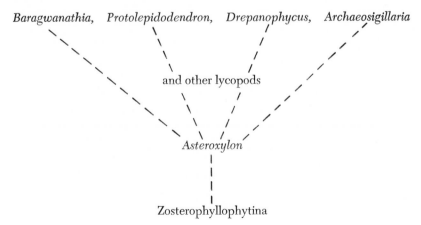

was much more complex in its branching pattern than had been assumed previously. Its ultimate appendages, borne spirally, forked trichotomously once or oftener. Every fork then dichotomized three times, resulting in a much-branched, planated, but not webbed, frond. Some fronds bore sporangia terminally. *Cladoxylon scoparium* Kräusel and Weyland (1926) (Fig. 5C) branched as profusely as *Pseudosporochnus* but more irregularly. Its ultimate appendages were much smaller and less branched and its fertile appendages were fan-shaped, bearing sporangia terminally. These genera are related on the basis of their gross morphological structure and their multifasciculate xylem. In fact the order *Cladoxy-*

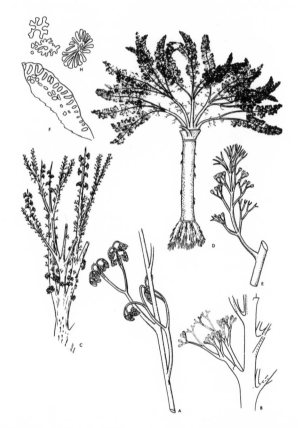

Fig. 5. Trimerophytina and Cladoxylopsida. A, *Dawsonites*. B, *Trimerophyton*. C, *Cladoxylon scoparium*. D, *Pseudosporochnus*. E, One of the spirally arranged fronds of *Pseudosporochnus*. F, *Xenocladia* with radially aligned peripheral xylem strands and some of the more circular central strands. G, *Schizopodium*, two variations of the much-lobed xylem strand. H, *Cladoxylon* with xylem strand similar to that found in *Pseudosporochnus*. (A, From Hueber, 1964; B, from Hopping, 1956; C, from Kräusel and Weyland, 1926; D, and E, from Leclercq and Banks, 1962; F, from specimen; G, from Hueber, 1960; H, from Hueber, 1960.)

lales was founded on petrified specimens of Mississippian age whose xylem was much divided; it is only the Devonian representatives for which external morphology is known.

There are two recent additions to the Devonian cladoxylaleans. Ananviev (1957) found a *Hyenia*-like axis and a *Pseudosporochnus*-like fertile branch system. He concluded the two were probably parts of one plant and erected a new Lower Devonian taxon *Protohyenia* for them. He chose this name because the sporangia were upright, not recurved. In 1964 he reported finding a cladoxylalean type of multifasciculate vascular system in the fertile branch system. Bonamo and Banks (1966b) suggest that the fertile branch system is therefore a *Pseudosporochnus* as Ananiev thought originally (it is not listed here on Table 6 because I am unconvinced that it is really of Lower Devonian age). The remaining piece of Ananviev's *Protohyenia* is probably *Hyenia*. Thus the new sphenopsid *Protohyenia* that was thought to be the earliest representative of that group no longer exists.

Table 6. Possible Evolutionary Trends from Rhyniophytina–Trimerophytina

	Cladoxylopsida	Coenopteridopsida	Progymnospermopsida
Tournaisian	Several genera and species	Several genera and species	*Callixylon* *Siderella* *Protopitys*
Famennian	*Pietzschia*	*Rhacophyton*	*Callixylon* *Archaeopteris* *Aneurophyton*
Frasnian	*Pietzschia* *Pseudosporochnus* *Xenocladia* *Cladoxylon* *Schizopodium*	*Rhacophyton* *Asteropteris* *Reimannia* *Arachnoxylon*	*Ginkgophyton* *Callixylon* *Archaeopteris* *Sphenoxylon* *Tetraxylopteris* *Aneurophyton*
Givetian	*Pseudosporochnus* *Cladoxylon scoparium* *Calamophyton* *Xenocladia* *Schizopodium*	*Asteropteris* *Iridopteris* *Reimannia* *Arachnoxylon*	*Actinopodium* *Svalbardia* *Sphenoxylon* *Protopteridium* *Aneurophyton*
Eifelian			*Aneurophyton*
Emsian	Trimerophytina	*Dawsonites* *Trimerophyton*	
	Rhyniophytina	*Eogaspesiea* ?*Rhynia*, ?*Horneophyton*	
Siegenian	Trimerophytina Rhyniophytina	*Dawsonites* *Taeniocrada, Yarravia* *Hedeia, Cooksonia*	
Gedinnian	*Cooksonia*		

Leclercq and Schweitzer (1965) have just reported the discovery of typical cladoxylalean anatomy in *Calamophyton bicephalum*. They are convinced therefore that *Calamophyton* is not a sphenopsid. It agrees with other Devonian cladoxylaleans in the branching of its main axis. (Leclercq and Andrews, 1960) and its numerous terminal sporangia. It agrees too in the morphology of its sterile appendages which are more like those of *Cladoxylon scoparium* than like those of *Pseudosporochnus*. However, the sporangia of *Calamophyton* are borne on recurved branches of sporangiophores whose morphology is more complex than the equivalent fertile leaves of *Pseudosporochnus* and *Cladoxylon scoparium*. This of course raises doubt about the systematic position of *Hyenia*, which shares many characteristics with *Calamophyton* (Bonamo and Banks, 1966b). It will be a matter of no small interest to learn whether *Hyenia* remains in Sphenopsida or must also be transferred. It will be equally interesting to see if the new anatomical information from *Calamophyton* that seems to make it a cladoxylalean continues to outweigh the morphological evidence that *Calamophyton* does have a primitive sphenopsid sporangiophore.

Trimerophytina seems a natural group to serve as a precursor of Cladoxylopsida, both anatomically and morphologically. Its stratigraphic occurrence is significant. Trimerophytina appear earlier in geologic time, at least so far as we can tell from present knowledge (Table 6). For the future, many details remain to be cleared up. Spores are known for *Dawsonites* (Hueber, 1964), *Calamophyton* (Bonamo and Banks, 1966b), and *Trimerophyton* only. Structure of sporangia is known only for *Dawsonites* (work in progress, Banks, Hueber and Leclercq) where their walls are several layers thick and are composed of cells similar to the cortex of the branches. They are supplied by large vascular strands and probably possessed stomates. Thus sporangia of *Dawsonites* fit the usual criteria for primitive organs. It is essential to find spores and sporangial structure for the other genera, to find external morphology for *Xenocladia* and *Schizopodium,* and to find anatomical structure and better-preserved spores for *Trimerophyton*. If ever all these data are forthcoming, we may have some exact knowledge of the role played by Cladoxylopsida in evolution. At present they are most commonly regarded as a plexus that might have had some connection to the medullosan pteridosperms or as an independent line that ended blindly. It seems just as likely to me that they represent one of several experimental lines developing during late Middle and Upper Devonian time. Each of the newly developing lines may have undergone the several possible changes such as lobing and dissection of the stele, aggregation or reduction in number of sporangia, and specialization of sporangia and their position. Certain individuals from each of the several lines may then have evolved in the direction of pteridosperms. In the present state of our knowledge I see no reason to single out one group (plexus or line) as the only one that was capable of evolving into pteridosperms, especially as continuing research enlarges each group in turn and shows it to be relatively specialized.

COENOPTERIDOPSIDA. A second plexus that might have evolved from Trimerophytina is Coenopteridopsida (Table 6). Arnold (1935, 1940) and Read (1938) described *Reimannia, Arachnoxylon,* and *Iridopteris* on the basis of small axes preserved only as petrifactions (Fig. 6). Xylem in *Reimannia* is three-lobed; in the other two it is five-lobed. The first collections of all three genera were made in rocks of Givetian age, but I have found *Reimannia* and *Arachnoxylon* in younger Frasnian rocks (Banks, 1961). Arnold (1940) erected Iridopteridineae, a suborder of Coenopteridales, for them and speculated about which part of a plant they might represent. We are really no better off today than when he wrote, as far as details of the three genera are concerned. All three are characterized by the production of simple, terete vascular strands. Nothing is known of the appendages supplied by the strands except that they are spirally arranged. Peripheral loops are found in the protoxylem areas, a characteristic associated with coenopterids.

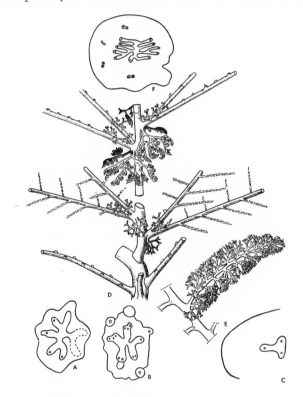

Fig. 6. Coenopteridopsida. A, *Arachnoxylon* with lobed, mesarch xylem strand. B, *Iridopteris*, lobed, mesarch xylem strand and circular, mesarch traces. C, *Reimannia* with lobed, mesarch xylem strand. D, *Rhacophyton*, three lowest pinnae unbranched and showing only bases of pinnules; four upper pinnae each showing the basal dichotomy, the catadromic pinnules (some fertile), and points of attachment of ultimate pinnules. E, One pinna of *Rhacophyton* enlarged to show the much-branched, unwebbed pinnules. F, *Asteropteris* with lobed, mesarch xylem strand and clepsydroid leaf traces. (A, From Read, 1938; B, from Arnold, 1940; C, from specimen; D and E, from Leclercq, 1951; F, from specimens.

Since Arnold's publication we have learned that some cladoxylaleans and some progymnosperms possess variously lobed or divided xylem strands from which arise simple terete strands (leaf traces?). Coenopterid ferns, on the other hand, often produce clepsydroid traces to their appendages. All three groups exhibit mesarchy. It seems perfectly possible therefore that Iridopteridineae may be related to cladoxylaleans or to progymnosperms just as easily as to Coenopteridales (Table 6). They may represent only plants that were at an evolutionary level just below that attained by cladoxylaleans, coenopteridaleans, and progymnosperms. Information is as yet too sparse to make a reassignment in the present classification system.

The Frasnian genus *Asteropteris* (Fig. 6F) has been called the oldest representative of coenopterid ferns. It possessed a much-lobed xylem strand off which leaf traces arose in a whorl. Peripheral loops are present in the tips of the arms of xylem, and they seem to remain closed as in the clepsydroid coenopterid ferns. The traces to the rachides have two peripheral loops even before they are free from the arms of xylem. They are typically clepsydroid in form. When seen farther out in the cortex, they have developed four peripheral loops, two at each end of the clepsydroid bundle. Bertrand (1914) confirmed Dawson's original interpretation that the many-rayed, central vascular strand is reminiscent of Cladoxylales. However, the appearance of four protoxylem strands in the leaf traces led him to conclude that its closest affinity lay with Coenopteridales, and he compared the xylem strand of the stem with that of *Asterochlaena*. If the peripheral loops in the clepsydroid traces are permanent and if they give rise to traces that are closed rings, then *Asteropteris* will be included among the clepsydroid coenopterids. To date, however, only short lengths of stem have been found petrified, and the leaf traces have never been seen outside the cortex. Dawson's single specimen came from marine rocks of Frasnian age in central New York, and Hueber (1960) collected several axes in continental deposits in eastern New York. Specimens showing external morphology have yet to be discovered. *Asteropteris* is one of the important plants badly in need of additional study.

Rhacophyton (Fig. 6D) is the one unquestioned member of Coenopteridales to be discovered in Devonian strata, and both its anatomy and morphology have been found. *R. zygopteroides* is the best-known species (Leclercq, 1951, 1954). The xylem strand of its stem is star-shaped, and its arms produce clepsydroid traces to the rachides. Both sterile and fertile fronds are borne spirally and are characterized by clepsydroid traces. Vegetative fronds bear pinnae in a distichous manner, and traces to the pinnae are small crescentic bundles whose departure leaves an open peripheral loop. Similar bundles supply the ultimate pinnules which are divided several times and are unwebbed (Fig. 6E). Fertile fronds, on the contrary, divide at their base into two primary pinnae whose xylem strand is again clepsydroid. Further branching of the fertile fronds resembles that of vegetative fronds. *Rhacophyton* has therefore certain features of both Clepsydropsidaceae and Etapteridaceae (Zygopterids). The four-ranked branching of fertile pinnae, the temporary peripheral loops, and the crescentic pinna bundles are similar to Etapteridaceae. The two-ranked branching of the vegetative fronds is a character of the Clepsydropsidaceae.

Sporangia of *Rhacophyton* are borne on a catadromic pinnule situated at the base of the paired pinnae. It is a dichotomously branched, concave cluster of fusiform sporangia that probably dehisced longitudinally and are reminiscent of sporangia of Trimerophytina and Rhyniophytina.

It must be admitted that Devonian representatives of the coenopterid lines are still sparse. Nevertheless, the distinctive anatomy and morphology of the Carboniferous coenopterids, which are rapidly becoming a large and diverse complex, make a search for Devonian precursors inevitable. Three characters that command attention are the tendency to produce leaves as modifications of large branch systems (Mamay and Andrews, 1950), the production of large masses of terminal sporangia, and the possession of a complex vascular system. All three characterize *Rhacophyton* as well as Carboniferous coenopterids. *Asteropteris* and the iridopterids are known only by their anatomy. The former is more coenopterid-like, whereas the latter are simpler and could be placed in any one of several groups. Most striking is the parallelism between the fronds of *Rhacophyton* and the large branch systems of progymnosperms, between the fertile pinnules of *Rhacophyton* and the fertile complexes of some progymnosperms, and between the sterile pinnules of *Rhacophyton* and those of Aneurophytales. In *Rhacophyton* the anatomy of the frond differs from that of the stem, whereas in progymnosperms a change in anatomical structure occurs only in the production of the ultimate appendages. Yet the ultimate appendages in most Devonian members of both groups are unwebbed telomic structures, whereas in both groups the lateral branch systems resemble large fronds. Clearly, parallel changes were occurring in the two groups. In the same way, the aggregation of numerous fusiform, terminal sporangia into complex fertile branch systems was advancing in parallel fashion in the two groups. Many gaps remain to be filled between Trimerophytina and *Rhacophyton*, but the outline of a series is evident.

PROGYMNOSPERMOPSIDA. Progymnospermopsida (Beck, 1960) are a third group that may have evolved from Rhyniaceae by way of Trimerophytaceae. It is a group about which data are accumulating rapidly and about which considerable evolutionary speculation is bound to emerge as the plants become better known. The group is characterized by secondary xylem with circular bordered pitting, usually narrow vascular rays as in many coniferophytic gymnosperms, and by pteridophytic reproduction. Some taxa are so preserved that they show anatomical structure only, some show morphological features only, some show both. Some taxa are apparently homosporous, some heterosporous. A tentative classification of the group is given in Table 7 and an idea of their occurrence in time is given in Table 6.

It is reasonable to speculate that Aneurophytales (Fig. 7) is the most primitive order in the group. *Aneurophyton*, *Tetraxylopteris*, and *Protopteridium* are all protostelic. *Protopteridium* is included here on the basis of work reported (Bonamo and Banks, 1967). Specimens of the first two genera are mesarch, those of the third

Table 7. Tentative Classification of Progymnospermopsida

Archaeopteridales

> *Svalbardia*
> *Actinopodium*
> *Ginkgophyton* sensu Beck
> *Archaeopteris*
> *Callixylon*
> *Siderella*

Protopityales

> *Protopitys*

Aneurophytales

> *Protopteridium*
> *Aneurophyton*
> *Tetraxylopteris*
> *Sphenoxylon*

probably are. Axes of *Aneurophyton* have a three-lobed protostele whereas those of *Tetraxylopteris* have four-armed protosteles. In both genera the stele is the same in all orders of branching except the ultimate divisions. It consists of elongate tracheids with multiseriate bordered pits on all walls and of high, mostly uniseriate, rays. The xylem of *Protopteridium* is less well known, but its primary xylem is reported to be three- or four-lobed (Kräusel and Weyland, 1938). *Sphenoxylon* was erected (Read, 1937) for a single petrified stem that seemed to have a pith surrounded by four radiating arms of primary xylem. Beck (1957), Hueber (1960), and Matten (1965) have contributed to the strong probability that *Sphenoxylon* and *Textraxylopteris* are synonymous. The genus *Sphenoxylon*, however, must be retained as an organ genus for petrifactions for which external morphology is lacking.

Secondary xylem like that of many gymnosperms seems to have become well established in Aneurophytales, hence, by late Eifelian time. Secondary phloem consisting of phloem rays, various kinds of parenchyma cells, and fibers has been described for *Tetraxylopteris* (Beck, 1957). In spite of good preservation there is no indication that typical sieve cells have evolved.

Branching in *Aneurophyton* is spiral, in *Tetraxylopteris* it is opposite, decussate, and in *Protopteridium* it is probably spiral although the ultimate branches may be dichotomous. In both of the first two genera there are several orders of branching which have been regarded as primitive fronds. The branch systems terminate in dichotomized ultimate appendages that are not planated and not webbed. In *Aneurophyton* the appendages are said to be without vascular supply whereas in *Tetraxylopteris* they are supplied by a terete xylem strand. This latter character indicates that the ultimate appendages may be equivalent to leaves. *Protopteridium* lacks these regularly arranged, dichotomized ultimate appendages. It may possess pinnately lobed appendages, some of which are sterile and some of which are fertile. These pinnately lobed sterile appendages have long been regarded as the earliest evidence for the origin of fern-like leaves (Fig. 7A), but see Bonamo and Banks (1967).

Sporangia of *Aneurophyton* are borne in clusters on small, recurved branches. Available evidence indicates that they are homosporous. Sporangia of *Protopteridium* are believed to be borne on the upper side of large, lateral, upcurved branch systems (Fig. 9C). These systems bear pairs of short pinnae whose branches carry large numbers of slender, pedicellate sporangia. In *Tetraxylopteris* (Fig. 9D), large sporangial complexes consist of dichotomously and pinnately branched appendages (Bonamo and Banks, 1966a). In all three genera the sporangia are elongate and fusiform, and they ·probably dehisce longitudinally. They seem clearly to be an extension of the evolutionary series initiated by *Rhyniophytina* that bore terminal sporangia and that was continued by *Trimerophytina*.

Spores referable to *Aneurospora* have been found in sporangia of *Aneurophyton* (Streel, 1964); *Rhabdosporites langi* has been isolated from sporangia of *Tetraxylopteris* (Bonamo and Banks, 1966a) and has been found in association with *Protopteridium* as well (Lang, 1926; Richardson, 1960).

Protopitys, a Mississippian genus, was long regarded as related to conifers or to pteridosperms because of its abundant secondary wood characterized by bordered pits on the walls of the tracheids. When its primary xylem was found, some placed the genus among the ferns, perhaps because of its predominantly

Fig. 7. Progymnospermopsida. A, *Protopteridium hostimense*, main branches attached spirally, lesser branches dichotomous; toward the apex there are sterile and then fertile pinnae. B, *Aneurophyton* showing forked, ultimate appendages. C, *Svalbardia*, fertile pinnules. D, *Svalbardia*, sterile pinnules. E, *Tetraxylopteris* fronds, arranged spirally on main axis; subsequent branching is opposite decussate. (A, Kräusel and Weyland, 1933; B, from specimens; C and D, from Høeg, 1942; E, from Beck, 1957.)

scalariform tracheids. No foliage has been observed, but leaf traces originate as crescent-shaped collateral bundles at either end of the elliptical pith. Arrangement of appendages is therefore distichous. Walton (1957) reported a new species of *Protopitys* that bears fertile branches in distichous fashion. Each fertile branch of *Protopitys* dichotomizes several times and then forks pinnately. The resemblance of these branches to the sporangial complexes of *Protopteridium* and *Tetraxylopteris* (Fig. 9) is striking.

The ultimate divisions in *Protopitys* terminate in sporangia, and a vascular strand extends to the base of the sporangium as in *Dawsonites*. Sporangia are elongate-fusiform, their walls are two to three cells in thickness, and stomates apparently were present as in *Archaeopteris* (Carluccio et al., 1966) and in *Dawsonites*. Dehiscence is longitudinal as in *Tetraxylopteris, Dawsonites,* and other genera. The sporangia are unique in having radially elongate epidermal cells when viewed in a transverse section of a sporangium. In surface view they are longitudinally elongate as in several other genera. Spores range from 82 to 163 μ in diameter, and Walton suggested incipient heterospory as one interpretation of this wide range in size. However, Richardson (1965) finds numerous genera of isolated spores in which the range in size is as great or greater.

The entire fertile branch system is recurved as it is in *Protopteridium* and *Tetraxylopteris* (Fig. 9). The tendency toward pinnate branching also recalls these two genera, and the position, shape, structure, and dehiscence of the sporangia can clearly be regarded as derived from such progenitors as Trimerophytaceae. Anatomically the fertile branch system is more highly evolved than in any of the genera mentioned. It is supplied by one large crescent-shaped leaf trace that is almost endarch (Walton, 1957). This trace dichotomizes in the proximal portion of the fertile branch, and thenceforth only more or less circular traces have been seen in the other divisions of the fertile branch. This suggests that the fertile branch is equivalent to a leaf or frond. Walton referred to it as a sporophyll. Whatever it is called, it is somewhat more highly evolved than fertile branches of Aneurophytaceae and Trimerophytaceae. In addition, the stem of *Protopitys* with its pith, almost endarch primary xylem bundles, and crescent-shaped leaf trace is more highly evolved than that of either of the two families named. Yet the inclusion of *Protopitys* in Protopityales in the Progymnospermopsida (Table 7) is justified by its combination of characters.

Archaeopteridales are known best for the two genera *Callixylon* Zalessky 1911 and *Archaeopteris* (Dawson) Stur 1875. Both occur in Frasnian and Famennian time, both have been found in strata that may prove to be uppermost Givetian, and *Callixylon* occurs also in Tournaisian. If *Siderella* proves to be synonymous with *Archaeopteris*, as suggested by Carluccio et al. (1966), then both *Callixylon* and *Archaeopteris* continue into Tournaisian. Beck (1960) was the first to find a branch determined as *Archaeopteris* attached to a stem assignable to *Callixylon*. As a result of this connection of a presumed gymnosperm and a presumed fern, Beck suggested the name Progymnospermopsida for plants whose reproduction is pteridophytic and whose secondary xylem is gymnospermous.

Archaeopteris (Fig. 8) has been regarded as a bipinnate frond of a fern to which the terms rachis, pinna, and pinnule were applied. On the basis of the newly discovered anatomy of this "frond," Carluccio et al. (1966) suggest that it is in fact a branching system whose ultimate appendages should be called leaves rather than pinnules. *Callixylon is* known from petrified axes up to 28 ft in length and 5 ft in diameter. Its pith is surrounded by discrete mesarch bundles that produce branch traces in spiral sequence. Each bundle divides tangentially, producing one trace and one reparatory strand so that the trace leaves no gap in the stele. The resulting branches may be rachides assignable to *Archaeopteris*. Proximally their anatomy in transverse section resembles that of *Callixylon* (Carluccio et al., 1966) the stem to which they are attached. More distally, their primary xylem is siphonostelic (Fig. 9A) with ten to twelve lobes. From the main axis (rachis) opposite lobes give rise to branch traces (pinna traces) that, in fertile *A. macilenta*, become siphonostelic like the main branch. The other lobes produce smaller

Fig. 8. *Archaeopteris* (modified from Beck, 1962). Branching system arranged spirally on stem (*Callixylon*); stipules clasping base of branch, rachial pinnules on main branch between laterals; laterals bear sterile and fertile leaves; sporangia in two rows on laminar, forked leaf. Anatomy of main axis (rachis): pith (lined), lobed siphonostele, bundles of sclerenchymatous cells (dotted), mesarch traces with two protoxylem strands, and divided traces.

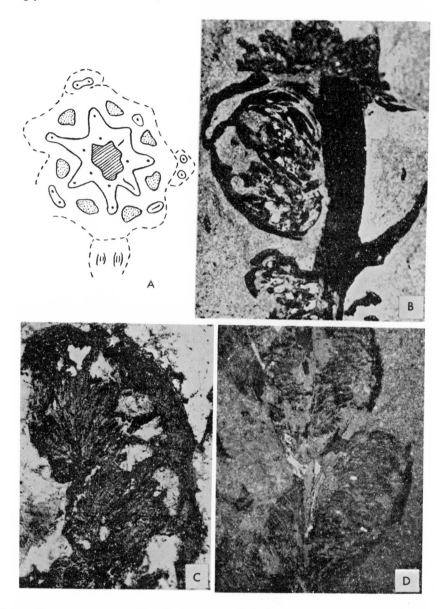

Fig. 9. Progymnospermopsida. A, Anatomy of *Archaeopteris*. B, Sporophyll of *Protopitys*. C, Sporangial complex of *Protopteridium*. D, Sporangial complexes of *Tetraxylopteris*. (A, From Carluccio et al., 1966; B, from Walton, 1957; C, from Kräusel and Weyland, 1938; D, from specimen.)

traces in spiral order. These traces appear to supply leaves (rachial pinnules) along the main axis. From the fertile lateral axes (branches or pinnae), small traces are produced in spiral order. They supply the leaves (pinnules) which therefore are spirally arranged despite their apparently bilateral symmetry.

The ultimate branches (pinnules) of fertile axes are spirally arranged. They are often several times dichotomized and bear two rows of sporangia on their adaxial surface. The epidermis of both fertile leaves and sporangia is composed of elongate cells and stomates (Carluccio et al., 1966). The fertile leaves are laminar, and the sporangia are probably primitive in construction. No sporangia have been found petrified, but the presence of stomates suggests that they had a wall several cells in thickness. Dehiscence was longitudinal (Andrews et al., 1965). Heterospory has been proved in some species (Arnold, 1939; Pettitt, 1965) and has been suggested in others (Kräusel and Weyland, 1941). Pettitt (1965) reported megaspores similar to the dispersed spore genus *Biharisporites* and microspores like *Cyclogranisporites*.

Svalbardia Høeg (1942) and *Actinopodiopsis* Høeg (1942) were described from Middle Devonian strata in Spitzbergen. The former (Fig. 7, C and D) has been regarded as a precursor of *Archaeopteris*. Carluccio et al. (1966) have suggested that *Actinopodiopsis* might represent petrified axes of *Svalbardia* although the two have not been found attached. The ultimate branches (pinnules) of *Svalbardia* are forked several times into filiform segments. In contrast to *Archaeopteris* they are unwebbed as in the Aneurophytales. This character along with the somewhat less regular arrangement of sporangia on the ultimate fertile branches may support the concept of *Svalbardia* as a Middle Devonian precursor of the predominantly Upper Devonian *Archaeopteris*. If axes assignable to *Actinopodiopsis* prove to be parts of the plant called *Svalbardia*, the difference between *Svalbardia* and *Archaeopteris* will be little more than the webbing of the leaves (pinnules) of the latter.

Ginkgophyton sensu Beck (1963) is an axis bearing spirally arranged, wedge-shaped, sterile leaves. Little is known of its gross morphology. Internally it resembles *Callixylon* except that it lacks banded pitting on the radial walls of the tracheids. The discovery that leaves (pinnules) of *Archaeopteris* are borne spirally suggests that Beck's *Ginkgophyton* is an oversized *Archaeopteris obtusa*. *A. macilenta* is borne on a stem (*Callixylon*) that has banded pitting (Beck, 1960, 1962). *A. macilenta* itself has banded pitting (Carluccio et al., 1966). All known species of *Callixylon* show banded pitting. However, it is unknown whether all fronds of *Archaeopteris* show this character. Thus only future discoveries can answer such questions as: Does the frond of *A. obtusa* show grouped pitting? Can the *Ginkgophyton* of Beck be synonymous with *Archaeopteris*? Are there two closely related genera that differ only in the arrangement of their pits on tracheid walls?

Progymnosperms are a group with considerable morphological significance regardless of whether they gave rise directly to gymnosperms (Beck, 1962; Meeuse, 1963) or merely paralleled the evolution of gymnosperms and ferns (Leclercq, 1962). The origin of the pteropsid leaf is one of the most significant questions to which progymnosperms contribute. It is unnecessary here to repeat all that has been written (e.g. Andrews, 1961, p. 84–87) about the origin of pteropsid leaves from branch systems, but it is important to point out that Aneurophytales exemplify this concept. Their anatomy is the same in all orders of branching except in the ultimate divisions, and their branching is three-dimensional. Nevertheless, the systems of lateral branches simulate fronds. Planation of these three-dimensional structures would produce even more obvious fronds, and webbing of the ultimate divisions would produce pinnule-like structures. In Archaeopteridales the result of planation and webbing can be seen. The "frond" of *Archaeopteris* bears "pinnae" in two rows (planated), but the ultimate leafy divisions (pinnules), though webbed, are still borne in a spiral sequence. Presumably descendants produced leaves (pinnules) in distichous fashion. Thus in the Archeopteridales (Pityales), just as in the Aneurophytales, leaves may have been evolving simultaneously in two ways, lateral branch systems were becoming fronds, and ultimate branchlets were becoming leaves. From Archaeopteridales (Pityales), Meeuse (1963, p. 157–64) has speculated that further evolution resulted in the cycadophyte leaf on the one hand and the coniferophyte leaf on the other. In the former case, the entire branch system (frond) of *Archaeopteris* became the large compound leaf of the cycadophytes, whereas only the ultimate pinnules (leaves) of *Archaeopteris* evolved into the coniferophyte leaf such as the sword-shaped leaf of *Cordaites*. All we have learned about progymnosperms to date supports this interpretation. In fact the discovery (Carluccio et al., 1966) that the leaves (pinnules) of *Archaeopteris* are borne spirally removes the one difficulty mentioned by Meeuse (1963, p. 159). He wrote of the "alternate or subopposite dictichous arrangement" in *Archaeopteris* changing to the helical arrangement in *Cordaites*. No such change was necessary.

Sporangia of progymnosperms are elongate cylindrical organs similar to those of Trimerophytaceae. Often they had a long attenuated apex. Where known, they had stomates on their surface and dehisced by a single longitudinal slit. Their wall probably consisted of several layers of cells, one of which broke down or sometimes separated from the others to form a sac-like structure in which the spores escaped as a mass (Pettitt, 1965). Only *Archaeopteris* is known to have been heterosporous.

Archaeopteris has been used by Meeuse (1963, p. 142ff.) as the starting point in the evolution of both pteridosperm and cordaite reproductive organs. His Figure 5 illustrates the possibility that some individual fertile pinnules of *Archaeopteris* evolved into pteridosperm male synangia such as those of *Crossotheca*, others into seeds. In the evolution of the integument, he assumes, with Benson (1935), that it was produced by sterile megasporangia enclosing one fertile one. It seems to me that an alternative, and equally unproved, hypothesis is that fertile pinnules lost all but one megasporangium which then became surrounded by the numerous dichotomized tips of the fertile pinnule. This suggestion follows more closely the evidence from other sources (e.g. Andrews, 1963) that integuments were formed by the fusion of sterile telomes around a megasporangium. Because the sterile leaf of *Archaeopteris* appears to have evolved from webbed, ultimate branchlets (telomes), it is reasonable to consider the much-divided fertile leaf to be the same. Thus if it were reduced to bearing only a single megasporangium, its divisions might well envelop that megasporangium after the fashion of the origin of integument postulated by Andrews (1961, Fig. 13–4).

Meeuse also derives coniferophyte reproductive organs from progymnosperms like *Archaeopteris*. He assumes (his Fig. 4) that each pinna becomes one male or one female short shoot (cone) of *Cordaites*. This involves the migration of one sterile pinnule to the axis (rachis) below the insertion of the pinna (short shoot) to form a subtending bract. It seems to me that a rachial pinnule of *Archaeopteris* (Fig. 8) might serve this function equally well. It involves also the reduction of the remaining sterile pinnules to scale-like structures aggregated closely (cone-fashion) around one or a few fertile pinnules. He derives other coniferophytes from the cordaite type.

In discussing the evolutionary significance of the progymnosperms and their role in the various hypotheses of origin of more highly evolved plant groups one important point stands out: our ignorance of the exact limits of axis and leaf. At least some of the controversy over the axial or appendicular nature of an organ is the result of a failure to look at the evolutionary origins of the organ. *Archaeopteris* is a case in point. Prior to learning its anatomical structure the custom was to speak of its frond, its pinnae, and its pinnules, either sterile or fertile, because those are the terms that would be applied to a living plant of similar appearance. On this premise one would call the sporangia foliar. Anatomy has shown (Carluccio et al., 1966) that this apparently flattened frond is a branch system whose penultimate branches (pinnae) are distichous but whose ultimate divisions are still spirally arranged. Only the ultimate divisions differ anatomically from the rest of the branch system and they can be called leaves. Some species of *Archaeopteris* have unwebbed leaves (*A. fissilis*) and related genera (*Svalbardia*) are similarly unwebbed. The leaves of the more primitive progymnosperms (e.g. *Aneurophyton* and *Tetraxylopteris*) are homologous. If we go back slightly farther to *Dawsonites* there is no particular organ that can be called leaf, and its sporangia, the apparent precursors of those of progymnosperms, are considered stem borne. It is clear that leaves of progymnosperms are merely slightly modified branches and that the distinction between leaf and branch (stem) is difficult to draw. Thus if one chose to regard the ultimate, sporangium-bearing branches of progymnosperms as axial rather than appendicular organs, he would call the sporangia axial or the plants stachyosporous. I would prefer to regard the ultimate appendages as appendicular and to call the progymnosperms phyllosporous, because I interpret the ultimate appendages as prototypes of leaves. I consider the fertile pinnules of *Archaeopteris* as homologues of the sterile pinnules. Thus no matter how modified these pinnules might become (e.g. reduced to bearing a single terminal sporangium) their sporangia (or seeds if *Cordaites* were derived from them) would be leaf-borne.

SPHENOPHYTINA AND FILICOPSIDA. The origin of these two groups is speculative. The sphenophytes may have been derived from Rhyniophytina. The ferns may have had a similar origin by way of Trimerophytina. Some characters associated with Filicopsida evolved in each of the three groups, Cladoxylopsida, Coenopteridopsida, and Progymnospermopsida, and the various evolutionary series seen among them could equally well have led to ferns. Beck (1962) has cited several reasons for believing that progymnosperms are neither ferns nor progenitors of ferns. Similar reasoning applies to cladoxylaleans and coenopterids, e.g. Delevoryas (1962, p. 79–80). Yet the existence of these three groups and the characters they share indicate that true ferns may be only one more expression of the morphological variation that produced these groups. It is from the early, plastic members that other

Table 8. Summary of Evolutionary Concepts

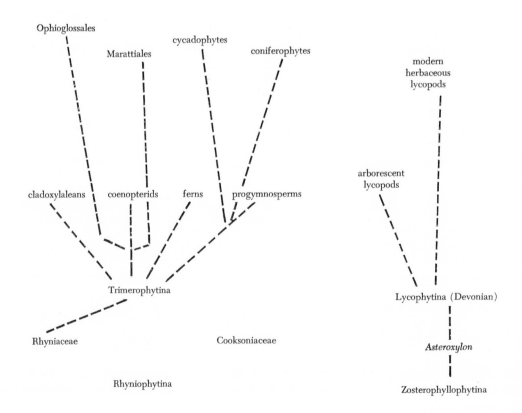

groups evolved, not from the easily recognized, obvious, highly evolved forms. The derivation of Ophioglossales and Marattiales from coenopterids has been argued pro and con, but it is more likely that early coenopterids, rather than those with fixed and definitive characters, were the progenitors (Table 8).

Speed of evolution of land plants. Banks (1965) has suggested that new habitats on the land and limited competition permitted rapid colonization and the development of variation. Further, it is possible that in Silurian–early Devonian time, slight genetic changes effected more pronounced morphological changes than is true today. On this basis some of the types reviewed here, plus others that are omitted, might easily have evolved in the relatively short time that was available.

Palynology. The study of spores found in Devonian strata is proceeding rapidly. In the area of stratigraphy the results will facilitate the correlation of marine and continental strata so that the latter can be placed more accurately than at present. They may improve interregional stratigraphic correlations, as Richardson (1965) has shown in his comparison of the microfloras of Scotland and Russia. The following publications are examples of the kind of extensive studies that will be needed to accomplish these results: Allen, 1965; Kedo, 1955; McGregor, 1964; Richardson, 1965; Streel, 1964; Tchibrickova, 1962; Vigran, 1964.

Some spores have been found in situ and described in full detail. This detail has permitted the application to them of names used in palynological nomenclature (Table 9). In many cases, e.g. *Calamophyton*, the spore has proved to belong to an existing taxon for sporae dispersae. Other spores have been found in situ in Devonian plants, but either their descriptions have been too meager or their preservation too poor to correlate them with names used in palynological nomenclature (Table 10).

Table 9. Devonian Plants Bearing Named Spores in Situ

Plant	Spore	Reference
Archaeopteris cf. *jacksonii*	*Cyclogranisporites* *Biharisporites*	Pettitt, 1965
Svalbardia polymorpha	*Lycospora*	Vigran, 1964
Tetraxylopteris schmidtii	*Rhabdosporites*	Bonamo & Banks, 1966a
Aneurophyton germanicum	*Aneurospora*	Streel, 1964
Dawsonites sp.	*Retusotriletes*	Hueber, 1964
Barinophyton richardsonii	*Calamospora*	Pettitt, 1965
Enigmophyton superbum	*Phyllothecatriletes* *Enigmophytospora*	Vigran, 1964
Calamophyton bicephalum	*Dibolisporites*	Bonamo & Banks, 1966b
Eviostachya høegii	*Acanthotriletes*	Leclercq, 1957

Table 10. Some Devonian Plants with Spores in Situ but Unnamed

Plant	Reference
Pseudosporochnus krejcii	Leclercq, 1940
Protopteridium spp.	Lang, 1926; Obrhel, 1961; Halle, 1936.
Hyenia elegans	Leclercq, 1940
Trimerophyton robustius	Hopping, 1956
Barrandeina dusliana	Obrhel, 1961
Zosterophyllum llanoveranum	Croft & Lang, 1942
Psilophyton ornatum	Hueber, 1964
Nothia aphylla (Asteroxylon)	Kidston & Lang, 1920b
Horneophyton Lignieri	Kidston & Lang, 1920a
Rhynia gwynne-vaughanii	Kidston & Lang, 1917
Cooksonia sp.	Croft & Lang, 1942
Sporogonites exuberans	Croft & Lang, 1942

Isolated spores whose parent plants are known will serve to predict the mega-fossils that may be found in nearby deposits. Spores, like megafossils, will contribute to our understanding of the time of origin of land plants and of the origin of various groups of land plants. Even now some generalizations are possible (Richardson, 1964). Lower Devonian spores are simple, trilete, and azonate with smooth, apiculate, or spinose exines. Examples are *Retusotriletes, Calamospora, Lophotriletes, Acanthotriletes, Punctatisporites, Apiculatisporites, Leiotriletes,* and *Emphanisporites*. Younger Devonian spores show more diversity of ornament, structure and size. *Archaeotriletes, Hystrichosporites,* and *Ancyrospora* possess bi-furcate spines. *Hymenozonotriletes* sensu Naumova is a zonate spore. *Rhabdospo-rites, Auroraspora, Calyptosporites,* and *Endosporites* are "cavate" spores. *Bihari-sporites* is an example of an Upper Devonian megaspore, and the first monolete spore appears in upper Eifelian in Russia. It is of particular interest to note that the appearance of simple spores probably belonging to land plants coincides fairly well with the appearance of simple vascular plants. This adds to the confidence with which one can think of late Silurian and early Devonian as the time of origin of vascular plants.

Seeds have not been demonstrated in Devonian strata, but heterospory may have appeared as early as Givetian time, with the spores associated with *Enigmo-phyton* in Spitsbergen. Heterospory is known in several plants in Frasnian time (e.g. Pettitt, 1965), and numerous isolated megaspores have been reported from Upper Devonian strata (Chaloner, 1959). The closest approach to the seed condition is demonstrated by *Cystosporites devonicus* (Chaloner and Pettitt, 1964) from the Frasnian of Quebec. This fossil is a megaspore tetrad in which one spore enlarges and three abort. *Cystosporites* is a Carboniferous genus and it has been found only in the genus *Lepidocarpon*. Thus the tetrads described by Chaloner and Pettitt may indicate an early form of the seed habit, the lycopod type. Because they found no associated fructifications, the authors speculate that *Cysto-sporites* could represent a species of *Archaeopteris* in which the number of mega-spores was much reduced. In view of the relative abundance and variety of lyco-pods in Upper Devonian and of our present knowledge of heterospory in *Archae-opteris*, I prefer to agree with the authors that this find is the beginning of the lycopod type of seed habit.

In summary, the importance of careful stratigraphic records of proved vascular plants is stressed. *Cooksonia*, a simple, leafless plant with terminal sporan-gia appears in late Silurian time as the first representative of Tracheophyta. Ad-ditional simple plants appear in lowest Devonian time, and the number and diver-sity of land plants increase markedly in succeeding deposits. The appearance of simple spores at first, and more complex ones subsequently, substantiates the re-sults from megafossils, although vascular plant spores appear somewhat earlier in Silurian time than present records of megafossils indicate. Evolutionary series are becoming clearer as the morphology–anatomy of the plants is clarified. Psilophy-tales are distributed between two new subdivisions: Rhyniophytina with terminal sporangia and Zosterophyllophytina with lateral sporangia. The latter may have given rise to lycopods with *Asteroxylon* as an intermediate type. Rhyniophytina, on the other hand, seems to have evolved through Trimerophytina, a new subdi-vision, toward four groups—the cladoxylaleans, the coenopteridaleans, the true ferns, and the progymnosperms. The last may have given rise to both cycado-phyte and coniferophyte lines. The importance of knowing whole plants is demon-strated by the changes in classification that are being effected, e.g. *Asteroxylon* is a lycopod, not a psilophyte; *Pseudosporochnus* is a cladoxylalean rather than a psilophyte; and *Archaeopteris* and *Callixylon* are names applied to different parts of one plant, neither a fern nor a gymnosperm. There is stronger support for the evolution of some leaves as enations, some as webbed, planated terminal branches, and some as entire, large branch systems. The evolution of branch sys-tems found in Devonian progymnosperms into fronds found in Mississippian strata should be studied carefully by means of anatomical data. Heterospory is becom-ing better known in Devonian plants, and definitive descriptions of spores in situ are increasing in number. Isolated spores (sporae dispersae) promise to add pre-cision to age determinations in continental strata and to facilitate interregional correlation of strata. Although Devonian seeds are still unknown, an approach to the seed habit is seen in the discovery of *Cystosporites*, heretofore found only within *Lepidocarpon* in Carboniferous rocks. The floras of oldest Devonian (Ge-dinnian) and youngest Devonian (Famennian) are the least well known. Both are extremely important. The older is significant because we are still groping for an understanding of the reasons for the abrupt and rapid increase in new kinds of plants after the earliest and simplest *Cooksonia*. The other is important because of the probable gradual transition from Devonian into Mississippian floras with the development of the seed habit, the true ferns, and several new subdivisions of Tracheophyta. Extensions in the stratigraphic range of Devonian plants are increasing in number and will lead to more detailed thinking about paleoecology. Gradually, as the flora is revealed in increasing detail, speculation about rates of evolution can go beyond the suggestion that early evolution could be rapid because the plants were invading a new area with an abundance of niches, because there was little competition, and because small genetic changes produced marked changes in morphology.

Acknowledgments. I wish to thank Miss Elfriede Abbe for her skillful preparation of the illustrations, and I am grateful for the opportunity to discuss this paper with Dr. Patricia Bonamo. This work was supported by a John Simon Guggenheim Memorial Fellowship and by National Science Foundation Grant GB 4493.

ADDENDUM

Since this manuscript was submitted in July 1966, new data have clarified and extended some of the tentative suggestions made originally. Foremost among these is the work on *Psilophyton*. Hueber and Banks (1967) selected a neotype for *P. princeps* Dawson 1859. It has spines and large clusters of terminal sporangia similar to those illustrated here as Figure 5A. Additional details are given in Hueber (in press). *Psilophyton princeps* should be added to the plants included in Trimerophytina. Other species of the genus undoubtedly will be added soon (e.g. *P. krauselii* Obrhel). *Dawsonites* can remain in Trimerophytina as a form genus for sporangia that are unconnected to an identifiable axis or that are not shown to occur in large clusters. Hueber and Banks (1967) showed also that *Psilophyton princeps* var. *ornatum* Dawson 1871 differs anatomically from *Psilophyton princeps*. Its lateral sporangia and its elliptic, exarch protostele relate it clearly to Zosterophyllophytina. In the present paper this variety has been referred to as *Psilophyton ornatum* or as *Psilophyton* (non Dawson, new name needed). Specifically this means that a new generic name should be erected for the variety *ornatum*.

Banks and Davis (1967) have extended the concept of Zosterophyllophytina by reporting a new genus with lateral sporangia.

Banks (in press) described the anatomy of *Hostinella* collected at Röragen in Norway. He accepted Obrhel's (1961) suggestion that this generic name be spelled with an *n* instead of an *m*. Its structure resembles that of a *Psilophyton*, thus reinforcing Halle's (1916) suggestion that his *Hostinella* might be part of his *Psilophyton goldschmidtii*. This raises the question whether *Hostinella* should remain in Rhyniophytina, as in the present paper, or should be transferred to Trimerophytina. No answer is possible until other specimens yield anatomical data.

Bonamo and Banks (1967) have now completed the description of fertile branches of *Tetraxylopteris*, comparing them in detail with those of *Protopteridium*. Their results bear directly on the problem of origin of megaphyllous leaves.

Matten and Banks (1967) have documented the evidence that the progymno-sperm genera *Sphenoxylon* and *Tetraxylopteris* are synonymous.

Chaloner (1967) has contributed a well-documented account of the early occurrences of the spores of vascular plants. He reached conclusions on the origin of land plants that are similar to the views presented here. Banks (in press) has added details to the time of occurrence of the first macrofossils of land plants.

Pettitt and Beck (1967) reported the existence of seeds in Upper Devonian time, a step in advance of the *Cystosporites* mentioned in the present paper.

REFERENCES

Allen, K. C., 1965. Lower and Middle Devonian spores of North and Central Vestspits-bergen. *Palaeontology, 8:* 687–748.

Ananiev, A. R., 1957. New fossil plants from the Lower Devonian deposits of the village of Torgashino, south-eastern zone of western Siberia. (Transl., Geol. Surv. Canada, 64104), *Bot. Zhur., 42:* 691–702.

——, 1964. Recent studies on the Devonian floras of Siberia. Tenth Int. Bot. Congr., Edinburgh, p. 17–18 (abstr.).

Andrews, H. N., Jr., 1961. *Studies in Paleobotany.* Wiley, New York and London, 487 p.

——, 1963. Early seed plants. *Science, 142:* 925–31.

Andrews, H. N., Jr., T. L. Phillips, and N. W. Radforth, 1965. Paleobotanical studies in Arctic Canada. I. *Archaeopteris* from Ellesmere Island. *Canad. J. Bot., 43:* 545–56.

Arnold, C. A., 1935. Some new forms and new occurrences of fossil plants from the Middle and Upper Devonian of New York State. *Buffalo Soc. Natur. Sci., Bull., 17:* 1–12.

——, 1939. Observations on fossil plants from the Devonian of eastern North America. IV. Plant remains from the Catskill Delta deposits of northern Pennsylvania and southern New York. *Univ. Michigan, Mus. Paleont. Contrib., 5:* 271–314.

——, 1940. Structure and relationships of some Middle Devonian plants from western New York. *Am. J. Bot., 27:* 57–63.

——, 1952. Observations on fossil plants from the Devonian of eastern North America. VI. *Xenocladia medullosina* Arnold. *Univ. Michigan, Mus. Paleontol. Contrib., 9:* 297–309.

Axelrod, D. I., 1959. Evolution of the psilophyte paleoflora. *Evolution 13:* 264–75.

Banks, H. P., 1961. The stratigraphic occurrence of Devonian plants with applications to phylogeny, p. 963–68, in *Recent Advances in Botany,* v. 2. Univ. Toronto Press.

——, 1964. Putative Devonian ferns. *Torrey Bot. Club Mem. 21:* 10–25.

——, 1965. Some recent additions to the knowledge of the early land flora. *Phytomorphology, 15:* 235–45.

——, 1966. Anatomy of a *Hostimella, Am. J. Bot., 53* (6/2): 628.

——, in press. The stratigraphic occurrence of early land plants and its bearing on their origin. Vol. II, *Proc. Int. Symposium on the Devonian System.* D. H. Oswald, ed., Calgary, Canada.

——, in press. Anatomy and affinities of a Devonian *Hostinella. Phytomorphology.*

Banks, H. P., and M. R. Davis, 1967. A new genus of Devonian zosterophylloids. *Am. J. Bot., 54:* 650.

Beck, C. B., 1957. *Tetraxylopteris schmidtii* gen. et sp. nov., a probable pteridosperm precursor from the Devonian of New York. *Am. J. Bot., 44:* 350–67.

——, 1960. The identity of *Archaeopteris* and *Callixylon. Brittonia, 12:* 351–68.

——, 1962. Reconstructions of *Archaeopteris* and further consideration of its phylogenetic position. *Am. J. Bot., 49:* 373–82.

——, 1963. *Ginkgophyton (Psygmophyllum)* with a stem of gymnospermic structure. *Science, 141:* 431–33.

Benson, M., 1935. The fructification, *Calathiops Bernhardti,* n. sp. *Ann. Bot., 49:* 155–60.

Bertrand, P., (1913) 1914. Étude du stipe de l'*Asteropteris noveboracensis.* Twelfth Congr. Geol. Int., Canada, Compt. Rend., p. 909–24.

——, 1935. Contribution à l'étude des Cladoxylées de Saalfeld. *Palaeontographica, 80B:* 101–70.

Bonamo, P. M., and H. P. Banks, 1966a. A study of the fertile branches of *Tetraxylopteris. Am. J. Bot., 53(6/2):* 628.

——, 1966b. *Calamophyton* in the Middle Devonian of New York State. *Am. J. Bot., 53:* 778–91.

——, 1967. *Tetraxylopteris schmidtii:* Its fertile parts and its relationships within the Aneurophytales. *Am. J. Bot., 54:* 755–68.

Bower, F. O., 1935. *Primitive Land Plants.* Macmillan, London.

Carluccio, L. M., F. M. Hueber, and H. P. Banks, 1966. *Archaeopteris macilenta,* anatomy and morphology of its frond. *Am. J. Bot. 53:* 719–30.

Chaloner, W. G., 1959. Devonian megaspores from arctic Canada. *Palaeontology, 1:* 321–32.

——, 1967. Spores and land plant evolution. *Review Faleobotany and Palynology, 1.*

Chaloner, W. G., and J. M. Pettitt, 1964. A seed megaspore from the Devonian of Canada. *Palaeontology, 7:* 29–36.

Croft, W. N., and W. H. Lang, 1942. The Lower Devonian flora of the Senni beds of Monmouthshire and Breconshire. *Phil. Trans. Roy. Soc., 231B:* 131–63.

Cronquist, A., A. Takhtajan, and W. Zimmermann, 1966. On the higher taxa of Embryobionta. *Taxon, 15:* 129–34.

Delevoryas, T., 1962. *Morphology and evolution of fossil plants.* Holt, Rinehart & Winston, New York, 189 p.

Eames, A. J., 1936. *Morphology of Vascular Plants, Lower Groups.* McGraw-Hill, New York.

Grierson, J. D., and H. P. Banks, 1963. Lycopods of the Devonian of New York State. *Palaeontographica America, 4:* 219–95.

Halle, T. G., 1916. Lower Devonian plants from Röragen in Norway. *Kungl. Svenska Vetenskapsakad. Handl., 57:* 1–46.

——, 1936. On *Drepanophycus, Protolepidodendron* and *Protopteridium,* with notes on the Palaeozoic flora of Yunnan. *Palaeontologia Sinica A., 1:* 1–38.

Harris, T. M., 1929. *Schizopodium Davidi* gen. et. sp. nov., a new type of stem from the Devonian rocks of Australia. *Phil. Trans. Roy. Soc., 217B:* 395–410.

Heard, A., 1927. On Old Red Sandstone plants showing structure from Brecon (South Wales). *Geol. Soc. (London) Quart. J., 88:* 195–208.

Høeg, O. A., 1942. The Downtonian and Devonian flora of Spitzbergen. *Norges Svalbard-Og Ishavs–Undersøkelser Skr., 83:* 1–228.

Hopping, C. A., 1956. On a specimen of "*Psilophyton robustius*" Dawson, from the Lower Devonian of Canada. *Proc. Roy. Soc. Edinb., 66B:* 10–28.

Hueber, F. M., 1959. "Fossil flora of the *Onteora* 'red beds' (Upper Devonian) in New York State, a preliminary survey." M.S. thesis, Cornell Univ., 55 p.

——, 1960. "Contributions to the fossil flora of the *Onteora* 'red beds' (Upper Devonian) in New York State." Ph.D. thesis, Cornell Univ. (Libr. Congr. Card No. Mic. 61–1432) 212 p., Univ. Microfilms, Ann Arbor, Mich. (*Diss. Abstr., 22:* 405–06).

——, 1961. Psilophytes in the Upper Devonian of New York. *Am. J. Bot., 48:* 541 (abstr.).

——, 1964. The psilophytes and their relationship to the origin of ferns. *Torrey Bot. Club Mem., 21:* 5–9.

——, in press. *Psilophyton:* The genus and the concept. Vol. II, *Proc. Int. Symposium on the Devonian System,* D. H. Oswald, ed., Calgary, Canada.

Hueber, F. M., and H. P. Banks, 1967. *Psilophyton princeps:* The search for organic connection, *Taxon, 16:* 81–85.

Jaeger, H., 1962. Das Alter der ältesten bekannten Landpflanzen (*Baragwanathia-flora*) in Australien auf Grund der begleitenden Graptolithen. *Paläont. Z., 36:* 7.

Kedo, G. I., 1955. Middle Devonian spores from north-east Belorussiya SSR. *Palaeont. i. stratig. BSSR, 1:* 5–47 (in Russian).

Kidston, R., and W. H. Lang, 1917. On Old Red Sandstone plants showing structure from the Rhynie chert bed, Aberdeenshire. Part I. *Rhynia Gwynne-Vaughani,* Kidston and Lang. *Trans. Roy. Soc. Edinb., 51:* 761–84.

——, 1920a. On Old Red Sandstone plants showing structure, from the Rhynie chert bed, Aberdeenshire. Part II. Additional notes on *Rhynia Gwynne-Vaughani,* Kidston and Lang; with descriptions of *Rhynia major* n. sp. and *Hornea Lignieri,* n. g., n. sp. *Trans. Roy. Soc. Edinb., 52:* 603–27.

——, 1920b. On Old Red Sandstone plants showing structure, from the Rhynie chert bed, Aberdeenshire. Part III. *Asteroxylon Mackiei* Kidston & Lang. *Trans. Roy. Soc. Edinb., 52:* 643–80.

Kräusel, R., and H. Weyland, 1926. Beiträge zur Kenntnis der Devonflora II. *Abhandl. Senckenberg. Naturforsch. Ges., 40:* 115–55.

——, 1938. Neue Pflanzenfunde im Mitteldevon von Elberfeld. *Palaeontographica, 83B:* 172–95.

——, 1941. Pflanzenreste aus dem Devon von Nord-Amerika. *Palaeontographica, 86B:* 1–78.

Kulp, J. L., 1961. Geologic time scale. *Science, 133:* 1105–14.

Lang, W. H., 1926. Contributions to the study of the Old Red Sandstone flora of Scotland, III. On *Hostimella (Ptilophyton) thomsoni* and its inclusion in a new genus, *Milleria. Trans. Roy. Soc. Edinb., 54:* 785–90.

——, 1937. On the plant-remains from the Downtonian of England and Wales. *Phil. Trans. Roy. Soc. B, 227:* 245–91.

Leclercq, S., 1940. Contribution à l'étude de la flore du Dévonien de Belgique. *Mém. Acad. Roy. Belg., 12:* 3–65.

——, 1951. Étude morphologique et anatomique d'une fougère du Dévonien Supérieur, le *Racophyton zygopteroides* nov. sp. *Ann. Soc. Géol. Belg., 9:* 1–58.

——, 1954. An Upper Devonian Zygopterid showing clepsydropsoid and etapteroid features. *Am. J. Bot., 41:* 488–92.

———, 1956. Evidence of vascular plants in the Cambrian. *Evolution, 10:* 109–14.

———, 1957. Étude d'une fructification de Sphenopside à structure conservée du Dévonien Supérieur. *Mém. Acad. Roy. Belg., 14:* 1–39.

———, 1962. Deux plantes du Dévonien. *Bull. Soc. Roy. Bot. Belg., 95:* 51–59.

Leclercq, S., and H. N. Andrews, Jr., 1960. *Calamophyton bicephalum,* a new species from the Middle Devonian of Belgium. *Ann. Missouri Bot. Gard., 47:* 1–23.

Leclercq, S., and H. P. Banks, 1962. *Pseudosporochnus nodosus* sp. nov., a Middle Devonian plant with cladoxylalean affinities. *Palaeontographica, 110B:* 1–34.

Leclercq, S., and H. J. Schweitzer, 1965. *Calamophyton* is not a sphenopsid. *Bull. Acad. Roy. Belg., 11:* 1394–1402.

Lyon, A. G., 1964. The probable fertile region of *Asteroxylon Mackiei* K. and L. *Nature, 203:* 1082–83.

Mamay, S. H., and H. N. Andrews, Jr., 1950. A contribution to our knowledge of the anatomy of *Botryopteris. Torrey Bot. Club Bull., 77:* 462–94.

Matten, L. C., 1965. "Contributions to the Upper Devonian flora of New York." Ph.D. thesis, Cornell Univ. (Libr. Congr. Card No. Mic. 65–14, 701) 141 p., Univ. Microfilms, Ann Arbor, Mich. (*Diss. Abstr., 26:* 2999–3000).

Matten, L. C., and H. P. Banks, 1967. Relationship between the Devonian progymnosperm genera *Sphenoxylon* and *Tetraxylopteris. Bull. Torrey Bot. Club, 94:* 321–33.

McGregor, D. C., 1964. Devonian miospores from the Ghost River Formation, Alberta. *Geol. Surv. Canada, Bull., 109:* 1–31.

Meeuse, A. D. J., 1963. From ovule to ovary: A contribution to the phylogeny of the megasporangium. *Acta Biotheoret., 16:* 127–82.

Nikitin, P. A., 1934. Fossil plants of the Petino horizon of the Devonian of the Voronezh region I. *Kryshtofovichia africani* nov. gen. et. sp. *Akad. Nauk SSSR, Izv., Ser. 7:* 1079–92 (in Russian).

Obrhel, J., 1961. Die Flora der Srbsko-Schichten (Givet) des mittelböhmischen Devons. *Sbornik Ustředniko Ústavu, Geologického, 26:* 7–44.

———, 1962. Die Flora der Pridolí-Schichten (Budňany-Stufe) des mittelböhmischen Silurs. *Geologie, 11:* 83–97.

Pettitt, J. M., 1965. Two heterosporous plants from the Upper Devonian of North America. *Brit. Mus. (Nat. Hist.) Geol. Bull., 10:* 83–92.

Pettitt, J. M., and C. B. Beck, 1967. Seed from Upper Devonian. *Science, 156:* 1727–29.

Pichi-Sermolli, R. E. G., 1958. The higher taxa of the Pteridophyta and their classification. *In* "Systematics of today," *Uppsala Universitets Årsskrift, 6:* 70–90.

Read, C. B., 1937. The flora of the New Albany shale. Part 2. The Calamopityeae and their relationships. *U.S. Geol. Surv. Prof. Paper, 186E:* 81–104.

———, 1938. Some Psilophytales from the Hamilton group in western New York. *Torrey Bot. Club Bull., 65:* 599–606.

Richardson, J. B., 1960. Spores from the Middle Old Red Sandstone of Cromarty, Scotland. *Palaeontology, 3:* 45–63.

———, 1964. Stratigraphical distribution of some Devonian and Lower Carboniferous spores, *Cinquième Congr. Int. Stratigr. Géol. Carbonifère, 13B:* 1111–14.

———, 1965. Middle Old Red Sandstone spore assemblages from the Orcadian basin north-east Scotland. *Palaeontology, 7:* 559–605.

Streel, M., 1964. Une association de spores du Givétian Inférieur de la Vesdre, à Goé (Belgique). *Ann. Soc. Géol. Belg., 87:* 1–30.

Tchibrickova, E. V., 1962. Spores from Devonian terrigenous deposits of the Bashkir region and the southern slopes of the Urals. *Akad. Nauk. Bashkir. SSR* 353–476. (in Russian).

Vigran, J. O., 1964. Spores from Devonian deposits, Mimerdalen, Spitsbergen. *Norsk Polarinstitutt Skr., 132:* 5–32.

Walton, J., 1957. On *Protopitys* (Göppert): With a description of a fertile specimen "*Protopitys scotica*" sp. nov. from the calciferous sandstone series of Dunbartonshire. *Trans. Roy. Soc. Edinb., 63:* 333–40.

Zimmermann, W., 1949. Geschichte der Pflanzen. Thieme, Stuttgart, 111 p.

Walter G. Kühne

3. KIMERIDGE MAMMALS AND THEIR BEARING ON THE PHYLOGENY OF THE MAMMALIA

There is no doubt that the most complete fossil record is the one most likely to yield relevant answers to paleontological and evolutionary questions. Filling a gap in the paleontological record demands from the scholar qualities utterly alien to paleontologists and to evolutionists, although many paleontologists have excelled in this task. Even now, when the problem has become more difficult, the challenge of completing the record is an attractive one.

Mesozoic mammals are as little known today as the now well-represented vertebrates were in 1820. Their stratigraphy is poor, owing to their occurrence in nonmarine sediments. Their systematization is poor owing to our inability to disentangle phylogenetic and homoeomorphic likenesses. Their morphology is poorly understood because their representation is almost wholly by dentitions and teeth. Hence, conclusions an investigator draws seldom find support from subsequent finds. A consensus is generally lacking; an author sticking to the subject for more than fifteen years will doubtless be forced to retract the generalizations he had expressed in the past in the form of a phylogenetic tree.

Any new locality is expected to yield specimens greatly changing the concepts previously gained. A new locality yielding a good fauna with good specimens is bound to alter our knowledge about Mesozoic Mammalia considerably. In a span of more than 110 million years, from the Rhaetic to the Lower Paleocene, I count only twelve good localities and almost twice this number of poor ones. Many of the latter have yielded few (but most important) specimens in their time.

Before I discuss my subject proper, I shall bring up some technical matters. Owing to their small size, the remains of Mesozoic Mammalia cannot be discovered in the field. They have been found accidentally during searches for larger objects. Two localities, yielding a single specimen each, were identified because the matrix of dinosaurs during their preparation was carefully investigated in the laboratory. They are the Red Beds near Mafeteng, Basutoland, with the skull of *Erythrotherium parringtoni;* and the Keuper of Halberstadt, Germany, which yielded a single haramiyd cheek tooth not yet described. Natural bone concentrations have been encountered only in England and Wales. J. B. Hatcher was the first to overcome the factual invisibility of the objects he was collecting by utilizing natural concentrating agents. The agents are ants and wind, operating in the scattered badland patches of the Lance Formation, Wyoming. Of far greater importance in our time, however, has been the work of Claude Hibbard, to whom all living collectors of Mesozoic mammals, and in all probability future ones too, are deeply obligated. There are predecessors beginning with Plieninger in 1847, but the great advances in the knowledge of Mesozoic mammals in Europe and North America since 1960 are largely due to the utilization of Hibbard's concentrating method, which he has used since 1936 and made known in 1949. Our Berlin team owes two new localities of Mesozoic mammals to Claude Hibbard. Each of them, having yielded only forty isolated teeth, I regard as poor localities; one is in the Kimeridge of the west coast of Portugal, Porto Pinheiro I, the other in the Spanish Wealden of Teruel Province, Galve II. The method used is based on Hibbard's but designed and developed by Henkel (1966).

GENERAL CONSIDERATION OF SYSTEMATICS

The title of this paper intentionally avoids a taxonomic term, and the first question I proffer is this: Is Mammalia a term comparable to the term Reptilia or to the term Aves? The Aves, as I understand Romer (*Vertebrate Paleontology*, 1945), are today regarded as a class, whose monophyletic origin is not in doubt. They stem from the subclass Archosauria in the class Reptilia (the latter, it is agreed, not being monophyletic). The sequel of this simple statement is that we can discuss the origin of Aves but that we have to discuss the origins of the reptiles if this ought to be our topic. The terms class Reptilia and class Aves (in Romer, 1945) are not commensurable terms.

When classes were defined for the first time, the concept of phylogeny could not be considered and fossil forms were practically unknown. It is most unlikely that such class concepts can still be useful, when phylogeny is regarded as an essential criterion in systematics, and many fossil forms are known which prove that the genera assembled under the old class concepts are not monophyletic (Hennig, 1965).

In my opinion it is not desirable to use the old class concept and to give it a further span of life by relying on a single character or on a single character group to be diagnostic for it. Among the Mesozoic mammals we do not yet have a fossil with the mammalian shoulder girdle, epiphyseal growth of vertebrae and long bones, and only the stapes as sound-conducting bone; I think one might well have existed, and tomorrow it might be found. The Monotremes, however, are existent and so are the Multituberculates and the Tritylodontids; the question whether these animals are mammals or therapsids cannot be decided, nor can the question be decided whether the Therapsids are mammals or vice versa. It is inconvenient not to be allowed to speak of the class Mammalia with regard to Mesozoic representatives as well as monotremes, but future generations will probably do so without any qualms.

The validity of a single-character diagnosis is affected, as is the one resting on multiple characters, by the deficiency of the record and by the present evaluation of the characters in question. The record, however, improves in time, and the significance of the diagnostic character is subject to the change of opinion and the increase of knowledge. The contradictions inherent in a single-character definition as a class criterion become evident if we consider Docodonta and Tritylodonta. The latter are mammals as good as the monotremes but for their jaw articulation. The docodonts have not one but two jaw articulations. If we erect a new class for them, which probably nobody is likely to do, we defy our own ends to argue with phylogenetic concepts. The evolution of the secondary jaw articulation can be conceived only if we postulate at a certain phase of the lineage, leading for instance to man, members having the primary as well as the secondary jaw articulation. Such fossil neither fits the reptilian nor the mammalian class definition. These fossils are real, but they do not fit into classes defined when they were unknown and authors were not concerned with the origination of classes.

Instead of discussing border questions and the applicability of typological concepts in phylogeny, I propose to allow certain fossils a position *incertae sedis* between classes. To do so would underline our dilemma but would also express the advances of phylogeny borne out by the availability of fossils transitional or intermediary between higher taxonomic units. In my opinion there ought to be no obligation to allot all taxonomic categories to a fossil, beginning with the species, if such allotment patently defies our intentions.

With increasing frequency old phylogenetic theory is replaced by phylogenetic practice. A monophyletic lineage during its range is bound to cross systematic boundaries which are nothing but the relics of our former ignorance. As soon as we consider lineages and give real fossils a definite position inside them, we are bound to replace old definitions with the verbal or mathematical expression of evolutionary tendencies.

The last common ancestor of the acknowledged Jurassic orders of mammals and of the haramiyds, Tritylodonts, and *Diarthrognathus* lived probably in the Lower Triassic and was a therapsid reptile. In the Mesozoic we have the best opportunity to observe the origin of a class. The origination of the mammals is fortunately a long process; it is not shrouded in mystery or darkness but can be studied by the application of known methods and repeatable processes. By discussing the many forms and form groups involved, we are in an excellent position to evaluate and to differentiate between typological and phylogenetic classification, that is, between a static systematic still adhered to but obviously unable to satisfy all, and a phylogenetic systematic—inconvenient, cumbersome, and often hypothetical but bound to be the systematics of the future.

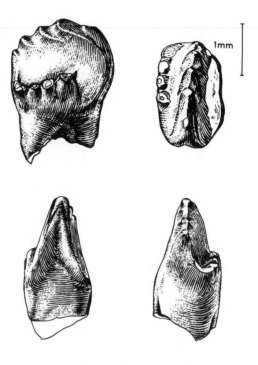

P₄ of Paulchoffatia

Fig. 1. Last lower premolar of Lower Kimeridge multituberculate, *Paulchoffatia* sp.

THE GUIMAROTA FAUNA

A new locality having yielded a good fauna of Mesozoic Mammalia is the little coal pit Guimarota near Leiria, Portugal. A tentative age of Lower Kimeridge has been determined by means of ostracods and characeans. The mammalian fauna has features indicating it is older than the fauna of the English Purbeck and the North American Morrison formations. The material collected consists of four cranial remains (three of Multituberculata and one of a Docodont) and seventy specimens augmented by more than a thousand isolated teeth. The former were collected with the well-organized help of Portuguese women, the latter by apply-ing ore-dressing methods. The many isolated teeth allow the investigator to study dental detail of specimens not covered by preservatives and to observe them from all sides. The project was successfully organized between 1961 and 1965 by Dr. S. Henkel.

The fauna has not yielded a single specimen of Symmetrodont, Triconodont, or Tritylodontid. Among 64 determinable specimens which have been obtained by splitting the coal, there are 38 of Pantotheria, 11 of Multituberculata, and 8 of Docodonta.

The Guimarota Multituberculata are in the hands of G. Hahn who, up to now, has dealt with the lower jaw and its dentition; in the following I rely on his manuscript. There is one genus only, *Paulchoffatia*. The P_4 of *Paulchoffatia* has two longitudinal rows of dental elements: the lingual row with five cusps and four serrations and the buccal row with four cusplets, well developed but early worn away (Fig. 1).

Three Upper Jurassic Multituberculates reveal a simple pattern of increase of cusps on the P_4:

	Buccal row of cusplets	*Lingual row of cusps*
Plagiaulax becklesii	6	8
Psalodon sp.	5	7
Paulchoffatia	4	5

Later in the Cretaceous and Tertiary the buccal row of cusplets almost disappears, and the lingual row increases its number of cusps and serrations to a maximal sixteen in *Neoplagiaulax*. An early Oxfordian Multituberculate is expected to have the numbers of cusps of inner and outer rows almost equal. P_4 of *Paulchoffatia* is worn flat on the top of its crown, hence it still serves for chewing and not exclusively for cutting as the P_4 of later Multituberculata (Fig. 2). An early Oxfordian Multituberculate is expected to have the lingual row of cusps only slightly higher than the buccal one. The anisomery of the lower premolars is least in the oldest Multituberculate *Paulchoffatia;* this is borne out by the ratio length P_4: length P_3. The respective ratios are

Paulchoffatia, specimen 1	1.33
Paulchoffatia, specimen 2	1.36
Paulchoffatia, specimen 3	1.16
Ctenacodon serratus	1.54
Psalodon marshi	1.76
Ctenacodon scindens	1.8
Ctenacodon minor	2.0
Plagiaulax becklesii	2.2

The early Oxfordian Multituberculate is expected to have the length of the lower anterior molar and the two last premolars subequal. In the Kimeridge, the reduction of the numbers of premolars is already underway: one species of *Paulchoffatia* has only three premolars. The anisomery later increases with the subsequent loss of P_1, P_2, and P_3. Among a considerable number of isolated rootless teeth there are many belonging to *Paulchoffatia;* hence the presence of a milk dentition of this early Multituberculate can be postulated with good reason. The presence of a third row of cusps in the upper teeth of *Paulchoffatia* has been proven.

A Multituberculate dentition has been developed at least three times from Theria. In those three cases the parent group has well-occluding cheek teeth. The origin of the daughter group can be envisaged by loss of fit, loss of occlusion, and lowering of the height of the cusps subsequent to a change of diet from one strictly insectivorous–carnivorous. The time to accomplish the morphological

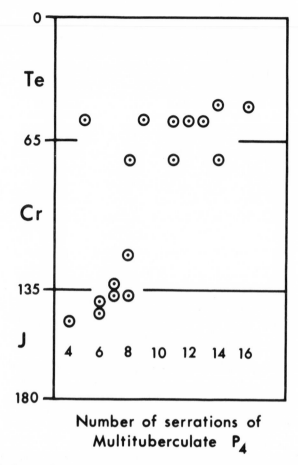

Number of serrations of
Multituberculate P_4

Fig. 2. From the Kimeridge to the Eocene the number of serrations on the multituberculate P_4 increases from four to sixteen. The range increases too because this tendency is
not shared by all, *Pentacosmodon* in the Paleocene, for instance, having advanced only
from four to five.

change seems to have been less than 15 million years in the Tertiary and not more
than the time between the Bathonian and the Kimeridge, which is the time when
the Multituberculata originated. Though I expect the parent group of Multituberculata to be related to the *Haramiya* group, I would not be very surprised if it
turns out to be the Symmetrodont from Wales or a Rhaetic Triconodont, of which
we know still very little. The absence of the angular process of the Multituberculata is shared with the Triconodonta and Symmetrodonta, and the absence of the
internal groove is unique among Mesozoic Mammalia.

The Guimarota Multituberculata necessitate an augmentation of the suborder
diagnosis Plagiaulacoidea given by Simpson in 1928: a rather large lachrimal is
present in *Paulchoffatia*. This is a rather trivial matter. If, however, the Oxfordian

Multituberculata should be found, the essential sentence of Simpson's diagnosis would have to fall; it reads: "premolars sharply differentiated from molars, the posterior ones forming a strong shearing device." The describer of this still unknown Oxfordian fossil will have to widen the old diagnosis to let the new species enter into the suborder, or he must create a new suborder for the new species. Both procedures are makeshifts; they cloud the issue and illuminate the dilemma by dealing with a phylogenetic lineage in terms of Linnaean—i.e. static—systematics.

The evolutionary change witnessed from the (at present) oldest to the youngest Multituberculate is by no means great but of such a degree that the attempt to formulate a diagnosis for all will fail, either because of its diffuseness or because the diagnosis will not last beyond the discovery of a still older representative of the lineage. The diagnosis does not and cannot express our present knowledge of Multituberculata and is, in fact, useless. I think we can do better by defining the Multituberculata as bearers of certain evolutionary tendencies, a few of which I express as follows:

> Multituberculata are fossil mammal-like Tetrapods, known from the Kimeridge to the Eocene. Cheek teeth have two to three longitudinal rows of cusps. The fourth lower cheek tooth undergoes a change from a chewing to a cutting device in the Jurassic. The buccal row of cusps of this tooth become vestigial in the Lower Cretaceous. The lingual row of cusps of this tooth increase the number of cusps from five in the Kimeridge to sixteen in the Eocene. The three lower anterior cheek teeth disappear at the same time from the first to the third.

Guimarota Docodonts

The Guimarota Docodonts surprisingly have a smaller number of cheek teeth than the younger genus *Docodon* from the Morrison Formation. Of three specimens (Fig. 3) the tooth formula can be given: (1) C P_3 M_5; (2) P_3 M_5; (3) I^4 C P^3.

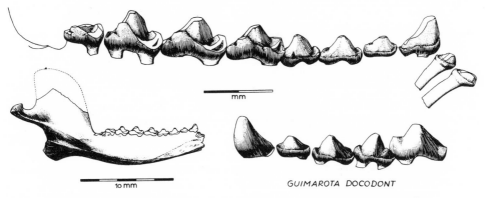

GUIMAROTA DOCODONT

Fig. 3. Lower jaw of docodont *Haldanodon* sp. from the Kimeridge of Portugal.

This contrasts with I⁴ C P⁴ M⁸ of *Docodon*. There is still evidence to relate phylogenetically *Morganucodon* and the Docodonta; the genus from Wales has seven cheek teeth and *Erythrotherium* as many. If the trend to increase the number of cheek teeth pertained to the whole recorded span of the order Docodonta, one could assume that it reacted to impacts requiring a change in the dentition only by polyisomerism, as did the Dryolestidae and *Amphitherium*. The time that I consider the Docodonta gave rise to any other systematic unit of the Mesozoic Mammalia lasts, however, from the Liassic to the Bajocian, from whence no fossils are yet known.

The two excellently preserved proximal ends of lower jaw corroborate the picture Simpson (1928b) gave of *Docodon*. They show the same deep and well-delimited trough ranging from the dental foramen to the rim between angular process and condyle, which is also found in the Morganucodontids. Our two maxillaries are worn, and isolated upper permanent molars are all broken owing to the third root supporting the protocone and a deep cleft between it and the buccal complex of para- and metacone, which are according to Simpson (1961) III, IV, and I. Behind the protocone is always a smaller cusp contributing to this heel-like part of the tooth. The isolated lower milk molars are rather elongated and have

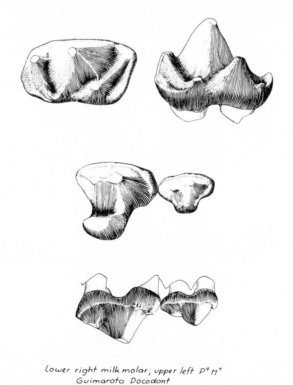

Lower right milk molar; upper left P⁴ M¹
Guimarota Docodont

Fig. 4. Lower right milk molar and upper left P⁴M¹ of *Haldanodon* sp.

four cusps (Fig. 4). The isolated permanent molars are less elongated and carry from four to seven cusps in different specimens.

Among the nonmultituberculate mammals from the Guimarota, the Docodonts have the most heavily worn teeth. Knoblike remnants of teeth are found; the diet apparently caused strong attrition of the teeth without incapacitating the animal's feeding. Wear facets are observed, but they are less sharp and straight than those found on the teeth of Pantotheria from the same locality. If preserved on enamel, the wear facets are striate. Cusp XIV of *Docodon* (Simpson, 1961) is found in all specimens of lower molars of the Guimarota Docodonts (Fig. 5). In regard to the corresponding r₃ of *Morganucodon*, this seemingly insignificant element has meanwhile been found in *Erythrotherium parringtoni* and in the Yunnan Morganucodont. The author of *Morganucodon*, while describing his single tooth in 1948, did not expect this genus to be found in such multitudes fifteen years later in Glamorgan, or that two single skulls with jaw attached would come to light, one in South Africa and the other in Yunnan. Nor did he expect in 1950 that cusp r3 would be found more prominent in respect to the cingulum cusps in front and behind. If we consider a phylogenetic relation between *Morganucodon* and the Docodontidae, it seems that only some of my predictions of 1950 regarding the transformation of the former into the latter have been confirmed: the anterior

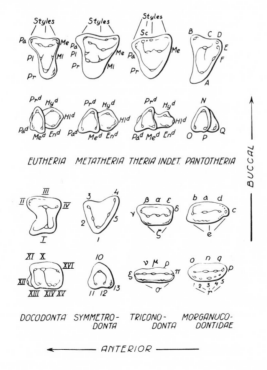

Fig. 5. Figure 1 from G. G. Simpson, 1961. In order to avoid hypothetical commitments on my part, attempted homologizations refer to symbols given by Simpson.

accessory cusp of *Morganucodon* has not disappeared but is XI—and in my opinion the paraconid. An antero-internal cingulum cusp, r1, may be XIII; it is not what in Docodonts I regard as the paraconid. The crest between X and XIV is well displayed in the Guimarota Docodonts; the homologization with n and r3 I regard as conclusive.

Among the six mandibles are two in the process of tooth replacement; a few of the isolated teeth are rootless, indicating that they are shed teeth.

Guimarota Pantotheria

Concerning tooth form, distinction of paurodont and dryolestid upper and lower molars is obvious: the paurodont molars are longer. Upper paurodont molars have low cusps, often poorly differentiated; dryolestid upper molars have high and well individualized cusps. The identical picture appears in the Morrison fauna: *Melanodon* a Dryolestid, *Pelicopsis* a Paurodontid. The dryolestid lower molars have a small talonid and the anterior root three times thicker than the posterior one; paurodont lower molars have a larger talonid and the two roots subequal.

There are ten specimens yielding the number of cheek teeth or the number of molars; the sequence of increasing number of elements reads as follows:

$$M^5 \qquad P^4\,M^6$$
$$P^3\,M^5 \qquad P_4\,M_8$$
$$P^4\,M^5 \qquad P^4\,M^8$$
$$P_4\,M_6 \qquad M^9$$
$$P_5\,M_5$$

If we consider tooth form, the specimens in the left column belong to Paurodontidae, those in the right to Dryolestidae (Fig. 6). The tooth formula P4M4 or less, which Simpson gave for Paurodontidae in 1928, does not fit any of the Guimarota specimens, though eight cheek teeth are found certainly once and possibly twice. There is no specimen with fewer than eight cheek teeth in the Guimarota fauna

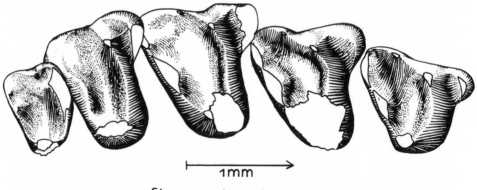

1mm

Simpsonodon splendens

Fig. 6. *Simpsonodon splendens,* a Kimeridge Pantothere with a paurodont tooth morphology and five molars.

but three genera do in the Morrison: *Paurodon* P_2 M_4, *Archaeotrigon* P_2 M_{3-4}, *Araeodon* P_3 M_4. Among the specimens in the right column with teeth of dryolestid form, the first specimen has a tooth formula at variance with the one Simpson gave as diagnostic for Dryolestidae: P_4M_7 or more. In fact a diagnostic criterion, the tooth formula, which is valid in the younger Purbeck-Morrison fauna has lost its validity to distinguish Paurodontidae from Dryolestidae in the Kimeridge.

Of isolated lower molars, 66 pertain to Paurodontidae, 78 to Dryolestidae; 18 additional teeth lack the root. The crown is preserved with its dentine core, the latter excavated and presenting a concave and cavernous surface, ending with a sharp rim. Some of these molars are worn and some are unworn; the surface of the enamel is well preserved. I do not hesitate to regard these eighteen specimens as shed deciduous teeth. Without exception they can be identified as paurodont (Fig. 7). Provided the designation as milk teeth is correct, there are three possible explanations for this evidence: (1) the Guimarota sediments were laid down with remains of adult Dryolestids but adult as well as juvenile individuals of Paurodontids; (2) Paurodonts have a deciduous dentition, Dryolestids have none; (3) Paurodonts as well as Dryolestids have milk molars of Paurodont type. I regard the third explanation as the most probable one. Evidence from twelve rootless isolated upper molars is not so striking but points in the same direction.

One dP^4 of a Paurodont has been found among the isolated upper cheek teeth. Several similar specimens are known from another Upper Jurassic locality, Porto Pinheiro in Portugal. This tooth is very similar to the anterior tooth in the specimen YPM 13751 of *Malthacolestes osborni*.[1] In all our specimens the root is lacking, owing to resorption. Because of its great length compared with dryolestid upper molars, this tooth displays, in my opinion, features hidden in the upper pantotherian molars; hence, I consider it significant for solving the problem of cusp homology of the Pantotheria. The evidence of this tooth, in my opinion, speaks unequivocally for a phylogenetic relationship of Symmetrodonta with Dryolestidae and Paurodontidae. The tooth displays a large elongate basin, bordered by five cusps and anteriorly a stout and low parastyle. The large, single, anterior cusp, the paracone, is the highest; posteriorly follows labially and lingually one cusp of lesser height; the posterior end of the basin, being open, is flanked by two cusps which are the smallest of the five. It is easy to identify the elements of this tooth with those of the Guimarota upper molars and with the outline of the pantotherian upper molar in Simpson (1961, Fig. 1, p. 70). It is less easy to perform this identification with the upper molars from the Morrison; it would be very difficult to do it with the Guimarota genus *Butlerigale*. The proposed homologization (Table 1) in terms of Simpson 1961 is compared with the one Patterson proposed in 1956.

Butler (1939) has conscientiously drawn cusp D but did not consider it, and Patterson (1956) has taken as typical the M^4 of *Melanodon oweni*, the only tooth I know that has a cusplet between A and C, his cac. The new homologization is the very opposite of the one I proposed in 1961.

---

1. In the Yale University Peabody Museum collection.

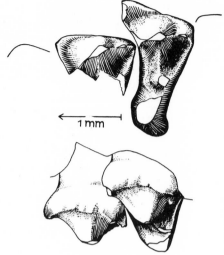

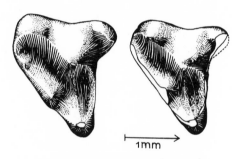

Butlerigale

Fig. 7. Guimarota Pantotheres. Top: *Butlerigale* sp. Upper molars showing extreme basin reduction. Middle: *Guimarota freyi*, two upper molars showing the pantotherian basin well developed. Bottom: (not to scale), right, DP⁴ in crown and buccal view, showing the pantotherian basin with the pentacuspid rim; cf. *Malthacolestes osborni*.

Guimarota freyi

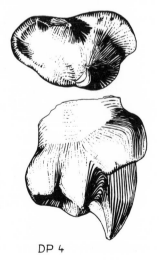

DP 4

Table 1. Upper Molar

1966		Patterson, 1956	
Dryolestid	Symmetrodont	Dryolestid	Symmetrodont
A	1	A	1
C	2	C	3
D	3	cac	2
F	5	D	No homologue
E	4	F	5
B	No homologue	E	4
		B	No homologue

A group of genera which differs in the construction of the back end of the mandible from Dryolestids and Paurodonts and approaches the condition found in *Docodon* is represented by *Amphitherium* (Bathonian), cf. *Peramus* (from Guimarota, Kimeridge), *Archaeotrigon* (Morrison), *Peramus* (Purbeck), and *Brancatherulum* (Tendaguru) (Fig. 8). Of this group only *Peramus* is represented with upper molars. *Amphitherium* and *Peramus* have recently been reviewed by Mills (1964). Before burial, the Guimarota specimen had lost all teeth but the second premolar, which carries behind the main cusp two small ones; one of them may be the posterior accessory cusp missing in all Pantotheria but present in Docodonts. According to the tooth formula, *Amphitherium,* with eleven cheek teeth, obviously has a number in excess of the other members of the group. The form of the molars of *Amphitherium* and *Peramus* corresponds, those of *Archaeotrigon* do not, there being no more than the typical four main cusps on its molars, as in Dryolestids. The teeth of *Brancatherulum* are unknown. Two isolated lower teeth have been found in the Guimarota material, fitting in size the specimen cf. *Peramus;* they are a left and a right molar. Both specimens have anteriorly two small and low accessory cusps. On the left specimen the talonid is unworn, unicuspid, and not provided with ridges. The right specimen displays only one buccal facet, worn by a large paracone. Below and inside the paraconid is a tiny cusplet, regularly found in *Amphitherium.* The two roots are equal. The two teeth show striking similarity to the Welsh Symmetrodonta from the Rhaetic.

I do not propose to unite the mentioned genera systematically, but I should like to point out the following: the form of the mandible is common in all; the earliest member *Amphitherium* has the greatest number of cheek teeth; *Archaeotrigon* has cheek teeth too simple to compare with the others; and lower molars designated as belonging to cf. *Peramus* do not provide positive evidence for a lingual cingulum on the unknown upper molars.

CONCLUSIONS

It is not surprising that the contribution this new fauna makes to the history of the Mammalia is not too great, if the small span of time between the Purbeck-

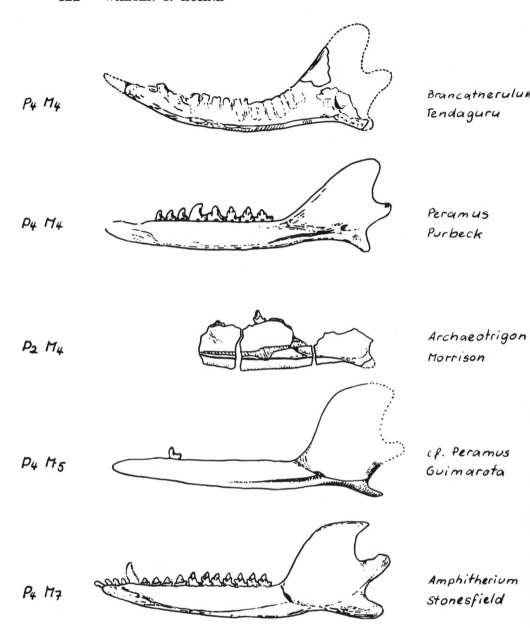

P4 M4   Brancatherulum Tendaguru

P4 M4   Peramus Purbeck

P2 M4   Archaeotrigon Morrison

P4 M5   cf. Peramus Guimarota

P4 M7   Amphitherium Stonesfield

Fig. 8. Six lower jaws of Mesozoic mammalian genera. The only common character is the shape of the angular process, which differs from that in Dryolestids.

Morrison faunas and the Guimarota is taken into account. Even in the Kimeridge the Multituberculata do not show signs of relationship to any other group of mammals in the Jurassic.

In the Tertiary, increase in the number of cheek teeth is extremely rare and practically confined to aquatic and myrmecophagous mammals. In the Jurassic, increase is recorded in the Docodonta, the Dryolestidae and, with good reason, in the ancestors of *Amphitherium*. If the last genus is considered ancestral to *Peramus,* we have to record a reversal of trend. The Dryolestidae and the Paurodontidae converge from the Portland to the Kimeridge. A group of fossils can be considered similar in respect of the dentary but heterogeneous in respect of tooth formula and tooth form. If Docodonta are not related to Theria, the angular process and the protocone have to develop twice during the Jurassic.

In order to put on a sound basis the ideas on the origin and the early (Mesozoic) history of the mammals, we require no sensational finds—no first specimen from a stage, a series, or a country—but a well-represented record from all continents. Measured by this unachieved ideal, the present situation is one in which most of the evidence is still unknown and most problems still unsolved.

REFERENCES

Butler, P. M., 1939. The teeth of Jurassic mammals. *Proc. Zool. Soc. London, 109:* 329.

Henkel, S., 1966. Methoden zur Prospektion und Gewinnung Kleiner Wirbeltierfossilien. *Neues Jahrb. Geol. Paläont. Monatsh.* 3: 178–84.

Hennig, W., 1965. Phylogenetic Systematics. *Ann. Rev. Entomol., 10:* 97–116.

Hibbard, C. W., 1949. Techniques of collecting microvertebrate fossils. *Univ. Michigan, Mus. Paleont. Contrib.,* 8: 7–19.

Kermack, K. A., et al., 1965. *Aegialodon dawsoni,* a new trituberculosectorial tooth from the Lower Wealden. *Proc. Roy. Soc. B. 162:* 535–54.

Kühne, W. G., 1950. A symmetrodont tooth from the Rhaeto-Lias. *Nature, 166:* 696.

———, 1961. A mammalian fauna from the Kimeridge of Portugal. *Nature, 192:* 274–75.

Mills, J. R. E., 1965. The dentitions of *Peramus* and *Amphitherium. Proc. Linn. Soc. London, 175:* 117.

Patterson, B., 1956. Early Cretaceous mammals and the evolution of mammalian molar teeth. *Fieldiana Geol. 13* (1).

Simpson, G. G., 1928a. A catalogue of the Mesozoic Mammalia in the Geological Department of the British Museum. British Museum, London.

———, 1928b. Mesozoic Mammalia XII. *Amer. Jour. Sci. XV* (5): 461–70.

———, 1961. Evolution of Mesozoic mammals. *In* Internat. Colloquium on Evolution of Lower and Nonspecialized Mammals, Brussels.

William G. Chaloner

4. THE PALEOECOLOGY OF FOSSIL SPORES

The use of fossil spores and pollen in studying ecological processes has its fiftieth anniversary this year. In 1916 Lennart von Post first produced a diagram using fossil pollen ratios as a basis for stratigraphic correlation of Quaternary deposits and so initiated the science of Quaternary palynology or pollen analysis. I intend to deal with paleoecological aspects of fossil spores and pollen in rocks older than the Quaternary, but the technique begun by von Post represents a model of methodology for anyone working with older material. For this reason it is worth reviewing briefly the principles underlying Quaternary work before considering how far they can be applied in a geologically earlier context.

Von Post was not the first person to identify fossil spores. Other workers in Europe did this in the eighties: Ehrenberg (1884) and Früh (1885) had both recognized fossil pollen in terms of living species. Lagerheim in Sweden had even counted the relative numbers of different pollen types and noted their changing proportions through a peat sequence (Erdtman, 1943). Von Post's contribution was to construct a pollen diagram, showing the changes in relative abundance of pollen types through peat sequences, and to establish the principle that this was the basis of a chronology of regional application. Changes in tree pollen ratios would be more or less constant in their time of occurrence in peat profiles throughout a region, and so would form the basis for a time correlation between adjacent sites. There are three features innate in Quaternary palynology:

1. The plants of Quaternary time are, with very few exceptions, still living. By comparing fossil pollen in peat with the pollen of living plants it is possible in most cases to identify the fossils in terms of extant species.

2. It is accordingly possible to concentrate attention on certain pollen or spore types in terms of their known ecological status. Early pollen analysis, for example, concentrated on tree pollen as representing the climatically sensitive regional forest cover.

3. Changes in the tree pollen ratios were interpreted as the response of climax vegetation to changing climate (and in the later part of European postglacial sequences, to interference by man). The changing climate acting on the vegetation thus formed the basis for a regional chronology. The correlation of postglacial pollen diagrams across northern Europe thus effected has been subsequently confirmed by radiocarbon dating.

Two basic assumptions are made in applying this method. The first is that the pollens identified represent plants of basically the same ecological requirements as their living counterparts. The second assumes that changes in the pollen ratios represent responses to climatic change (or to man's influence) and that the vegetation had time to come into equilibrium with the climate at any phase in the process. Both assumptions have been largely vindicated by the overall consistency of the results and the proven synchroneity of the major changes for northern Europe. But the same assumptions obviously cannot be made with equal conviction for deposits of different physical character or very much greater age.

To some extent, the methods of Quaternary work can be applied in older rocks for at least as far back in time as the angiosperms dominate the land flora. Many Tertiary spores and pollen can be identified in terms of living genera or families (rather than at the specific level, as in most Quaternary work). Through the Tertiary, as in the Quaternary, slow response to climatic change appears to have been the prime cause of progressive changes in successive floras. The assumption that the present ecological requirements (insofar as these are clear-cut at the generic or familial level) have been generally maintained through Tertiary time seems justified by the consistency of the results both among themselves and with other biological data. The general climatic control mechanism of Tertiary floras has been recently reviewed by Barghoorn (1964) and Dorf (1964) and its particular application in a palynological context by Traverse (1955).

As we go farther back in time beyond the origin of angiosperms, or at least beyond their dominance of fossil floras, the method of extrapolating back the ecological associations of living plants breaks down. It is a futile exercise to try to interpret the paleoecology of Mesozoic floras by reference to the ecology of the living survivors of the important groups. The present-day distribution of cycads, for example, is now surely largely controlled by competition with the angiosperms. As Harris (1961) has pointed out, it is evident from their mode of occurrence as fossils that some, at least, of the Jurassic cycads must have been dominant plants of delta swamps or riverbanks, habitats in which the living representatives of the group are unknown. For the purposes of paleoecology we must make a distinction between the period of dominance of the angiosperms, roughly the Quaternary and Tertiary periods in which we may extrapolate the ecological requirements of living plants backward in time, and all earlier time in which we clearly cannot. It is mainly with this "pre-extrapolatory" phase of plant paleoecology that I wish to deal.

TERTIARY PALYNOLOGICAL PALEOECOLOGY

I would like to consider one piece of Tertiary palynological work done at University College as illustrating a principle equally applicable to earlier periods. This is the work of Ma Khin Sein (unpublished thesis, 1961). One of the motives for this particular study was the problem of the degree to which a pollen assemblage, especially in clastic rocks (as distinct from an autochthonous peat), gives the same picture of the flora as other fossil evidence. The London Clay was selected for the study because it contains a rich early Eocene fossil flora in the form of fruits and seeds which have been intensively studied for many years (Reid and Chandler, 1933; Chandler, 1964) and represents one of the best known and most important of all Tertiary floras. It may be said that in general it has a composition pointing to a tropical lowland flora with strong Indo-Malayan affinities, in terms of the present-day distribution of its constituents. The most abundant and characteristic of the fossil fruits is *Nipa,* a stemless palm occurring at present only in marine swamps in the Indo-Malayan region.

Ma Khin Sein's study of the London Clay pollen confirmed this general conclusion. Figure 1 is a diagram from her thesis, comparing the climatic implications of the micro- and macroflora. What is of particular interest in the present context is that the pollen study revealed the presence of various plants unknown in the macroflora, and with slightly different ecological associations. *Nipa,* for instance, is a rare pollen type, in contrast to its fruit (Plate IG). Living *Nipa* is a poor pollen producer, as Muller (1964) has pointed out, and its large pollen would in any case probably tend to aggregate close to its source instead of being carried out to sea (cf. behavior of *Avicennia* pollen in Recent sediments, Muller, 1958). Away from the immediate *Nipa* swamp environment the pollen of other plants would show up to a relatively greater degree in the overall pollen assemblage. Figure 1 shows the per cent occurrence of the genera recorded from the London Clay flora in different regions at the present time. The histogram with oblique shading represents the results based on macrofossils (the fruits and seeds). These show a clear peak for Indo-Malaya, with diminishing proportions in other areas at increasing distance from that region. However, whereas the pollen results (stippled) show a similar general aspect, the extreme peak of the microfossils is "removed" and in effect "redistributed" by the presence of forms with affinity with present-day temperate Europe and North America. *Tilia,* (linden or basswood) is an example of a genus with present-day distribution in both New and Old World temperate latitudes. This genus is common among the London Clay pollen (Pl. I, C–E), but is unknown in the form of its fruit. This is perhaps not surprising since its fruit is small and relatively perishable. An example of a North American temperate form is *Carya* (hickory) (Pl. I, A and B) which is again unknown in the fruit flora. It appears that in general the pollen is simply representing a wider aspect of the flora, probably including plants growing well away from the *Nipa* swamp environment, and hence with diminished opportunity of being preserved as fossil fruit or seeds in the marine environment. It is a plausible supposition that the *Tilia* and *Carya* represent constituents of a community occupying the hinterland. This would be consistent both with their present climatic association and their occurrence in the pollen flora but not the fruit flora. Gray (1960) has shown a comparable extension of the records of temperate plants in the pollen obtained from the Eocene of Alabama.

The interest in these London Clay results is their illustration of what is perhaps self-evident, and yet not always acknowledged. Any fossil flora is biased by

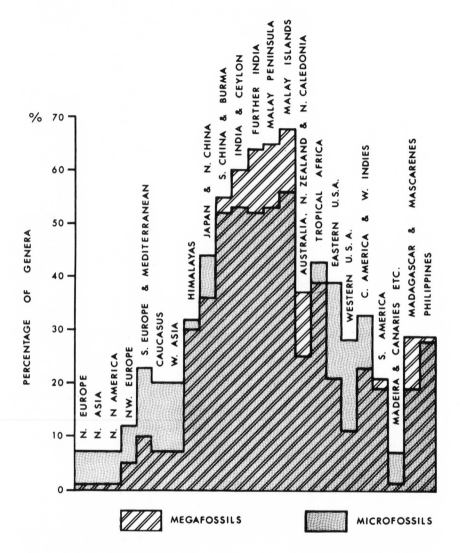

Fig. 1. A histogram showing the percentages of those genera of plants known as fossils in the London Clay, which now occur in various parts of the world. The data from the macrofossils (based on Reid and Chandler, 1933) is shown shaded; that from the microfossils (pollen and spores) is stippled. The agreement of the fossil macroflora with that of present-day Malaya is less pronounced in the microfossils, which include more representation of what are now temperate genera of Europe, Asia, and North America (from the unpublished thesis of Ma Khin Sein, 1961).

the conditions of its preservation. The London Clay fruit flora is biased in favor of large or robust fruits and seeds which readily survived to become fossils in the marine environment, and also toward plants growing in the *Nipa* swamps or close to rivers and delta distributaries. Any pollen flora, on the other hand, is biased in favor of wind-pollinated flowers rather than entomophilous ones. Because of the potentialities of wind and water transport of pollen and spores, it is likely that a pollen flora (especially if derived from offshore detrital rocks rather than an autochthonous peat) will represent a broader sample of the flora spatially than the associated fossil macroflora. Neither the macroflora nor the microflora is "more complete" or "more correct." Each gives an incomplete picture of the contemporaneous flora; the two pictures have large areas of overlap, but each complements the omissions of the other.

PRE-TERTIARY SPORE STUDIES

The palynology of pre-Tertiary rocks developed primarily as a form of applied micropaleontology, especially of coals, rather than as a botanical and ecological exercise, as it had done in the Quaternary. By the 1930s many workers in Europe were already using spores occurring in Carboniferous coals for stratigraphic correlation, but their approach was essentially an empirical one. The spores were categorized at first by letters and numbers, and later by binomials, simply as a means of referring to them as isolated fossils and without reference to their parent plants. In the years following World War II, similar work was extended to the study of spores obtained from lithologies other than coal in the context of oil exploration. The ecological methodology of Quaternary palynology and the more practical approach of Carboniferous work became merged in the great surge of palynological work that followed its successful application in the oil industry in the 1950s. Enormous numbers of fossil spores were described and named without any knowledge of their parent plants. (Potonié, 1956, 1958, 1960). A few paleobotanists began to explore the possibility of extracting spores from those rather rare occurrences of spore-bearing structures attached to larger identifiable fragments of known fossil plants. This offered the possibility of correlating pre-Tertiary spores with their parent plants, and perhaps eventually of using dispersed spores in Mesozoic and Paleozoic rocks for paleoecological interpretation (cf. Chaloner, 1962). On the basis of such work, Potonié (1962) has recently published a review of all known records of such *sporae in situ,* known in connection with their fossil parent plants.

   Much work has been done in the last five years on the relationship between spores and the lithology of the rock in which they occur, not only in Carboniferous coal (Smith, 1957, 1964a,b; Habib et al., 1966) but in associated detrital rocks (Neves, 1958, 1961; Peppers, 1964; Marshall and Smith, 1965). In the face of growing knowledge of the parent plants responsible for many of the pre-Tertiary dispersed spores, various attempts have been made to explain the ecological mechanism behind such relationships (Chaloner, 1958; Smith, 1962, 1964a). Per-

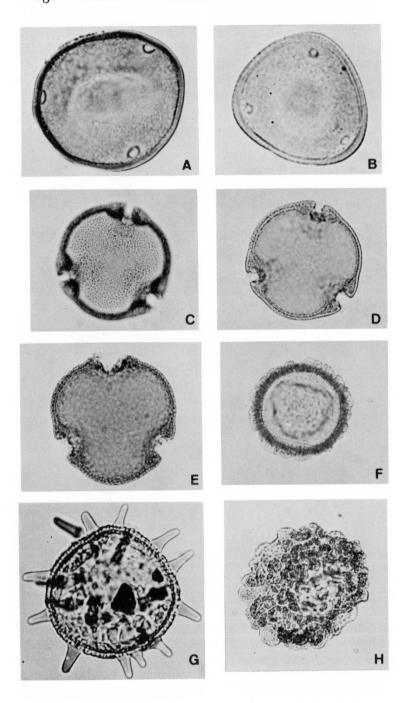

haps the most significant fact to emerge from this Paleozoic work is the strong correlation between the composition of a fossil spore assemblage and the sedimentary environment in which it became fossilized. At first this situation seems at variance with what would be expected. One of the most attractive aspects of spores as microfossils for stratigraphic correlation is their independence of the lithofacies. The same species of spore borne on the wind or subsequently transported by water is available for fossilization in a variety of habitats. Spores from the same species of parent plant have the potentiality of surviving in lithologies as diverse as shale, limestone, coal, and evaporite. The dispersal of its spores into any variety of sedimentary environments has no effect on the continued life of the parent plant in some possibly remote source area. In this independence from direct facies control, spores surpass even those groups of fossils such as graptolites and planktonic forams which on account of their floating nature may appear more or less synchronously in widely separated environments. From the early work on sediments associated with coal (Hoffmeister et al., 1955; Neves, 1958; Staplin, 1960) it became evident that, while in a qualitative sense the same kinds of spores can occur simultaneously in different environments, the ratios in which different types occurred differed radically in closely adjacent samples of contrasted lithology. Neves has pointed out that the assemblages in Carboniferous marine shales are commonly rich in Cordaites pollen while more or less synchronous coals and nonmarine shales are rich in lycopod spores. The present author (Chaloner, 1958) suggested that this was consistent with a situation in which the Cordaites were abundant in an upland community remote from the coal-forming swamps and least affected by a marine invasion. In order to investigate whether a comparable mechanism was operating in an analogous but different setting, a study of spores in all available lithologies was undertaken by Dr. Muir on the Yorkshire Middle Jurassic Deltaic Series (Muir, 1964: Chaloner and Muir, in press). This sequence shows rhythmic alternations from small coal seams to marine limestones, resembling to some extent the cyclothems of the Carboniferous coal measures. One aspect of the results of this study is shown in Figure 2. It can be seen that here, as in the Carboniferous, the spore assemblages show strong correlation with the

---

Plate I. A, Pollen of *Carya tomentosa* (white-heart hickory) from the United States. B, Fossil pollen of *Carya* (hickory) from the London Clay, Alum Bay, Isle of Wight (prepared by Ma Khin Sein). Note the small subequatorial pores and the thin depressed circular area in the center of each grain. C and D, Pollen of *Tilia cordata* (lime or linden) from Britain; the same grain at two focal planes. E, Fossil pollen of *Tilia* sp. from the London Clay of Herne Bay, Kent, England. Note that the flattening of the fossil has splayed out the apertures. G, Fossil pollen of *Nipa* sp., from the London Clay, Alum Bay, Isle of Wight (prepared by Ma Khin Sein). F, Pollen of *Tsuga yunanensis*, a species of hemlock-spruce from China. H, The dispersed pollen called *Tsugaepollenites mesozoicus* from the Middle Jurassic Estuarine Series, Yorkshire (prepared by M. Muir). Note that the recent *Tsuga* pollen is seen as an optical section of the spherical grain, whereas the sculpture of a complete hemisphere is seen in the flattened fossil.

All the photos are × 850 except F and H which are × 425.

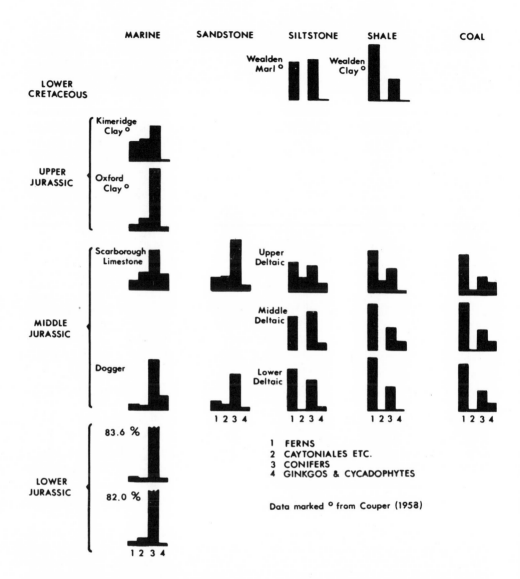

Fig. 2. Histograms to show the composition of spore assemblages in British Jurassic and Lower Cretaceous rocks of different lithology. The spores are grouped as far as possible into four categories of botanical significance. In general there is closer agreement in the broad composition of the assemblages between samples from the same type of lithology (i.e. vertically in the diagram), regardless of their stratigraphic position, than between more or less synchronous assemblages (horizontally aligned in the diagram) from widely different types of lithology. The cause of this apparent influence of the depositional environment on the composition of the spore assemblage is discussed in the text (from the unpublished thesis of Muir, 1964).

environments of deposition. There is a closer superficial agreement between assemblages from the same type of rock throughout the sequence than between more or less synchronous rocks of the same lithology. The fern spores, for example, are abundant in the nonmarine clays, in contrast to the conifer pollen which is most abundant in the marine shales. Now a comparable result would be obtained if, for example, one compared pelecypods, grouped on a family or higher level, through a series of Jurassic rocks. A freshwater assemblage would have a greater resemblance in its general makeup with any other Jurassic freshwater assemblage than with a marine one, even of close proximity stratigraphically. But the mechanism controlling the population of spores and pelecypods is totally different. Generally speaking, the hard parts of invertebrate fossils are preserved more or less in the environment in which they were living. If conditions had become unfavorable they would have had to migrate or perish. The spores in contrast fell or were transported into the environment of deposition, the nature of which could not directly affect the survival of the parent plant, except in the case of an autochthonous deposit. The environmental control of a spore population is clearly an indirect one. A change in the environment reflects itself in a change in the relative proximity of different communities on the adjacent land surface. It appears that in both the Mesozoic and the Carboniferous rhythmic deposition, a similar mechanism is operating. During a marine phase the coal-forming community is either remote enough or sufficiently reduced in area that its spores form only a trivial part of the assemblage incorporated in the marine sediments. In each case the main regional spore producers growing in situations away from the swamp environment are most abundant in the sediment being laid down most remote from the delta.

The occurrence of spores in detrital rocks evidently raises problems of rather different nature than those encountered in the context of pollen analysis of Quaternary peat bogs. It has been stated in the context of such Quaternary work (Faegri and Iversen, 1950, p. 37) that "50–100 km forms a natural limit to pollen dispersal." This is no doubt a valid observation if one is considering the pollen rain over a peat bog surrounded by woodland. The vegetation within a 50-km radius will produce so much pollen that any contributed from outside that radius will form an insignificant part of the assemblage. However, if one gets more than 100 km away from any land vegetation, *all* the pollen transported into that site will have exceeded the "natural limit." Erdtman's (1943) memorable study of pollen collected from the air during a transatlantic crossing adequately demonstrates this. He obtained relatively high percentage values of pine and birch in the samples that he took more than 1,000 km from land. This is probably a reflection of the fact that for northwest Europe and eastern North America, these two tree genera are the principal large-scale pollen producers. One might visualize that in the Carboniferous the Cordaites, and in the Mesozoic various conifers, played a comparable role in the contemporaneous floras.

INTERRELATIONS OF LITHOLOGY, CLIMATE, AND SPORE ASSEMBLAGE

The relationship between a spore assemblage and the lithology of its enclosing sediment is evidently both indirect and complicated. I have considered a single example in the British Middle Jurassic and compared it with the British Coal Measures. We are still at the stage of making models or tentative hypotheses which require testing by the investigation of analogous but different situations at other horizons and under different conditions. The mechanism of changing proximity of different plant communities suggested for the Jurassic and Carboniferous data is perhaps the simplest, but is only one of many possibilities. We know far too little about the role of minor climatic fluctuations in the past. Climax vegetation would be much more susceptible to these than would the physical character of sedimentary rocks. As Hollingworth (1962) has emphasized, geologists have tended to ignore the possible occurrence of such minor climatic fluctuations, except under the two extreme conditions of glaciation and evaporite formation, when the effects of such oscillation are inescapably manifest. An interesting example of the effect of minor climatic change acting simultaneously on a spore assemblage and the lithology can occur in an interglacial phase in a borderline environment between the marine and the nonmarine. The climatic change is then simultaneously controlling the eustatic sea level (via the melting of landlocked ice) and keeping the climax vegetation in phase with it. Such a situation is illustrated in the sequence of infilling of the Clacton Channel in southeastern England during the Clactonian Interglacial (Fig. 3) when rising sea level caused a change from freshwater to estuarine conditions in the depositional environment (Pike and Godwin, 1953). At approximately the same horizon, the pollen contents of the sediment indicate a rise in the proportion of conifers (in the form of silver fir, *Abies*) displacing the thermophilous mixed oak wood.

I have tried to set out some of this possible interaction of factors controlling spore assemblages in Figure 4. Two factors (shown in capital letters) are ultimate causes: climate and isostatic movement of the land surface. The evolution of the land flora—the total pool of species from which many different communities may be drawn at any one phase of time—is in a sense fixed for that phase of time. The classic Quaternary palynology of von Post and his successors has usually involved a system comprising a single site, spore transport mainly by wind, and a study of pollen from one or a limited number of communities whose basic struc-

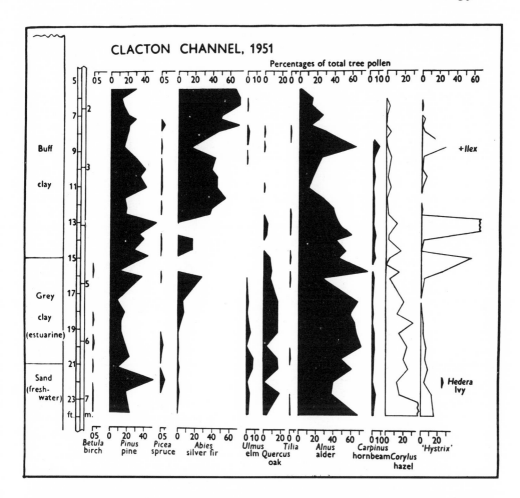

Fig. 3. Pollen diagram showing the percentages of tree pollen (in solid black) through an interglacial sequence in the Clacton Channel in eastern England. Note the marked rise in the percentage of Abies (silver fir) pollen in the upper part of the diagram, corresponding with a fall in the elm and oak. This floral change more or less coincided with a marine transgression, shown in the changing lithologies (left-hand side). The coincidence results in this case from their both being controlled in effect by the climate; the sea level change in this instance was probably a result of subsidence of the North Sea basin due to delayed compensation for the isostatic rise of Scandinavia following removal of ice load—an indirect result of climatic change, and not a direct, eustatic sea level rise (from Pike and Godwin, 1953).

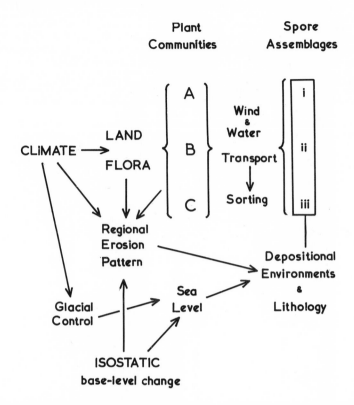

Fig. 4. The interaction of factors controlling an assemblage of fossil spores and the lithology of the rock in which it is incorporated. Two factors, climate and base-level change, may be regarded as ultimate causes influencing others. The land flora at any one period of time will be represented under a given climatic pattern by a series of different plant communities (A–C). Spore assemblages at sites i–iii (at right) will reflect different proportions of the communities A–C according to their innate spore production capacity, their proximity, and the influence of wind and water transport. However, the type of rock being formed at sites i–iii will be influenced by the depositional environment, which will itself be affected in turn by the base level and the regional pattern of erosion. Climate can control both of these, the latter directly and the former by a glacial control of sea level.

ture is understood. In these relatively straightforward circumstances, change in climate is reflected via its effect on plant communities seen in the spore assemblage accumulating in a fixed site of deposition. Sometimes a more complex situation may exist, such as that just cited for the Clactonian Interglacial. Here, climatic change had a dual effect on flora and sea level, so that spore assemblage and lithology changed synchronously.

The study of spore assemblages through a sequence of rocks of changing lithology, in say the Mesozoic or Paleozoic, involves many more unknown factors. The situation in the British Middle Jurassic described above was interpreted in terms of changing base level under supposedly constant climate. The correlation of spore assemblage with lithology was attributed to changing base level changing the relative area of different communities, and their proximity to the sampling site. However, this is evidently only one possible explanation. In the Pennsylvanian, at least, it is possible that climatically controlled sea level would to some extent keep pace with any response of the land flora to climatic fluctuation. The high proportion of *Cordaites* pollen in the Pennsylvanian marine phases of Britain may represent not so much an upland flora as a flora induced by that particular climatic phase of a cyclothem. These and other possibilities need exploring.

The study of the paleoecology of fossil spore assemblages is still very young —at least in the pre-Tertiary context. Spore assemblages in clastic rocks seem to be simultaneously facies-independent qualitatively, but directly related in a quantitative sense to the sedimentary environment. Spore studies have the great practical advantage that we may use them qualitatively to effect stratigraphic correlation while we are still exploring the mechanism governing the quantitative relationship with the environment of deposition.

REFERENCES

Barghoorn, E. S., 1964. Quantitation of sequential change in North American Cenozoic floras as a clue to palaeoclimates. In *Problems in Palaeoclimatology*, A. E. M. Nairn, ed. Wiley, New York, p. 31–39.

Chaloner, W. G., 1958. The Carboniferous upland flora. *Geol. Mag.*, 95: 261–62.

——, 1962. Palaeo-ecological data from Carboniferous spores. In *Recent Advances in Botany*, Univ. Toronto Press, p. 980–83.

——, and M. Muir, in press. Spores and floras. In *Coal and Coal-bearing Strata*, D. G. Murchison and T. S. Westoll, eds. Oliver & Boyd, London.

Chandler, M. E. J., 1964. *The Lower Tertiary Floras of Southern England. IV.* Brit. Mus. (Nat. Hist.), London, 151 p.

Dorf, E., 1964. The use of fossil plants in palaeoclimatic interpretations. In *Problems in Palaeoclimatology*, A. E. M. Nairn, ed. Wiley, London, p. 13–31.

Ehrenberg, C. G., 1884. *Microgeologie*. Leipzig.

Erdtman, G., 1943. *An Introduction to Pollen Analysis*. Chronica Botanica, New York.

Faegri, K., and J. Iversen, 1950. *Text-book of Modern Pollen Analysis*. Munksgaard, Copenhagen.

Früh, J., 1885. Kritische Beitrage zur Kenntnis des Torfes. *Jahrb. K.K. geol. Reichsanst.*, 35.

Gray, J., 1960. Temperate pollen genera in the Eocene (Claiborne) flora, Alabama. *Science, 132*: 808–10.

Habib, D., W. Riegel, and W. Spackman, 1966. Relationship of spore and pollen assemblages in the Lower Kittanning Coal to overlying faunal facies. *J. Paleont., 40*: 756–59.

Harris, T. M., 1961. The fossil cycads. *Palaeontology, 4*: 313–23.

Hoffmeister, W. S., F. L. Staplin, and R. E. Malloy, 1955. Mississippian plant spores from the Hardinsburg Formation of Illinois and Kentucky. *J. Paleont., 29:* 372–99.

Hollingworth, S. E., 1962. The climatic factor in the geological record. *Quart. J. Geol. Soc. London, 118:* 1–21.

Marshall, A. E., and A. H. V. Smith, 1965. Assemblages of miospores from some Upper Carboniferous coals and their associated sediments in the Yorkshire coalfield. *Palaeontology, 7:* 656–73.

Muir, M., 1964. "The palaeoecology of the small spores of the Middle Jurassic of York-shire." Ph.D. thesis, University College, London University.

Muller, J., 1958. Palynology of Recent Orinoco delta and shelf sediments. *Micropaleon-tology, 5:* 1–32.

——, 1964. A palynological contribution to the history of the Mangrove Vegetation in Borneo. In *Ancient Pacific Floras, The Pollen Story*, L. M. Cranwell, ed. University of Hawaii Press, Honolulu, p. 33–42.

Neves, R., 1958. Upper Carboniferous plant spore assemblages from the *Gastrioceras subcrenatum* horizon, north Staffordshire. *Geol. Mag., 95:* 1–19.

——, 1961. Namurian plant spores from the southern Pennines, England, *Palaeontol-ogy, 4:* 247–79.

Peppers, R. A., 1964. Spores in strata of late Pennsylvanian cyclothems in the Illinois Basin. *Illinois State Geol. Surv. Bull., 90:* 1–89.

Pike, K., and H. Godwin, 1953. The Interglacial at Clacton-on-Sea, Essex. *Quart. J. Geol. Soc. London, 108:* 261–72.

Post, L. von, 1916. Om skogsträdpollen i sydsvenska torfmosslagerföljder. *Geol. Foren. Stockholm Forh., 38:* 384.

Potonié, R., 1956. Synopsis der Gattungen der Sporae dispersae I. *Beih. Geol. Jahrb., 23:* 1–103.

——, 1958. Ibid. II. Ibid. *31:* 1–114.

——, 1960. Ibid. III. Ibid. *39:* 1–189.

——, 1962. Synopsis der Sporae in situ. Ibid. *52:* 1–204.

Reid, E. M., and M. E. J. Chandler, 1933. *The flora of the London Clay*. Brit. Mus. (Nat. Hist.), London, 206 p.

Sein, Ma Khin, 1961. "Fossil Spores of the London Clay." Ph.D. thesis, University College London.

Smith, A. H. V., 1957. The sequence of microspore assemblages associated with occur-rence of crassidurite in coal seams of Yorkshire. *Geol. Mag., 94:* 345–63.

——, 1962. The palaeoecology of Carboniferous peats based on the miospores and petrography of bituminous coals. *Proc. Yorkshire Geol. Soc., 33:* 423–74.

——, 1964a. Palaeoecology of Carboniferous peats. In *Problems in Palaeoclimatology*, A. E. M. Nairn, ed. Wiley, London, p. 57–66.

——, 1964b. Zur Petrographie und Palynologie der Kohlenflöze des Karbons und ihrer Begleitschichten. *Fortschr. Geol. Rheinland Westfalen, 12:* 285–302.

Staplin, F. L., 1960. Upper Mississippian plant spores from the Golata formation, Al-berta, Canada. *Palaeontographica, B 107:* 1–40.

Traverse, A., 1955. *Pollen Analysis of the Brandon Lignite of Vermont*. U.S. Bureau of Mines Rept. Inv. 5151, 107 p.

H. Barraclough Fell

5. THE BIOGEOGRAPHY AND PALEOECOLOGY OF ORDOVICIAN SEAS

The Ordovician period covers a span of some sixty million years, beginning at the epoch 500 million years before the present (MY B.P.). It was marked by initial marine transgressions over most of the continental plates and, as the period progressed, the epeiric seas became so extensive that little more than the ancient shields remained as exposed land areas. Consequently we possess in the wide-ranging marine sedimentary rocks of Ordovician age a rich source of biotic data in the shape of fossils, the great majority of which are marine invertebrates. Our knowledge of the biogeography and environmental conditions under which the Ordovician faunas evolved and lived remained, however, quite fragmentary, since we were unaware of the disposition of warmer and colder seas and hence could not relate any fauna to any other. Confusion was still worse confounded by the existence of two opposed geological theories about the position and interrelationships of the continents. Proponents of the hypothesis of continental drift have advocated the view that the southern continents were all united as a single super-continent, Gondwanaland, and it has been held that this great southern land mass did not fragment into the existing southern continents until mid-Jurassic times (Adie, 1965; Creer, 1966). Others have held that the continents are permanent features. This latter view would seem to imply that the Pacific, Indian, and Atlantic Oceans (at least) must also have been permanent basins, yet we lack any specific information of the size or shape of these basins prior to the Mesozoic (Menard, 1964). Some writers have even dated the Atlantic Ocean as late as the Cretaceous (Furon, 1963).

Faced with such uncertainties about the fundamental geographic features of the planet during early Paleozoic times, it is small wonder that so little has been written on the subject of the biogeography of Ordovician faunas, and that the only substantial contributions to paleoecology have been limited to regional studies, such as that of Cloud and Barnes (1957) on the early Ordovician seas of Texas.

The symposium at which this contribution was read took place before the parameters of the drift equation of speciation had been determined (Fell, 1967a), and therefore before it became possible to compute the track of the polar wandering curve. The article is to be viewed, then, as one of several background studies which led to these developments. The general pattern of the inquiry was set by observations of transoceanic decay sequences in speciation intensity (Fell, 1962) noted during the program of research in the southern oceans during the International Geophysical Year (1957–58).

EPEIRIC SEAS AND GEOSYNCLINES

The principal areas flooded by the marine transgressions of the period are as follows. Most of North America, save for western Alaska, shield regions around the Arctic and Hudson Bay, Labrador, some islands in the south and west, and Mexico, was covered by shallow seas. The eastern and western margins of the continent formed geosynclines, and so were also under the sea, with bounding island arcs (Kummel, 1961). Mexico, with Panama, formed an elevated island. The PreCambrian shields of South America were elevated, but two major geosynclines, the Andean and the Amazonian, brought extensive seaways into the interior and along the western margin (Jenks, 1956). Most of Africa was elevated, but much of the northwestern region became inundated by an epeiric Barbary Sea as the period progressed; the faunas of this sea, however, are poorly known (Furon, 1963, p. 12–14, 106–34). Much of central Europe was flooded, as well as western Russia and large areas of Asia, particularly Siberia, China, and the southeastern areas of the continent. An epeiric sea, the Amadeus Sea of Australian geologists, covered western Australia; the eastern margin of that continent comprised the Tasman geosyncline. New Zealand was submerged (David, 1959).

The sediments deposited in the floors of these seas contain the fossils by which we judge the world faunas. At first sight it might seem that we have no evidence of the existence or nature of the major oceans themselves, but, as is now clear, the reverse is true, for the fossils of the epicontinental seas prove upon detailed analysis to be so remarkably distributed as to leave no doubt about major geographic features of the earth at that period.

SOURCES

Regional handbooks (Jenks, 1956; Furon, 1963; David, 1959) and some original sources such as Kobayashi's long series of memoirs (1959) have served as material for the present study, but in the main I have depended upon the immense repository of information on systematics and distribution in the volumes so far published of the *Treatise on Invertebrate Paleontology;* it is impossible to acknowledge adequately the value of this work, containing as it does the considered taxonomic evaluations of the largest group of internationally recognized specialists ever to combine in a project of this nature (Moore, 1953 continuing).

For the southern continents, where our knowledge of Ordovician faunas is less complete than for the northern hemisphere, I have utilized available recent assessments of the systematics and distribution of the groups which have so far been revised for the *Treatise on Invertebrate Paleontology*. After eliminating cosmopolitan genera, there remain some 208 genera about which we have sufficient information to permit their employment in a biogeographic analysis. They belonged to the following groups, listed in approximate order of importance (in numbers): trilobites, nautiloids, graptolites, brachiopods, rugose and tabulate corals, ostracods, and gastropods. For the northern continents the amount of available information was so extensive that it was necessary to restrict the study mainly to the four most abundant groups—trilobites, nautiloids, graptolites, and brachiopods. After discarding cosmopolitan forms, some 850 northern genera came under review. Thus the conclusions here reached are based on a total of over a thousand genera.

HEMISPHERIC PATTERN

It soon became apparent that the broad pattern of distribution of Ordovician invertebrates in no way matched that of the present-day earth. As Figure 1 shows, there are two great faunal provinces, but arranged in a configuration which is unfamiliar to the eye when it is plotted on the customary Mercator projection of the earth. One major province comprises Europe, Africa, and South America. These three regions share many genera in common. The African fauna shares 95 per cent of its genera with Europe, and the South American fauna shares 44 per cent of its genera with Europe (as against 37 per cent with North America). However, although both the African and South American faunas are related to the European, they are only remotely related to each other, for South America shares no more than 5 per cent of its genera with Africa. Appendix A gives the data on which these percentage ratios are based.

Australia does not belong with the other two southern continents, for it shares 75 per cent of its genera with the northern continents, and only 9 per cent with South America, and 2 per cent with Africa. Australia shares 61 per cent of its genera with North America, of which 10 per cent is shared exclusively with North America, and comprises only pelagic forms (chiefly nautiloids). South America similarly proves to share 14 per cent of its fauna exclusively with Europe, and (as in the case of the Australian–North American assemblage) this also proves to comprise exclusively pelagic forms (trilobites and graptolites). In each of these cases, where a southern continent shares a substantial part of its fauna with a northern hemisphere continent, separated by a present-day ocean gap, the northern continent proves to lie to the northeast.

As already reported (Fell, 1967a), all these unexpected findings have a simple explanation, for when the faunal zones are transferred to a globe it is found that they form two symmetrically disposed belts around the earth, bounded by small circles and disposed on either side of a great circle, inclined at an angle of about 70° of arc to the plane of the existing equator. Clearly the two great faunal regions are in fact the northern and southern hemispheres of the Ordovician

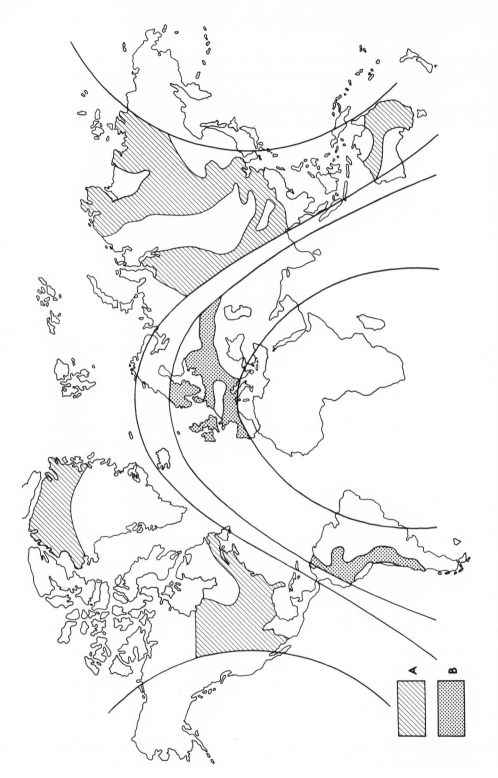

Fig. 1. Broad pattern of distribution of Ordovician faunas. A, northern hemisphere assemblage; B, southern hemisphere assemblage.

earth, and the great circle is the Ordovician equator. Thus the poles were displaced by an angle of 70° from their present positions, the north pole lying in the Pacific, west of Hawaii, the south pole in the Atlantic, off southwest Africa. With the altered directions of the Coriolis forces on the oceans and the changed direction of the trade winds allowed for, it is also clear that the pelagic invertebrates shared by Australia and North America, and by South America and Europe, owe their apparent discontinuous distribution to the action of the ocean currents, which would flow between the pairs of continents indicated. Hence the distribution is not really discontinuous; we have merely observed the continental terminations of what were two continuous bands of pelagic organisms, carried on their respective gyres (Fell, 1967b).

Figure 2 is a modified Mercator projection of the earth to geographic coordinates based on the Ordovician earth axis. The sinusoidal zones of Figure 1 are now converted to east–west zones of uniform width (as is also the case if the zones are plotted on a globe), and we can recognize the climatic belts and classify the faunal elements according to position in these fundamental parameters.

Coelenterata

As might be expected, the coral reef communities now prove to fall into a broad equatorial belt, and what has hitherto been interpreted as a cosmopolitan distribution is merely due to our having mistaken a sinusoidal pattern, swinging 70° north and south of the modern equator, as being a belt 140° wide. In reality the belt was no wider than that on the existing earth, which would seem to suggest that climates in Cambro-Ordovician times differed little from those of today.

The reef belt was apparently lacking from the South American part of the equatorial region, as all the deposits so far examined have an argillaceous facies, containing little more than graptolites and brachiopods, and in places a trilobite fauna; water depths here presumably were too great, and the only deposits were shaly, lacking carbonate. However, along the miogeosyncline associated with the Andean system we would expect islands with fringing reefs to occur, and presumably some traces of these will eventually be discovered.

Along all the rest of the equatorial belt the reef faunas are rich. The miogeosyncline associated with the Appalachian geosyncline provided the required shallow-water conditions and islets for a system of reefs supporting an associated hermatypic fauna. The present northeast–southwest orientation of the geosyncline is seen to conform closely to the equatorial zone, whereas the otherwise comparable but differently located Cordilleran geosyncline on the west coast touched the equatorial zone only at its Mexican end. Hence we find coral reefs only in the Mexican and adjacent portions of the Cordilleran geosyncline. The localities where reefs are particularly known, or where corals occur, are as follows, the list reading in sequence from Ordovician west to Ordovician east: the northernmost provinces of Mexico; Texas; Oklahoma; South Dakota; Missouri; Iowa; Minnesota; Mississippi; Georgia; Tennessee; Virginia; Kentucky; Indiana; Michigan; Wisconsin; Ohio; Pennsylvania; Maryland, Virginia; New York; New Jersey; On-

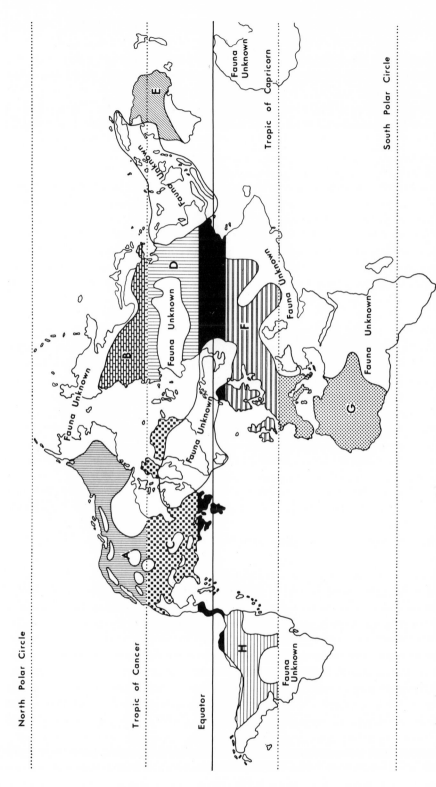

Fig. 2. An interpretation of Ordovician biogeography, based on inferred geographic coordinates derived from the distribution pattern observed in Figure 1.

tario; Quebec; Hudson Bay regions; Baffin Island; Franklinland; Ellesmereland; northern Greenland; Spitzbergen; Britain; Norway; Sweden; Estonia; western U.S.S.R.; Novaya Zemlya; central Russia; Karakorum (C. Asia); western Siberia; Himalayan region; Australia.

Reference to the map on Cambro-Ordovician projection indicates that these regions all lie in the expected belt. The affinity of the Tasmanian fauna with that of central Asia is well illustrated by the occurrence in the latter region of *Tetradium tasmaniense*.

In the list of places above, the reefs are rich and varied. However, some impoverished and evidently temperate outliers, usually only of one or two genera, sometimes a single species, are known from small regions to the Ordovician north of the equatorial zone (such as British Columbia and Alaska, on the North American continent), and to the south (such as Italy, with *Striatopora;* Laval, France, with *Favosites*). The principal coral genera present in the reef faunas include *Favosites, Halysites, Heliolites, Tetradium,* and others, as listed by Bassler (1950) and Hill (1956). Hill has already discussed the sequence in which the families appeared and noted the involvement of the Appalachian geosynclinal region from lower Ordovician time onward. It should be noted, however, that Hill's conclusion that all coral faunas first appeared in the Appalachian Blackriveran stage and then rapidly became cosmopolitan, needs some qualification. The lowest Ordovician is not yet recognized in Europe and Asia, and when it is found, if ever, there is good reason to suppose that it, too, will contain faunas like those of the North American Blackriveran stage; and, as already noted, the coral fauna did not become cosmopolitan, but, rather, pantropical and subtropical wherever suitable water depths existed.

It is also of interest to note that we should expect Ordovician coral faunas to be discovered in eastern Antarctica, which lay wholly within the equatorial belt, unless the Ordovician facies there proves to be pelitic, in which case it would yield the *Kainella* trilobite faunule of the corresponding regions of South America. Reef faunas are unlikely ever to have existed in central or southern Africa, which lay in cold temperate and subpolar zones. Even northern Africa has so far yielded only one genus, *Halysites,* despite the widespread Ordovician epeiric seas over that region toward the latter part of the period. If Ordovician rocks are discovered on the peninsula of India they should yield reef corals. Easternmost Siberia and westernmost Alaska are unlikely to yield reefs, since they lay in the northern subpolar belt and would therefore probably have carried only solitary corals.

Other coelenterates are known only from very poor data. It appears that the Cambrian saw the development of various orders of Scyphozoa, so these presumably would continue into the following period, though we lack this evidence. Some doubtful Hydrozoa are reported, including a possible siphonophore assemblage, based on genera such as *Discophyllum, Palaeoscia,* and others, which inhabited the waters of the Appalachian reef region. The Conulata, now recognized as a group of extinct tetraradiate coelenterates allied to the Scyphozoa, are listed in the *Treatise* (Moore, 1953 continuing) as coming from localities which imply that the group was essentially, if not entirely, confined to the Ordovician tropics, a distribution that also seems likely for the other periods in which these animals lived, though a detailed check has not yet been carried out. Here again the cautionary qualification is needed, that supposedly cosmopolitan forms are likely to be found really to have had a distribution based upon the equatorial zone.

Porifera

The review of the distribution and ecology of Paleozoic sponges given by Okulitch and Nelson (1957) suggests very strongly that the faunas evidently followed, for the most part, the same tropical zone that was occupied by the reef corals, and that the sponges at this epoch were largely hermatypic constituents. They also occupied, however, the muddy facies, where these occurred, and hence were able to spread through all parts of the tropical zone, irrespective of the substrate.

Graptolites

As already inferred by previous workers, the graptolites were evidently planktonic in habit, and achieved a near cosmopolitan distribution, in the strict sense of the term. Thus nearly all genera occur in several zones. However, some are at present known only from particular regions, and if our present knowledge is an adequate basis for judgment, they may constitute true endemic markers of the faunas with which they are associated. These few genera are listed later in this paper, therefore, in the section where the faunal divisions are defined.

Cephalopods

Nautiloid cephalopods have proved to be by far the most valuable elements in this biogeographic study, for it is clear that they were extremely sensitive to temperature and restricted in their tolerance of environmental temperature ambience. Broadly, the nautiloids fall into three main distributional assemblages: 103 genera restricted to the Ordovician northern hemisphere; 32 restricted to the Ordovician southern hemisphere; 183 occurring in both hemispheres.

The majority of the third category are found in a broad equatorial zone, following the coral reef belt. The other two categories lie in the subtropical and temperate zones to the north and south of the equatorial belt, separated by a zone of avoidance which is marked along the equator in Figure 2 by the solid black belt. These two latter categories include the assemblages of genera which follow east–west isotherms (by Ordovician geographic reckoning), and hence have proved so important in establishing transcontinental and intercontinental arcs, by which the Paleozoic continents can be triangulated.

The oldest and most generalized nautiloids are, interestingly, the most stenothermal. Thus the Ellesmerocerida exhibit the following hemispheric distribution: 61 genera (88%) restricted to the Ordovician northern hemisphere; 3 (4%) restricted to the Ordovician southern hemisphere; 5 (8%) cross the equator. The corresponding figures for the later-evolved order Tarphycerida prove to be 63, 32, and 5 per cent respectively. This shows that the nautiloids gradually adapted to a more eurythermal habit, with the majority eventually becoming adapted to living in the equatorial zone. Evidently nautiloids originated in the Cambrian northern hemisphere.

The following important faunules can be recognized.

1. The *Anthoceras* assemblage, comprises 26 genera distributed along an east–west axis which lies north of the Ordovician equator and passes from eastern North America (region C in Fig. 2), through the present Arctic region, into region D of central Asia, to terminate in region E, Australia. The Indonesian region was occupied in Ordovician times by a land mass (Aequinoctia), and hence we have no information on the fauna, though it is obvious that the Aequinoctian coasts must have carried the *Anthoceras* faunule also. These 26 genera can be further subdivided:

(1) *Anthoceras, Eothinoceras, Proterocameroceras,* and *Coreanoceras*, which all ranged over the entire arc from Texas to Western Australia, in regions C, D, and E.

(2) *Selkirkoceras*, which ranges from Manitoba to Korea, delineating the isotherm that bounds the Ordovician Tropic of Cancer.

(3) *Parendoceras, Vaningenoceras,* and, for brevity, one tribolite which has the same range, *Protopliomerops*, may be mentioned here; ranging regions C and D. The trilobite, unlike the cephalopods, also entered region H, evidently as a benthic form able to cross the equator. This point is of interest when the habits of nautiloids are considered a little later in this discussion.

(4) *Tofangoceras, Eremoceras, Orthonybyoceras, Ellesmeroceras, Albertoceras, Clarkoceras, Levisoceras, Clitendoceras, Cotteroceras, Narthecoceras, Cyrtovaginoceras, Cyrtonybyoceras,* and *Centroonoceras*, all of which range substantial east–west segments of the northern hemisphere.

(5) *Thylacoceras, Lobendoceras,* and *Manchuroceras*, which range regions D and E and, together with the trilobite genus *Asaphopsis* and the graptolite genus *Cardiograptus*, constitute an Asian–Australian assemblage.

2. The *Arkoceras* assemblage is restricted to regions A and E and evidently owes its apparently discontinuous distribution to the agency of the North Pacific gyre. It comprises *Arkoceras, Bassleroceras, Ectocycloceras, Allopiloceras, Aphetoceras, Pycnoceras, Trocholitoceras,* and two genera of graptolites, *Sigmagraptus* and *Zygograptus*.

Thus, whereas the *Anthoceras* assemblage was distributed along coastlines and shallow seas, the *Arkoceras* assemblage has a transoceanic distribution. In both cases the axes of symmetry of the distribution zones are east–west parallels of Ordovician latitude, both in the northern hemisphere by Ordovician reckoning. These facts suggest that the nautiloids shared by Australia and North America exclusively, i.e. the *Arkoceras* assemblage, had habits which permitted them to adopt a prolonged pelagic habit, since otherwise the Pacific would have presented an impassable barrier. They fall in three orders. Three of the genera are members of the archaic Ellesmerocerida, for which group Furnish and Glenister (1964) have inferred creeping or nektobenthic habits, on the basis of shell structure. I would prefer to view them as successful swimmers, able to utilize surface currents on an east–west transit with uniform isotherms. The endocerid genus, similarly, must have been a good swimmer, since its heavy shell would barely provide flotation; and here also Furnish and Glenister have inferred nektobenthic or vagrant benthic habits. The remaining nautiloids of the assemblage are regarded by the same authors as active swimmers and posthumous floaters, a conclusion which the present data support.

Trilobites

Trilobites exhibit much greater freedom in their ability to occupy regions on either side of the Ordovician equator. Of 341 genera which inhabit the Ordovician northern hemisphere, only 93 genera are restricted to one or other of the regions A to E; 167 restricted genera inhabit the southern hemisphere as three faunas, each restricted to Europe, Africa, and South America. But a further large assemblage inhabits both hemispheres. Since these are valueless in determining faunal relationships, their precise number has not been assessed, but obviously the group as a whole was widely distributed and tolerant of temperature changes in the surface waters. More probably, it might be inferred, they tended to have benthic habits and so were immune to surface isotherm changes. However, it seems clear that some trilobites at least were able to swim for prolonged periods.

In particular I call attention to the *Angelina* assemblage, comprising the 12 genera *Angelina, Gallagnostus, Saltaspis, Tropidopyge, Paramegalaspis, Niobina, Ogygiocaris, Illaenopsis, Ceratopyge, Orometopus, Pliomera,* and *Pharostomina.* Every one of these genera is remarkable for a discontinuous distribution pattern that includes some species in Europe and some in South America, with no species occurring in any other part of the world. It was this assemblage, together with the graptolite *Janograptus* (with species restricted to Scandinavia and South America), which led to my originally recognizing the former existence of the Capricorn gyre (Fell, 1967a), as part of the investigation of the location of the Ordovician equator. It is clear that all members of this assemblage were transported between Europe and Brazil through the vectorial agency of this gyre, whose subsequent history, it now appears, was to transport other genera between Europe and South America in later Paleozoic periods, until the tilt of the earth's axis no longer directed the current along a northeast–southwest axis.[1] The Capricorn current was apparently captured by the South Atlantic gyre about Jurassic times, and thereafter the current transfers of pelagic forms across the Atlantic occurred chiefly between west Africa and Brazil, as is still the case today.

1. This is speaking, of course, in the frame of reference of a fixed earth, since actually the earth's sphere itself was doing the shifting around the relatively *fixed* axis, tilted at 23.5°, with respect to the orbital plane around the sun.

The morphology of a trilobite implies an active swimmer as well as a benthic crawler. But the data elicited by this study suggest also that the majority of trilobites did not spend much time in mid-water, for if they had, more would have been transported by the ocean currents across ocean gaps. Possibly the *Angelina* assemblage represents a minority group which had developed nektonic habits, like shrimps or euphausiaceans today. No trilobite thus far has been recognized to have accomplished a trans-Pacific journey in Ordovician times. The *Angelina* arc resulting from the distribution of this group of genera is one of the major fixes in the Paleozoic triangulation of South America and Africa, since it limits the possible direction of continental drift of South America relative to Europe and, by its intersection with the Devonian *Calmaria* arc, in fact demonstrates that no movement of South America can have occurred since the early Paleozoic.

Brachiopods

Brachiopods are numerous and important as index fossils in Ordovician sediments but have little value in biogeography. The genera have roughly the same distribution as trilobites but exhibit no evidence whatever of transportation on ocean currents. Evidently they utilized the continental shelf as their migration highway, with minor crossings of narrow sea gaps by larval stages. I have not extracted global distribution figures since they would have little interest; instead, I have isolated the generic groupings which apparently characterize each of the main faunal regions that are recognized in this paper.

Other Invertebrates

Ostracods have one special feature of interest in this study: they include long-ranging genera which help us to build up a picture of relatively stable environments over long time intervals. Since it now appears that a misunderstanding of the location of the tropical zone has led in the past to exaggeration of the supposed warmth of earlier geological periods, and it would seem therefore that the oceans have been in a steady state since Cambrian times, one is compelled to seek evidence wherever it may be found, to test whether significant changes in solar radiation (or other heat sources) could indeed have occurred. It seems to me that the evidence for this would have to be strong indeed before we could entertain the idea, and that any evidence suggesting continuity of environmental conditions should not be overlooked. Here then, our attention is arrested by the Ordovician genus *Bairdia*. Competent systematists cannot distinguish the Ordovician species as forming a grouping distinct from extant species placed in the same genus. This remarkably long time range deserves scrutiny. The modern species occur in all seas. If Ordovician seas were significantly colder or warmer than present seas, we might expect to find the Ordovician species restricted to either a warm or a cold zone. This does not appear to be the case. Hence we have either to conclude that the overall range of Ordovician sea temperatures matched that of the present time or, alternatively, that all modern species of *Bairdia* have changed their temperature preferences to a different gamut. But if the genus (unlike the cephalopod genera considered above) has been so conservative morphologically, why should we suppose it has changed dramatically in its physiology? Hence I infer no major change in sea temperatures.

In the case of salinity, the echinoderms seem important. The Ordovician period saw the transformation of the older echinoderm faunal assemblages into a pattern in which all the modern classes and subclasses emerged. Some of the Ordovician genera are so close to modern ones that they are classifiable in the same families as modern genera. But echinoderms are, in general, extremely intolerant of lowered salinities; even a heavy rainstorm at sea is capable of causing mass mortality of young stages. I interpret the rise of modern echinoderms in early Ordovician seas as implying that the salinity of the ocean had probably already reached equilibrium, with losses balancing accretions, at the present level of ca. $33^o/_{oo}$ mean.

Ordovician echinoderms and gastropods and bivalve mollusks are otherwise of less interest ecologically, perhaps, than the cephalopods, since they seem to have been more tolerant of ambient factors. On the other hand, the morphology of members of these three groups has proved to be of prime importance, and recent work has been devoted largely to important systematic and morphological research. Nonetheless, the autecology of genera and species can be related to their morphology in such way as to have a bearing on the paleoecology of particular habitats and of particular systematic groups.

These notes and inferences are not based on a detailed study of groups, for a general survey of the echinoderms, gastropods, and bivalves suggested that a more detailed survey would probably not yield much in proportion to the amount of time entailed in carrying it out. Since the aspect of the brachiopod distribution is similar to what these other groups offer, and the brachiopod survey having proved unrewarding, other study was discouraged that seemed likely to yield much the same outcome. On the other hand, the statistical study of cephalopods and trilobites, and also those graptolites that did not have cosmopolitan distributions, offered obvious anomalies which demanded an answer, and most of my effort was directed to solving the problems that were presented by such materials.

REGIONAL BIOGEOGRAPHY

The remainder of this contribution is devoted to a summary of the regional faunas which seem to constitute the Ordovician marine provinces, together with a listing of the restricted biota characteristic of each.

A. Northwest Temperate Region (Fig. 2, A)

This province comprises the part of North America that lies by modern reckoning west of the 100° west meridian. It shares many genera with the remainder of the North

American continent but is in general a rather impoverished region faunistically. The restricted genera apparently include the following:

Trilobites (26)

Hyperagnostus	Scinocephalus	Licnocephala
Paenebeltella	Lingukainella	Gonioteloides
Moxomia	Aulacoparia	Dimeropygiella
Benthamaspis	Lachnostoma	Tesselacauda
Goniophrys	Stenorhachis	Kanoshia
Hardyia	Trigonocercella	Protopliomerella
Evansaspis	Kobayashia	Pseudocybele
Remopleuridella	Parabellefontia	Isalaux
Menoparia	Eleutherocentrus	

Brachiopods (14)

Cymbithyris	Oligorthis	Taphrodonta
Orthidella	Anomalorthis	Hesperinia
Lordorthis	Goniotrema	Kirkina
Fasciculina	Hesperomena	Lirocamera
Desmorthis	Syndielasma	

Nautiloids (3)

Kirkoceras	Landeroceras	Alaskoceras

It may be noted that the trilobite genus *Kainella*, usually cited in college texts as characteristic of the West Coast fauna, is omitted from the foregoing list since it is also present in South America and evidently is a pan-American facies indicator. *Neoagnostus* has a similar distribution.

B. Northeastern Temperate Region (Fig. 2, B)

This faunal province comprises that part of eastern Asia lying east of the 125° east meridian by modern reckoning. By Ordovician reckoning it is that part of Asia lying to the north of the Tropic of Cancer. The restricted genera are few, though the fauna as a whole is not depauperate, as it shares many species with the adjacent subtropical margin of the central Asian tropical region. The boundary of the region is delineated along the Tropic of Cancer by the *Selkirkoceras* arc, which also follows the Tropic of Cancer westward into Manitoba. The restricted genera are as follow:

Trilobites (7)

Hukasawia	Plethopeltella	Parabasilicus
Temnoura	Ogygitoides	Dolerobasilicus
Koldinioidea		

Nautiloids (5)

Sinoeremoceras	Discoactinoceras	Sigmocycloceras
Wanwanoceras	Parormoceras	

C. Northwestern Tropical Region (Fig. 2, C)

This province comprises the remainder of North America, including the Arctic islands Baffinland, Ellesmereland, Washingtonland, and Greenland and adjacent small Arctic islands. An Ordovician landmass occupied the area made up of northern Quebec, part of Baffinland, most of central and southern Greenland, Iceland, and northern Scandinavia. Hence no marine invertebrates are recorded from these areas, but they would have been present around the coasts of this land, which touched the equator between Iceland and Greenland. The coasts of New Brunswick, Nova Scotia, Newfoundland, and Maine all lay along the equator. Numerous small and larger islands rose from the Appalachian miogeosyncline, and larger islands lay in the epicontinental sea covering the North American shield. Mexico was mainly emergent, save for the northern provinces. The whole region was populated by a rich marine invertebrate fauna, of which some of the restricted elements are here noted:

Trilobites (32)

Leiobienvillea	Lutesvillea	Hadrophybus
Glaphurus	Platyanax	Heliomera
Glaphurina	Rananasus	Metapliomerops
Cholopilus	Mesotaphraspis	Leiostrototropus
Perischodory	Paratrinucleus	Strotactinus
Ectenaspis	Novaspis	Bevanopsis
Nileoides	Ampyxina	Missisquoia
Cyclopyge	Anisotonella	Holdenia
Hyboaspis	Edmundsonia	Hapsiceraurus
Goniotelus	Endymionia	Remipyga
Jeffersonia	Seleneceme	

Brachiopods (15)

Scaphelasma	Dictyonites	Pelonomia
Rhysotreta	Pleurorthis	Apatomorpha
Torynelasma	Cyclocoelia	Paucicostella
Ephippelasma	Tropidothyris	Rhipidomena
Oxlosia	Elasmothyris	Parallelelasma

Nautiloids (67)

Vassaroceras	Mysticoceras	Franklinoceras
Woosteroceras	Phragmosiphon	Antiphragmoceras
Quebecoceras	Platysiphon	Clarkesvillea
Smithvilloceras	Pliendoceras	Lavaloceras
Dwightoceras	Retroclitendoceras	Reedsoceras
Manitouoceras	Stenosiphon	Simardoceras
Bridgeoceras	Liskeardia	Sinclairoceras
Chepuloceras	Humeoceras	Moreauoceras
Clelandoceras	Colpoceras	Pilotoceras
Copiceras	Saffordoceras	Seelyoceras
Stemtonoceras	Eotripteroceras	Clytoceras
Anguloceras	Pleurorthoceras	Shumardoceras

Diaphoroceras	Anaspyroceras	Beekmanoceras
Dyscritoceras	Glenisteroceras	Jasperoceras
Monogonoceras	Oxfordoceras	Litoceras
Rudolfoceras	Mesnaquaceras	Barrandeoceras
Ogygoceras	Protokionoceras	Antiplectoceras
Pachendoceras	Whiteavesites	Avilionella
Shideleroceras	Isorthoceras	Centrocyrtoceras
Meniscoceras	Monomuchites	Paquettoceras
Proendoceras	Garryoceras	Eskimoceras
Escharendoceras	Subspyroceras	
Lobosiphon	Maelonoceras	

Graptolites (2)

Anomalograptus   Calamograptus

Coelenterates (3)

Ctenoconularia   Conularina   Sphenothallus

Asterozoans (2)

Hudsonaster   Anorthaster

Echinozoans (11)

Bassleridiscus	Foerstediscus	Isorophus
Carneyella	Lebetodiscus	Isorophusella
Cincinnatidiscus	Lepidoconia	Thresherodiscus
Cystaster	Streptaster	

D. Central Northern Tropical Region (Fig. 2, D)

This province comprises central Asia, lying by Ordovician reckoning between the equator and the Tropic of Cancer; by modern reckoning it is that part of Asia lying to the east of an arc joining Finland to Burma, and west of Korea. It evidently had a rich fauna, though it is probably only partly explored at present. A large landmass lay emergent in this epicontinental sea area, and to the east (by Ordovician reckoning) lay Aequinoctia, the Indonesian landmass already referred to earlier. The region is broadly related faunistically to both North America and to Australia, as would be expected from its central location between these two northern hemisphere marine provinces of the Ordovician world.

The restricted genera are:

Trilobites (21)

Shumardops	Birmanites	Emsurina
Eoisotelus	Omeipsis	Encrinurella
Tungtzuella	Dactylocephalus	Calymenesun
Seisonia	Boschchekulia	Reedocalymene
Hangchungolithus	Dipleuropyge	Monorakos
Ningkianolithus	Digrypos	Ceratevenkaspis
Nankinolithus	Pliomerina	Lyralichas

Brachiopods (9)

Sinorthis	*Evenkina*	*Alimbella*
Eostrematorthis	*Metorthis*	*Medesia*
Lepidorthis	*Kassinella*	*Lepidocycloides*

Nautiloids (12)

Shantungendoceras	*Parapiloceras*	*Cyclocyrtendoceras*
Bajkaloceras	*Chihlioceras*	*Padunoceras*
Changkiuoceras	*Intejoceras*	*Ordosoceras*
Talassoceras	*Evencoceras*	*Stolbovoceras*

E. Eastern North Tropical Region (Fig. 2, E)

The region comprises Australia and New Zealand, which lay at this epoch in the northern hemisphere. In passing it may be noted that investigations similar to the present one have shown that New Zealand and southern Australia began to pass over the equator to enter the southern hemisphere during Carboniferous times, and that the transition was completed by New Zealand early in the Permian; Australia required a longer time and did not complete the transition until Jurassic time. Australian faunas reflect northern hemisphere affinities, therefore, in the Paleozoic. New Zealand faunas reflect northern affinities until the Permian, at which epoch the island group came under the influence of the South Pacific gyre for the first time, with dramatic effects on the marine fauna, which acquired the first South American immigrants (Fell, 1967 b).

The restricted genera included:

Trilobites (3)

Etheridgaspis	*Tasmanaspis*	*Tasmanocephalus*

Graptolites (2)

Mimograptus	*Skiagraptus*

Brachiopod (1)

Spanodonta

Nautiloids (14)

Hemichoanella	*Diastoloceras*	*Madiganella*
Lebetoceras	*Notocycloceras*	*Hecatoceras*
Loxochoanella	*Campendoceras*	*Aethoceras*
Ventroloboceras	*Lobendoceras*	*Hardmanoceras*
Apiocrinoceras	*Tasmanoceras*	

The fauna is by no means impoverished, and the shortness of the above lists reflects probably no more than the fact that 75 per cent of the fauna was shared with the central north tropical region, and also that the Ordovician sediments of Australia have not yet been fully mapped or explored. As can be seen, there is little evidence of isolation in the fauna, since so much was shared with Asia and so few restricted local genera had arisen; also the *Arkoceras* group of nautiloid genera was shared with North America, as noted above, and therefore does not appear on the foregoing list. The evolution of restricted Australian and New Zealand genera, which is so marked a feature of Tertiary and Recent faunas, evidently was inhibited so long as Australia and New Zealand lay in the northern hemisphere in close geographic proximity to Asia. Once the transition of the equator had occurred, the area (partcularly New Zealand) became much more isolated, since the northern hemisphere gyre of the Pacific had retreated from these coasts, and no further influxes of pelagic current-borne elements could occur from the northeast.

F. Central South Tropical Region (Fig. 2, F)

The region comprises northern Europe and western Russia, the Caucasus, Turkestan, Afghanistan, Pakistan, and the Indian peninsula; the last area, however, was elevated, so no marine faunas are known from it. This region was by far the richest faunal province of the southern hemisphere and doubtless owes this circumstance to its lying in immediate contiguity with the central Asian region and to the existence of a coastline linking Europe with the North American region via Greenland and Scandinavia. It is evident that Europe was the central distributing area for the whole Ordovician southern hemisphere, both Africa and South America exhibiting close faunistic links with Europe, though not with each other.

The following are the restricted genera:

Trilobites (128)

Corrugatagnostus	Hungioides	Ityophorus
Geragnostella	Leimitzia	Krattaspis
Girvanagnostus	Aspidaeglina	Osekaspis
Homagnostoides	Ellipsotaphrus	Remipyga
Gallagnostoides	Pricyclopyge	Cyrtometopus
Leiagnostus	Psilacella	Actinopeltis
Sphaeragnostus	Stygina	Eccoptochile
Hospes	Bronteopsis	Pseudosphaerexochus
Acanthopleurella	Prostygina	Reraspis
Boeckaspis	Cekovia	Stubblefieldia
Amphytrion	Octillaenus	Pompeckia
Teratorhynchus	Panderia	Hemisphaerocoryphe
Tramoria	Platillaenus	Areia
Lichapyge	Ectillaenus	Plasiaspis
Asaphus	Zbirovia	Anacheirurus
Ogmasaphus	Zdicella	Parapilekia
Plectasaphus	Theamataspis	Diaphantometopus
Pseudasaphus	Agerina	Dindymene
Pseudobasilicus	Phaetonellus	Oedicybele
Pseudomegalaspis	Proetidella	Platycalymene
Ptychopyge	Astroproetus	Ptychometope
Xenasaphus	Clypoproetus	Bathycheilus
Homalopyge	Paryfenus	Pharostoma
Homotelus	Warburgaspis	Bavarilla
Lannaeus	Philipsinella	Zeliszkella
Megalaspides	Celmus	Ormathops
Hunnebergia	Tornquistia	Eudolatites

Megistaspis
Niobe
Bohemopyge
Niobella
Norinia
Homalopteon
Ogyginus
Ogygiocarella
Ogygites
Borogothus
Varvia
Eoasaphus
Barrandia
Bunastides
Asaphopsoides
Dikelocephalopsis

Eoharpa
Paraharpes
Selenoharpes
Broeggerolithus
Reuscholithus
Salterolithus
Marrolithoides
Lloydolithus
Talaeomarrolithus
Protolloydolithus
Eirelithus
Dionidella
Trinucleoides
Cnemidopyge
Raymondella
Falanaspis

Kloucekia
Josephulus
Uralichas
Leiolichas
Dicranopeltis
Conolichas
Hoplolichas
Lichakephalus
Proceratocephala
Whittingtonia
Isocolus
Cyphoniscus
Pradesia
Myinda
Sarkia

Brachiopods (90)

Oslogonites
Kjaerina
Kjaerufina
Boreadorthis
Ladogiella
Iru
Ukoa
Sampo
Keyserlingia
Hisingerella
Bancroftia
Harknessella
Horderleyella
Smeathenella
Cliftonia
Ahtiella
Aulonotreta
Tomasina
Pseudopholidops
Acrotreta
Clistotrema
Orbithele
Orthisocrania
Pseudocrania
Pseudometoptonia
Volbarthia
Jivinella
Eostrophomena
Portranella
Glossorthis

Prantlina
Ranorthis
Panderina
Poramborthis
Barbarorthis
Spinorthis
Corineorthis
Schizophorella
Rhactorthis
Cremnorthis
Saukrodictya
Comatopoma
Drabovinella
Hirnantia
Cryptothyris
Dedzetina
Eodalmanella
Heterorthina
Howellites
Planoharknessella
Svobodina
Angusticardina
Apatorthis
Clinambon   •
Ilmarinia
Pahlenella
Gonambonites
Anchigonites
Antigonambonites
Estlandia

Lacunarites
Raunites
Bicuspina
Progonambonites
Epacroplecia
Plectotreta
Plectambonites
Plectella
Inversella
Leptestia
Grorudia
Tetraodontella
Anoptambonites
Leptelloidea
Merciella
Leptestina
Eochonetes
Aegiromena
Alwynella
Chonestoidea
Actinomena
Luhaia
Mjoesina
Maakina
Foliomena
Bekkeromena
Kiaeromena
Lycophoria
Metacamerella
Holorhynchus

Nautiloids (30)

Oelandoceras	*Balticoceras*	*Broeggeroceras*
Suecoceras	*Leurocycloceras*	*Eichwaldoceras*
Tallinnoceras	*Troedssonella*	*Tragoceras*
Estonioceras	*Clinoceras*	*Ancistroceras*
Lituites	*Heloceras*	*Angelinoceras*
Ringoceras	*Metephippiorthoceras*	*Cyclolituites*
Zittelloceras	*Protobactrites*	*Holmiceras*
Orthoceras	*Piersaloceras*	*Rhynchorthoceras*
Bifoveoceras	*Hadoceras*	*Trilacinoceras*
Ctenoceras	*Kiaeroceras*	*Tyrioceras*

Graptolites (6)

Holograptus	*Parazygograptus*	*Nanograptus*
Anorthograptus	*Lonchograptus*	*Archiretiolites*

Coelenterates (4)

Trochiscolithus	*Coelostylis*	*Brachyelasma*	*Anaconularia*

Asterozoa (10)

Archegonaster	*Petraster*	*Phragmactis*
Archophiactis	*Girvanaster*	*Aulactis*
Platanaster	*Siluraster*	
Palaeura	*Eophiura*	

Echinozoa (4)

Bothriocidaris	*Aulechinus*	*Ectinechinus*	*Eothuria*

G. South Temperate Region (Fig. 2, G)

The region comprises southern Europe and all of Africa except the southernmost part; however, marine conditions prevailed only over southeast Europe and northwest Africa, and so from these regions alone our knowledge of the marine fauna derives. The fauna is so far poorly known, and most genera occur in Europe generally as well as in this region, so that only a very few restricted forms can be listed. These are:

Trilobites (9)

Marrolithus	*Calymenella*	*Selenopeltis*
Lehua	*Brongniartella*	*Onchometopus*
Placoparia	*Plesiacomia*	*Trinucleus*

Brachiopods

Drabovia

H. Western South Tropical Region (Fig. 2, H)

The region comprises South America, save for eastern Brazil, most of which lay in the south temperate zone; since, however, that part of Brazil was emergent, we have no knowledge of its fauna. Of the rest of South America, the distinctive restricted genera are:

Trilobites (16)

Incaia	Hapalopleura	Cuyanaspis
Zuninaspis	Araiopleura	Deltacare
Guandacolithus	Rhadinopleura	Nannopeltis
Famatinolithus	Metapilekia	Sphaerocare
Australoharpes	Leiostegina	
Mendolaspis	Bodenbenderia	

Nautiloids (2)

Desioceras   Paracyclostomiceras

Brachiopods (2)

Bistramia   Andobolus

The South American fauna also includes the following elements of a pan-American fauna:

Hintzeia	Porterfeldia	Neoagnostus
Rossaspis	Plicatolina	Schizambon
Kainella		

Another important shared element is the *Angelina* complex, found only in Europe and South America; these genera are listed above (p. 148). Their presence in the fauna is due to the east–west flow of the Capricorn current between Europe and Brazil.

Antarctica

We lack at present any information on the Ordovician faunas of the Antarctic continent. It is predictable, on the basis of the inferences here made, and dispersal vectors already noted in previous papers (Fell, 1967a, 1967b), that the fauna will belong to the southern tropical assemblage and will contain the following elements.

(1) Genera of the *Angelina* arc complex, derived from Europe and carried to South America by the Capricorn current. These genera would probably also traverse the gap between Patagonia and West Antarctica, to become established on the Bellingshausen, Weddell, and Ross Sea areas of the continent.

(2) Pan-American genera, as listed above.

(3) South American genera, as above.

(4) Genera of the central south tropical region (Fig. 2, F) which would probably enter the Indian Ocean by way of a narrow connection between that ocean and Tethys, between India and Thailand; and some genera from region D (Fig. 2) would probably enter the Indian Ocean by the same route.

Thus the Ordovician fauna of Antarctica can be expected to contain genera which have species represented in the European, Eurasian, and South American areas.

If the interpretations here presented are soundly based, the Antarctic fauna should have essentially the equatorial character of the regions to which it is inferentially affiliated. If calcareous facies are found, they should contain reefs; if pelitic facies occur, they should yield the fauna noted in (1), (2), and (3) above. The Antarctic fauna would be unlikely to contain African elements. If the age of West Antarctica is less than that of East Antarctica, and in particular, if the Scotia arc is a post-Paleozoic structure, as geologists believe, then we should expect the Antarctic marine fauna of the Ordovician to contain a proportion of restricted endemic genera evolved in isolation but derived from equatorial stocks of the regions noted above.

Acknowledgments. This research was carried out in part during tenure of a grant from the National Science Foundation. I am also indebted to James Freeman Clark who prepared Figures 1 and 2 from my pencil sketches.

APPENDIX A

SOUTHERN ORDOVICIAN MARINE INVERTEBRATE FAUNAS

The genera are arranged in systematic groups, under each of the three continents. Cosmopolitan genera are omitted. After each genus is given its known distribution beyond the limits of the continent under which it has been listed. Abbreviations: Afr, Africa; As, Asia; Eu, Europe; NAm, North America; SAm, South America; Aust, Australasia (Australia, Tasmania and/or New Zealand).

1. AUSTRALIA

Trilobites

Carolinites SAm, NAm, Eu
Telephina NAm, Eu
Asaphopsis As
Proceratopyge SAm, Eu, As
Sphaerexochus NAm, Eu, As

Staurocephalus NAm, Eu, As
Gravicalymene Eu, As
Dicranogmus Eu
Ceratocephala NAm, Eu, As

Etheridgaspis
Tasmanaspis
Tasmanocephalus

Nautiloids

Ellesmereoceras NAm, As
Hemichoanella
Lebetoceras
Loxochoanella
Ventroloboceras
Bassleroceras NAm
Apiocrinoceras
Catoraphiceras NAm, Eu, As
Diastoloceras

Eothinoceras NAm, As
Thylacoceras As
Proterocameroceras NAm, Eu, As
Anthoceras NAm
Campendoceras
Lobendoceras
Piloceras NAm, EU
Allopiloceras NAm
Tasmanoceras

Kionoceras NAm, Eu
Columenoceras NAm, Eu
Protokionoceras NAm, Eu
Mysterioceras Eu
Ephippiorthoceras NAm, Eu
Madiganella
Hecatoceras
Aethoceras
Aphetoceras NAm

Ectocycloceras NAm
Kyminoceras NAm
Notocycloceras
Bactroceras Eu
Bathmoceras SAm, Eu,
  ?As

Manchuroceras As
Cyrtendoceras Eu
Nybyoceras NAm, Eu, As
Michelinoceras NAm, Eu,
  As
Plagiostomoceras Eu

Pycnoceras NAm
Arkoceras NAm
Hardmanoceras
Trocholitoceras NAm

Graptolites

Adelograptus Eu
Bryograptus NAm, Eu
Staurograptus NAm, ?Eu
Triograptus NAm, Eu
Ptilograptus NAm, Eu
Mastigograptus SAm,
  NAm
Goniograptus NAm, ?Eu
Brachiograptus SAm,
  NAm, ?As
Pterograptus SAm, Eu

Sigmograptus NAm
Trichograptus SAm, Eu
Zygograptus NAm
Schizograptus ?SAm, Afr,
  NAm, Eu
Mimograptus
Trochograptus NAm, Eu
Cardiograptus NAm, Eu
Skiagraptus
Oncograptus NAm, Eu
Leptograptus NAm, Eu

Nemagraptus NAm, Eu,
  As
Dicellograptus NAm, Eu,
  As
Trigonograptus NAm, Eu
Neurograptus NAm, Eu
Nymphograptus Eu
Plegmatograptus ?NAm,
  Eu
Didymograptus NAm, Afr,
  Eu

Ostracods

Aechmima NAm, Eu   *Aparchites* NAm, Eu, As

Brachiopods

Siphonotreta NAm, Eu, As
Dicoelosia NAm, Eu, As

Spanodonta
Syntrophopsis NAm, Eu

Porambonites NAm, Eu,
  As

Gastropods

Tremanotus NAm, Eu   *Mourlonia* NAm
Helicotoma NAm, Eu, As   *Murchisonia* NAm, Eu, As

Rugose Coral

Streptelasma NAm, Eu, As

Tabulate Corals

Tetradium NAm, Eu
Billingsaria NAm
Nyctopora NAm, Eu
Protaraea NAm, Eu

Acidolites Eu
Plasmoporella NAm, Eu,
  As

Halysites NAm, Afr, Eu,
  As

2. SOUTH AMERICA

Trilobites

Neoagnostus NAm
Geragnostus NAm, Eu, As
Trinodus NAm, Eu, As
Anglagnostus NAm, Eu
Gallagnostus Eu
Machairagnostus

Hoekaspis
Megalaspidella ?N.
  Afr, ?Eu
Niobides
Paramegalaspis Eu
Niobina Eu

Incaia
Orometopus Eu
Lonchodomas NAm, Eu,
  As
Mendolaspis
Hapalopleura

Shumardia NAm, Eu, As
Parabolina NAm, Eu
Mekynophrys
Jujuyaspis NAm, Eu
Parabolinopsis
Saltaspis Eu
Triarthrus NAm, Eu
Angelina Eu
Parabolinella NAm, Eu
Plicatolina NAm
Porterfeldia NAm
Hypermecaspis
Tropidopyge SAm, Eu
Carolinites NAm, Eu, Aust
Lloydia NAm
Apatokephalus NAm, Eu
Kainella NAm
Pseudokainella As

Ogygiocaris Eu
Thysanopyge
Australopyge
Zuninaspis
Illaenopsis Eu
Lakaspis
Symphysurus NAm, Eu
Ceratopyge Eu
Dichelepyge
Onychopyge
Proceratopyge Eu, As, Aust
Pseudohysterolenus
Australoharpes
Harpides NAm, Eu, As
Guandacolithus
Onnia Afr, Eu
Famatinolithus

Araiopleura
Rhadinopleura
Pliomera Eu
Metapilekia
Protopliomerops NAm, As
Hintzeia NAm
Rossaspis NAm
Synhomalonotus Afr, Eu, As
Pharostomina Eu
Leiostegina
Phacopina NAm, Eu
Bodenbenderia
Brackenbuschia
Cuyanaspis
Deltacare
Nannopeltis
Sphaerocare

Nautiloids

Desioceras

Paracyclostomiceras

Bathmoceras Eu, As, Aust

Graptolites

Aspidograptus NAm, Eu
Anisograptus NAm, Eu
Mastigograptus NAm, Aust
Brachiograptus NAm, ?As, Aust

Pterograptus Eu, Aust
Trichograptus Eu, Aust
Schizograptus NAm, Eu, Aust
Azygograptus NAm, Eu, As

Janograptus Eu
Lasiograptus ?NAm, Eu, Aust

Brachiopods

Bistramia
Broeggeria NAm, Eu, As
Andobolus

Craniops NAm, Eu, As
Schizambon NAm

Apheorthis NAm, Eu, As
Anisopleurella NAm, Eu

Gastropods

Bucanella NAm, Afr, Eu   *Tropidodiscus* NAm, Eu, As

3. AFRICA

Trilobites

Onnia SAm, Eu
Marrolithus Eu
Lehua Eu, ?As
Placoparia Eu
Synhomalonotus SAm, Eu, As

Calymenella Eu
Brongniartella Eu
Colpocoryphe NAm, Eu, As
Plesiacomia

Selenopeltis Eu
Dalmanitina NAm, Eu, As
Onchometopus Eu
Trinucleus Eu

Brachiopods

Elkania (?Afr), NAm   *Syntrophina* NAm, Eu, As
Drabovia Eu   *Pionodema* NAm, Eu

Gastropods

Bucanella SAm, NAm, Eu   *Sinuites* NAm, Eu, As   *Gyronema* NAm, Eu

Tabulate Coral

Halysites NAm, Eu, As,
Aust

Graptolites

Didymograptus NAm, Eu,   *Schizograptus* ?SAm,
Aust   NAm, Eu, Aust

REFERENCES

Adie, R. J., 1965. Antarctic geology and continental drift. *Sci. J.*, *1*: 65–73.

Bassler, R. S., 1950. Faunal lists and descriptions of Paleozoic corals. *Geol. Soc. Am. Mem. 44.*

Cloud, P. E., Jr., and V. E., Barnes, 1957. Early Ordovician Sea in Texas. *Geol. Soc. Am. Mem., 67:* 163–214.

Creer, K. M., 1966. Continents on the move. *Sea Frontiers, 12*(3): 148–57.

David, T. W. E., 1959. *The Geology of the Commonwealth of Australia.* Arnold, London.

Fell, H. B., 1962. West-wind-drift dispersal of echinoderms in the southern hemisphere. *Nature, 193:* 759–61.

——, 1967a. Resolution of Coriolis parameters for former epochs. *Nature, 214,* 1192–98.

——, 1967b. Cretaceous and Tertiary surface currents of the ocean. *Oceanogr. Mar. Biol. Ann. Rev., 5:* 317–41.

Furnish, W. M., and B. F. Glenister, 1964. Paleoecology (of Nautiloidea). In *Treatise on Invertebrate Paleontology*, pt. K. Univ. Kansas Press, Lawrence.

Furon, R., 1963. *Geology of Africa.* Oliver & Boyd, Edinburgh.

Hill, D., 1956. Rugosa and Tabulata. In *Treatise on Invertebrate Paleontology*, R. C. Moore, ed. pt. F. Univ. Kansas Press, Lawrence.

Jenks, W. F., 1956. Handbook of South American geology. *Geol. Soc. Am. Mem., 65:* 1–378.

Kobayashi, T., 1959. (For bibliography of relevant papers, see *Treatise on Invertebrate Paleontology, Arthropoda*, R. C. Moore, ed. pt. L: 529–30. Univ. Kansas Press, Lawrence.)

Kummel, B., 1961. *History of the Earth.* Freeman, San Francisco.

Menard, H. W., 1964. *Marine Geology of the Pacific.* McGraw-Hill, New York.

Moore, R. C., ed., 1953 continuing. *Treatise on Invertebrate Paleontology.* Univ. Kansas Press, Lawrence.

Okulitch, V. J., and S. J. Nelson, 1957. Sponges of the Paleozoic. *Geol. Soc. Amer. Mem. 67:* 763–69.

Francis G. Stehli

6. TAXONOMIC DIVERSITY GRADIENTS IN
POLE LOCATION: THE RECENT MODEL[1]

During the last few decades, much speculation has attached to the related hypotheses of continental drift and polar wandering, but unequivocal evidence bearing on these subjects has been limited. The reconstruction of past climatic zones by paleontological or geochemical means has been generally recognized as potentially the most effective way of testing the hypotheses. But while paleoclimatic evidence appears to deny significant polar wandering or latitudinal shift in the continental positions during Cenozoic time, data relating to the earlier history of the earth have not produced definitive results.

Greatly intensified interest in the investigation of rock magnetism during the last few years has suggested an alternative means of testing the polar wandering and continental drift hypotheses. The paleomagnetic data thus far collected appear strongly to support both continental drift and polar wandering in pre-Cenozoic time. The evidence from this source appears to be internally consistent and in many respects seems quite compelling.

In applying paleomagnetism to the problems of continental drift and polar wandering, it is well to remember, however, that the paleomagnetic method locates the magnetic, not the rotational, pole. The location of the rotational pole by this technique rests entirely on the assumption that the earth's magnetic field is and has been, through the period of interest, an axial dipole. Though this assumption is not known to be valid, and a considerable body of evidence suggests that it is not, it nevertheless receives support from the fact that during most of Cenozoic time the average position of the magnetic pole seems to have fallen close to that of the present rotational pole (Cox and Doell, 1960).

In pre-Cenozoic time a different condition exists. As we go back, we find that the magnetic pole as indicated by paleomagnetic measurements is increasingly distant from the position of the present rotational pole. One is forced to conclude that something in the system under consideration has undergone a basic change.

1. Contribution No. 28 of the Department of Geology, Case Western Reserve University, Cleveland, Ohio.

There seem to be two possibilities. It may be assumed (1) that the rotational pole as well as the magnetic pole has shifted or (2) that the magnetic pole has moved independently of the rotational pole. If the first assumption (basic to most current interpretations of paleomagnetic data) is selected, it leads to the conclusion that both polar wandering and continental drift have occurred. The second assumption leads to the conclusion that the earth's magnetic field is not, or at least has not always been, an axial dipole, and that paleomagnetic data cannot readily be brought to bear on either the polar wandering or the continental drift hypothesis. If either of these assumptions could be shown to be correct, it would be of immense interest. At present, however, one conclusion appears as likely as the other, and information that would allow a selection between them is eminently to be desired.

I have been interested in this problem for a number of years and have attempted to formulate an experiment that would provide a criterion for selecting one of the alternatives. The rudiments of such an experiment are easily designed. One must find a way to make a determination of the position of the rotational pole which is independent of the magnetic pole. Then for a suitable period of geologic time the location of both the magnetic and rotational poles must be determined. If the magnetic and rotational poles coincide, the earth's field has been an axial dipole, and there have been both polar wandering and continental drift. If the two poles differ significantly in position, then the earth's field was not an axial dipole and polar wandering can be rejected; therefore paleomagnetic data no longer can be accepted as evidence of either polar wandering or of continental drift.

While the critical experiment is easily formulated, means to conduct it are less readily apparent since suitable techniques to locate the position of the rotational pole are difficult to discover. It is desirable that any technique employed should be based on few and simple assumptions; that it be quantitative; that it be broadly applicable with relative ease to the geologic record; and that it be susceptible to considerable extension back into geologic history. These requirements rule out most of the techniques that have been tried in the past, either because they are not quantitative (presence or absence distribution data for fossil organisms or other geologic materials) or because they cannot yet be broadly enough applied to older rocks (paleotemperature determinations). The taxonomic diversity gradients[2] which exist among organisms and are covariant with latitude seem, however, to fulfill all the requirements set forth above and have been selected for testing as a technique for rotational pole location and hence an implementation of the experiment outlined above.

Taxonomic diversity gradients were apparently first noted in a qualitative way by Wallace (1878). They were probably first put into a quantitative form by Tillyard (1914), who used them to study the distribution patterns of certain

2. Taxonomic diversity is the number of kinds of organisms at any given taxonomic level that are found at a given locality or within a given area.

animals. The utility of taxonomic diversity gradients in locating past rotational poles was pointed out in a crude way by Stehli (1957); their overall relation to the earth's planetary temperature gradient has been discussed by many workers and subjected to a recent review by Fischer (1960). The first attempt to use them in a quantitative manner as a technique for locating the earth's rotational poles appears to have been that reported by Stehli (1964).

It is the purpose of this paper to evaluate the taxonomic diversity gradient as a potential geologic tool. In so doing, an attempt is made to set up a model based on the diversity gradients of Recent organisms and to test it as a means for rotational pole location. Taxonomic diversity is primarily, and very strongly, responsive to latitude, but it is also affected to a lesser degree by secondary causes. For the purpose of rotational pole location, the primary or latitudinal response may be termed "signal" and the secondary and largely nonlatitudinal responses may be termed "noise." To realize the potential of taxonomic diversity gradients for the purpose at hand, it is desirable to minimize the complicating effects of the noise components and consider the signal component in its least complicated form. This end may be achieved by computation of simple mathematical surfaces best fitting the raw data distributions. The mathematical procedure confers the advantage of allowing more objective examination and comparison of diversity distributions and makes possible the precise location of maxima and minima related to equatorial or polar positions.

On the basis of the tests made with the Recent model, diversity gradients are found to be suitable for rotational pole location and to provide rather high resolution. Only the Recent model is considered here, though preliminary application of the technique to the fossil record has been successfully made and extensive testing is in progress.

BASIS OF DIVERSITY GRADIENT MODEL

To locate the rotational pole, one must find some one of its properties that uniquely defines it. The most obvious such property is the occurrence of characteristic minima in solar energy capture at the rotational poles (Fig. 1). The existence of a gradient in solar energy capture between the equator and the poles has many consequences, most pronounced of which is a strong planetary temperature gradient which, like the energy gradient that generates it, varies as a function of latitude (Fig. 1). Because temperature is such a pervasive factor in both physico-chemical and biochemical reactions, it is to be expected that the planetary temperature gradient will produce a great variety of secondary effects. Some of these temperature-dependent effects should be such that they will leave an impress on the geologic record. It is among this group of effects ultimately related to the gradient in solar energy capture and so to the position of the rotational pole that we must seek a model suitable for locating the position of the rotational pole.

If a reflection of the planetary temperature gradient is being considered as a means for locating the rotational pole, then it is of interest to determine the ac-

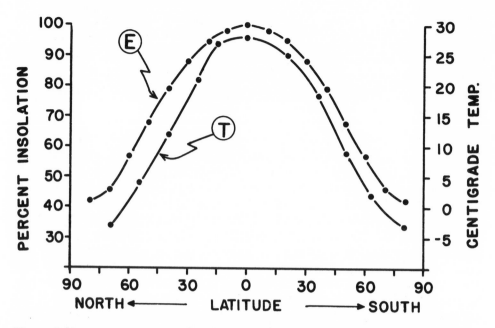

Fig. 1. Solar energy capture gradient (E) and planetary temperature gradient (T) as a function of latitude. Energy capture gradient shown as a per cent of total solar energy received at the equator (data from Blair, 1942). Planetary temperature curve from smoothed data for ocean surface water temperatures (data from *U.S. Navy Climatic Atlas of the World*, 1959).

curacy with which the temperature gradient, itself, can locate the pole. The distribution of sea-surface temperatures, if winter is assumed in both hemispheres, is shown in simple contoured form in Figure 2. The basic relationship of the planetary temperature gradient to latitude is clearly evident. It is also evident, however, that secondary or "noise" effects due to ocean currents, etc., somewhat deform the simple gradient. Application to the data of a best-fitting second-order spherical harmonic surface permits an effective separation between the signal and the noise components of this distribution. The form of the fitted surface is shown in Figure 3, and its utility in segregating the primary from the secondary responses is clearly seen. The inflection of the second-order surface indicates the position of the heat equator of the earth as determined from the sea-surface temperatures and, because of the cause-and-effect relationship between the solar energy capture gradient and the planetary temperature gradient, it must closely approximate the geographic equator. From the position of the equator thus determined, it is possible to provide a unique location for the rotational pole. The pole position determined in this way is shown in Figure 4 and is found to lie very close indeed to the actual position of the rotational pole.

Viewed in terms of the planetary temperature gradient, the northern and southern hemispheres are theoretically mirror images. In practice, the two hemi-

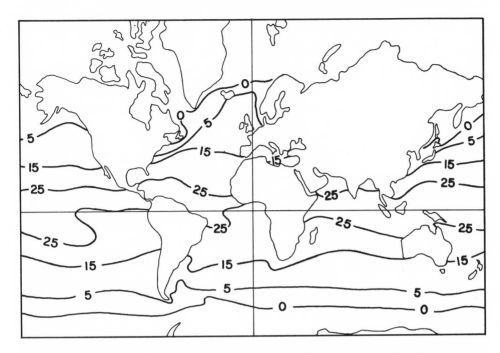

Fig. 2. Contour map of sea surface temperatures, in degrees centigrade, winter in both hemispheres. Note the basic latitude dependence (signal) and the various secondary effects (noise) (data from *U.S. Navy Climatic Atlas of the World*, 1959).

spheres depart somewhat from this ideal condition because of the unequal distribution of land and the resulting differential effectiveness of ocean currents as agents of thermal transfer. The raw temperature data may be smoothed one hemisphere at a time and the rotational pole position determined by application of a best-fitting nonorthogonal polynomial surface. Such surfaces fitted to the two hemispheres are shown in Figure 5, A and B, and their minima represent the position of the rotational poles for the two hemispheres. Comparison of the two poles located in this way (Fig. 4) shows them to be slightly different but not importantly so and suggest that, within rather broad limits of variation, the distribution of land and sea exercises relatively little overall effect on sea-surface temperature gradients, at least in terms of their ability to locate the rotational pole. The close correspondence between the poles determined for the individual hemispheres and for the earth as a whole (Fig. 4) indicates that data for a single hemisphere are quite adequate to establish the global pattern and provide accurate pole location.

It is well at this stage in developing the model to review the assumptions that will have to be made in its application. We must consider not only whether these assumptions are correct at the present time but also whether they can be justified in extrapolations into the past. The following assumptions are required with the model up to this point: (1) the earth is and has been basically spherical; (2)

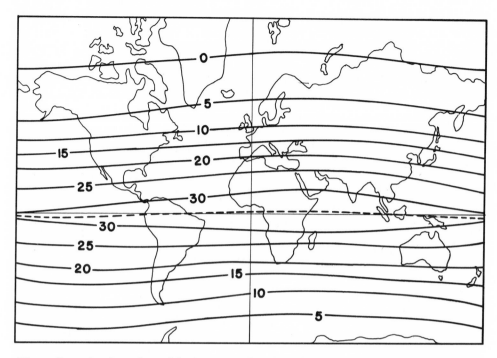

Fig. 3. Second-order spherical harmonic surface best fitting the sea surface temperature data shown in contoured form in Figure 2. Note that the surface presents in simple form the primary or planetary component of the temperature gradient (signal) while minimizing the secondary components (noise). The dashed line represents the position of the heat equator as derived from sea surface temperature data; it is found to be very nearly coincident with the actual geographic equator.

the earth's major source of energy has been the sun (effectively a point source); and (3) the inclination of the earth's axis with respect to the ecliptic plane has not varied greatly from its present condition. The first two of these assumptions seem virtually unassailable. The third also seems sound, for though the inclination of the earth's axis apparently does vary between 21° 8′, and 24° 4′ (Brouwer and Van Woerkom, 1950), a very much larger change would be required to destroy the model. It would therefore appear that the model is sound, to this point, as a means for locating the rotational pole.

Having concluded that the planetary temperature gradient itself can be used to locate the rotational pole, it is possible to proceed to the question of how the planetary temperature gradient may best be recognized in the geologic record. Several possibilities, both geochemical and paleontological are available for consideration. From among these possibilities, taxonomic diversity gradients have been selected as most likely to yield sufficient data to allow a unique answer, and they have been subjected to testing by study of their present-day characteristics and relation to latitude. As an initial model, we may take the taxonomic diver-

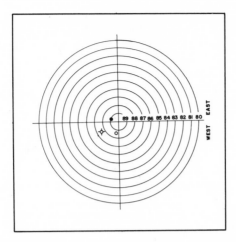

Fig. 4. Rotational pole locations (temperature mimima) as determined from best-fitting mathematical surfaces applied to the sea surface temperature data shown in contoured form in Figure 2. The crossed open circle represents the pole found from the spherical harmonic surface of Figure 3. The black dot represents the pole found from the best-fitting second-order nonorthogonal polynomial surface applied to the northern hemisphere data shown in Figure 5A. The open circle represents a northern hemisphere projection of the south pole found for a second-order nonorthogonal polynomial surface applied to the southern hemisphere data shown in Figure 5B. Note that none of the pole positions lies more than 2.5° from the actual rotational pole position.

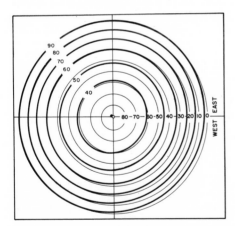
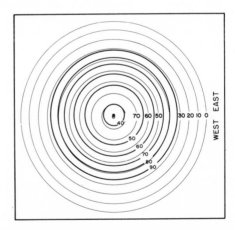

Fig. 5. Second-order nonorthogonal polynomial surfaces best fitting sea surface temperature data for each of the two hemispheres. A: The best-fitting surface for northern hemisphere sea-surface temperatures in February. B: The best-fitting surface for southern hemisphere sea-surface temperatures in August. The open circles represent the rotational poles, the black dots the temperature poles (data from *U.S. Navy Climatic Atlas of the World,* 1959).

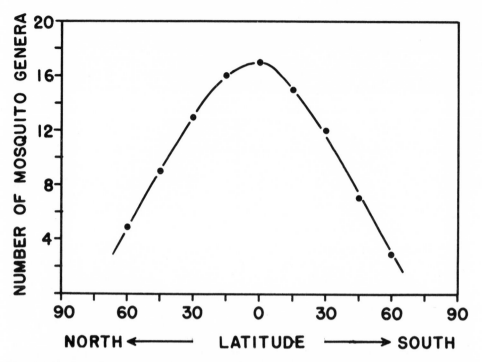

Fig. 6. Number of Recent genera of mosquitoes as a function of latitude. In preparing this diversity gradient the number of genera was averaged for 15° latitude classes. Note the similarity of this curve to those for solar energy capture and planetary temperature gradient shown in Figure 1. Diversity appears to be approximately as latitude-dependent as either of the other two curves (data compiled from ranges of species given by Stone et al., 1959).

sity of a particular group of organisms and test its utility in rotational pole location in the same manner in which we tested the utility of the planetary temperature gradient itself. The diversity, at the generic level of mosquitoes Culicidae) has been chosen for this purpose since the group has received extraordinarily thorough study. A plot of the mosquito data against latitude is seen in Figure 6, and it is clear that the diversity curve for this group is generally covariant with those for solar energy capture and the planetary temperature gradient seen in Figure 1. Thus it seems probable that diversity gradients will be as useful in rotational pole location as either the temperature or solar energy capture gradient. The contoured raw data for mosquito diversity on a worldwide basis are seen in Figure 7. The basic latitudinal control of diversity is once more evident. Also to be noted, however, are the aberrations of the simple form of the gradient which are analogous to the ocean current distortions seen in the sea-surface temperature data (Figure 2). These aberrations are, in this case, due to the distribution of

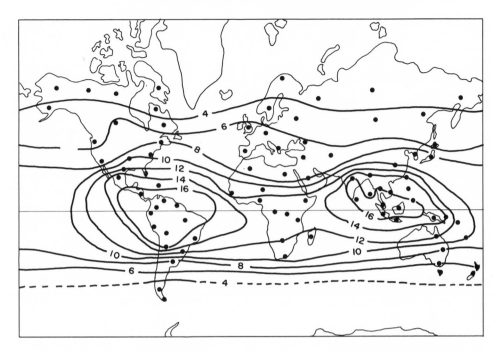

Fig. 7. Contoured raw generic diversity data for Recent mosquitoes. The overall form of the gradient and its pronounced latitude dependence (signal) are apparent. The sharp east–west attenuation between the two pronounced faunal provinces (noise) is also apparent as a secondary component of the distribution. Black dots represent control points (data from Stone et al., 1959).

land, imperfect collecting or study, and especially to the existence of faunal provinces. To see the portion of the mosquito diversity gradient most simply responsive to latitude, it is therefore necessary once again to employ mathematical surface-fitting procedures to segregate the response, or signal, from the disturbing effects, or noise.

In Figure 8 is shown the second-order spherical harmonic surface best fitting the diversity data for mosquito genera. The equator (equals diversity maximum) derived from this model is as close to the position of the geographic equator as was that determined for the temperature gradient itself (Fig. 3) and thus fully as useful in rotational pole location. The actual rotational pole determined from this taxonomic diversity gradient is shown in Figure 9.

Employing the diversity data for the two hemispheres separately, as was done with temperature, we find that information from a single hemisphere is, once more, adequate for accurate rotational pole location (Fig. 10, A and B). We find also that despite the great difference in land–sea distribution evident between

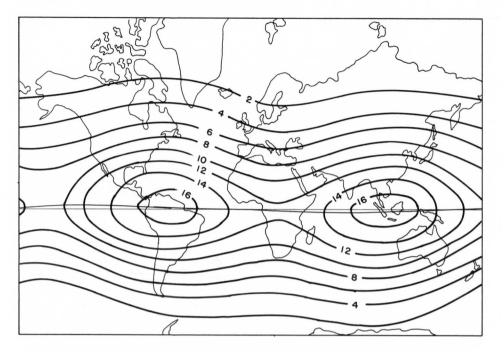

Fig. 8. Second-order spherical harmonic surface best fitting the data for generic diversity of Recent mosquitoes shown in contoured form in Figure 7. Note that this surface emphasizes the planetary contribution to the gradient (signal) and minimizes the faunal province and other noise contributions. The position of the diversity maximum (trace of point of zero rate of change in slope of the surface) lies very close to the geographic equator.

the two hemispheres, the difference in the poles determined is slight (Fig. 9). In brief, this initial model suggests that gradients in taxonomic diversity are about as strongly dependent on latitude as is temperature itself, and that they can be used for relatively high resolution determination of rotational pole position.

From the point of view of a model for location of past rotational poles, the use of taxonomic diversity gradients requires the addition of one further assumption: that the response of organic diversity to the planetary temperature gradient, or to latitude, has in the past been the same as it is today. This assumption is strongly supported by the fact that diversity gradients characterize not just a few groups of organisms but virtually all large, well-established, widely distributed groups among plants and animals. It appears that diversity gradients are a sweeping response to temperature and perhaps directly to solar energy capture and that they can be carried back into the geologic record without fear that increasingly tenuous relationship to Recent organisms will alter them, since they are at present expressed independently of relationships between major groups.

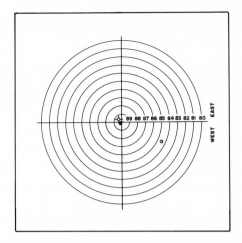

Fig. 9. Rotational pole locations (diversity minima) as determined from best-fitting mathematical surfaces applied to the generic diversity for Recent mosquitoes shown in Figure 7. The crossed open circle represents the pole found from the spherical harmonic surface of Figure 8. The black dot represents the pole found from the best-fitting second-order nonorthogonal polynomial surface applied to the northern hemisphere data shown in Figure 10A. The open circle represents a northern hemisphere projection of the south pole found for a second-order nonorthogonal polynomial surface applied to the southern hemisphere data shown in Figure 10B. Note that none of the pole position lies more than 5.5° from the actual rotational pole position.

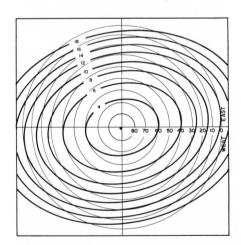 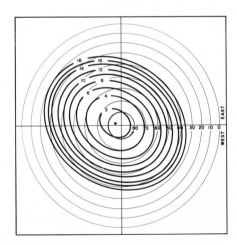

Fig. 10. Best-fitting second-order nonorthogonal polynomial surfaces applied to the generic diversity gradient for Recent mosquitoes. A: Data for northern hemisphere treated separately yields a diversity pole virtually coincident with the true rotational pole position. B: Data for the southern hemisphere treated separately yields a diversity pole at 84° 30′ N.

SOME GENERAL CHARACTERISTICS OF TAXONOMIC DIVERSITY GRADIENTS

Taxonomic diversity gradients seem to embody considerable potential as a geologic tool, not only in rotational pole location but also in study of climatic variations, ocean circulation patterns, and migrations of organisms through time. If they are used, however, their limitations as well as their potential must be determined in order that the most favorable material may be selected for any specific problem. In order to determine the limitations of diversity gradients in geology, a large number of groups of Recent organisms characteristic of a variety of major environments has been studied. Some general conclusions regarding the limitations of these or similar groups are noted below. Suggestions regarding the time dependence of some of the limitations that might be encountered in geological application of diversity gradients are also included.

Cosmopolitan Versus Endemic Elements

In dealing with features of the earth as a whole, it is clearly desirable to work with groups of plants or animals that have a very broad and preferably almost cosmopolitan distribution. Endemic groups do indeed develop diversity gradients related to the planetary temperature gradient (north–south gradient), but they also have, because of their finite distribution, strong gradients in other directions (Fig. 11). In such cases it is not always possible, from the diversity gradient alone, to recognize the portion that represents a response to the planetary temperature gradient. Even when distribution of a particular group of organisms is more or less worldwide, the inclusion in it of many endemic elements can cause the development of pronounced faunal provinces within which the gradient in an east–west direction may be almost as strong as the more general north–south gradient. An excellent example of this condition has been presented by Simpson (1964), and others will be given below. It will be seen, however, that while the existence of pronounced faunal provinces can locally distort the form of the gradient, it rarely does so to a degree that seriously threatens our objective of locating the rotational pole as long as worldwide control or good coverage of a single hemisphere is employed.

Environmental Effects

In addition to selecting groups of organisms characterized by widespread distributions, it is desirable to employ the forms that are most directly exposed to the effects of the planetary temperature gradient. Included in this category would be virtually all elements of the terrestrial biota and those marine forms living in shallow water. Forms which prefer deeper water environments may exist permanently below the thermocline and thus, from the equator to the poles, be exposed only to low temperatures regardless of latitude. One may question the importance of this problem in nonglacial times for, as has been shown for the Middle Cenozoic by

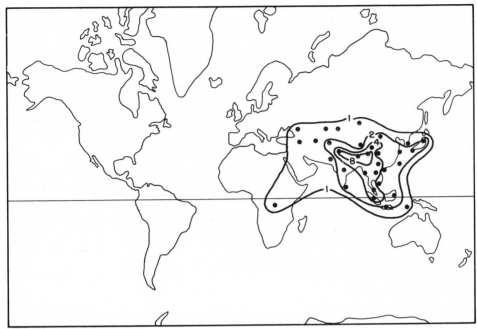

Fig. 11. Diversity of an endemic group, the pheasants (Phasianinae) at the generic level. Note that it is difficult, if not impossible, to tell the north–south gradient in diversity from that oriented east–west. For this reason endemic groups are rarely suitable for the application of diversity to geologic problems (data from Delacour, 1951).

Emiliani (1954) and for the Cretaceous by Lowenstam (1964), even the deep waters of the ocean may have been warm during much of the earth's history. It seems an inescapable conclusion, however, that the deep waters must always have shown a minimal expression of the planetary temperature gradient and that shallow-water marine forms or terrestrial organisms from low elevations are to be preferred for most geological applications of taxonomic diversity gradients. Even within the shallow-water marine environment, organisms occupying some niches seem to be superior to others. It appears, for instance, from the work of Thorson (1957) that epifaunal elements that are directly exposed to changes in the temperature of ambient water masses show a pronounced diversity gradient, whereas infaunal elements that inhabit the more stenothermal bottom muds may not do so.

Distribution Potential

Closely related to the environmental effects considered above, yet worthy of separate treatment, is what might be called *distribution potential*. Clearly, organisms vary greatly in the ease with which they may be dispersed, and types with limited distribution potential have concomitantly little potential in the application of diversity gradients to the geologic record. Perhaps the point is best illustrated by considering extremes. As an example of low distribution potential, one might imagine a group of stenothermal, freshwater fish, specialized for existence in lakes and slow-flowing streams and feeding on the larvae of a particular insect. Such animals are limited by temperature and salinity barriers, are tied to a specific source of food, are limited by the existence of aridity barriers such as the major deserts of the earth, and are commonly limited to one or a few drainage basins by the absence of a convenient connection with other systems. It is apparent that this group of organisms is not likely to be widely distributed, is very likely to be as strongly controlled by local conditions as by the response to the planetary temperature gradient, and thus would be of little value for our purposes.

At the other end of the spectrum one could imagine a eurythermal, euryhaline, phytoplanktonic group. Such organisms would be distributed throughout the oceans, lakes, and rivers of the earth and so be represented over some 70 per cent of the earth's surface; they would be extremely useful in applying diversity gradients to the geologic record. In general, since it appears likely that the oceans have always dominated the earth's surface, shallow-water marine forms with long-lived planktonic larval stages may be expected to be most useful.

Nonequatorial Optima

Major groups in the taxonomic hierarchy, if they have a good distribution potential, generally exhibit a relatively simple response to the planetary temperature gradient, which is characterized by high diversity near the equator and a decline into the higher latitudes of both hemispheres. Since higher taxonomic categories, unless they represent remnant stocks, tend to occupy broad adaptive zones, there is within each of them more or less specialization for narrower zones. Occasionally, such specialization results in the exploitation of an adaptive zone which finds its optimum expression in latitudes far removed from the equator. Such a condition is exemplified by the penguins of the southern hemisphere and their ecological counterparts, the alcids in the northern hemisphere. Though the diversity gradients of these forms are not equatorially centered, there is nevertheless a pronounced gradient which, in each case, declines both north and south from the optimum latitude. Thus even these atypical diversity gradients seem to be latitude-dependent and potentially useful in pole location.

Evolutionary Position

In the evolutionary history of any group of organisms, there are time-dependent variations in diversity upon which are superimposed geographic variations. An examination of the diversity patterns which result from variations in evolutionary rate (Simpson, 1953) suggests that there is an optimum time in the evolution of any group for its employment in diversity gradient studies. A newly evolving group is almost of necessity restricted both in geographic distribution and in diversity and is thus not likely to furnish suitable data. A relic group or "living fossil" is also likely to be restricted both in distribution and in diversity and thus to be unsuitable for diversity gradient study. The most favorable evolutionary position in the development of a group would seem to be at or near its maximum development. For instance, the brachiopod order Spiriferida with a total range in time from Middle Ordovician to Middle Jurassic would be unsuitable for diversity gradient work either in the Middle Ordovician (a total of about seven genera) or in the Middle Jurassic (a total of about three genera). During the Middle Devonian, however, the group might be excellent, since it then included a total of about ninety genera (figures from Williams, 1965).

"Noise"

While diversity gradients normally show a primary response to the planetary temperature gradient or the energy capture gradient or both, there are, as we have just seen, secondary responses of various kinds as well. For the purpose of locating the rotational pole, the primary response of diversity gradients may be considered as signal and the secondary responses as noise. Some of the major sources of noise have been considered above. Many minor sources can be identified in the various Recent diversity gradients that have been investigated in the course of this study. Some of the noise is unavoidably caused by incomplete collecting, differences in taxonomic philosophy, etc., but most diversity gradients are so strong that such minor and more or less random effects cause little significant distortion. Another source of noise is found in real diversity responses to minor anomalies in the planetary temperature gradient or to other special departures from the optimum ecological conditions for the group in question. This aspect of diversity gradients has been examined in some detail by Simpson (1964). For pole location, it is desirable to separate the noise and signal components in the data, and means whereby this may be accomplished are considered below. In certain cases the noise contains real and often quite interesting information, as has been noted elsewhere (Stehli, 1965).

Summary of Intrinsic Limitations

One can conclude that while there are limitations that must be heeded in applying taxonomic diversity gradients to the problem of rotational pole location, a careful selection among the wide spectrum of organisms available can avoid most of them. The problems of selecting the optimal group with which to work involve a knowledge of the environmental preferences of living groups and a knowledge of functional morphology which, in fossils, may help to determine environmental preferences. Also involved is the problem of preservation, and it is clear that some groups well suited for use by their environmental preferences will be eliminated because of poor potential for preservation or for recovery, when one deals with the fossil record. Selecting a suitable group thus requires judgment, but is not a particularly difficult problem.

SAMPLING PROBLEMS

Once a group of plants or animals believed appropriate to the problem at hand has been selected, there exists a problem in sampling. It is, in the first place, necessary to make some decision regarding the appropriate geographic limits which are to be assigned to a sample station or "control point." It is desirable that the area used be large enough to include a variety of environments and so reveal something approaching maximum diversity or, if a single major environment is used, that it be widely enough available to be used consistently. On the other hand, the area included in the control point must have a reasonably limited extent if much resolution is not to be lost. In the most detailed study of diversity yet made, Simpson (1964) has considered the specific diversity of mammals in North America, using a standardized sampling area of 22,500 square miles. This procedure provided unusual resolution, but the present study shows that most diversity gradients are so strongly expressed that the primary response suffers little damage even when very much larger control points are employed. If the sample is being taken from the literature, as has been the case with the data employed in this study, it is apparently an adequate precaution to use only those works reporting a comprehensive study of a compact geographic region. This procedure has been used in a study of diversity among Recent bivalves and has been found satisfactory (Stehli et al., 1966).

When literature data are used, they often include the results of studies spanning a considerable interval of time during which taxonomic concepts and practices may have changed. To avoid such problems it is desirable, where feasible, to reduce the nomenclature to a uniform system by reference to a competent modern treatise on the group being studied (Simpson, 1964; Stehli et al., 1966). If original collections are being made, precautions can be taken to ensure internal consistency in the sampling.

Even among the best-studied groups of Recent plants and animals, it is not always possible to know with certainty when the total diversity at any taxonomic level has been discovered. This situation poses a problem in knowing when a sample is adequate. The problem is much greater in dealing with fossils than is the case with recent materials, because the former are in general less well known. Possibilities for minimizing the sampling problem through the use of various ratios seem to exist and are considered further below in connection with some examples.

METHODS OF PRESENTING DIVERSITY GRADIENT DATA

Latitude Versus Diversity Plots

The simplest technique that can be used in graphical presentation of diversity gradient data is to plot diversity against latitude (Fig. 6). If a group of organisms is relatively well known, such a plot is often all that is required to see the form of the gradient and to determine whether it is related to the system of latitude being used. This procedure has the disadvantage, since it ignores longitude, that the plot may exhibit considerable scatter. If faunal province effects are very strong, and especially if the data are not of high quality, the plot may be very noisy. In such cases, it is well to recall that the highest value at any latitude is most likely to be significant since it is least likely to be affected by sampling problems. Plots of this simple type are sometimes adequate to reveal or at least suggest the existence of persistent latitudinally controlled anomalies as well as a response to the planetary temperature gradient.

Diversity Contour Maps

The work of Tillyard (1914) represents an early attempt, if not the earliest, to handle diversity data in a contoured form. While he applied the technique only to one group of insects within a single zoogeographic region, he suggested the possibility of both worldwide plots and the relation of plots to ecological conditions. Wells (1954) went much farther and showed in a contour map the distribution and diversity of hermatypic corals in the Indo-Pacific faunal province. The distribution and diversity of planktonic Foraminifera were shown on a worldwide basis by Stehli and Helsley (1963) and that for pelecypods by Stehli et al. (1966). Simpson (1964) has presented a contoured map of the specific diversity of mammals in North America which is based on extremely refined data. It is clear from these studies and from the maps in succeeding pages that, in general, the contoured diversity data show the presence of a pronounced response to the planetary temperature gradient. Superimposed on this relatively simple surface are many aberrations caused by various sources of noise. While a considerable portion of the noise represents a real response to environmental conditions and, as noted above, may include real and valuable information, it does not relate directly to the planetary temperature gradient and thus detracts from the clarity of the contoured surface and the precision with which the rotational pole position may be determined.

Trend Surface Analysis

The trend surface technique of applying best-fitting mathematical surfaces to geologic data has been discussed by Grant (1957), Krumbein (1959), and Mandelbaum (1963) and has been quite widely applied in the treatment of geologic data, particularly in stratigraphic studies. The technique is readily adapted for use with diversity gradients by determining the location of control points on an x–y coordinate system applied to a suitable map. It is possible by this technique to make a reasonably good separation between the primary form of a diversity surface (signal) and secondary effects which tend to distort it (noise). The technique is thus most valuable in the problem of rotational pole location. For most purposes, a quadratic surface fitted to diversity data as located on a map appears to be quite adequate to separate signal from noise, and the inflection of the surface approximately locates the equator, as shown by Stehli and Helsley (1963). The distortions inherent in the map projection used as a base in calculating such a surface as well as the "edge effects" resulting from lack of control at the edges of a map may make the technique undesirable if maximum resolution is required. When a higher level of resolution is required, the diversity data may be fitted with a spherical harmonic surface which avoids the distortions inherent in the use of maps. A second-order spherical harmonic is generally adequate to fit the primary form of the diversity surface.

POSSIBLE CAUSES OF ORGANIC DIVERSITY

Viewed at the most basic level, it appears that diversity gradients must result directly or indirectly from the existence of a latitudinally controlled gradient in the efficiency of solar energy capture. As yet, information is not sufficiently detailed or precise to permit recognition of either the solar energy gradient directly or the planetary temperature gradient, itself an indirect expression of the basic energy gradient, as the more probable cause of diversity. Regardless of which may ultimately prove to be directly responsible, it seems certain, since organisms may be considered as energy-using machines, that a higher level of available energy near the equator must, during the course of a year, result in a greater total biomass[3] there.

Two mechanisms might be suggested for the development of greater biomass, in the regions of highest energy flux. The condition might occur through the development of a constant number of species characterized by increasing numbers of individuals per unit area toward the equator. It might also occur if the number of individuals per species changed little or not at all as a function of latitude while the number of species increased as the equator is approached.

It has been suggested by Klopfer and MacArthur (1960) that, at least among the passerine birds, the number of individuals per unit area within species decreases as the equator is approached. If this conclusion is generally correct, the increased biomass is not achieved by increase in the number of individuals within a species. On the contrary, it appears, and much of the evidence presented here will tend to show, that biomass increases toward the equator by proliferation in the number of species (or higher taxa for that matter). It is interesting to speculate, as many have done, about the factors that have caused the development of increased biomass more through the evolution of greater numbers of species than through larger populations within the species. The problem appears to be one of population dynamics or evolutionary rates, or both, and probably is more susceptible to biological than paleontological attack. One approach is suggested by Klopfer and MacArthur (1961), who have noted that tropical forms exhibit a

3. Exceptions might be imagined in cases in which secondary effects locally assume the primary control. The availability of chemical nutrients in the sea might provide such an example in areas of upwelling or convergence.

greater tolerance for niche overlap than do those of higher latitudes. On the other hand, Manten (1953), using evidence based on the occurrence of polyploids in ferns, has provided evidence suggesting that evolution may indeed be proceeding at a higher rate in tropical than in temperate areas.

A detailed understanding of the mechanism through which diversity gradients are produced would be of much interest. For our present purposes it is adequate, however, that a relationship be established between latitude and diversity, and this can be done empirically.

It is pertinent to this investigation to consider whether or not diversity gradients characterize fossil organisms as well as those of the present day. In an extended review of possible causes of diversity, Fischer (1960) suggests that the relatively diverse biotas of the warm, humid tropics owe their existence to a more constant environment and to relative freedom from climatic disasters. His discussion makes it clear that he considers the vicissitudes of Pleistocene glaciation and associated rigorous climate to be, to some degree, responsible for the low diversity of polar regions at the present time. Undoubtedly this is correct, and we may expect severe polar climates to cause steepened diversity gradients since they tend to push the point of zero diversity equatorward without necessarily affecting in a substantial way diversity levels in equatorial regions.

It is worth a moment's digression to ascertain whether diversity gradients could be wholly due perhaps to "climatic disasters" of the Pleistocene; if this were the case, one could not contemplate the use of diversity gradients in non-glacial intervals of geologic time. Two tests of this hypothesis suggest themselves. The more direct, but at the same time the more difficult, would be to plot the diversity distribution of some group of organisms for an aglacial interval of the earth's history, such as the late Mesozoic or early Cenozoic. Such a test is underway but, as yet, complete data are not available. The second method, though less direct, is far easier. One can examine the diversity of groups of organisms whose distribution lies wholly within the tropics and subtropics—the warm, humid and generally constant environment relatively free of climatic disasters to which Fischer refers. If diversity begins to decrease well within this highly stable region, it would seem to suggest that climatic disasters play, at most, a minor part in the long-term propagation of diversity gradients. In Figure 12 we see the generic diversity of the butterfly family Danaidae, plotted against latitude. The entire range of this family occurs within the tropical-subtropical zone lying between 25° N and 25° S, yet a pronounced diversity gradient is evident within a few degrees of the equator. This pattern in diversity is commonly observed. One must conclude, it appears, that diversity gradients now commonly exist within areas essentially free of climatic disasters, and that they therefore would probably occur even through subtropical conditions extended to the poles, though doubtless the slope would generally be more gradual. There seems to be every reason, therefore, to believe that diversity gradients should characterize aglacial times as well as our present glacial or near-glacial climatic conditions.

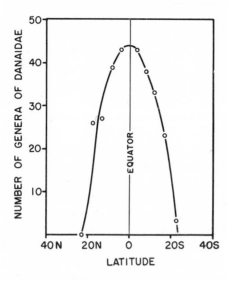

Fig. 12. Latitude vs. generic diversity plot for the butterfly family (Danaidae), showing the abrupt decline in diversity which begins within a few degrees of the equator and reaches zero only slightly beyond 20° north and south latitudes, still well within the tropical—subtropical faunal realm (data from Hovanitz, 1958).

EXAMPLES OF RECENT DIVERSITY GRADIENTS

In order to test the model developed above, it has been necessary to study the diversity of a number of groups of Recent organisms. The accumulation of sufficient data to permit consideration of diversity on a worldwide scale has proved both difficult and time-consuming. It appears, predictably I suppose, that biologists have accorded most attention to organisms that are harmful to man's activities, or are of commercial value, or are particularly striking in appearance. Most other groups have received only sporadic and local attention. This problem is especially noticeable among marine invertebrates, an unfortunate situation for the geologist who, in applying diversity gradients to the fossil record, must deal primarily with this assemblage. Because of the limited information available for many groups, some originally scheduled for testing were ultimately abandoned and some forms unlikely to have left a fossil record have been used instead. Nevertheless, an attempt has been made to test representatives of many environments and to include as well some groups that show atypical distributions.

Plots of Diversity Versus Latitude

The presentation of diversity data as a simple plot against latitude can be quite useful as a first approximation, though it lacks the third dimension. This simple treatment is sometimes adequate to reveal whether or not the diversity is truly related to the latitudinal framework being employed. In all the plots shown in Figures 13 to 15, the procedure of selecting the highest diversity value occurring within each 5° latitude class has been followed. This treatment of the data reduces the scatter due to inequalities in the thoroughness of collecting and study at many localities as well as that due to other sources of noise. The data are shown in semi-log plots. The smooth curves applied to the data have been fitted to the higher values in each distribution because, in view of the prevalence of incomplete collection, it is considered that these points are most likely to approach the true maximum diversity.

Though diversity versus latitude plots are very simple, they demonstrate the existence of several general kinds of diversity gradients. The most common form appears to be the curve that declines rather symmetrically both north and south from the equator. The decrease in diversity is frequently apparent within a few degrees of the equator, though the slope of the gradient may vary considerably as may the latitude at which the gradient reaches a zero diversity level. An example is seen in Figure 13A; a variant showing a relatively constant high diversity through the tropics and subtropics with a rapid decline in the temperate zones is seen in Figure 13B.

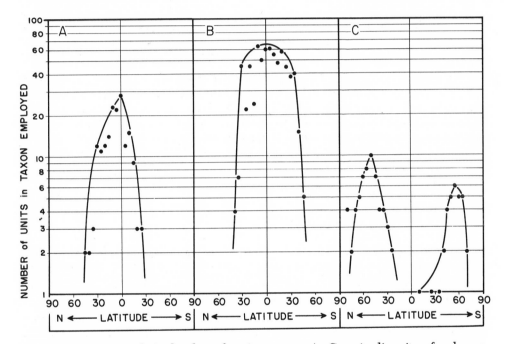

Fig. 13. Diversity vs. latitude plots of various types. A: Generic diversity of palms, a leptokurtic distribution pattern found in many tropical–subtropical forms (see data sources in Appendix). B: Specific diversity of Cypraeid gastropods, showing a diversity distribution pattern frequently encountered in tropical–subtropical shallow water benthonic animals (data from Schilder, 1938–39). C: The atypical distributions sometimes encountered among small groups occupying only a portion of the total ecological niche available to the larger group to which they belong. Southern hemisphere data refer to specific diversity of penguins (data from Peters, 1931). The northern hemisphere data refer to genera of Alcids (Peters, 1931). For all groups the data plotted are the highest diversity in each 5° latitude class and the curve has been fitted to the higher points which presumably show less effect of poor sampling (an exception occurs in the Alcids where one point is clearly due to the disturbing effect of the Gulf Stream).

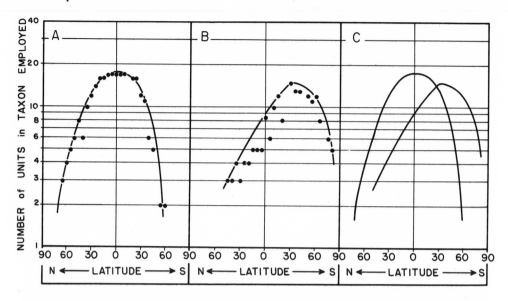

Fig. 14. Diversity vs. latitude for genera of Recent mosquitoes. A: Highest number of mosquito genera in 5° latitude classes plotted against present-day latitude framework. B: Highest number of mosquito genera in 5° latitude classes plotted against paleomagnetic latitude framework for the Permo-Carboniferous as given by Irving and Brown (1966). The deformation of the curve when applied to the improper latitude framework is evident. C: Curves from A and B superimposed for comparison. It is clear that plots of this kind could be used as a first approximation test of whether or not a particular latitude framework is related to a given set of data (data from Stone et al., 1959).

The diversity of mosquitoes at the generic level (Fig. 14A) shows a somewhat asymmetric distribution with a relatively abrupt decline in the southern hemisphere and a more gentle decline in the north. Knowing that the distribution of land in the two hemispheres is unequal, strongly favoring the north, one might suggest that the asymmetry in slope reflects this situation. That one could present such a suggestion based on a fossil distribution is, however, questionable.

The diversity of some terrestrial animals can show persistent anomalies that may be quite informative. The diversity of amphibians, lizards, and snakes shown in Figure 15 A–C represents such cases. Each of these groups shows a marked shoulder in both hemispheres between 15° and 30°, which, it seems reasonable to conclude, represents reduced diversity due to the unfavorable conditions associated with the major desert belts tending to occur in each hemisphere between these latitudes. Such a phenomenon might be recognized in the fossil record of some appropriate group of organisms (pulmonate gastropods, perhaps), at least during the Cenozoic and, thus, perhaps the nature and extent of expansion and contraction of climatic zones during climatic changes would become apparent.

Each of the diversity distributions so far discussed is more or less typical in being equatorially centered. This seems to be the common pattern for widely dis-

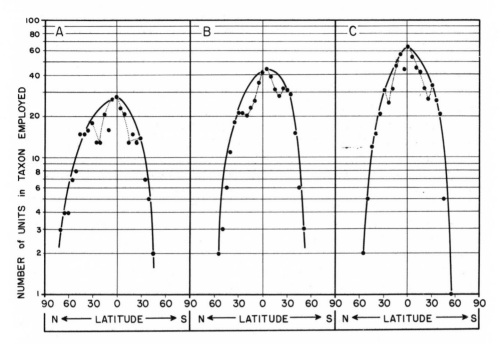

Fig. 15. Diversity vs. latitude plots for three groups of terrestrial poikilotherms, showing what appear to be latitude-related anomalies in the region 15–30° that are probably a response to the less favorable conditions prevailing in the desert regions often found in those latitudes. Data showing highest number of genera in 5° latitude classes. Solid curve smoothed through points indicating highest diversity, dotted curve following the points suggestive of persistent anomaly. A: Genera of amphibians. B: Genera of lizards. C: Genera of snakes (sources of data given in Appendix).

tributed groups occupying relatively broad adaptive zones. Within major groups there is, however, more or less specialization of subgroups for particular subzones which may or may not be equatorially centered. The penguins in the southern hemisphere and their northern hemisphere ecological counterparts, the alcids, both show diversity gradients which are not equatorially centered (Fig. 13C). Despite the fact that neither of these groups is equatorially centered, each shows a diversity gradient that slopes both equatorward and poleward from an optimum zone.

Plots of diversity against latitude respond quickly to the use of a grossly invalid latitudinal framework by departure of the resulting curve from the typical equatorially centered form. This property imparts to them a potential value in providing a simple test of the latitudinal configurations required by the various continental drift and polar wandering curves that have been proposed. As a simple test, the continental masses have been placed in the positions required for Permo-Carboniferous time according to the paleomagnetic model presented by Irving and Brown (1966). To this model of the earth has been fitted the diversity gradient for mosquitoes. The control points have retained their observed values and their relative positions on the continental blocks, but their latitudes have been reassigned to fit the Permo-Carboniferous model. A comparison of the resulting plot (Fig. 14B) with the plot using the correct latitudinal values (those of the present earth model to which the mosquito data correctly apply; Fig. 14A), shows clearly the distortion resulting from the use of an improper earth model. It seems evident that even so simple a use of diversity data as the plot against latitude can perhaps distinguish between probable and improbable configurations of the continents with respect to latitude. A possibility of confusion with diversity distributions which actually are not equatorially centered (e.g. penguins) remains, however, and a discrimination between correct and incorrect latitude frameworks would have to depend on the use of data for many groups, the use of groups of high taxonomic level, and the recognition and elimination thereby of the relatively infrequent nonequatorial distributions. This source of ambiguity suggests, however, that a means of data presentation with resolution superior to that of the latitude-versus-diversity graph is to be preferred in testing goodness of fit of diversity to various latitudinal frameworks.

CONTOURED RAW DIVERSITY DATA

Though plots of diversity versus latitude may yield considerable information, a three-dimensional display is frequently more useful. A plot of this type may be produced by contouring raw diversity data located on an appropriate base map. For some purposes, the raw data contain too much detail, and simplifying procedures are required. In many instances, however, the detail obtainable in raw diversity data may provide useful information. The contoured diversity data for a number of groups of Recent organisms is presented below, and attention is called to some of its potentially useful properties. It is desirable to consider these plots in terms of the major and minor responses they reveal. Because it seems probable that the major responses are most likely to be of geological significance, they will be discussed first.

Major Responses

The north–south gradient. The most impressive response to be seen in the plots is the strong north–south gradient revealed by each of them. It was pointed out earlier that this gradient may not always be uniquely identified in the contoured diversity of endemic groups, and a plot for the pheasants (Phasianinae) was shown as an example (Fig. 11). In the plots of worldwide groups of organisms show in Figures 16 through 23, this powerful gradient can be readily and uniquely recognized.

Two examples of the north–south gradient may be singled out for discussion. Figure 7 shows the raw diversity surface for mosquitoes (Culicidae) at the generic level. This is a very widespread group, and it reaches quite high levels of

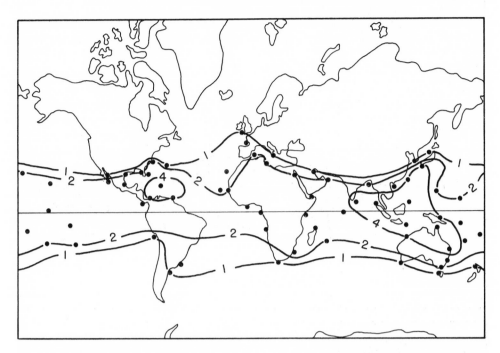

Fig. 16. Contoured raw diversity data for Recent species in the pelecypod family Pinnidae. Although the diversity is consistently low, the relationship to the equator is clear. Note, however, the apparent existence of the Caribbean faunal province associated with the extensive, warm, shallow-water shelf in this region (data from Turner and Rosewater, 1958; Rosewater, 1961; Keen, 1958; and pers. comm. from Rosewater).

generic diversity in the equatorial regions. The gradient is relatively flat near the equator but declines more rapidly near the margins of the subtropics. Where data continue into the high latitudes in the northern hemisphere, the gradient flattens abruptly north of the general region of the temperate–subtropic boundary and continues with almost negligible slope essentially to the northern extremities of land.

The contoured raw diversity surface for species of the bivalve family Pinnidae shows another extreme (Fig. 16). In this case the total distribution is limited to the tropics, subtropics, and the warmest parts of the temperate zone. The diversity is nowhere very high, but the gradient is nevertheless quite clear.

Because the north–south gradient in diversity distributions is so strong and of such potential interest in locating the position of the equator and rotational poles, it is often desirable to see it in a simpler form than the contoured raw data permit. Further attention will be given in a succeeding section to the north–south gradients and to means of simplifying them. It is clear, however, that all the other features of the diversity distributions, no matter how strong, are subordinate to the latitude dependence in the examples studied.

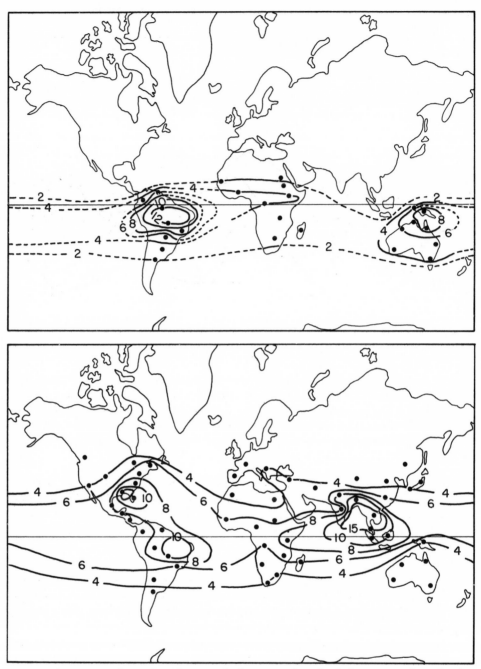

Fig. 17. A: Contoured raw data for specific diversity of turtles belonging to the suborder Pleurodira. Note the principal development of this group slightly south of the equator. The fossil record of this group is geographically more extensive, and range contraction may be due to competition with Cryptodires. Note also the two strong faunal provinces in the relatively isolated southern continents of South America and Australia–New Guinea and the relative paucity of Pleurodires in Africa–the least isolated southern continent (data from Wermuth and Mertens, 1961).

B: Generic diversity of Recent turtle genera. Both Cryptodira and Pleurodiras are included (data from Wermuth and Mertens, 1961).

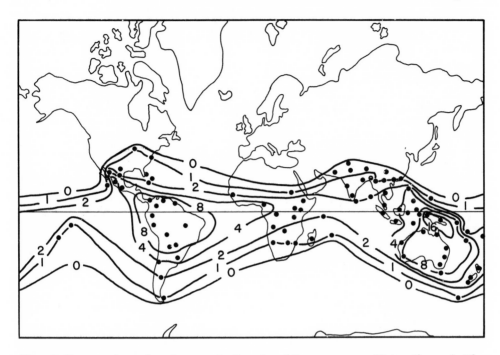

Fig. 18. Contoured raw data for generic diversity of Recent parrots (Psittaciformes). The north–south diversity gradient is apparent, but the center of diversity is slightly south of the equator, especially in the Australia–New Guinea region. Quite possibly the parrots, like the Pleurodira, are a declining group since they are not strongly developed in the northern continents, are weakly developed in Africa, and show their principal development in the most isolated regions—South America and the Australia–New Guinea area (data from Peters, 1937).

Faunal provinces. Second only to the north–south gradient in the strength with which it is expressed is what might be termed the faunal province effect. This effect is evident in both plots already considered (Figs. 7 and 16). Perhaps it is somewhat misleading to use the term faunal province since it actually is a diversity province that is being considered, but to a very large extent the two appear to be coincident and the familiar term is retained in the discussion that follows.

If we turn our attention to Figure 7, we find that at the generic level, at least, two pronounced faunal provinces exist for the Culicidae. One of these, which might be called East Indian, includes India, extreme Southeast Asia, and the East Indies, and shows a maximum number of seventeen culicid genera. The second, or South American province, includes equatorial South America and part of Central America, and also exhibits a maximum of seventeen Culicid genera. The east–west gradient in diversity that exists between these two faunal provinces is quite strong. The generic diversity drops, for instance, to 75 per cent of its maximum value in the equatorial regions of Africa and falls far lower (50 per cent) on the islands of the central Pacific. Despite this fact, the east–west gradient resulting

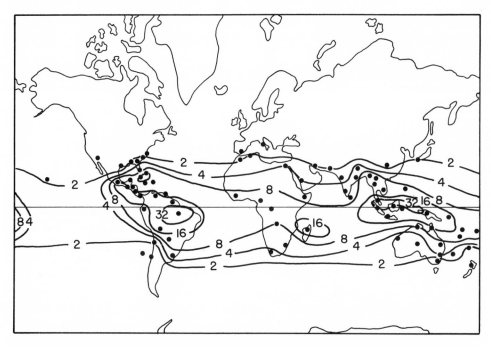

Fig. 19. Contoured raw data for generic diversity of Recent palms. This group shows a diversity distribution centered very close to the equator. Two centers of diversity occur, one in the East Indies and one in South America. Africa shows low diversity even at the equator. Madagascar, however, far more isolated than mainland Africa, shows much higher diversity. There appears to be a suggestion in the data that palms are a waning group tending to decline in competition with some other group except in relatively isolated regions (data sources in Appendix, but map checked by H. E. Moore).

from the faunal province effect is subordinate to the north–south gradient. The attenuation that occurs between the centers of faunal provinces is presumably a result of dispersal barriers of one kind or another. In the case of terrestrial organisms such as the culicids just considered, the barrier is commonly a major expanse of ocean, though it may also be a temperature or humidity barrier lying athwart an otherwise suitable land connection. The effectiveness of dispersal barriers is related to the dispersal potential of a particular group of organisms. Forms that can fly, swim, be distributed by the wind, or withstand exposure to salt water are likely to be most uniformly distributed. Those organisms that lack such mobility, and are in addition strongly restricted by temperature, tend to show the most pronounced faunal provinces. The relative strength or weakness of faunal provinces is, however, not solely a function of the present environment but may reflect, as well, such features as the place and time of origin, climatic events of the recent past, or the effectiveness of a particular group in coping with the competing organisms.

Faunal provinces are abundantly represented in the marine as well as the ter-restrial biota. The diversity gradient of species of Pinnidae (Fig. 16) shows a representative example. In this case there is a strong Indo-Pacific province cen-tered in the East Indian region and a smaller, secondary province in the Carib-bean. These provinces seem to a large degree to coincide with extensive areas of warm water and shallow shelf. Marine faunal provinces are clearly limited by temperature barriers lying across otherwise suitable shallow-water migration routes. They are also restricted by great expanses of deep ocean such as the east-ern Pacific, a feature presumably related to the duration of planktonic stages in larval life and to the velocity and direction of ocean currents.

It is of some interest to examine a little more closely the nature of similari-ties and differences in faunal provinces as indicated by diversity data. If the Culi-cidae are taken as a relatively well-studied example (Fig. 7), the two major faunal provinces already discussed, each containing a maximum of seventeen genera, dominate the distribution. One might suppose that these regions owe their greater diversity to the occurrence in the humid tropics of a greater part of a more or less worldwide mosquito fauna and that a great number of genera would be common to these two areas and absent elsewhere. But this is not the case. The two faunal provinces (Sumatra and Brazil have been taken to represent them) do show eight genera in common, but each of these eight also occurs in equatorial Africa and is thus pantropical in its distribution. The genera which produce the extraordinarily high diversity in the two main faunal provinces are mutually exclusive. This fact is significant because it suggests that diversity at any place will develop to the level dictated by the number of ecological niches available to a particular group and that this is in a large part, at least, latitude-dependent. An interesting ques-tion remains, however. Why does Africa, with apparently similar geographic op-portunities, have a lower diversity than other equatorial regions? Are there actu-ally fewer ecological niches available to mosquitoes in Africa, perhaps due to competition with other organisms? Or is the lower diversity a time-dependent effect due to a temporary disequilibrium caused by climatic or some other major change?

Archaic forms. A feature of the distribution of faunal provinces, particularly among terrestrial organisms, is the concentration of archaic groups in the south-ern hemisphere. The diversity distributions seem to support the conclusions of Simpson (1953) and others that the most important feature of the southern conti-nents permitting the existence of archaic biotic elements is their relative isolation from the nearly continuous northern hemisphere landmass rather than their once closer association with each other.

A particularly interesting example of this phenomenon of persistence of archaic types in the southern hemisphere may be seen among the turtles, as an-cient a group of reptiles as still exists. Turtles belonging to the order Pleurodira (Fig. 17) comprise a small group (thirteen genera) which are at present confined to the southern hemisphere. The fossil record indicates, however, that they pre-viously occurred in the northern hemisphere as well (Colbert, 1955). The Pleuro-

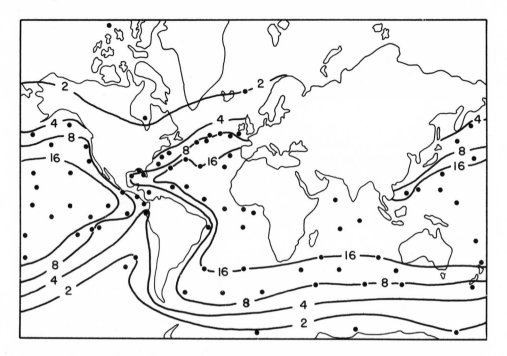

Fig. 20. Contoured raw diversity for Recent species of planktonic Foraminifera. Equatorial centering of the diversity gradient is clear, as is the major source of noise introduced by ocean current transport of these planktonic organisms (for data sources see Appendix).

dira diversity shows two centers, one in the very isolated New Guinea–Australia region and a second in South America which, until late Tertiary time, was almost equally isolated. Both of these diversity centers lie slightly south of the equator, probably because of competitive pressure from the Cryptodira, which has allowed them to flourish only in isolated areas. Africa, the least isolated of the southern continents in question, shows a sparse development of Pleurodira (three genera), which have apparently been reduced by Cryptodira (nine genera) competition. In this case, however, the surviving Pleurodira and the Cryptodira have apparently achieved a balance, since the equilibrium condition of an equatorially centered diversity maximum exists for both groups (Figs. 17 A and B).

A further example of this same phenomenon may be seen among the far more mobile parrots (Fig. 18). This group of birds, though reasonably strong fliers presumably capable of wide dispersal, shows a distribution strongly skewed toward the southern hemisphere. If the now extinct Carolina parakeet were eliminated from the plot, distribution would be even more asymmetrical. Once more, Africa shows a very low diversity while both South America and the Australian region show high diversity. It is probably reasonable to assume that the Psittaci-formes, as a group, are in competition with some aggressive northern hemisphere group of birds which is gradually displacing them.

Still a further striking example may be seen among the palms—the only group of plants that was studied (Fig. 19). Again, diversity is very low in Africa but high in South America and in the East Indian region. In this case, both the dispersal centers are equatorial rather than skewed toward the south. An interesting sidelight in the distribution of palm genera in Africa is the fact that the isolated island of Madagascar has not suffered the depletion of its palm flora that has characterized the mainland (8 genera vs. 18). Presumably Madagascar, by virtue of its isolation, has preserved more of an archaic palm flora than has survived in mainland Africa.

Minor Responses

The minor responses that can be easily identified in contoured raw diversity data seem to be primarily related to anomalies in the planetary temperature gradient, marked variations in rainfall, etc. The most pronounced of these responses, so far noted, is that due to ocean currents. The effect is easily seen in the diversity distribution of planktonic Foraminifera (Fig. 20), which responds negatively to cold currents and positively to warm currents (Stehli, 1965).

A second source of minor variation in diversity surfaces based on raw data is due to inadequacies of collection and study. An example of extreme taxonomic splitting and the resulting anomaly in the diversity surface for species of bivalves has been pointed out by Stehli et al. (1966). The same investigators have shown that the use of higher taxa and standardization of some taxonomic system to provide internal consistency can greatly reduce aberrations due to differences in taxonomic treatment.

Atypical Diversity Patterns

Although the equatorially centered diversity gradient is by far the most common type and apparently represents an equilibrium condition for most organisms, there are, as we have seen, modifications in this pattern which may be related to the archaic nature of certain biotic elements. Far more extreme departures from the equatorially centered pattern exist, however, and their significance must be assessed. Two groups of sea birds, the penguins and the alcids (Fig. 21), illustrate atypical distributions.

Each of these two groups of birds shows a diversity distribution centered far from the equator. The penguins show the simpler of the two distribution patterns with a well-defined optimum zone, containing four or more species, which occupies the region between 45° S and 60° S. Toward the south, diversity decreases to two species along the Antarctic coast. Toward the north, diversity decreases to zero between 30° S and the equator, but the boundary is irregular, and it seems

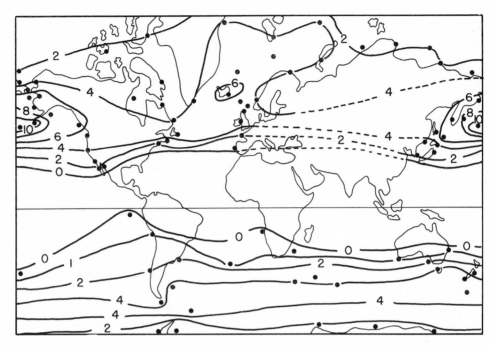

Fig. 21. Contoured raw diversity data for species of penguins in the southern hemisphere and genera of alcids in the northern hemisphere. Latitude dependence is clear in both cases, as is a gradient in diversity declining both poleward and equatorward from the region of optimum conditions. The relatively simple surface circulation pattern of the southern hemisphere is reflected in the penguin data which show a large departure from simple latitude dependence only in the region of the Humboldt Current west of South America. The much more complex current pattern of the northern hemisphere and in particular the Gulf Stream is reflected in the greater complexity of the alcid diversity. Atypical distributions of this kind seem to be relatively rare, at least in large groups of organisms tending to occupy major environmental niches fully. They should probably be avoided in geological applications of diversity, though they can be used if necessary.

clear that these fish-eating birds are influenced in their distribution by the existence of upwelling water masses with their high nutrient values and great productivity.

The alcids (puffins, auks, etc.) are essentially the ecological equivalent in the northern hemisphere of the penguins (in fact their convergence produced the penguin-like, flightless, and now extinct great auk). The alcids show a zone of maximum diversity lying generally between 45° N and 65° N. From this optimum zone, diversity decreases toward both pole and equator. The center of this distribution, like that of the penguins, is essentially parallel to latitude. The more complex oceanic circulation induced in the high latitudes of the northern hemisphere by the occurrence of continental masses produces variations in the diversity pattern of alcids which are more pronounced than those of the penguins. The Gulf

Stream, for instance, produces a pronounced northern deflection of high diversity levels.

Although both of the atypical groups considered do vary in diversity primarily as a function of latitude and so could be used in pole location, they also show a response to current-induced variations in temperature and productivity that constitute an important source of noise. For this reason they are less desirable as material in the geologic application of diversity than are more typically distributed groups. Atypical distributions seem generally to reflect specialization for some subzone within a major adaptive zone. The problems they may cause can commonly be avoided by employing the larger group occupying the entire zone rather than a small group occupying only part of it. If, e.g., all birds, or even all sea birds, were used as the basis for a diversity gradient, the distribution would be expected once more to show an equatorial center. This suggests, as has been advocated for other reasons as well, that diversity gradients are best studied at high taxonomic levels if the results are to be applied to geologic problems of planetary scale (Stehli et al., 1966).

Despite the fact that contouring raw diversity data does little to suppress the effect of noise in the data, it is nonetheless commonly adequate to show clearly the form of the primary surface. Because this is true, such contoured diversity maps are frequently sufficient to provide a test of the latitudinal framework used in plotting. In Figure 22 the control stations for mosquito diversity on each continental block have been placed in the positions suggested by Irving and Brown (1966) for Permo-Carboniferous time. When the diversity gradient is contoured for this model of the earth, it becomes readily apparent that the fit is poor. Comparison of a present earth model in Figure 7 with the paleomagnetic earth model in Figure 22 for Permo-Carboniferous time shows clearly the deterioration of good fit that accompanies the use of an improper latitudinal framework.

APPLICATION OF SURFACE-FITTING TECHNIQUES

As we have just seen, contoured raw diversity data can clearly show the general nature of the strong north–south component of a diversity distribution and suggest the general position of the equator or the poles, but an exact location of these cardinal reference points is difficult. The utility of surface-fitting techniques in providing unique equatorial or polar locations from the diversity distributions has been noted previously and will now be further considered. By the use of these techniques, one deliberately suppresses those components of the diversity surface not related to the primary form of the gradient. For this reason, the data in this form do not show to a significant degree the secondary and tertiary effects that have just been discussed in considering contoured raw diversity surfaces. As applied to diversity data, fitted mathematical surfaces of this kind are useful primarily in problems related entirely or principally to the contribution of the planetary energy capture and temperature gradients to diversity.

Two kinds of surface-fitting procedures have been found useful in the prob-

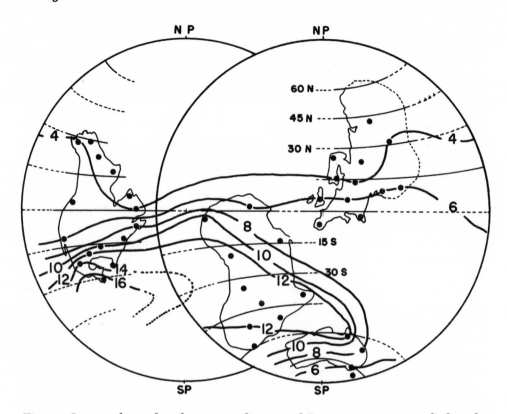

Fig. 22. Contoured raw data for generic diversity of Recent mosquitoes applied to the continents dispersed according to paleomagnetic latitude determinations as given by Irving and Brown (1966) for the Permo-Carboniferous. (Irving and Brown did not locate South America, and data for that region are therefore omitted.) The intense distortion of the gradient for generic diversity of mosquitoes that accompanies the use of an improper latitude framework shows that contoured diversity data should be quite effective in discriminating proper from improper latitude frameworks.

lem of pole location from diversity gradient data. One can be applied to the data for a single hemisphere as seen in polar projection, by calculating the best-fitting nonorthogonal polynomial surface (Grant, 1957; Krumbein, 1959; Mandelbaum, 1963). Normal, equatorially centered diversity distributions which drop to minimum values in polar regions have a basically bowl-shaped form, as may be seen by inspection of the raw data (Fig. 23). The primary form of such a distribution may be expressed by a surface with but a single inflection (second-order surface). Since the surface is not allowed further inflections, it is not free to fit in any detail the secondary or tertiary features of the distribution and thus must provide the best fit for the primary feature of the whole distribution. The point of zero rate of change on this surface (lowest point in terms of diversity) will, according to our model, represent the position of the rotational pole.

In attempting to apply the diversity gradient techniques for pole location to

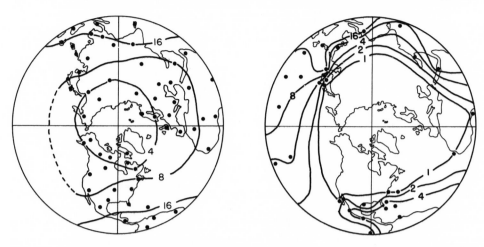

Fig. 23. Contoured surface drawn on the generic diversity of Recent mosquitoes for the northern hemisphere (see Appendix for data sources).

Fig. 24. Contoured surface drawn on raw data for species diversity of the gastropod genus *Strombus* on north polar projection map. Note the very strong faunal province effect in the Indo-Pacific region and the much smaller one in the Caribbean region (see Appendix for sources of data).

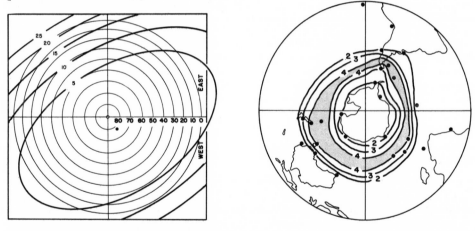

Fig. 25. Second-order non-orthogonal polynomial surface best fitting the northern hemisphere species diversity data for *Strombus*. The narrowness of the equatorial belt occupied by *Strombus* and the strength of the Indo-Pacific faunal province (see Fig. 24) cause the fitted surface to yield a pole position that is shifted 12° from the true rotational pole position in a direction away from the high diversity of the Indo-Pacific region.

Fig. 26. Contoured surface drawn on the raw data for the species diversity of penguins, a group wholly restricted to the southern hemisphere. Note that even though the distribution is atypical in not being equatorially centered, there is nevertheless a latitudinally controlled zone of maximum diversity from which a gradient slopes both poleward and equatorward. While it is apparent that this distribution could be used for pole location, a surface of relatively high order is required to fit it (see Appendix for data sources).

Fig. 27. Sixth-order nonorthogonal polynomial surface best fitting the species diversity data for penguins. The calculated pole determined from this complex surface is shown as an open circle; the position of the true rotational pole is shown by the black dot.

the fossil record, it appears likely that data of adequate quality and quantity may commonly be found to be available for only one hemisphere. The technique for locating the pole with single-hemisphere data is thus of great potential value, and it has been tested on a number of sets of data in order that its advantages and disadvantages might be determined. We have already seen in Figures 5 and 10 how well the procedure works for actual temperature data and for the diversity data of the mosquitoes at the generic level. Figure 24 representing the diversity of the gastropod genus *Strombus* at the species level suggests a major disadvantage of the single-hemisphere approach. Forms belonging to this tropical genus are restricted to the relatively narrow tropical and subtropical zone around the equator, and there is thus no control over most of the area of the map. Further, there is an immensely strong faunal province effect contributed by the shallow-water shelf areas of the Indo-Pacific. The restricted area covered by control and the strong distorting effect of the powerful faunal province combine to give a pole location far from the rotational pole (Fig. 25). It is clear that when data from a single hemisphere are used, they must be for a widely distributed group (such as mosquitoes; Fig. 10), not for a group restricted to a narrow geographic belt (*Strombus;* Fig. 25). Further, it is desirable to avoid groups that exhibit unusually strong faunal province effects. Invoking these two simple precautions should allow single-hemisphere data to provide pole locations of high accuracy, such as those obtained for the mosquito distribution.

When nonequatorially centered diversity distributions are considered on a single hemisphere, a more complex general form is represented, and a more complex surface is required to fit it. In polar projection, the diversity distribution of penguins (Fig. 26) is no longer approximated best by a simple bowl shape but is instead like a bowl whose edges have been turned down until they touch the table. Such a surface requires not the single inflection of the mosquito data but at least three inflections and thus would require at least a fourth-order polynomial to generate a best-fitting surface. When, as is the case with the penguins, the margins of the bowl are uneven in elevation as well, a still higher order of surface is required. A sixth-order surface fitted to the penguin data is shown in Figure 27. As can be seen, this is a complex surface, and though it does define with considerable accuracy a point of minimum diversity, which according to the model is equal to the rotational pole position, it is more difficult to interpret than the simpler surfaces fitting normal or equatorially centered distributions. Thus, while atypical distributions can be used for pole location, they are less desirable than are typical diversity gradients.

When data for both the northern and southern hemisphere are available, it is of course desirable to employ both in pole location. This can be done through the use of the same nonorthogonal polynomial surfaces discussed above if the data are mapped on a Mercator or some similar projection. An example of this approach, that uses data from species of planktonic Foraminifera, is seen in Figure 28. Such an approach has, however, two significant limitations: it involves gross distortions and introduces severe edge effects at the borders of the map since, in the calculation of the best-fitting surfaces, these edges are not continuous as they would be on a sphere. As Figure 28 shows, these problems are relatively minor and for many applications do not introduce serious problems; they can, however, be avoided by calculating a surface best fitting the diversity data actually distributed on a sphere. This purpose may be accomplished by using best-fitting spherical harmonic surfaces. Typical, equatorially centered diversity gradients which form a belt, tent-shaped in cross section, around the earth may be fitted by a second-order spherical harmonic surface. Such a surface will have a general great-circle symmetry but may also have a minor egg-shaped term; its major inflection, how-

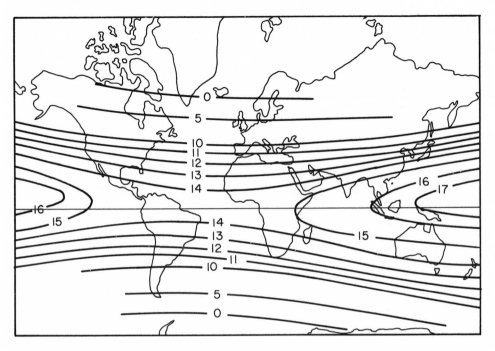

Fig. 28. Second-order nonorthogonal polynomial surface fitted to species diversity data for Recent planktonic Foraminifera. Despite the distortions inherent in the map projection used and the edge effects, especially at the east and west edges of the map, the equatorial plane as determined from the inflection of the surface is remarkably close to that of the true equator. The near coincidence of the two equators is the more remarkable in view of the high noise level in the data induced by the effect of ocean currents on the distribution of these planktonic animals.

ever, represents the position of the diversity equator and thus, according to our model, the position of the geographic equator as well. From the position of this equator it is of course a simple matter to determine the location of the corresponding poles.

The diversity data available for each of the groups of Recent organisms used in testing the model for rotational pole location has been subjected to second-order spherical harmonic analysis where the technique is applicable. For each of these sets of diversity distributions the contoured surface is shown in Figures 29 to 51. Figure 52 shows the location of the pole determined for each set of data. Figure 53 shows the position of the average pole as determined by the Fisher statistic commonly employed in paleomagnetic work and the position of the 95 percent confidence cone around this point. From this plot the diversity gradient model for rotational pole location appears to be a reasonable one, and it provides a rather high resolution result if sufficient data are available. It seems quite clear that if the technique can be successfully applied to the fossil record, the

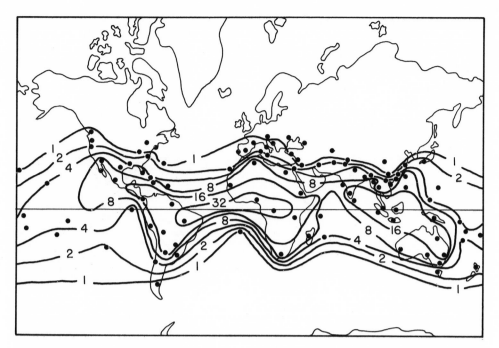

Fig. 29. Contoured surface drawn on the raw diversity data for genera of Recent termites (see Appendix for sources of data).

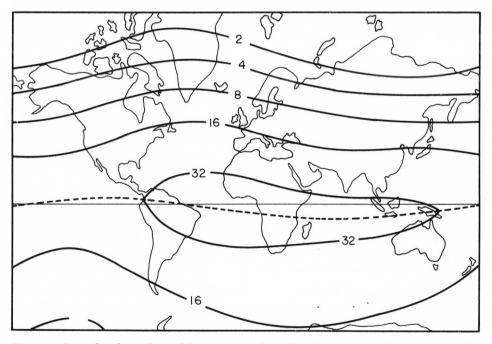

Fig. 30. Second-order spherical harmonic surface fitted to generic diversity data for Recent termites seen in Figure 29.

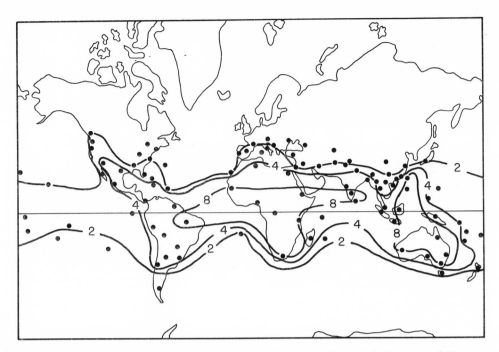

Fig. 31. Contoured surface drawn on the raw data for subfamilial diversity of Recent termites (see Appendix for data sources).

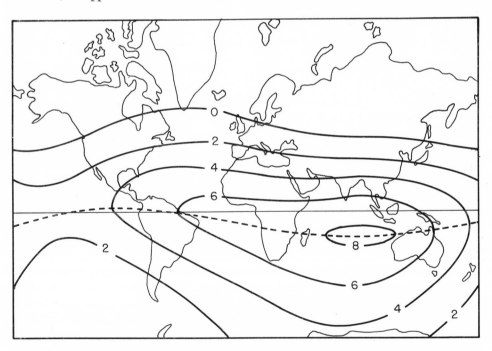

Fig. 32. Second-order spherical harmonic surface fitted to the subfamilial diversity of Recent termites.

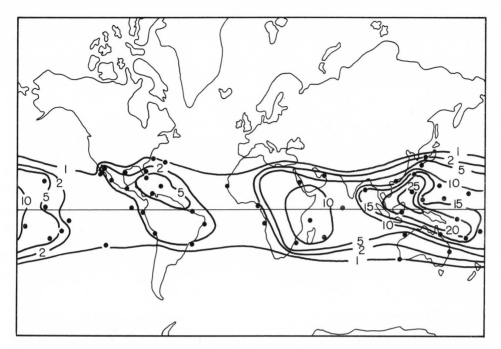

Fig. 33. Contoured surface drawn on the raw data for species diversity in the gastropod genus *Strombus* (see Appendix for data sources).

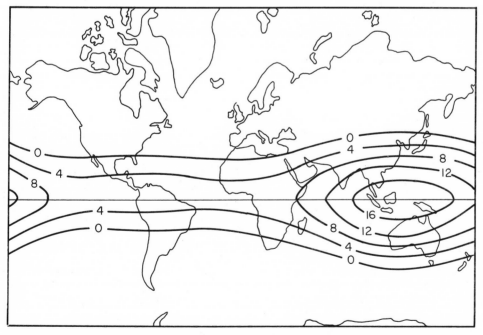

Fig. 34. Second-order spherical harmonic surface fitted to the species diversity of the gastropod genus *Strombus* seen in Figure 33. Note the persistence of a strong effect from the powerful Indo-Pacific faunal province seen also in the raw data in Figures 24 and 33.

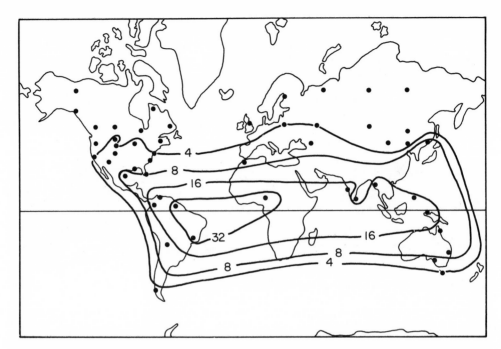

Fig. 35. Contoured surface drawn on the raw data for generic diversity of Recent frogs. Note the paucity of data for Africa, which may be partly responsible for the relatively large departure of the diversity equator from the true equator seen in Figure 36 (see Appendix for data sources).

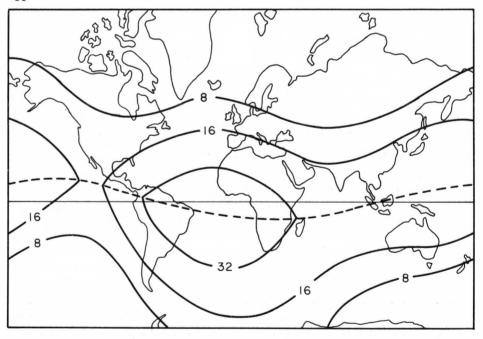

Fig. 36. Second-order spherical harmonic surface fitted to the data for generic diversity of Recent frogs seen in Figure 35.

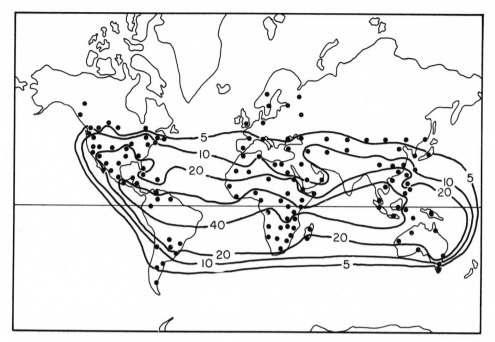

Fig. 37. Contoured surface drawn on the raw diversity data for genera of Recent snakes (see Appendix for data sources).

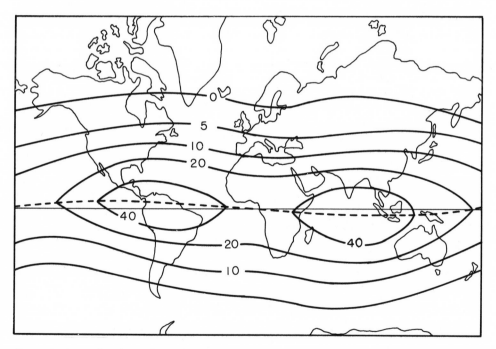

Fig. 38. Second-order spherical harmonic surface fitted to the raw data for generic diversity of Recent snakes seen in Figure 37.

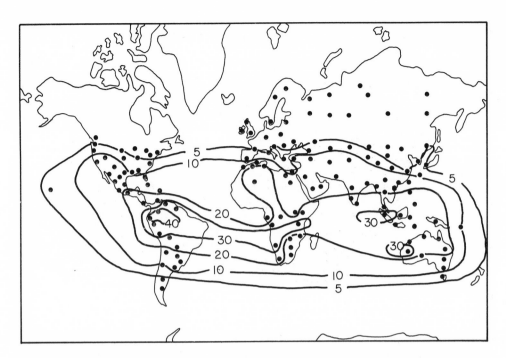

Fig. 39. Contoured surface drawn on the raw diversity data for genera of Recent lizards (see Appendix for data sources).

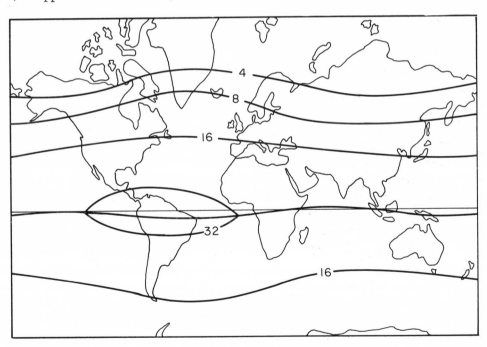

Fig. 40. Second-order spherical harmonic surface fitted to the raw diversity data for Recent genera of lizards seen in Figure 39.

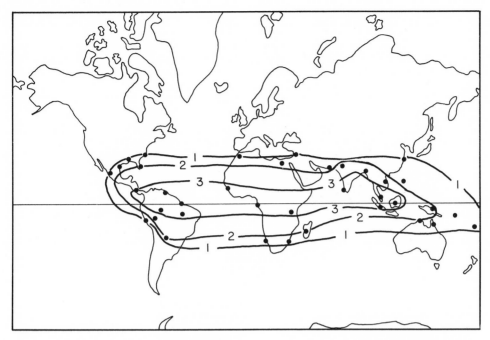

Fig. 41. Contoured surface drawn on the raw data for species diversity of Recent croc-odilians. These data taken from older literature, principally an 1889 catalog of speci-mens in the British Museum and Schmidt (1919, 1928, 1932). Compare it with Figure 43 showing a similar map based on the most recent revision of the crocodilians available to me. Although this was the only such test made, it appears that taxonomic revisions and refinements are not likely to alter significantly the form of a diversity surface once the basic distribution is known (see Appendix for data sources).

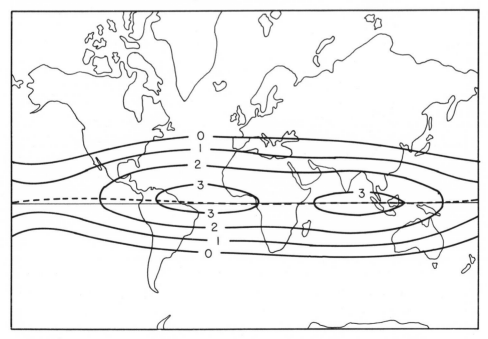

Fig. 42. Second-order spherical harmonic surface fitted to the raw diversity data for species of crocodilians as reported in the older literature and shown in Figure 41.

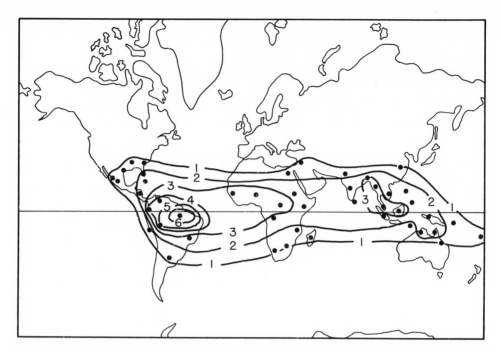

Fig. 43. Contoured surface drawn on the raw diversity data for species of crocodilians as reported in the most recent available revision of the group. Compare with similar surface based on older literature and seen in Figure 41 (see Appendix for data references).

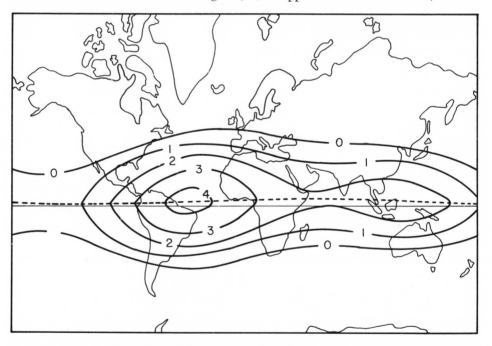

Fig. 44. Second-order spherical harmonic surface fitted to the raw data for species diversity of Recent crocodilians as given by a recent revision of the group (see Appendix for data sources).

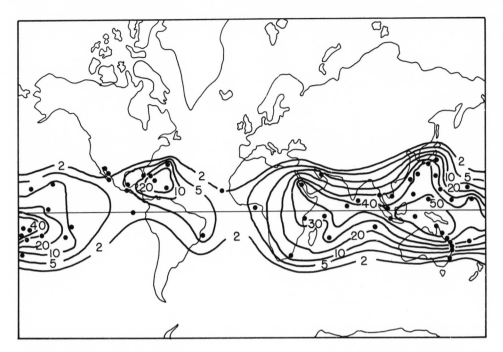

Fig. 45. Contoured surface drawn on the raw data for generic diversity of Recent hermatypic corals (see Appendix for data sources; map checked and corrections made by J. W. Wells).

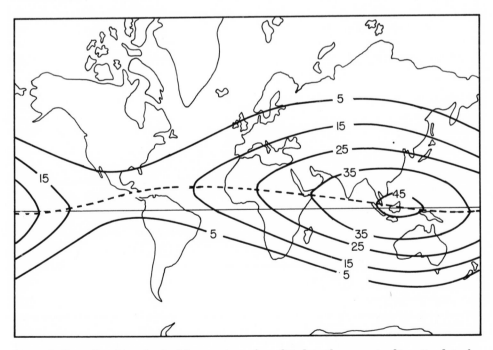

Fig. 46. Second-order spherical harmonic surface fitted to the generic diversity data for Recent hermatypic corals seen in Figure 45.

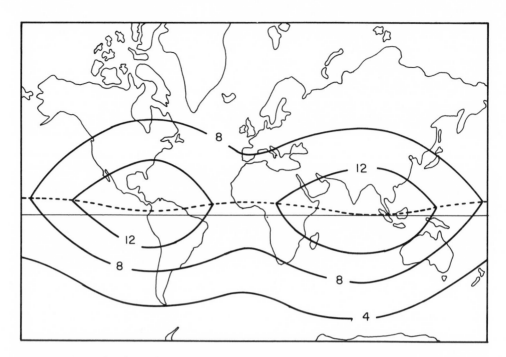

Fig. 47. Second-order spherical harmonic surface fitted to the raw diversity data for genera of Recent turtles (both Cryptodira and Pleurodira) as seen in Figure 17B.

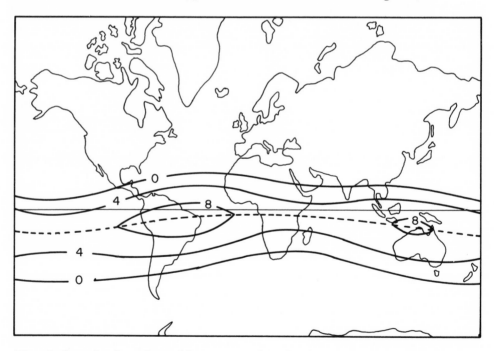

Fig. 48. Second-order spherical harmonic surface fitted to the raw diversity data for species of Pleurodira as shown in Figure 17A.

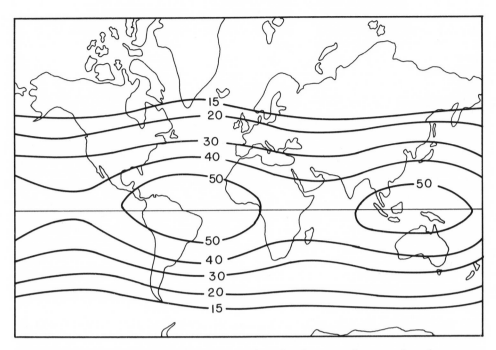

Fig. 49. Second-order spherical harmonic surface fitted to raw diversity data for genera of Recent palms as shown in Figure 19. Note that because the surface must best fit all the data and is prohibited from dropping abruptly to zero where palm distribution ends at the margins of the subtropics, it suggests the presence of palms far north and south of their actual range limits. This does not alter the position of the diversity equator which is the subject of concern here.

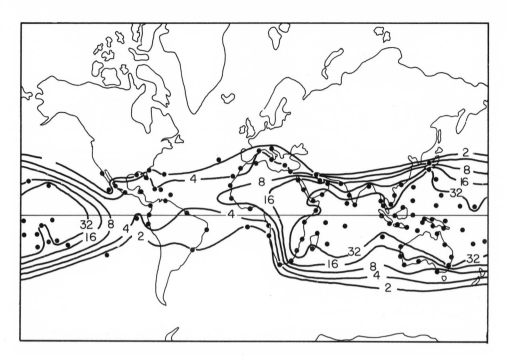

Fig. 50. Contoured surface drawn on the raw diversity data for species diversity of Cypraeid gastropods (see Appendix for data sources).

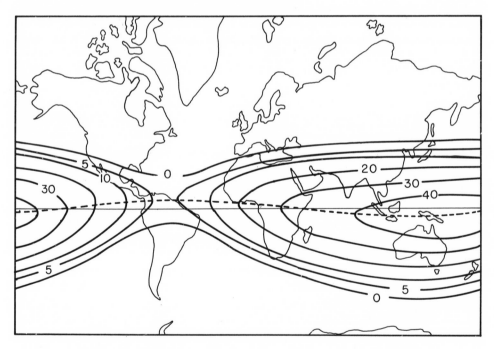

Fig. 51. Second-order spherical harmonic surface fitted to the raw diversity data for Recent species of Cypraeid gastropods seen in Figure 50.

desired tests can be made of the polar wandering and continental drift hypotheses and of the axial dipolar nature of the earth's magnetic field through time.

SOME FURTHER ASPECTS OF DIVERSITY DATA

It has been noted by Stehli et al. (1966) that diversity gradients persist to high taxonomic levels and that this fact enhances the possibility that they can be applied to the fossil record since higher taxonomic categories are more objectively defined and identified than those of lower rank. These authors failed to note, however, another interesting conclusion that can be drawn from the persistence of diversity gradients through several levels of the taxonomic hierarchy. In Figures 54 and 55 are shown the diversity gradient for Recent bivalves at the generic and family levels. It will be noted that, though the general form of the gradient is the same in both cases, the slope is different. Because this is the case it is evident that a ratio such as number of genera/number of families will vary systematically as a function of latitude. This fact may be important in the application of diversity gradients to the fossil record, because it may simplify sampling problems if it is no longer necessary to achieve a close approximation of actual diversity but only to have established a close approximation of the ratio between generic and familial diversity. As an example of the application of such a ratio, Figure 56 shows a second-order spherical harmonic surface fitted to data for the ratio number of genera/number of families for Recent pelecypods. The equator found by this technique is approximately the same as that found for diversity data in pure form and apparently is quite as useful in pole location.

A further variation of the ratio approach suggests itself when it is noted that the diversity gradients for various groups of organisms tend to have different slopes. This fact suggests that many kinds of ratios are available and that one need not be limited to ratios of different taxa within a single group. It is quite clear, for instance (though geologically and biologically absurd) from examination of Figures 8 and 42 that a ratio of number of mosquitoe genera/number of crocodile species would be latitude-dependent and thus useful in rotational pole location.

CONCLUSIONS

The foregoing consideration of taxonomic diversity gradients has been undertaken as a means of assessing their applicability to the geologic record in general and, in particular, their applicability to a test of the hypotheses of continental drift and polar wandering. The conclusions reached are summarized here.

1. The diversity gradients of all the widely distributed major groups of organisms studied exhibit a form that is latitude-dependent.

2. With the exception of two groups (penguins and alcids) deliberately selected because they were known to be peculiar, all groups examined show a diversity gradient reaching maximum levels at or near the equator.

3. The application of surface-fitting procedures to suitable taxonomic diver-

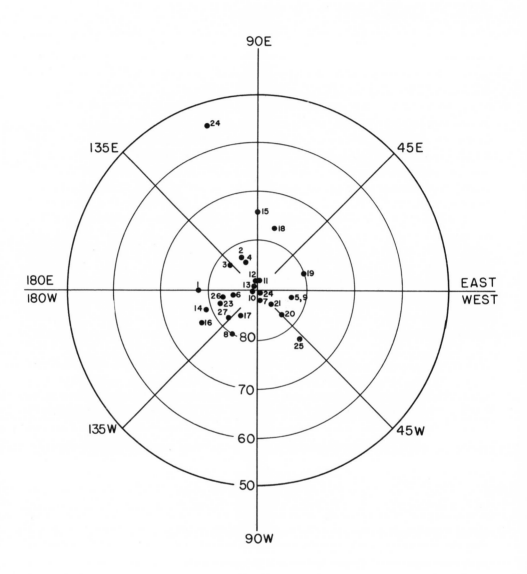

Fig. 52. Summary plot of the diversity poles obtained from second-order spherical har-monic or nonorthogonal polynomial surfaces fitted to Recent diversity distributions. Note that the plot extends out from the pole only to 50°N. The numbered poles refer to the following groups, and all are derived from spherical harmonic surfaces unless otherwise noted: 1, Parrots. 2, Cypraeid gastropods. 3. Hermatypic corals. 4, Pinnidae. 5, Clam ratio genera/families. 6, Clam families after Stehli et al. 7, Clam genera after Stehli et al. 8, Clam species after Stehli et al. 9, Termite subfamilies. 10, Mosquito genera. 11, *Strombus*. 12, Crocodilians, older literature. 13, Crocodilians, newest revision. 14, Pleu-rodira turtles. 15, Planktonic Foraminifera. 16, Frogs. 17, Snakes. 18, Termite genera. 19, Turtle genera. 20, Lizards. 21, Palms. 22, Southern hemisphere mosquito genera nonorthogonal polynomial, pole-projected into northern hemisphere. 23, Northern hemi-sphere mosquito genera nonorthogonal polynomial. 24, Southern hemisphere *Strombus* data, nonorthogonal polynomial, pole-projected into northern hemisphere. 25, Northern hemisphere *Strombus* data, nonorthogonal polynomial. 26, Penguin data sixth-order non-orthogonal polynomial, pole-projected into northern hemisphere. 27, Northern hemisphere data for clam ratio genera/families, nonorthogonal polynomial; note that two of the points most distant from the rotational pole, 24 and 25, are from single-hemisphere treatment of *Strombus* data which as noted in the text are not suitable for single-hemisphere treatment and which we would normally treat by spherical harmonics using both hemispheres to give pole (11). A third point, 15, is for planktonic Foraminifera which, because of the distorting effect to their gradient by ocean currents, would not normally be used for pole location.

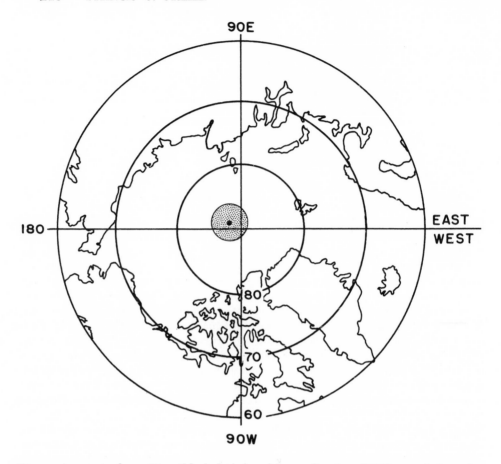

Fig. 53. Average pole position (black dot) found by application of Fisher statistic to the pole positions shown in Figure 52. The pole lies at 149°E, 88°N. At the 95 per cent level the calculated cone of confidence about the pole has a radius of 3° 37′ (stippled area).

sity data permits the objective and precise determination of a pole position whether the data involve the entire earth or a single hemisphere.

4. The application of Fisher statistic to diversity pole locations shows a high degree of homogeneity in the data, since at the 95 per cent confidence limit a cone of confidence about the average pole determined for the assembled data is small.

5. The average poles found from diversity data and from temperature data do not coincide exactly with the rotational pole. It is therefore clear that there is some still unexplained imperfection in the model used since it assumes that there should be an exact coincidence between the rotational, and the temperature and the diversity poles. The discrepancy found between the various poles is small, and

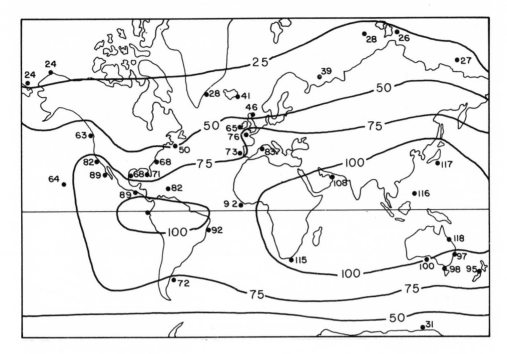

Fig. 54. Contoured surface drawn on the raw diversity data for genera of Recent bivalves (after Stehli et al., 1966).

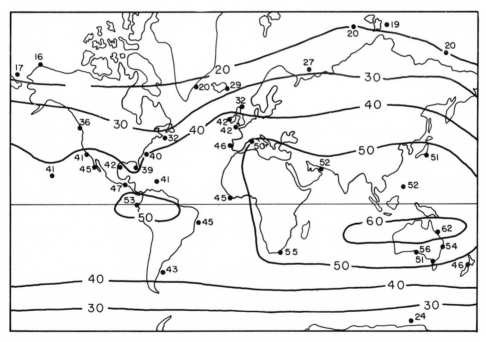

Fig. 55. Contoured surface drawn on the raw diversity data for families of Recent bivalves (after Stehli et al., 1966).

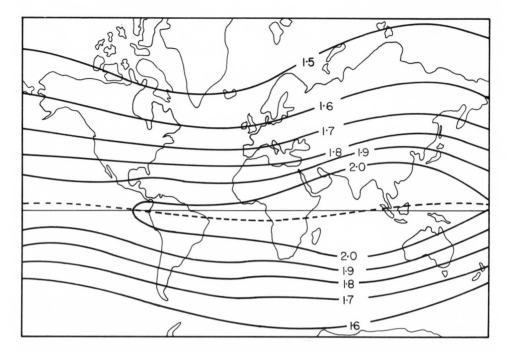

Fig. 56. Second-order spherical harmonic surface fitted to a ratio of bivalve genera/ bivalve families for the Recent forms shown in Figures 54 and 55. It is clear that this kind of ratio (and many others) are as latitude-dependent as simple diversity. The use of such ratios may considerably reduce the sampling problems involved in using populations of fossils for rotational pole location.

it is evident that the feature as yet not taken into consideration in the model (if it is not simply a matter of imperfect sampling) is not of great importance and certainly will not materially affect the use of diversity gradients or of the temperature gradient in locating the approximate position of the rotational pole. The discrepancy involved is very much smaller than that involved in using the present magnetic pole as an indication of the present rotational pole position.

6. The resolution attainable in the use of diversity gradients for rotational pole location is sufficient to suggest that the application of the technique to fossil record is capable of providing a conclusive test of the polar wandering hypothesis (and of course, at the same time, a test of the hypothesis that the earth's magnetic field in the past must always have been an axial dipole).

7. Diversity gradients have also sufficient resolution for the displacement of continental masses across latitude to permit their application to the fossil record for a definitive test of whether or not there has been significant continental drift across latitude.

8. Diversity gradients have no resolution for continental displacements that do not involve shifts across latitude.

9. The use of taxonomic diversity gradients for higher taxa and the employment of various kinds of ratios both suggest that application of diversity gradients to the fossil record may be less difficult than previously anticipated.

Acknowledgments. In compiling the data which have been used in developing the Recent model, the writer has been fortunate in having the advice and assistance of many individuals. Fred Sizer and Yadwiga Kuncaitis have located for me and obtained through interlibrary loans all manner of obscure journals. I have had the able assistance of Gail Ashley, James Bugh, James Noble, Karen Olesen, Timothy Saylor, Stephen Stanley, and Bruce Williams in compiling distribution and diversity information from the literature. Helpful advice has been given on the taxonomy and distribution of many groups by specialists including R. T. Abbott, C. M. Bogert, B. H. Brattstrom, D. Cochran, W. K. Emerson, A. L. McAlester, H. E. Moore, Jr., W. E. Olds, Jr., J. A. Peters, J. Rosewater, J. W. Wells, and R. G. Zweifel.

Assistance in selecting the mathematical procedures employed in fitting surfaces to the raw data was generously offered by a number of individuals. Quadratic, cubic, and higher order nonorthogonal polynomial surfaces fitted to the data for several groups of organisms were provided by D. Boyne, J. M. Forgotson, Jr., and W. R. Walton of the Research Department of the Pan American Petroleum Corp. A program for spherical harmonic analysis was initially provided by G. J. F. MacDonald and was modified to better suit the purposes of this study by C. E. Helsley. The Gulf Oil Corp., through the courtesy of Richard McCammon and Augustine Pyre, made available a program which was used in calculating the critical point (zero rate of change) in quadratic and higher order nonorthogonal polynomial surfaces; IBM cards were punched and verified by Paul Weidig. Typing and basic editing of the manuscript was provided by Joyce Brewton and Mary Baldrey. The manuscript has been read and criticized by P. O. Banks and J. R. Dodd, with resultant great improvement. Finally, without the support of the National Science Foundation (Grant GP-2206) and the Petroleum Research Fund (Grant 1614-82) the study would not have been possible.

APPENDIX

SOURCES OF DATA USED

Danaidae (butterflies)
Hovanitz, W., 1958. Distribution of butterflies in the New World. In C. L. Hubbs, ed., *Zoogeography*. Am. Assoc. Adv. Sci. Publ. 51, Washington, p. 321.

Phasaninae (pheasants)
Delacour, J., 1951. *The Pheasants of the World*. Scribners, New York.

Culicidae (mosquitoes)
Stone, A., K. L. Knight, and H. Starcke, 1959. *A Synoptic Catalog of the Mosquitoes of the World (Diptera, Culicidae)*, Thomas Say Foundation, v. 6. Horn-Shafer, Baltimore.

Palmacea (palms)
Blatter, Ethelbert, 1926. *The Palms of British India and Ceylon*. Oxford Univ. Press, London.

Burret, Max, 1943. Die Palmen Arabiens. *Bot. Jahrb. Syst.* 73(2): 175–90.

Dahlgren, Bror Eric, ed., 1936. *Index of American Palms;* Fossil Palms, by A. C. Noe. Chicago (no publisher given).

Gagnepain, F., 1936. *Flore générale de l'Indochine.* (1907 1st ed.) Masson, Paris.

Jumelle, H., 1933. Palmae. In *Catalogue des plantes de Madegascar.* L'Academie Malagaché, Tananarive.

McCurrach, James C., 1960. *Palms of the World.* Harper, New York.

Moore, H. E., 1965. Personal communication, including many recent and unpublished data.

Ridley, Henry N., 1925. *Flora of the Malay Peninsula,* v. 5, publ. under authority of the Government of the Straits Settlements, 1922–25. Reeve, London.

Small, John Kunkel, 1931. Palms of the continental U.S. *Science,* 32(3): 240–55.

Cypraeidae (cowries)

Schilder, F. A., 1938–39. Prodrome of a monograph on living cypraeidae. *Proc. Malacological Soc. London* (1938), 23(3), 119–80; graph, table, text figs., 9 distribution maps (1939), 23(4), 181–231.

Alcidae (puffins, auks, etc.)

Peters, James Lee, 1934. *Checklist of Birds of the World,* v. 2. Harvard Univ. Press, Cambridge, p. 350.

Psittaciformes (parrots)

Peters, J. L., 1937. Ibid., v. 3.

Spheniscidae (penguins)

Peters, J. L., 1931. Ibid., v. 1, p. 29.

Lacertillia (lizards)

Anderson, J., 1896. *Herpetology of Arabia with a Preliminary List of the Reptiles and Batrachians of Egypt.* 8 v. Porter, London.

Barbour, Thomas, and Arthur Loveridge, 1930. Reptiles and Amphibians from Liberia. In *The African Republic of Liberia and the Belgian Congo,* Richard P. Strong, ed., Cambridge, Mass., pp. 769–85.

Boulenger, George A., 1890. On the reptiles and batrachians of the Solomon Islands. *Trans. Zool. Soc. London,* 12: 35.

——, 1895. Catalog of the reptiles and batrachians of Barbary (Morocco, Algeria, Tunisia) based chiefly upon the notes and collections made in 1880–1884 by M. Fernand Lataste. *Trans. Zool. Soc. London,* 13: 93.

——, 1897. A list of reptiles and batrachians from the Congo Free State, with descriptions of two new snakes. *Mag. Nat. Hist.,* 19(ser. 6): 276–81.

——, 1900. A list of the batrachians and reptiles of the Gaboon (French Congo) with descriptions of new genera and species. *Proc. Zool. Soc. London,* p. 433–56.

——, 1910. A revised list of South African reptiles and batrachians with synoptic tables, special reference to the specimens in the South African Museum and descriptions of new species. *Ann. So. African Mus.,* 5(9): 455–538.

——, 1912. A *Vertebrate Fauna of the Malay Peninsula, Reptilia and Batrachia.* Taylor & Francis, London, p. 1–294.

Burt, C. E., and D. M. Burt, 1933. A Preliminary Check List of the Lizards of South America. *Trans. Acad. Sci. St. Louis,* 28(½): 1–104.

Cochran, Doris M., 1941. *The Herpetology of Hispaniola*. U.S. Nat. Mus. Bull. 177.

Crawford, S. C., 1931. Field keys to the lizards and amphibians of British Guiana. *Ann. Carnegie Mus.*, 21: 11–42.

Devencenzi, G. J., 1926–28. Fauna erpetalúgica del Uruguay. *Anales del Museo de Historia Natural de Montevideo* 2 (ser. 2): 1–65.

Dunn, Emmet R., 1945. Los Generos de amphibios y reptiles de Colombia, 2. Segunda parte, Reptiles, orden de los Saurios. *Caldasia*, 3: 72–110.

Flower, Stanley S., 1933. Notes on Recent reptiles and amphibians of Egypt, with a list of the species recorded from that kingdom. *Proc. Zool. Soc. London* (pt. 2), p. 735–851.

Koslowsky, J., 1898. Enumeracion sistemática de los reptiles argentinos. *Revista de la Plata*, 8: 161–200.

Lord, C. E., and H. H. Scott, 1924. *A synopsis of the vertebrate animals of Tasmania*. Oldham, Beddome & Meredith, Hobart.

Loveridge, Arthur, 1923. List of the lizards of British Territories in East Africa. *Proc. Zool. Soc. London*, p. 841–63.

Mertens, Robert, and L. Müller, 1928. Liste der Amphibien und Reptilien Europas. *Abh. Senckenberg. Naturforsch. Ges.*, 41: 1.

Nikolskii, A. M., 1915. Fauna of Russia and adjacent countries. In *Reptiles*, v. 1, *Chelonia and Sauria*, pp. vi, viii. Compiled mainly from the collections of the zoological Museum of the Russian Acad. Sci., N. B. Nasonov. ed.

Pope, C. H., 1935. The Reptiles of China: Turtles, Crocodilians, Snakes, Lizards. In *Natural History of Central Asia*, v. 10. Am. Mus. Nat. Hist., New York.

Ruthven, Alexander C., 1922. *The Amphibians and Reptiles of the Sierra Nevada de Santa Marta, Columbia*. Univ. Michigan Mus. Zool., Misc. Publ. no. 8.

Smith, Albert Charles, 1962. *Studies of Pacific Island plants*. XVII, The genus Geniostoma (*Loganiacene*) in the New Hebrides, Fiji, Samoa, and Tonga. Smithsonian Inst., Washington.

Smith, Hobart Muir, 1946. *Handbook of Lizards: Lizards of the U.S. and Canada*. Comstock, Ithaca.

Smith, Hobart M., and Edward Taylor, 1950. *Annotated Checklist and Key to the Reptiles of Mexico*. U.S. Nat. Mus. Bull. 199.

Smith, Malcolm A., 1943. *The Fauna of British India: Ceylon and Burma*. V. 3, *Reptilia and Amphibia*. Taylor & Francis, London.

Stejneger, Leonhard, 1907. *Herpetology of Japan and Adjacent Territory*. U.S. Nat. Mus. Bull. 58.

——, 1911. The batrachians and reptiles of Formosa. *Proc. U.S. Nat. Mus.*, 38: 91–114.

——, 1926. The land reptiles of the Hawaiian Islands. *Proc. U.S. Nat. Mus.*, 21: 783–813.

Taylor, Edward H., 1922. *The Lizards of the Philippine Islands*. Philippine Bureau of Science, publ. 17.

——, 1956. A Review of the Lizards of Costa Rica. *Univ. Kansas Sci. Bull.*, 38(1).

Werner, Franz, 1930. *Contribution to the Knowledge of the Reptiles and Amphibians of Greece, Especially the Aegean Islands*. Schweitzerbart, Stuttgart.

Zietz, F. R., 1920. Catalogue of Australian Lizards. *Records of So. Australian Mus.*, 1: 181–288.

Zweifel, R. G., 1965. Personal communication, containing much information extracted from literature unavailable to me.

Ophidia (snakes)

Anderson, J. A., 1896. *A Contribution to the Herpetology of Arabia: With a Preliminary List of the Reptiles and Batrachians of Egypt.* Porter, London.

Angel, F., 1946. *Fauna de France.* Lechanelieu, Paris.

Barbour, Thomas, and A. Loveridge, 1930. Reptiles and Amphibians from Liberia. In *Strong's African Republic of Liberia and the Belgian Congo.* Cambridge, Mass., p. 786–96.

Bleakney, Sherman, 1952. The amphibians and reptiles of Nova Scotia. *Canad. Field Naturalist, 66:* 125–29.

Bogert, C. M., and J. A. Oliver, 1945. A preliminary analysis of the herpeto fauna of Sonora. *Bull. Am. Mus. Nat. Hist.,* 83: 301–420.

Boulenger, G. A., 1910. Reptiles of Africa south of Angola and the Zambesi. *Ann. So. African Mus.,* 5: 455.

——, 1912. *A Vertebrate Fauna of the Malay Peninsula: From the Isthmus of Kra to Singapore, Including the Adjacent Islands. Reptilia and Batrachia.* London.

——, 1915. List of snakes from Portuguese Congo, Northern Rhodesia and Angola. *Proc. Zool. Soc. London,* p. 193.

——, 1915. List of snakes of Madagascar. Comoro, Mascarenez. *Proc. Zool. Soc. London,* p. 369–82.

——, 1915. List of snakes of North-east Africa, from tropic to the Soudan and Somaliland, including Socotra. *Proc. Zool. Soc. London,* p. 641–58.

——, 1915. List of snakes of East Africa, north of Zambesi and south of Sudan and Somaliland, Nyassaland. *Proc. Zool. Soc. London,* p. 611–40.

——, 1919. List of snakes of West Africa from Mauritania to the French Congo. *Proc. Zool. Soc. London,* p. 267–98.

——, 1919. Snakes of North Africa. *Proc. Zool. Soc. London,* p. 299–307.

Boyer, D. A., and A. A. Heinze, 1933–34. An annotated list of amphibians and reptiles of Jefferson Co., Mo. *Trans. Acad. Sci. St. Louis,* 28: 185–200.

Breckenridge, Walter J., 1944. *Reptiles and Amphibians of Minnesota.* Univ. Minn. Press, Minneapolis.

Carr, A., and G. Goin, 1955. *Guide to the Reptiles, Amphibians and Fish of Florida.* Univ. Florida Press, Gainsville.

Cochran, Doris M., 1941. *The Herpetology of Hispaniola.* U.S. Nat. Mus. Bull. 177.

De Rooj, N., 1917. *The Reptiles of the Indo-Australian Archipelago.* Brill, Leiden.

Ditmars, Raymond, 1935. *Serpents of the Northeastern States.* New York Zoological Soc., New York.

Dunn, Emmett, 1945. *Los Generos de anfibias y reptiles de Colombia:* Reptiles, v. 3. Caldasia, Bogota.

——, 1957. *Contributions to the Herpetology of Colombia 1943–1946.* Private print., M.T.D.

Flower, S. S., 1933. The Recent reptiles and amphibians of Egypt. *Proc. Zool. Soc. London,* p. 735–851.

Funkhouser, William D., 1945. *Kentucky Snakes.* Univ. of Kentucky, Lexington.

Graf, W., S. G. Jewett, and K. L. Gordon, 1939. *Records of Amphibia and Reptilia of Oregon.* Encyclopedia, Ann Arbor, p. 7–13.

Guthrie, J. E., 1926. *The Snakes of Iowa.* Iowa State College, Agric. Exp. Sta. Bull. 239, p. 145–92.

Hurter, Julius, and John Strecker, 1909. The amphibians and reptiles of Arkansas. *Trans. Acad. Sci. St. Louis.*, *18*(2): 11–27.

Kinghorn, J. R., 1956. *The Snakes of Australia*. Angus & Robertson, Sidney.

Logier, E. B. S., and G. C. Toner, 1961. *Checklist of the Amphibians and Reptiles of Canada and Alaska*. A revision of contribution no. 41, Royal Ontario Museum, Toronto, Contrib. 53.

Lord, C. E., and H. H. Scott, 1924. *A Synopsis of the Vertebrate Animals of Tasmania*, v. 8. Hobart, Oldham.

Marx, Hymen, 1956. *Key to the Lizards and Snakes of Egypt*. Cairo, U.S. Naval Medical Res. Unit, no. 3, Res. Rep. N Moo5 q50.39.45, p. 1–8.

Maslin, T. Paul, 1959. *Annotated Checklist of the Amphibians and Reptiles of Colorado*. Univ. Colorado Study Series in Biology, no. 6.

Mertens, R., 1930. *Die Amphibien und Reptilien der Inseln Bali, Lombok, Sumbawa und Flores*. Schweitzerbart, Stuttgart. (*Abh. Senckenberg. Naturforsch. Ges., 42:* 117–342.

——, 1952. *Die Amphibien und Reptilien von El Salvador*. Kramer, Frankfort am Main.

——, 1955. *Die Amphibien und Reptilien Sudwest Afrikas*. Kramer, Frankfort am Main.

Mertens, R., and L. Muller, 1928. Liste der Amphibien und Reptilien Europas. *Abh. Senckenberg. Naturforsch. Ges., 41:* 1–62.

Nikolskii, A. M., 1915. *Fauna of Russia and Adjacent Countries, Reptiles*. V. I, *Chelonia and Sauria*. Compiled mainly from the collections of the zoological Museum of the Russian Acad. Sci., N. B. Nasonov, ed.

Parker, H. W., 1935. The frogs, lizards and snakes of British Guiana. *Proc. Zool. Soc. London* (pt. 2), p. 505–30.

Peters, James A., 1960. The snakes of Ecuador. *Harvard Mus. Comp. Zool. 122*(9): 491–541.

Pope, C. H., 1935. *The Reptiles of China, Turtles, Crocodilians, Snakes, Lizards. Natural History of Central Asia*, v. 10. Am. Mus. Nat. Hist., New York.

Ruthven, Alexander C., 1922. *The Amphibians and Reptiles of the Sierra Nevada de· Santa Marta, Columbia*. Univ. Michigan Mus. Zool., Misc. Publ. no. 8, p. 5–69.

Ruthven, Alexander C., Crystal Thompson, and Helen Thompson, 1911. *The Herpetology of Michigan*. Michigan Geol. Biol. Survey, publ. 10 (biol. ser. 3).

Schmidt, Karl P., 1919. Contributions to the herpetology of the Belgian Congo based on the collection of the American Museum Congo Expedition, 1905–1915. *Bull. Am. Mus. Nat. Hist., 39:* 385–624.

——, 1941. *Amphibians and Reptiles of British Honduras*. Field Mus. Nat. Hist., 22, publ. 512.

Shannon, Frederick A., 1956. Reptiles and amphibians of Korea. *Herpetologica, 12:* 22–49.

Smith, Hobart M., 1958. Handlist of snakes of Panama. *Herpetologica, 14:* 222–24.

Smith, Hobart M., and Edward H. Taylor, 1945. Annotated checklist and key to the reptiles of Mexico. *Smithsonian Inst. 95:*(no. 3185): 521–613.

Smith, M. A., 1943. *The Fauna of British India, Ceylon and Burma Including the Whole of Indo-China Subregion*. Taylor & Francis, London.

——, 1943. *The Fauna of British India, Reptilia and Amphibia*, v. 8. Taylor & Francis, London.

——, 1949. *British Reptiles and Amphibians*. King Penguin Books, no. 47, London.

Stejneger, Leonhard H., 1907. *Herpetology of Japan and Adjacent Territory*. U.S. Nat. Mus. Bull. 57–58.

——, 1911. The batrachians and reptiles of Formosa. *Proc. U.S. Nat. Mus., 38:* 91–114.

Strecker, John K., 1915. *Reptiles and Amphibians of Texas*. Baylor Univ. Bull. 18 (no. 4).

Stuart, Lawrence C., 1948. The amphibians and reptiles of Alta Verapaz, Guatemala. *Univ. Michigan Mus. Zool. Misc. Publ., 56:* 1–53.

——, 1963. *Checklist of the Herpeto Fauna of Guatemala*. Univ. Michigan Mus. Zool. Misc. Publ., 122.

Taylor, Edward H., 1922. *The Snakes of the Philippines*. Philippine Bureau of Science, no. 15–17.

——, 1953. Review of the lizards of Ceylon. *Univ. Kansas Sci. Bull., 35:* 1525–85.

——, 1958. Report on collection of amphibians and reptiles from Harbel, Republic of Liberia. *Univ. Kansas Sci. Bull., 38:* 1191–1230.

——, 1963. Lizards of Thailand. *Univ. Kansas Sci. Bull., 44*(14): 687–1077.

Terentev, P. V., and S. A. Chernov, 1949. *Encyclopedia of Reptiles and Amphibians*, 3rd ed. State Publ. House of Soviet Science, Moscow.

Van Denborgh, John, 1922. The reptiles of Western North America. *California Acad. Sci. Occasional Pap., 10*(pt. 2): 623–1005.

Waite, E. R., 1929. *The Reptiles and Amphibians of South Australia*. Weir, Adelaide.

Werner, Franz, 1930. Contribution to the knowledge of the reptiles and amphibians of Greece, especially the Aegean Islands. *Univ. Mich. Occasional Pap. Mus. Zool.*, 211, p. 1–47.

Wright, Albert, and Anna (Allen) Wright, 1933. *Handbook of Snakes of the U.S. and Canada*. Cornell Univ. Press, Ithaca.

Zweifel, R. G., 1965. Personal communication.

Chelonia (turtles)

Wermuth, H., and R. Mertens, 1961. *Schildkröten, Krokodile, Bruckenechsen*. Fischer, Jena.

Pinnidae (pinna)

Keen, A. M., 1958. *Sea Shells of Tropical West America. Marine Mollusks from Lower California to Columbia*. Stanford Univ. Press, Stanford.

Nickles, M., 1955. *Scaphodes et lamellibraches recoltes dans l'Ouest Africain*. Atlantide Report no. 3. Danish Science Press, Copenhagen.

Rosewater, J., 1961. The family Pinnidae in the Indo-Pacific. *Indo-Pacific Mollusca, 1* (4): 175–85.

——, 1964. Personal communication.

Turner, R., and J. Rosewater, 1958. The family Pinnidae in the western Atlantic. *Johnsonia, 3*(38): 285–326.

Planktonic Foraminifera

Akers, W. H., 1952. General ecology of the foraminiferal genus *Eponidella* with description of a recent species. *J. Paleont. 26*(4): 645–49.

Bandy, Orville L., 1953. Ecology and paleocology of some California Foraminifera. Part 1, The frequency distribution of Recent Foraminifera off California. *J. Paleont., 27*(2): 161–82.

Bradshaw, John S., 1959. Ecology of Living planktonic Foraminifera in the north and equatorial Pacific Ocean. *Contrib. Cushman Found. Foram. Res., 10:* 25–64.

Brady, Henry B., 1884. Report on the Foraminifera dredged by H.M.S. *Challenger* during the years 1873–1876. In *Challenger Reports*, v. 9, *Zoology*. Macmillan, London.

Cushman, J. A., 1921. *Foraminifera of the Philippines and Adjacent Seas*. U.S. Nat. Mus. Bull. 100(4).

———, 1922. Shallow-water Foraminifera of the Tortugas region. *Carnegie Inst. Wash.*, 17: 1–85.

———, 1948. *Foraminifera, Their Classification and Economic Use*, 4th ed. Harvard Univ. Press, Cambridge.

Höglund, Hans, 1947. *Foraminifera in the Gullmar Fjord and the Skagerrak*. Uppsala Universitet, Zoologiska Bidrag fran Uppsala, v. 26.

Jeifzer, C. J., 1936. On variability in East Indian Foraminifera. *Temminickia, 1*: 75–151.

Kane, J., 1953. Temperature correlations of planktonic Foraminifera from the North Atlantic Ocean. *Micropaleontologist, 7*(3): 25–50.

Kustanowick, S., 1963. Distribution of planktonic Foraminifera in surface sediments of the Southwest Pacific Ocean. *New Zealand J. Geol. Geophys., 6*: 534–65.

Nagahama, Masaho, 1951. Studies on the foraminiferal fauna of small or almost enclosed bays in Japan. *Misc. Repts. Res. Inst. Nat. Resources*, no. 19–21, p. 142–48.

Parker, F. L., 1948. Foraminifera of the continental shelf from the Gulf of Maine to Maryland. *Bull. Mus. Comp. Zool., 100*(2): 211–41.

———, 1952. Foraminiferal distribution in Long Island–Buzzards Bay area. *Bull. Mus. Comp. Zool., 106*(10): 425–73.

Parker, F. L., F. B. Phleger, and J. F. Peirson, 1953. Ecology of Foraminifera from San Antonio Bay and environments, southwest Texas. *Contrib. Cushman Found. Foram. Res.*, Sp. Publ. no. 2, p. 1–75.

Phleger, F. B., Jr., 1952. Foraminifera ecology off Portsmouth, New Hampshire. *Bull. Mus. Comp. Zool., 106*(8–9): 315–90.

Post, R. J., 1951. Foraminifera of the South Texas coast. *Publ. Inst. Marine Sci., 2*(1): 165–76.

Said, Rushdi, 1950. The distribution of Foraminifera in the northern Red Sea. *Contrib. Cushman Found. Foram. Res., 1*: 9–29.

———, 1951. Foraminifera of Narragansett Bay. *Contrib. Cushman Found. Foram. Res., 2*: 75–86.

———, 1953. Foraminifera of Great Pond, East Falmouth, Massachusetts. *Contrib. Cushman Found. Foram. Res., 4*: 7–14.

Todd, Ruth, 1957. Geology of Saipan, Mariana Islands, Part 3, Paleontology. *U.S. Geol. Surv. Prof. Paper*, no. 280–H, p. 265–320.

Strombus (conches)

Abbott, R. T., 1960. The genus *Strombus* in the Indo-Pacific. *Indo-Pacific Mollusca, 1*(2): 33–144.

———, 1964. Personal communication.

Clench, W. J., and R. T. Abbott, 1941. The genus *Strombus* in the western Atlantic. *Johnsonia, 1*(1).

Nickles, M., 1950. Mollusques testaces marins de la Côte occidental d'Afrique. In *Manuels Ouest-African*, v. 2. Lechevalier, Paris.

Olds, W. E.; 1964. Personal communication.

Crocodilia (crocodiles)

Bogert, C. M., 1964. Personal communication.

Boulenger, G. A., 1889. *Catalog of the Chelonians, Rhynchocephalians and Crocodiles in the British Museum (Natural History)*. Taylor & Francis, London.

Loveridge, A., 1957. Checklist of the reptiles and amphibians of East Africa (Uganda, Kenya, Tanganyika, Zanzibar). *Harvard Mus. Comp. Zool. Bull., 117*(2): 153.

Schmidt, Karl P., 1919. Contributions to the herpetology of the Belgian Congo based on the collections of the American Museum Congo Expedition 1909–1915: Part 1, Turtles, Crocodiles, Lizards and Chameleons. *Bull. Am. Mus. Nat. Hist. 39:* 385–624.

——, 1928. Notes on South American caimans. *Field Mus. Nat. Hist., Publ. 252, Zool. Ser., 12*(17): 205–31.

——, 1932. Notes on New Guinean Crocodiles. *Field Mus. Nat. Hist., Publ. 310, Zool. Ser., 18*(8): 167–72.

Wermuth, H., and R. Mertens, 1961. *Schildkröten, Krokodile, Bruckenechsen.* Fischer, Jena.

Hermatypic corals (reef corals)

Branner, J. C., 1904. The stone reefs of Brazil: Their geological and geographical relations, with a chapter on the coral reefs. *Harvard Mus. Comp. Zool., 44:* 1–285.

Crossland, C., 1905. Ecology and deposits of the Cape Verde Islands marine fauna. *Proc. Zool. Soc. London,* p. 170–86.

Durham, J. W., 1947. Corals from the Gulf of California and the North Pacific coast of North America. *Geol. Soc. Am. Mem. 20:* 1–68.

Smith, Frederick George Walton, 1942. *Atlantic Reef Corals.* Univ. Miami Press, Coral Gables (dist. by Farrar, Straus, New York, 1948).

Verill, A. E., 1906. The Bermuda Islands. Part 5, Account of the characteristic life of Bermuda coral reefs Madreporaria. *Connecticut Acad. Arts Sci. Trans., 12:* 204–47.

Wells, John W., 1954. Recent corals of the Marshall Islands. *U.S. Geol. Surv. Prof. Pap.,* no. 260–61; p. 385–486.

——, 1955. A survey of the distribution of reef coral genera in the Great Barrier Reef region. *Reports of the Great Barrier Reef Committee, IV*(2): 21–29.

——, 1963–64. Personal communication.

Isoptera (termites)

Snyder, Thomas E., 1949. *Catalog of the Termites (Isoptera) of the World.* Smithson. Misc. Coll., v. 112.

REFERENCES

Blair, T. A., 1942. *Climatology, General and Regional.* Prentice Hall, New York.

Brouwer, D., and A. J. Van Woerkom, 1950. The secular variations of the orbital elements of the principal planets. *Astronomy Papers Am. Ephem. (Washington) 13:* 81.

Colbert, E. H., 1955. *Evolution of the Vertebrates.* Wiley, New York.

Cox, A., and R. R. Doell, 1960. Review of Paleomagnetism. *Bull. Geol. Soc. Am., 71:* 645.

Emiliani, C., 1954. Temperatures of Pacific bottom waters and polar surficial waters during the Tertiary. *Science, 119:* 853–55.

Fischer, A. G., 1960. Latitudinal variations in organic diversity. *Evolution, 14:* 64–81.

Grant, F., 1957. A problem in the analysis of geophysical data. *Geophysics, 22:* 309–44.

Irving, E., and D. A. Brown, 1966, in press. Labyrinthodont Abundance and Diversity: A reply to F. G. Stehli. *Amer. J. Sci.*

Klopfer, P. H., and R. H. MacArthur, 1960. Niche size and faunal diversity. *Am. Naturalist, 94:* 293–300.

———, 1961. On the causes of tropical species diversity; Niche overlap. *Am. Naturalist, 95:* 223–26.

Krumbein, W. C., 1959. Trend surface analysis of contour-type Maps with irregular control point spacing. *J. Geophys. Res., 64:* 823–34.

Lowenstam, H., 1964. Paleotemperatures of the Permian and Cretaceous Periods. In *Problems in Paleoclimatology,* A. E. M. Nairn, ed Interscience: North Atlantic Treaty Organization Paleoclimates Conference, Newcastle Upon Tyne and Durham, England, 1963.

Mandelbaum, H., 1963. statistical and geological implications of trend mapping with non-orthogonal polynomials. *J. Geophys. Res., 68:* 505–19.

Manten, I., 1953. The cytological evolution of the fern flora of Ceylon. *Symposia on the Soc. for Exp. Biol. no. 7, Evolution:* pp. 174–85.

Simpson, G. G., 1953. *The Major Features of Evolution.* Columbia Univ. Press, New York.

———, 1953. *Evolution and Geography.* Oregon State System of Higher Education, Eugene, Ore.

———, 1964. Species density of North American Recent mammals. *Systematic Zool. 13:* 57–73.

Stehli, F. G., 1957. Possible Permian climatic zonation and its implications. *Am. J. Sci., 255:* 607–18.

———, 1964. Permian zoogeography and its bearing on climate. In *Problems in Paleoclimatology,* A. E. M. Nairn, ed. Interscience: North Atlantic Treaty Organization Paleoclimates Conference, Newcastle Upon Tyne and Durham, England, 1963.

———, 1965. Paleontological technique for defining ancient ocean currents. *Science, 148:* 943–46.

Stehli, F. G., and C. E. Helsley, 1963. Paleontologic technique for defining ancient pole positions. *Science 142:* 1057–59.

Stehli, F. G., A. L. McAlester, and C. E. Helsley, 1966, in press. Taxonomic diversity of Recent bivalves and some implications for geology. *Geol. Soc. Am. Bull.*

Thorson, G., 1957. Bottom communities (sublittoral or shallow shelf). In *Treatise on Marine Ecology and Paleoecology,* Ladd, ed. *Geol. Soc. Am. Mem. 67:* 461–534.

Tillyard, R. J., 1914. On the study of zoogeographical regions by means of specific contours, with application to the Odonata of Australia. *Proc. Linn. Soc. New South Wales, 39:* 21–43.

Wallace, A. R., 1878. *Tropical Nature and Other Essays.* Macmillan, London, New York.

Wells, J. W., 1954. Recent corals of the Marshall Islands. *U.S. Geol. Surv. Prof. Paper 260-I:* 385–479.

Williams, A., 1965. Stratigraphic Distribution. In *Treatise on Invertebrate Paleontology,* R. C. Moore, ed. *Part H (Brachiopoda):* H 237–50. Univ. Kansas Press, Lawrence.

Léo F. Laporte

7. RECENT CARBONATE ENVIRONMENTS AND THEIR PALEOECOLOGIC IMPLICATIONS

In the last several years great advances have been made in understanding the physical, chemical, and biological factors responsible for the formation of Recent shallow-water marine carbonate deposits. Stratigraphers, paleontologists, and sedimentologists have become increasingly aware of the significance of these investigations in interpreting ancient limestone deposits and fossil assemblages and are now viewing the ancient rock record in light of these studies in the Recent.

The results of research in Recent carbonate environments are readily accessible in the geologic literature and include such diverse topics as the skeletal mineralogy of shelly invertebrates and calcareous algae, reef initiation and development, origin and distribution of carbonate muds, organosedimentary structures formed by blue-green algal mats, and penecontemporaneous formation of dolomite. Even a cursory review of this literature gives one the impression that, by and large, many of the critical questions regarding the genesis of different carbonate sediment types have been answered and that few significant problems remain. Many investigators, for example, are turning to the study of carbonate diagenesis to establish the processes responsible for transforming loose, wet carbonate sediments of diverse carbonate mineralogy into dense, compact, essentially monominerallic rocks.

Because of these advances in understanding Recent shallow-water marine carbonate lithofacies and biofacies patterns, it behooves paleoecologists to attempt to interpret the ancient carbonate rock record in accordance with some of the major observations and concepts elucidated in the Recent. It might thus be appropriate to summarize what seem to be some of the more important working principles of Recent carbonate sedimentation and ecology. The choice of principles I present clearly reflects a bias resulting from personal experience in the ancient and the Recent as well as the influence of professional associations. Consequently, other carbonate paleoecologists may prefer principles that are not mentioned. Be that as it may, this paper will review and synthesize some of the data and ideas regarding Recent shallow-water marine carbonate environments that should be especially interesting to students of similar ancient environments and biotas. As will be apparent, all but the last several principles have been originally articulated and substantiated elsewhere by other workers. Nevertheless, it seems worthwhile to integrate in one place these various principles which are scattered throughout an ever-burgeoning literature in Recent carbonate geology and to underline their paleoecologic implications. A word of warning to the unwary reader: although there is in every case substantial evidence supporting each principle, the truth of each ought not to be taken as definitive or absolute. In fact, these principles are rules of thumb for the initial analysis and interpretation of ancient carbonate rocks and fossil assemblages. Much yet is to be learned about the detailed dynamics of carbonate sedimentation and ecology; hence an uncritical application of these principles to particular ancient situations is premature and unwarranted.

PRINCIPLES FROM THE RECENT

Intrabasinal control of carbonate facies genesis. Carbonate marine sediments, unlike silicate clastic rocks, form entirely within the local sedimentary basin and usually show little or no influence from the extrabasinal environment. Coarser-grained silicate clastic rocks such as arkoses, greywackes, and quartzose sandstones reflect different weathering and erosion rates as well as variable rock composition in the area of provenance. The finer-grained, argillaceous mudstones and shales similarly record strong environmental influence in the source area as well as postdepositional diagenetic effects. By contrast, virtually all the types of carbonate grains, whether of inorganic or organic origin (i.e. oolites, aggregate or grapestone grains, intraclasts, pellets, and skeletal debris), form within the sedimentary basin as direct products of local, specific environmental factors (Fig. 1). This means, therefore, that reliable inferences of an ancient shallow-water marine carbonate environment can be drawn from the petrologic character of the constituent carbonate grains of a given carbonate rock by reference to their modern counterparts. For this reason, then, it seems that paleoecological study of *carbonate* sedimentary rocks is particularly fruitful for defining, in broad terms at least, ancient marine habitats of many now extinct marine invertebrates.

This principle is well articulated and thoroughly substantiated by Ginsburg and others (1963, p. 554) who state:

> Carbonate sediments contain a faithful record of the hydrographic milieu and the activities of organisms at the time of sediment deposition. This record is frequently more complete and more subtle than that presented by sediments composed of terrigenous clastics, for in the latter only the depositional features of the sediments—their grain size, packing and sedimentary structures—reflect the environment of deposition. In the carbonate sediments, the particles themselves are produced in the environment of deposition. As a re-

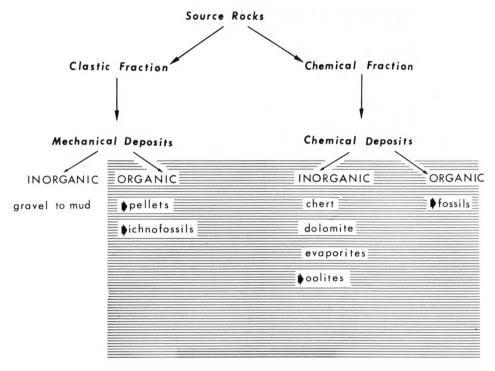

Fig. 1. Major inorganic and organic constituents (arrows) of shallow-water marine carbonate deposits form entirely within the sedimentary basin and bear little or no extrabasinal influences.

sult, the variety and abundance of the constituent particles can be related to hydrographic conditions.

Carbonate sands accumulate where produced. Carbonate grains which are sand-sized and larger are deposited and accumulated in the same local area of the sedimentary basin where they are originally produced. Problems of mixtures within the sedimentary basin of unlike environmental products are therefore minimized in carbonate environments. In contrast with the very significant net lateral movement of grains that occurs in noncarbonate sedimentary environments, as Ginsburg et al. (1963, p. 572) have pointed out, there is relatively little net lateral transportation of sand-sized and coarser skeletal and nonskeletal carbonate grains within shallow-water carbonate environments. Owing to much local relative relief within carbonate environments (shoals, islands, reefs) there is little opportunity for currents to move grains from one major environmental regime to another. The proliferation of benthic organisms (algal mats, grasses, encrusting algae, hydrocorallines, etc.) also helps stabilize the accumulating grains at the sediment/water interface and inhibit their movement by current traction. More-

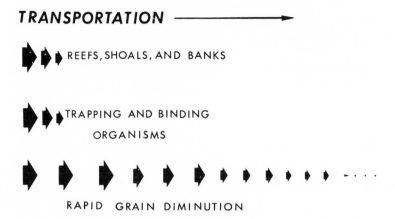

Fig. 2. Shallow-water marine carbonate sands tend to accumulate where produced (see text).

over, the relatively great susceptibility of carbonate grains to size diminution by abrasion results in rapid reduction (and hence obliteration into indeterminate matrix) of grains should they be exposed to current traction (Fig. 2). In those instances where sand-sized grains are moved laterally—in most cases in the high-energy, intertidal zone—there are other criteria that allow correct environmental identification.

Role of geometry and water energy of the sedimentary basin in carbonate facies genesis. Studies of Recent shallow-water carbonate environments have demonstrated that the geometry of the sedimentary basin where the sediments are accumulating and the water-energy level are the two dominant controls in carbonate facies genesis and differentiation. The geometry of the basin refers to the local geography (distribution of land and water masses) and hydrography (bottom relief relative to water depth). The geometry of the basin together with the energy regime of its water masses will control the abundance and distribution of not only the various nonskeletal grain types (i.e. oolite, pellets, intraclasts, and aggregate grains) but also, of course, the associated carbonate-secreting benthic organisms (Fig. 3).

The observations supporting this principle have been especially well confirmed by the work of Ginsburg (1956) and Ginsburg and others (1963) in South Florida, and of Newell et al. (1959) and Purdy (1963) in the Bahamas (Fig. 4). Investigations in ancient carbonate rocks support these conclusions from the Recent regarding the importance of the geometry and energy of the sedimentary basin in determining facies patterns (e.g. Lowenstam, 1957; Imbrie et al., 1964).

It should also be emphasized here that while in certain specific instances variation in water depth may be an important environmental factor, usually it is only a necessary, but not a sufficient, condition for carbonate facies differentiation. For example, while most Bahamian facies can be found forming at all water depths present on the Great Bahama Bank, other environmental parameters such

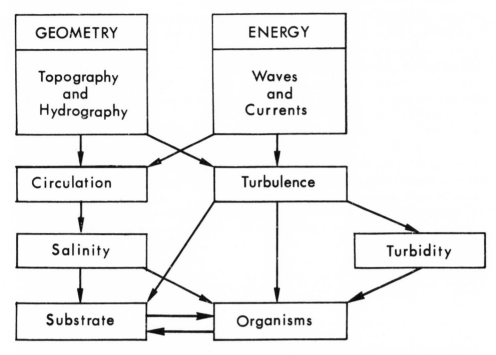

Fig. 3. The relationships between geometry and water-energy level of a marine shallow-water carbonate environment and their influence on the substrate and organisms. In the geologic record the substrate will be the "lithofacies" and the organisms will be the "biofacies" of an ancient carbonate unit (modified from Newell et al., 1959).

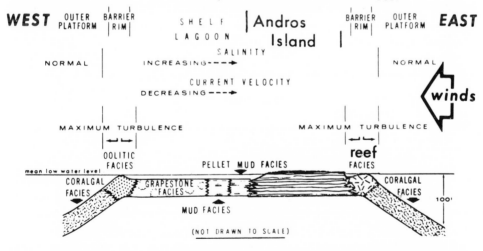

Fig. 4. Composition and distribution of calcareous sediments from the Great Bahama Bank and their relationship to salinity, current velocity, topography, and hydrography of the Bahamian platform. Note windward position of reef facies and sheltering influence of Andros Island (modified from Purdy, 1963).

as water energy, restriction of circulation, salinity, and so on are at least as critical in controlling facies patterns (Purdy, 1963). Thus, while it is true that Bahamian oolites form in waters less than six feet deep, other influences such as water agitation and sharp physicochemical gradients in calcium carbonate solubility are at least as important in oolite formation (Newell et al., 1960). If water depth alone were the limiting factor, there are many other shallow portions of the Bank where oolite should be forming. Similarly, organic reefs flourish in shallow water. But once again, many shallow-water environments in the Bahamas lack reef development because they are without direct connection with open ocean water which has relatively constant temperature, salinity, oxygen, and nutrient content, or they are unprotected from periodic flooding by overheated, hypersaline waters of the Bank interior (Ginsburg and Shinn, 1964).

Carbonate lithofacies and biofacies are therefore the result of several dominant environmental factors including water circulation, agitation, salinity, temperature, and turbidity, which in turn are strongly controlled by the geometry and water energy of the sedimentary basin. Water depth alone is of secondary importance only, in carbonate facies differentiation, and it ought not to be invoked uncritically by paleoecologists to explain ancient carbonate facies patterns.

Correlation of carbonate biofacies and lithofacies. In modern shallow-water carbonate environments the distribution patterns of carbonate grain types (lithofacies) are paralleled by those of benthic organism assemblages (biofacies). There are several related reasons for this. First and most obvious, some carbonate lithofacies such as reefs and skeletal and pelletal sands are the direct result of organic activity. Second, those same environmental factors such as salinity, water circulation, and agitation, which control deposition of inorganic grain types such as oolite, aggregate grains, and intraclasts, also influence the abundance and distribution of the associated benthic organisms. Third, accumulating carbonate grains, of whatever type, form substrates of varying texture, sorting, and packing which in turn determine the organic detritus and water content of the substrate, qualities important to epifaunal and infaunal invertebrates (Fig. 5).

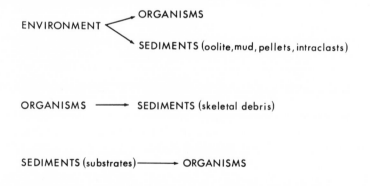

Fig. 5. The distribution patterns of shelly benthos parallel the distribution patterns of the calcareous sediments (see text).

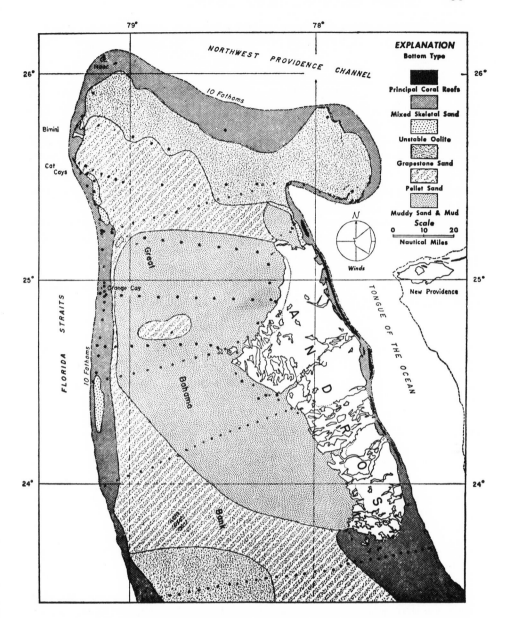

Fig. 6. Generalized map of the principal types of calcareous sediments (lithofacies) of the Great Bahama Bank. Recent revisions (Purdy, 1963) do not change the major patterns indicated here (from Newell et al., 1959).

An excellent example of the correlation between distributional patterns of carbonate lithofacies and biofacies is illustrated by the Recent situation found in the Bahamas (Figs. 6, 7). Data from other carbonate environments support this principle (e.g. South Florida; Ginsburg, 1956).

The particular significance of this principle is that paleontologists, especially those working with Paleozoic marine invertebrate biotas, are continually faced with the problem of interpreting the habitats and habits of fossil organisms which, almost always, are either extinct (e.g. fusulinids, solitary rugose corals, blastoids, trilobites) or whose modern living representatives are filling quite different ecologic niches (e.g. most articulate brachiopods, comatulid crinoids, certain coleoid cephalopods). It is therefore difficult to obtain direct evidence regarding the local ancient environment from the fossil biotas. But it is possible to interpret the depositional conditions of associated carbonate lithofacies—which fortunately have not become "extinct"—and to draw some tentative conclusions about the paleoecology of the associated biotas because of this principle of environmental parallelism between carbonate lithofacies and biofacies genesis.

Organic abundance and diversity gradients are reliable despite preservational bias. Only a small fraction of the individual members of a carbonate marine community actually is preserved in the accumulated sediments. Soft-bodied organisms such as algae, grass, sponges, sea anemones, various worms, and arthropods are never seen among the constituent grains of these sediments. What skeletal remains are preserved are not always recognizable as such, owing to extreme size reduction beyond the limit of reproducible identification. Trituration of calcareous skeletal debris by scavengers and predators, bacterial decomposition of the organic matrix which welds together individual crystallites making up a shell, and diminution by current abrasion are responsible for hard-part disintegration and removal.

Yet, despite this systematic loss of many of the original components of a marine benthic community before final burial in the sediments, the *relative* abundance and diversity of the community remains approximately the same, as compared with other communities (Fig. 8). For example, surveys of living benthic organisms on the Great Bahama Bank by Newell et al. (1959) closely parallel abundance and diversity gradients reported in the sediments of the same area by Purdy (1963). Ginsburg (1956, p. 2415, 2420) records similar impressions for the carbonates of South Florida.

While further verification of this principle is highly desirable, there is a strong suggestion that among marine carbonate benthic communities *relative variations* in abundance and variety of the "standing crop" are roughly the same as those seen in the coarser skeletal fraction of the accumulating calcareous sediments. Consequently, regular and systematic variations in the composition of fossil assemblages within an ancient carbonate rock may be taken as presumptive evidence of original environmental variations rather than fortuitous removal of different sorts of organisms by various postmortem diagenetic phenomena. This

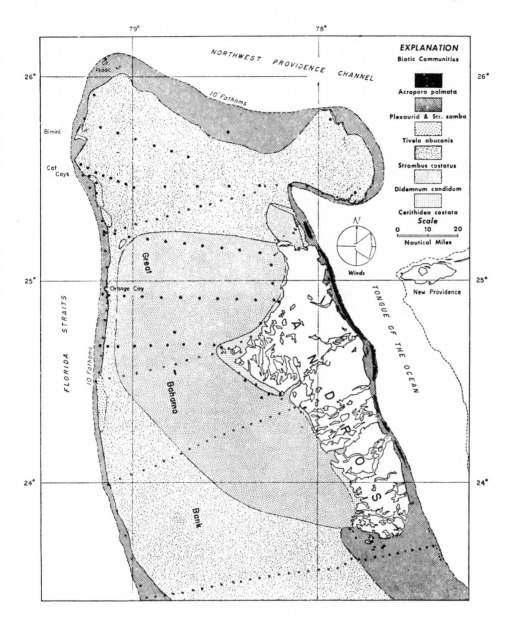

Fig. 7. Generalized map of the benthic assemblages (biofacies) of the Great Bahama Bank. Compare with previous figure and notice close similarity in lithofacies and biofacies patterns (from Newell et al., 1959).

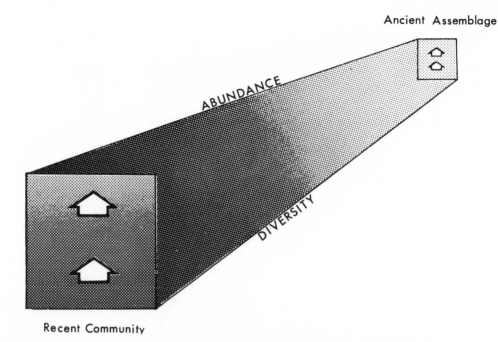

Fig. 8. The relative abundance and diversity as seen in an ancient fossil assemblage will be essentially the same as that originally found in the living community. These *relative* gradients (arrows) will usually be preserved even though many individuals and taxa of the original community will not be preserved in the fossil record.

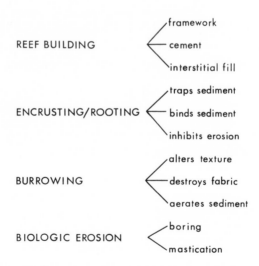

Fig. 9. Major ways in which organisms are important rock builders and sediment modifiers (see text).

would permit, for example, recognition and identification of ecological gradients within an ancient depositional environment.

Organisms are important environmental modifiers. The concept that organisms are important rock builders and sediment modifiers is well known. Yet, paradoxically, a discussion of this principle is appropriate because paleoecologists in emphasizing the role of the environment on organisms often pay too little attention to the organisms' role in altering or influencing the environment (Fig. 9). Organic reefs, of course, are among the best examples of how calcium carbonate-secreting biotas can build significant rock masses, thereby altering patterns of sedimentation. But there are other though less dramatic ways that organisms modify the local environment.

Some organisms burrow through sediments and destroy internal primary structures and fabrics formed by inorganic agencies (e.g. cross-stratification, graded bedding). Burrowing may also improve circulation of water and nutrients at the sediment/water interface with the sediments well below the interface. Such improved circulation may enable an interstitial biota to exist where it was formerly excluded because of deteriorated pH, Eh, and O_2 conditions. Organisms feeding directly on the sediment for its included organic matter (either organic detritus or microorganisms) will deposit large numbers of fecal pellets. Such pelleting may result in a coarsening of the sediment texture and improve interstitial water circulation, permitting a rich interstitial biota to survive.

Encrusting and rooted plants and animals such as algae, grass, sponges, hydrocoralline and madreporian corals help stabilize sediment at the depositional interface, thereby allowing other organisms, such as epifaunal sedentary forms, to

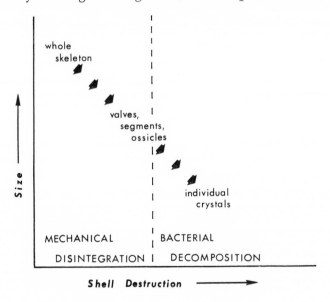

Fig. 10. Mechanical disintegration and bacterial decomposition result in size reduction of organic tests and skeletons.

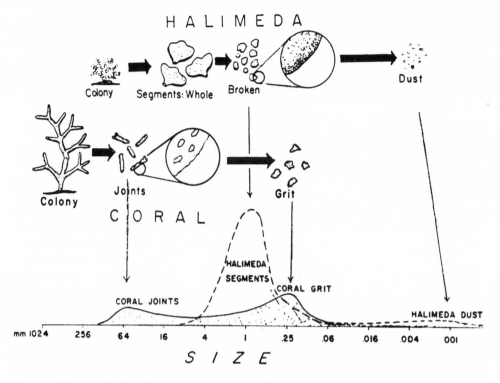

Fig. 11. Estimated abundance and size distribution of a coral (*Acropora*) and a calcareous alga (*Halimeda*) upon postmortem disintegration and decomposition. Note wide size range of skeletal debris which covers several orders of magnitude and depends upon degree of disarticulation and comminution (modified from Folk and Robles, 1964).

flourish. Some of the encrusting and rooted forms grow sufficiently high above the sediment surface that they check the bottom traction currents, providing a quieter water habitat. Slowing of bottom currents by organisms may cause increased deposition of suspended sediment in some places so that relative rates of sediment accumulation may cause local development of a carbonate shoal or bank. Such topographic rises, although small perhaps in absolute dimensions, may provide enough relief in a shallow carbonate sea to alter patterns of water circulation and transport. There may be restriction of water circulation and consequent changes in water characteristics such as salinity, temperature, oxygen, and nutrient content landward of such a rise, while just a small distance away on the ocean side, water characteristics may be quite normal, owing to better circulation with the open oceanic reservoir.

Besides contributing skeletal debris to the sediments and influencing depositional patterns, organisms are also responsible for biologic erosion and comminution of carbonate rocks and shelly remains. In the intertidal and shallow subtidal zones along carbonate rock coasts there are many such boring organisms as filamentous algae, clams, chitons, echinoids, and barnacles which penetrate the rocks and weaken them for further mechanical disintegration by surf action. On a smaller scale, skeletal debris is bored into by filamentous algae and sponges which create internal galleries within the shell material. Bacterial decomposition and oxidation of the organic matrix in these galleries result in the release into the sediments of many small crystals and aggregates of crystals such as aragonite needles and calcite prisms which compose the skeleton. Further discussion of this principle with many interesting examples can be found in Ginsburg (1957), Ginsburg and Lowenstam (1958), Cloud (1959), and Purdy (1963), among others.

Textures of carbonate sands are dependent upon the nature of the contributing skeletal producers. Textural studies of Recent carbonate sediments indicate that the size, shape, and sorting of grains are as dependent upon the nature of the architecture of the skeletons being produced in an environment as they are upon the local current regimen. This principle has been carefully documented by Folk and Robles (1964) and termed the "Sorby Principle" after H. C. Sorby, who originally demonstrated this relationship between skeletal architecture and sediment type.

As noted earlier, calcareous skeletal material is usually secreted as a mosaic of many small crystalline units within a proteinaceous organic matrix. Larger skeletal units like segments of a calcareous alga, clam valves, and echinoderm ossicles are held together by organic ligaments or tissue. After death, the organic matrix binding individual crystals or packets of crystals, as well as the larger separate parts of the organism, is decomposed by microorganisms or oxidized. The skeleton, consequently, disintegrates (Fig. 10) into various larger fragments (segments, valves, ossicles) and smaller grains (aragonite needles, calcite prisms). The total range of sediment sizes can be produced by just a few different organisms, dependent upon their original skeletal architecture and degree of disarticulation and disintegration. For example, the reef coral *Acropora cervicornis*, and the green calcareous alga *Halimeda*, can together produce calcareous grains that range from blocks up to several tens of centimeters long down to very fine-grained dust just a few microns in diameter (Fig. 11).

Current activity, of course, also plays a complementary role in determining sediment texture. Currents contribute to skeletal disintegration and may remove the finer-grained fraction as rapidly as it is being produced, leaving behind a coarse skeletal residue. Awareness of this principle should obviate the overly simplified conclusion that coarse-grained carbonate rocks are merely the depositional products of an area with strong water currents whereas fine-grained carbonates are quiet-water products. A corollary to this principle of biologic sorting is that the grain size of a pelletal carbonate sand, if fecal in origin, may provide little or no information about the local current regime; it indicates only something about the physical size of the pelleting organism.

Amount of mud matrix as a guide to water energy and circulation. From the foregoing principles it might reasonably be asked that if the constituent grains of a carbonate sediment are strongly dependent upon the nature of the organic skel-

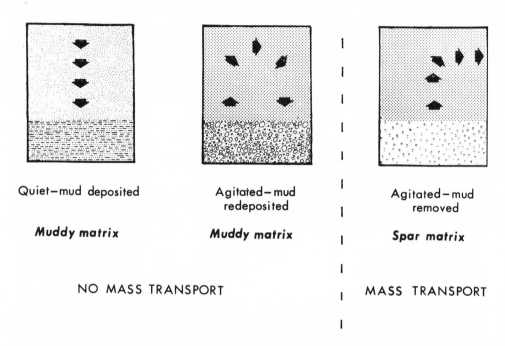

Fig. 12. Mutual importance of water agitation *and* mass transport in removing fine-grained carbonate sediment from its site of production (see text).

etal debris being locally formed, and if there is little lateral transportation of sand-sized calcareous particles, then is there *any* hydrodynamic significance to the texture of a carbonate sediment? Fortunately, the answer is a qualified yes.

The accumulation of the finer-grained, muddy fraction of a carbonate sediment, roughly the amount less than 1/16 mm in diameter, is indeed dependent upon local conditions of water agitation and mass transport. Other things being equal, carbonate sediments that are deposited in quieter water will have a muddy matrix, while sediments deposited in more agitated water will have the mud fraction winnowed out with only the coarser fraction left behind. Upon burial and diagenesis the mud becomes a fine-grained, dark, "lithographic" matrix; in mud-free calcareous sediments, a matrix of calcite spar is deposited within the interstices of the grains. (Actually, aragonite cement is usually deposited initially and later inverts to calcite.)

The relative proportion of mud matrix (micrite) to spar matrix (sparite), therefore, becomes an index of water agitation or energy. Several different classification schemes have been recently proposed for carbonate rocks, which use the relative abundance of mud to spar as a major descriptive parameter (Ham, 1962). The practical value of this parameter is that it can be easily measured in thin sections or acetate peels of carbonate rocks; it does not require physical disaggregation of the rock, which is, of course, impossible for ancient carbonates.

Mud accumulation, however, is a function not only of water agitation but also of the mass transport of the local waters, so that even if water is turbulent owing to the action of waves and tides, mud will not be removed unless the suspended material can be transported away from the site of mud production (Fig. 12). This means that a muddy, calcareous sediment may be the result of restricted water circulation as well as of "quiet water" accumulation. For example, the waters of the interior of the Great Bahama Bank and Florida Bay are regularly stirred up by storms but, because these water masses have relatively poor circulation with the deeper open ocean, the mud thrown into suspension eventually resettles and continues to accumulate (Ginsburg, 1956; Purdy and Imbrie, 1964, p. 28). Hence, relative rates of mud production (whether by organic secretion, skeletal disintegration, or inorganic precipitation) and mud removal by mass transport will control the net accumulation of a muddy matrix, possibly masking any local differences in water agitation. This discussion should also make it apparent that mud-to-spar ratios by themselves provide little information regarding depth of deposition.

Relative rates of physical and organic reworking have environmental significance. Many bottom-dwelling marine invertebrates, including clams, snails, arthropods, and polychaete worms, seek shelter or food below the sediment/water interface. As noted earlier, their burrowing activities will destroy internal, inorganic primary structures such as bedding, cross-stratification, grain sorting and orientation, and textural variations. Studies by Seilacher (1964) and Moore and Scruton (1957), among others, have discussed the morphology of organic burrows as well as the sedimentologic effect of burrowers in terrigenous clastic sediments. These authors point out that preservation of a sediment which has been physically reworked by wave and tidal currents or biologically reworked by burrowers depends upon the relative rates at which these two forces operate. For instance, beach sediments which are continuously reworked by surf action show excellent primary stratification, while sediments accumulating in a quiet lagoon are thoroughly homogenized by the abundant local infauna.

Carbonate sediments have not been as extensively studied from this particular point of view, but preliminary results reported by Imbrie and Buchanan (1965) indicate that the same conclusions apply here as in terrigenous marine deposits. For example, sediments accumulating along the margin of the Great Bahama Bank (coralgal or skeletal sands, and oolite) are being constantly reworked by flooding and ebbing tides as well as by oceanic swells so that they preserve their primary stratification and fabric. However, sediments from the Bank interior which are relatively protected from reworking by current traction are thoroughly stirred up by organisms and lack any primary current structures (Fig. 13). Biogenic structures, therefore, characterize quieter, more protected submarine deposits where the rate of current reworking of the sediments is less, com-

BEACH DEPOSIT
current stratified

LAGOON DEPOSIT
burrow mottled

Fig. 13. Two box cores from the top foot or so of calcareous sediments from the Great Bahama Bank. Left: Well-preserved laminations in beach deposit formed by wave wash and backwash in coarse skeletal sands. Right: Burrow-mottled grapestone sands from shallow subtidal area protected from strong bottom current action (from Imbrie and Buchanan, 1965).

pared to rates of organic reworking. Conversely, abundant, well-preserved primary structures ought to characterize higher-energy, more open marine waters where the rate of physical reworking is greater than organic reworking. Consequently, presence and relative abundance of inorganic and organic sedimentary structures when used with other supporting evidence may be useful for interpreting ancient environments.

These nine principles from studies of Recent carbonate environments have been selected for their level of general paleoecological significance, variety of informational content, and high degree of substantiation in a readily accessible literature. As has been pointed out, they are also extremely useful in the analysis and interpretation of ancient carbonate rocks and associated fossil assemblages. But, once established, in what sort of investigative framework can these principles be

most effectively used? In the remainder of this paper some of the tactical problems and principles in studying the paleoecology of ancient rocks and fossils will
be considered.

SOME TACTICS FOR PALEOECOLOGICAL ANALYSIS

Need for Lateral Facies Studies

Because of the strong historical factor inherent in geology, many geological investigations emphasize a "vertical" approach; that is, they describe and interpret
phenomena at just a few localities from the oldest to youngest set of available observations. While such studies are often quite informative, it is at least as important to hold time constant and to observe geologic phenomena as they vary laterally. Lateral variations result, of course, from differing initial conditions or rate
changes among geologic processes.

In paleoecological studies where the desired goal is to understand and relate
the original environmental factors which limit the abundance and distribution of
fossil assemblages, it is particularly critical to examine a relatively thin stratigraphic interval that is essentially parallel in time to see how different fossil assemblages vary from place to place in response to changing environmental conditions
that are inferred from the lithologic attributes of the enclosing rocks (Figs. 14,
15). Obviously, such lateral facies studies are best done where the strike of the
stratigraphic interval of interest is normal to the original depositional strike. In
this way one can proceed from one environment to the next and observe organism
interactions with the laterally varying environments. Recent sediment–organism
studies are pursued in this way, and similar tactics for the ancient ought to be employed.

Now, while such lateral facies studies were originally proposed long ago by
Gressly (1838, p. 10–11) only rather recently have paleoecologists followed this
specific approach. Too often, instead, paleoecological interpretations have been
made from a few vertical sequences of rocks, the assumption being that the observed vertical variations in composition of the rocks and fossil assemblages are
due to differing but related sedimentary environments. Such an assumption, while
reasonable, may be unwarranted because major breaks in environmental regimen
may occur within such sequences without being conspicuously recorded within.
For example, local regressions and transgressions may occur, leaving only subtle
traces too easily overlooked (Perkins, 1966). Lateral facies studies will detect
changes in overall regimen by the sudden juxtaposition of a new facies which
cannot be integrated with the other changing but interrelated facies.

But even more important than this is the fact that only lateral facies studies
can define the geometry, hydrography, and water-energy level of the original
sedimentary basin, factors which bear critical relationships to the accumulating
sediment types and to the ambient organic communities. Shoreline position, eco-

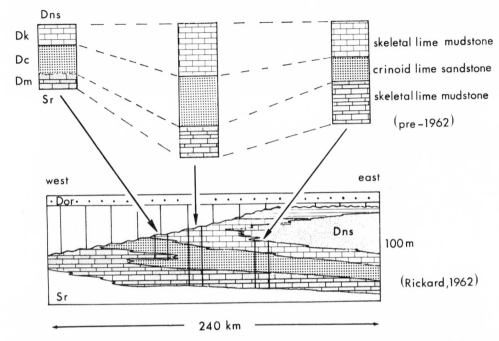

Fig. 14. Restored section of the Lower Devonian Helderberg group of New York State. Upper part of figure shows original interpretation of Helderberg stratigraphy where Manlius, Coeymans, and Kalkberg limestones (Dm, Dc, and Dk respectively) were correlated as time stratigraphic units. Lower part of figure shows re-interpretation of these Helderberg units as laterally interfingering carbonate units which migrated westward with time (Rickard, 1962). This new interpretation was made possible by very careful lateral tracing of these units across central New York from west of Syracuse eastward to the Hudson Valley. The Helderberg carbonates are underlain gradationally by the late Silurian–early Devonian Rondout Formation (Sr); higher Helderberg units—New Scotland Formation (Dns) and younger strata—are also shown. The Helderberg sequence is truncated by a pre-Oriskany erosion surface and is overlain by the Oriskany Sandstone (Dor).

logical gradients, and location of shoals, banks, and deeps can only be reliably predicted by lateral facies analysis. As Fischer (1964) indicated, integrated vertical and lateral stratigraphic analysis is necessary to unravel paleoecological problems. They are complementary, each providing a feedback and check on the other.

The Rule of Analogy

While it is currently fashionable in certain geologic circles to agonize over the truth of the venerable Lyellian dictum that the present is a key to the past, it is nevertheless true that many analogues between processes and products of Recent carbonate sedimentation can be found in the geologic record. In fact, some an-

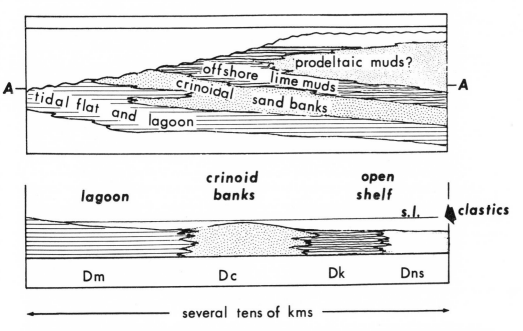

Fig. 15. Paleoecologic interpretation of the Helderberg carbonates as based on principles of Recent carbonate deposition. Lower part of figure shows diagrammatic cross section of major Helderberg depositional environments; upper part of figure shows stratigraphic result as these environments migrated westward during the early Devonian Helderberg transgression in New York State.

cient sequences simply could not be correctly understood until their modern counterparts were discovered and explained (e.g. algal stromatolites, supratidal dolomitization, oolite formation).

Paleoecological studies require, therefore, collateral search for modern, environmental analogues that can serve as models with which to compare the ancient examples. It may well be that not all ancient geologic processes and situations exist today but experience has shown that one cannot assume this unless and until careful search proves otherwise. Naturally, the paleoecologist must have sufficient imagination and flexibility to realize that details will indeed be different in comparisons of the Recent and the ancient. But by and large, it seems that most of the same sorts of environmental processes, products, and relationships that existed in the past are extant today.

Need of an Environmental Datum

A paleoecological study following facies variations laterally requires the establishment somewhere within the ancient framework of an environmental datum with which all facies can be referred and integrated. For example, certain modern carbonate facies like coral reefs, oolite shoals, and supratidal laminites are reasonably well known and ecologically restricted so that their presence in the ancient

Table 1. Comparison of Various Inorganic and Organic Features of the Manlius Formation (Lower Devonian) with Recent Carbonate Environments of South Florida and the Great Bahama Bank

Manlius	Recent analogue	Reference
Algal stromatolites and oncolites	Intertidal and just below low tidal level in Florida Keys and Andros Island, Bahamas	Ginsburg, 1960; Logan et al., 1964
Laminated dolomitic pelletal muds with mudcracks and birds-eye	Supratidal areas in Florida Keys and Andros Island	Shinn & Ginsburg, 1964; Shinn et al., 1965
Limestone-pebble conglomerates; interbedded skeletal sands and lime muds	Intertidal zone of Florida Keys	Baars, 1963; Laporte, personal observation
Scattered oolites and coated grains	Just below intertidal zone, Great Bahama Bank	Newell et al., 1960; Purdy, 1961

immediately provides a reliable datum for interpreting related but less well understood facies, particularly those containing extinct groups of organisms and lacking distinctive lithologic attributes.

Table 1 shows a comparison of various inorganic and organic features of the Manlius Formation (Lower Devonian) with Recent carbonate environments of South Florida and the Great Bahama Bank. The rule of analogy indicates that the depositional environments of the Manlius were very shallow, subtidal to supratidal in origin. Recognition of these environments provides an environmental datum for interpreting other related Helderberg facies. Such environmental keys usually provide information regarding shoreline direction or position of open oceanic environments. Consequently, intelligent guesses can be made about the position of depositional strike and ecological gradients, thereby permitting additional highly relevant observations to be made in the ancient which might otherwise have been ignored.

Lateral Migration of Facies to Form a Vertical Stratigraphy

Stratigraphers for a long time now have been aware that major depositional environments shift laterally with time, typically during major marine transgressions and regressions. Such shifts, however, can also occur on much smaller, more local scales so that within a thin stratigraphic interval, specific individual horizons may record changing sites of facies deposition. These horizons might have significant lateral persistence up to several miles or more and yet may still represent the locus of a migrating, areally restricted, subenvironment rather than a short depositional interval occurring simultaneously across the entire sedimentary basin.

Such shifting of facies is especially characteristic of carbonate deposition where water depths are ordinarily quite shallow, so that even minor changes in rates of sediment deposition and accumulation can effect rather large environmental changes. For example, the accretion of carbonate banks and shoals in shallow water can change surrounding sedimentation patterns markedly. Lateral migration of such topographic highs will produce a variable vertical stratigraphy which is a complex mosaic of advancing and retreating carbonate environments (Fig. 16). Too often such sequences are interpreted as the result of eustatic sea-level changes rather than as local migrations of related shallow-water carbonate environments.

Recognition of small-scale migrations of different subenvironments within a carbonate sequence is facilitated by lateral facies studies, so that the geometry of individual units can be defined and interrelated. Facies studies emphasizing vertical relationships usually result in hypotheses of multiple eustatic sea-level fluctuations that strain geologic credulity.

DIAGNOSIS AND PROGNOSIS

Having attempted to synthesize some principles for the study and paleoecological interpretation of ancient carbonate rocks and fossils, it is appropriate to conclude with a few remarks about where carbonate paleoecology stands today and what future developments appear likely.

Despite the tone and emphasis of this paper, and in most paleoecological investigations in general, paleoecology is really much more than definition and interpretation of sedimentation patterns within a stratigraphic interval. The ambient depositional environment must, of course, be initially established but, once established, serious further effort must be made to explain the particular factors operating in the environment in limiting the presence and abundance of the associated fossils. Furthermore, it is necessary to make comparative analyses of fossil assemblages of differing composition to determine the reasons for recurring associations of specific taxa within them (Johnson, 1962; Moore, 1964; Valentine and Mallory, 1965; see also Table 2 and Fig. 17).

In some instances the aggregations of different species may be the result of overlapping ecologic tolerances of the individual component species (Fig. 18). In other cases these aggregations may represent a complex system of energy transfer operating through several different feeding levels (Fig. 19). Assemblages of organisms, therefore, while definitely influenced by the local environment, may be either "statistical associations" on the one hand or "integrated communities" on the other. The actual degree to which assemblages of organisms are either one or the other is a source of debate among marine ecologists (Thorson, 1957). The important point, however, is that whatever the degree of species interaction, the composition of the assemblage is environmentally controlled and must be so explained.

Further paleoecological interpretation enters the area of autecology where the adaptive relationships of individual taxa to the environment are analyzed. Studies of living, related taxa, their functional morphology, and comparative anatomy become especially relevant here. We may conclude, therefore, that current

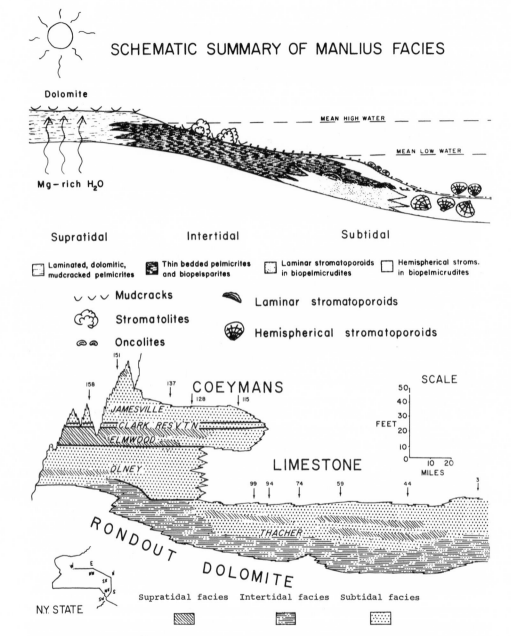

Fig. 16. Three facies found in Manlius Formation (Lower Devonian) of New York State (upper figure). Lateral migration of facies within Manlius depositional regime results in complex facies mosaic as seen today in Manlius stratigraphy (lower figure). Supratidal flats at times built out or prograded across intertidal and shallow subtidal deposits; at other times the supratidal deposits themselves were overridden by intertidal and subtidal sediments (from Laporte, 1967).

Table 2. *Composition of Groups of Mutually Associated Species in Pennsylvanian Collections.* From Johnson, 1962.

GROUP I

2	*Fenestrellina* sp.	Bryozoa
3	*Fistulipora carbonaria*	Bryozoa
8	*Chonetes granulifer*	Articulate brachiopod
10	*Cleiothyridina orbicularis*	Articulate brachiopod
11	*Composita* sp.	Articulate brachiopod
13	*Derbyia* sp.	Articulate brachiopod
14	*Dictyoclostus* sp.	Articulate brachiopod
15	*Echinoconchus semipunctatus*	Articulate brachiopod
16	*Hustedia mormoni*	Articulate brachiopod
21	*Marginifera splendens*	Articulate brachiopod
24	*Neospirifer* sp.	Articulate brachiopod
26	*Punctospirifer kentuckyensis*	Articulate brachiopod
63	Crinoid sp.	Crinoid

GROUP II

12	*Crurithyris planoconvexa*	Articulate brachiopod
31	*Cymatospira montfortianus*	Gastropod
33	*Euphemites carbonarius*	Gastropod
34	*Glabrocingulum grayvillense*	Gastropod
38	*Pharkidonotus percarinatus*	Gastropod
40	*Strobeus* sp.	Gastropod
43	*Pseudorthoceras knoxense*	Cephalopod
45	*Astartella* sp.	Pelecypod
52	*Nuculopsis girtyi*	Pelecypod

GROUP III

7	*Orbiculoidea missouriensis*	Inarticulate brachiopod
46	*Cardiomorpha missouriensis*	Pelecypod
47	*Clinopistha radiata*	Pelecypod
49	*Lima* sp.	Pelecypod
55	*Solemya radiata*	Pelecypod
56	*Solemya trapezoides*	Pelecypod

GROUP IV

6	*Lingula* sp.	Inarticulate brachiopod
48	*Dunbarella* sp.	Pelecypod
50	*Myalina* sp.	Pelecypod
58	*Spirorbis anthracosia*	Polychaete

GROUP V

5	*Rhombopora lepidodendroides*	Bryozoan
9	*Chonetina* sp.	Articulate brachiopod
22	*Mesolobus m. decipiens*	Articulate brachiopod
61	*Ditomopyge parvulus*	Trilobite

GROUP VI

30	*Bucanopsis tenuilineata*	Gastropod
32	*Donaldina robusta*	Gastropod
36	*Meekospira choctawensis*	Gastropod
41	*Trepospira*	Gastropod

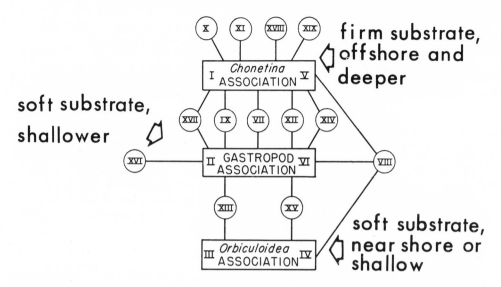

Fig. 17. Integration of nineteen separate groups of mutually associated fossil invertebrates from the Pennsylvanian into three major associations. Preliminary paleoecologic analysis suggests some of the ecologic factors that differentiate these major associations. See Table 2, which shows six of the nineteen groups (from Johnson, 1962).

paleoecological investigations are just beginning to provide data which tell us what organisms occur where. But the more significant contribution of paleoecology is to tell us *why* these organisms occur where they do—an adaptive rather than a teleological why, of course.

A second area for future paleoecological research is that once biofacies patterns are established through time—no small task in itself—the temporal changes of the biofacies must be explained through the geologic record, even though the associated lithofacies have remained essentially the same. For example, what can we say about the evolution of organic reefs through time, where sedimentation patterns are relatively similar but the specific taxonomic categories have changed considerably? Have the ecologic roles of the individual members of the community remained constant with only the taxonomic actors changing, or have there indeed been significant changes in the community structures as well? E. C. Olson has written a provocative paper regarding the evolutionary changes in the community structure of late Paleozoic and early Mesozoic terrestrial tetrapods and how these changes were linked to the rise of mammals (Olson, 1961; and Figs. 20, 21). Similar studies of community evolution in marine carbonate fossil communities will undoubtedly shed light on the evolution of marine shelly invertebrates as a whole. In fact, it is here that I believe carbonate paleoecology will make its major contribution to the study of the history of life. For if carbonate lithofacies are essentially the same in the ancient record as they are today, then it is possible to define and interpret the environmental conditions under which they formed, by using the present as a guide to the past. And, if ancient carbonate

RANGE OF ENVIRONMENTAL TOLERANCE

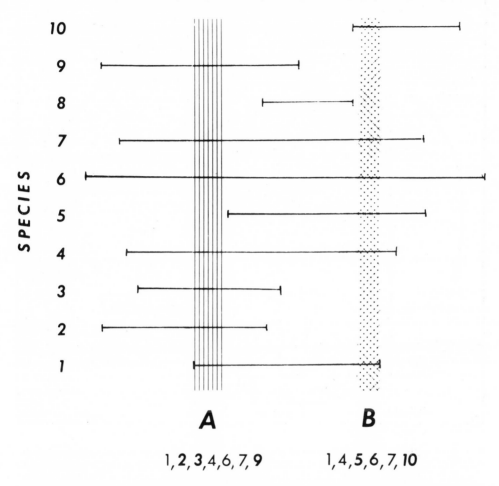

Fig. 18. How two different fossil assemblages will share some species in common (species 1, 4, 6, 7) because of overlapping ecologic tolerances; the other species are unique to each assemblage. In both cases the association of the individual species is the result of mutual ecologies with a minimum of species interaction.

biofacies and lithofacies share common environmental causes, once we under-stand lithofacies origins we will be able to explain biofacies patterns and their change through geologic time. Finally, if evolutionary changes in carbonate bio-facies parallel those of other marine invertebrate fossil assemblages, which they seem to do, knowledge of the factors that explain temporal variations in carbo-nate biofacies ought to shed light on marine invertebrate evolution as a whole. Invertebrate fossil history will then be explained not so much in terms of "what happened?"—as it is today—but "why did it happen?"

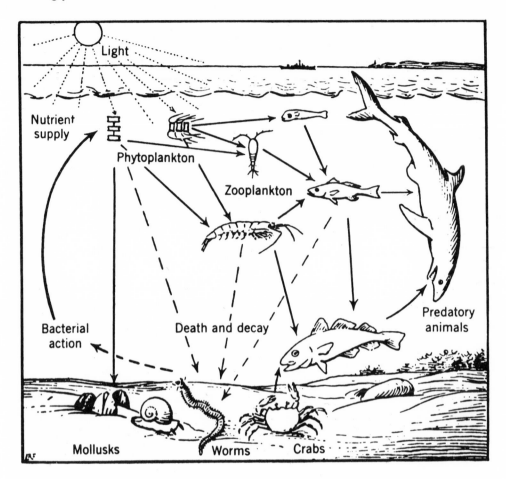

Fig. 19. Feeding relationships and trophic levels within a Recent marine community. In this case the association of the individual species is the result of feeding requirements as well as mutual ecologies with a maximum of species interaction (from Clarke, 1954).

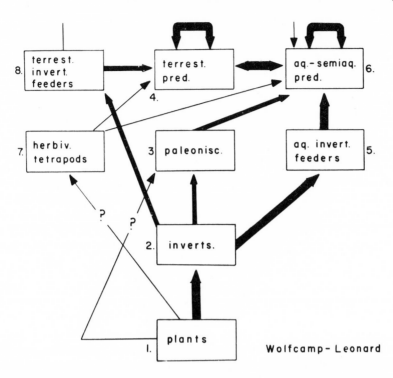

Fig. 20. Food web among early Permian organisms; terrestrial predatory tetrapods (4) besides feeding on each other have as their main food source terrestrial invertebrate feeders (8) and aquatic and semiaquatic predators (6). Compare with Figure 21 (from Olson, 1961).

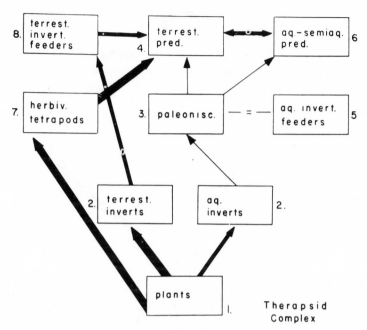

Fig. 21. Food web among certain early Triassic organisms; terrestrial predators now have as their chief food source terrestrial herbivorous tetrapods (7), relying less on the terrestrial invertebrate feeders and aquatic and semiaquatic predators. Hence this particular early Mesozoic community shows a distinct shift in the flow of energy from one trophic level to the next, culminating in the therapsid, or mammal-like reptiles, compared with the late Paleozoic community shown in Figure 20 (from Olson, 1961).

REFERENCES

Baars, D., 1963. Petrology of carbonate rocks. In *Shelf Carbonates of the Paradox Basin,* R. O. Bass, ed. Four Corners Geol. Soc., 4th Field Conf. Symp., p. 101–29.

Clarke, G. L., 1954. *Elements of Ecology.* Wiley, New York, 560 p.

Cloud, P. E., Jr., 1959. Geology of Saipan, Mariana Islands: Part 4. Submarine topography and shoal-water ecology. *U.S. Geol. Surv. Prof. Paper 280–K,* p. 361–445.

Fischer, A., 1964. Stratigraphic basis of paleoecology. In *Approaches to Paleoecology,* J. Imbrie and N. D. Newell, eds. Wiley, New York, p. 32–42.

Folk, R. L., and R. Robles, 1964. Carbonate sands of Isla Perez, Alacran reef complex, Yucatán. *J. Geol., 72:* 255–92.

Ginsburg, R. N., 1956. Environmental relationships of grain size and constituent particles in some South Florida carbonate sediments. *Am. Assoc. Petrol. Geologists Bull., 40:* 2384–27.

——, 1957. Early diagenesis and lithification of shallow-water carbonate sediments in South Florida. In *Regional Aspects of Carbonate Deposition,* R. J. Le Blanc and J. Breeding, eds. Soc. Econ. Paleontologists and Mineralogists Spec. Publ. no. 5, p. 80–99.

——,1960. Ancient analogues of recent stromatolites. Internat. Geol. Cong., 21st sess., pt. 22, p. 26–35.

Ginsburg, R. N., and H. A. Lowenstam, 1958. The influence of marine bottom communities on the depositional environment of sediments. *J. Geol., 66:* 310–18.

Ginsburg, R. N., and E. A. Shinn, 1964. Distribution of the reef-building community in Florida and the Bahamas. *Am. Assoc. Petrol. Geologists Bull., 48:* 527 (abstr.).

Ginsburg, R. N., R. M. Lloyd, K. W. Stockman, and J. S. McCallum, 1963. Shallow-water carbonate sediments. In *The Sea,* v. 3, M. N. Hill, ed. Interscience, New York, p. 554–82.

Gressly, A., 1838. Observations géologiques sur le Jura Soleurois. *Neue Denkschr. allg. Schweiz. Ges. ges Naturw., 2:* 1–112.

Ham, W. E., ed. 1962. Classification of carbonate rocks. *Am. Assoc. Petrol. Geologists Mem., 1:* 1–279.

Imbrie, J., and H. Buchanan, 1965. Sedimentary structures in modern carbonate sands of the Bahamas. In *Primary Sedimentary Structures and their Hydrodynamic Interpretation,* G. V. Middleton, ed. Soc. Econ. Paleontologists and Mineralogists Spec. Publ. 12, p. 149–72.

Imbrie, J., L. F. Laporte, and D. F. Merriam, 1964. Beattie Limestone facies (Lower Permian) of the northern midcontinent. *Kansas Geol. Surv. Bull., 169:* 219–38.

Johnson, R. G., 1962. Interspecific associations in Pennsylvanian fossil assemblages. *J. Geol., 70:* 32–55.

Laporte, L. F., 1967. Carbonate deposition near mean sea level and resultant facies mosaic: Manlius Formation (Lower Devonian) of New York State. *Am. Assoc. Petrol. Geologists Bull., 51:* 73–101.

Logan, B., R. Rezak, and R. N. Ginsburg, 1964. Classification and environmental significance of algal stromatolites. *J. Geol., 72:* 68–83.

Lowenstam, H. A., 1957. Niagaran reefs in the Great Lakes area. In *Treatise on Marine Ecology and Paleoecology,* v. 2. J. W. Hedgpeth and H. S. Ladd, eds. Geol. Soc. Am. Mem. 67, p. 215–48.

Moore, D. G., and P. C. Scruton, 1957. Minor internal structures of some recent uncon-solidated sediments. *Am. Assoc. Petrol. Geologists Bull.*, 41: 2723–51.

Moore, R. C., 1964. Paleoecological aspects of Kansas Pennsylvanian and Permian cy-clothems. *Kansas Geol. Surv. Bull.*, 169: 287–380.

Newell, N. D., J. Imbrie, E. G. Purdy, and D. L. Thurber, 1959. Organism communities and bottom facies, Great Bahama Bank. *Am. Mus. Nat. Hist. Bull.*, 117: 177–228.

Newell, N. D., E. G. Purdy, and J. Imbrie, 1960. Bahamian oolitic sand, *J. Geol.*, 68: 481–97.

Olson, E. C., 1961. The food chain and the origin of mammals. In *International Col-loquium on the Evolution of Lower and Nonspecialized Mammals*, v. 1. Konink-lijke Vlaamse Academie voor Wetenschappen, Letteren en Schone Kunsten van Belgie, p. 97–116.

Perkins, B. F., 1966. Rock-boring organisms as markers of stratigraphic breaks. *Am. Assoc. Petrol. Geologists Bull.*, 50: 631 (abstr.).

Purdy, E. G., 1961. Bahamian oolite shoals. In *Geometry of Sandstone Bodies*, J. A. Peterson and J. C. Osmond, eds. Am. Assoc. Petroleum Geologists, Tulsa, Okla., p. 53–62.

——, 1963. Recent calcium carbonate facies of the Great Bahama Bank (Parts 1 and 2). *J. Geol.* 71: 334–55, 472–97.

Purdy, E. G., and J. Imbrie, 1964. Carbonate sediments, Great Bahama Bank. In *Guide-book Field Trip 2, November, 1964.* Geol. Soc. Am. Annual Convention, Miami, Fla.

Rickard, L. V., 1962. Late Cayugan (Upper Silurian) and Helderbergian (Lower De-vonian) stratigraphy in New York. *N.Y. State Mus. Sci. Service Bull.* no. 386, 157 p.

Seilacher, A., 1964. Biogenic sedimentary structures. In *Approaches to Paleoecology*, J. Imbrie and N. D. Newell, eds. Wiley, New York, p. 297–316.

Shinn, E., and R. N. Ginsburg, 1964. Formation of recent dolomite in Florida and the Bahamas. *Am. Assoc. Petrol. Geologists Bull.*, 48: 547 (abstr.).

Shinn, E., R. N. Ginsburg, and R. M. Lloyd, 1965. Recent supratidal dolomite from Andros Island. In *Dolomitization and Limestone Diagenesis*, L. Pray and R. C. Murray, eds. Soc. Econ. Paleontologists and Mineralogists Special Publ. 13, p. 112–23.

Thorson, G., 1957. Bottom communities (sublittoral or shallow shelf). In *Treatise on Marine Ecology and Paleoecology* v. 1., J. W. Hedgpeth and H. S. Ladd, eds. *Geol. Soc. Am. Mem. 67*, 1: 461–534.

Valentine, J. W., and B. Mallory, 1965. Recurrent groups of bonded species in mixed death assemblages. *J. Geol.*, 70: 32–55.

James Edward Heath

8. THE ORIGINS OF THERMOREGULATION

Some years ago C. Ladd Prosser observed that the real marvel of living things is that they are so similar (1960). Much of the excitement of modern molecular biology derives from this fact. Yet the generality that is so clearly seen at the molecular or even cellular level often becomes obscured at higher levels of integration. In spite of similarity, delineation of distinctions between a veneer of adaptations, either general or special, and the more profound pattern is often difficult and hazardous. The study of thermoregulation proves to be no exception.

Over 2,000 years ago Aristotle proposed an organization of the mineral and living world which included warm versus cold blood as an important distinction between higher and lower animals. His arrangement of living forms was flexible, and it admitted of some fine gradations between levels of complexity.

A recent study of behavioral versus physiological regulators (Yamamoto, 1965) reveals that this ancient Greek dichotomy is as lively as ever. However, the accumulation of knowledge has changed greatly the definition of the two categories. Perhaps equally important is a new viewpoint developed by systems engineers and lately applied to biological problems (Ashby, 1956; Hardy, 1961). This approach is concerned less with the nature of regulatory mechanisms than with the way a mechanism operates to accomplish regulation. It discards superficial differences and promises to expose the essential fabric of regulatory mechanisms.

Yamamoto (1965) has proposed that behavioral or poikilostatic responses can be distinguished from homeostatic ones by only two basic properties. First, poikilostasis does not require internal receptors since it can depend upon external senses. It is therefore not necessarily error-actuated. Second, poikilostasis does not alter "sources and sinks" (in a narrow context, heat production and heat loss) but acts by altering the "class of random processes" the animal is exposed to (behavioral responses). I wish to examine these properties critically, and then, with a clearer vision of the nature of thermoregulation among terrestrial organisms, to suggest trends in the evolution of thermoregulation.

THE RECEPTORS

The location of receptors can be examined in two ways. First, are all physiological responses to temperature necessarily cued internally? Second, are some behavioral responses independent of external sensation?

Among mammals, current research shows that deep internal thermal receptors, especially the hypothalamus, can no longer be considered the absolute control point for body temperature. Often responses to heat and cold are initiated by
peripheral receptors. A few examples will make this clear.

One component of mammalian and avian thermoregulation involves changes
with temperature in the rate of perfusion of peripheral tissues. These vasomotor
changes influence the flux of heat from the body. Experimental heating and cooling of the hypothalamic region cause major changes in the perfusion of superficial
structures. For example, the pinna of the ear may act alternatively as an insulator
or heat exchanger (Hammel, 1965). On the other hand, insulative changes due to
vasomotion occur more generally as "anticipatory" responses to stress (Hardy,
1961, 1965). A sudden exposure to cold ambient conditions causes constriction of
superficial vessels and an increase in insulation before there is a detectable change
in hypothalamic temperature. The hypothalamic temperature may even increase
temporarily (Hardy, 1961). Presumably, receptors located at the extreme periph-
ery sense a sudden temperature change and initiate vasomotor adjustments. The
amount of vasomotor change depends on the rate of change of temperature at
peripheral receptor sites. Among reptiles, and perhaps other vertebrates, vasomotor response to temperature is present (Cowles, 1958b; Bartholomew and
Tucker, 1963). It is largely a peripherally sensed, rate-control process. In lizards, vasomotion favors increased heat flux between a cold animal and hot surroundings, and decreased flux between a hot animal and cold surroundings (Bartholomew and Tucker, 1963). However, warming and cooling of the reptilian
hypothalamus produces vasomotor adjustments in turtles similar to those of mammals (Rodbard, 1948; Rodbard et al., 1950; Heath et al., MS).

Panting among reptiles, birds, and mammals begins when the internal temperature exceeds some set-point value (Hardy, 1961; Heath, 1965; King and
Farner, 1961). Evaporative hyperventilation occurs even in insects in response
to high temperature of the interior of the body (Edney and Barrass, 1962; Adams
and Heath, 1964a). Among sheep, hyperventilation and evaporative cooling depend more upon the temperature in the scrotum than upon hypothalamic temperature (Waites, 1961, 1962; Waites and Voglmayr, 1963).

Even the more internalized mechanisms of temperature control such as heat
production are subject to modification by external temperature receptors. Table 1
relates heat production to hypothalamic temperature in a man. Both the critical
temperature for the initiation of increased heat production and the magnitude of
the response are sensitive to external temperature conditions (Benzinger et al.,
1963). Clearly, even large mammals under nearly ideal conditions rely upon
peripheral receptors to trigger adjustments in heat production.

Among higher taxa there are no purely poikilostatic or homeostatic animals.
Externally sensed, non-error-actuated behavioral responses to temperature are
found among all the groups. There are also internally sensed error-actuated behavioral responses in each group (Satinoff, 1964; Heath, 1964a). Yamamoto's criteria based upon receptor site fail in all ways to distinguish a homeostat from a
poikilostat.

Table 1. *Set Points of Human Temperature Regulation*
From Benzinger et al., 1963.

Ambient temperature (°C)	Critical temperature, cranial (°C)	Heat production (cranial temp. 36.4°C) (cal/sec)
30	36.8	~40
28	37.0	~52
26	37.1	~64
20	37.1	~88

CONTROL OF SOURCES AND SINKS

The second specific set of criteria relates to effector mechanisms. Physiological regulators control production and loss of heat whereas behavioral regulators alter their location and postures. The previous discussion of panting and vasomotor control applies equally to the effector side of the argument. For example, whether one chooses reptiles (Warburg, 1965), birds (King and Farner, 1961), or mammals or insects (Edney and Barrass, 1962), the net result of panting and hyperventilation is a decrease in body temperature, provided random processes of ambient temperature and humidity are favorable. At high temperatures all of these animals are homeostatic.

Ignoring some special mechanisms, such as sweating in mammals or special evaporative devices of moths (Adams and Heath, 1964a), the distinction between homeostat and poikilostat reduces to a single criterion, the production of heat to resist cooling. Birds and mammals adjust their heat production against heat loss to arrive at a balance that keeps their internal temperature constant. The rate of heat loss depends upon the amount of insulation and the area of the interface between the organism and the environment (Scholander et al., 1950). Mammals have arrived at a thermal balance in three ways. The arctic fox is an insulative specialist. Its heat production is low over a wide range of temperatures. At ambient temperatures above a critical level it must lose heat largely by vascular, evaporative, and behavioral changes, or suffer hyperthermia. An elephant is a surface-to-volume expert. Simply by being large, its rate of heat loss is low over a wide range of temperatures (Benedict, 1936). The shrew is a heat-production expert (Morrison et al., 1959). Its small size precludes a long, dense pile. However, a large scope of metabolism permits this animal to maintain its body temperature in very hostile situations. All other mammals and also birds fall within the extreme limits represented by the fox, elephant, and shrew.

These three animals, and in fact most birds and many mammals, maintain their body temperatures at high and relatively constant levels from birth to death. However, some mammals and birds have compromised their thermal homeostasis to some extent either seasonally or even daily (Pearson, 1960). Hibernators, aestivators, and animals which undergo regular daily torpor restrict thermal homeostasis in the ordinary sense to critical periods in their lives. During these periods they carry out the prime functions of existence. Similarly, reptiles and insects may restrict their activity to critical times of day or season when ambient conditions are favorable. The line between poikilostat and homeostat becomes tenuous in this context.

Among vertebrates, only birds and mammals have developed external insulative materials—fur and feathers. However, some insects have an external pile. Beneath the "furry" surface of a large moth, for example, lies one of the most energetic tissues in the entire animal kingdom—flight muscle. The machinery for heat production and an insulative material to decrease heat loss are both present. A thermocouple implanted in the thorax reveals that a moth can produce sufficient heat to warm many degrees centigrade above ambient temperature (Dotterweich, 1928; Oosthuizen, 1939; Krogh and Zeuthen, 1941; Dorsett, 1962). Periods of an hour or more of high heat production may occur regularly and spontaneously in these insects (Adams and Heath, 1964b) and over a wide range of ambient temperatures (Heath and Adams, 1965). Figure 1 shows a spontaneous period of activity measured from sphingid, saturniid, and arctiid moths, and a hummingbird. During active periods the moths feed and seek mates. The initiation of a period of activity begins by a special "warmup" behavior (Dotterweich, 1928; Dorsett, 1962). In all these moths the warmup is not an accidental result of flight. Indeed, one of the traces shown is from *Celerio lineata* (Sphingidae), and this moth cannot fly at all below 28°C. Except for the duration of activity and the range and apparent set points of temperatures, there is little to distinguish these traces from those of warm-blooded vertebrates. The extent and importance of heat production among insects is unknown. Insulative materials are found among Lepidoptera (Church, 1960), Hymenoptera and Coleoptera (Krogh and Zeuthen, 1941), and Neuroptera (Adams, personal communications). Church (1960) discovered that some dragonflies have a series of air sacs, lying just beneath the surface of the thorax, which restrict the outward flow of heat. Increased thoracic temperature resulting from heat production in the flight muscles has been described for only a few species of each order. Until more is learned of the thermostat and integrative mechanisms involved in insect heat regulation, it is perhaps best to call their responses behavioral thermogenesis.

Even the so-called cold-blooded vertebrates occasionally generate noticeable heat. Some large varanid lizards produce an internal heat excess of 2°C during artificially stimulated activity (Bartholomew and Tucker, 1964). However, the most significant case is that of brooding pythons. Female pythons not only warm their clutch of eggs by violent contraction of their trunk muscles but also regulate the temperature of the clutch to 31–32°C at ambient temperatures from 26–30°C (Hutchinson et al., 1966).

Cold-blooded vertebrates have also had their bulk specialists. Undoubtedly, the giant Mesozoic saurians encountered only small fluctuations in body temperature from day to day (Colbert et al., 1946). Given a small heat production and the vasomotor mechanisms of modern reptiles, it is conceivable that these giants were as thermally stable as any bird or mammal.

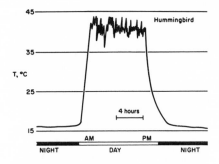

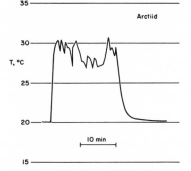

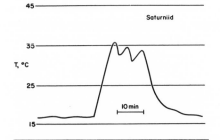

Fig. 1. Heat production during activity by moths and a bird. The arctiid weighed 0.13 gm; the other moths averaged 1–2 gm. The hummingbird curve was synthesized from data given by Pearson (1950), Bartholomew et al., (1957), and Lasiewski (1964). Note the difference in time scale.

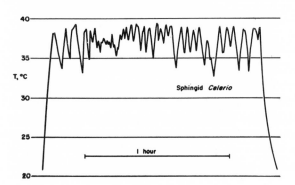

In summary, all properties of warm-bloodedness are found at least incipiently in reptiles and insects. Peripheral temperature receptors are more important in mammalian thermoregulation than was realized a few years ago. On the other hand, the cold-blooded terrestrial animals may rely largely on internal receptors. Most of the effectors of mammalian and avian thermoregulation are present among reptiles. However, sustained and controlled heat production is perfected only by birds and mammals and to a lesser extent by insects.

Cowles (1962) recognized this and suggested that the temperature responses of terrestrial organisms be divided into two broad categories. Animals which rely upon internal heat production to regulate temperature he called endotherms. Those that rely upon external heat sources he called ectotherms. This classification disposes of confusion generated by misleading terminology and focuses upon the essential difference, and it will be adopted here. Part of my task is to account for the development of heat-producing mechanisms in pre-avian and pre-mammalian reptiles and to account for a paralellism by some insects. However, this will require some background information on behavioral regulation of temperature.

BEHAVIORAL REGULATION

Just as there are similarities between endotherms and ectotherms, there are also some important differences. Most terrestrial organisms regulate internal temperature by more or less elaborate systems of motor patterns. If one allows for the diversity of morphology and adaptation between groups such as butterflies and lizards, some general properties of behavioral regulators emerge. Temperature is maintained not to a single level but to a range of temperatures. The limits of the range are often sharp, and each limit is associated with a set of distinctive behavior patterns. The execution of one of these patterns results in the return of body temperature to the prescribed range. Within the regulated range the organism need do little to alter heat flux. Table 2 compares ranges, set points, and motor patterns for several animals. The range is usually 5°C or more wide. Under natural conditions the organism often reaches and stays within the range for long periods in thermal equilibrium and without need for regulatory adjustment (Heath, 1964, a and b; Heath, 1967). A regulated range rather than a single set point means the animal need not alter repeatedly the arena of its activity in order to regulate temperature. One can hardly imagine a more commodious arrangement.

Each limit of the regulatory range is to some extent independently determined by the demand of the habitat. Thus, the desert horned lizard *Phrynosoma m'calli* has a set point of 40.4°C for the shade-seeking motor pattern, whereas the coastal species *Phrynosoma coronatum* exhibits the same pattern at 37.7°C. Both species leave the shade between 34° and 35°C. This relationship is repeated among several other thermoregulatory patterns (Table 3).

The set points of the regulatory range are largely insensitive to the rate of heat flux, and they remain constant in spite of varying thermal conditions. Horned lizards change the frequency of shuttling movements between sunlit areas and shade with time of day (Heath, 1965). Even when the average duration of forays into direct sunlight averages as little as two minutes, the animals still retreat to shade at about 37.7°C. This is strong evidence that the pattern is elicited by a central receptor sensing deep-body temperature. On the other hand, peripheral

Table 2. Set Points of Behavioral Temperature Regulation

Animal	Range (°C)	Set point (°C)	Motor pattern
Ectotherms			
Iguanidae			
Phrynosoma coronatum	3.5	37.7	Shade-seeking
		34.2	Leave shade
Phrynosoma m'calli	5.5	40.4	Shade-seeking
		34.9	Leave shade
Cicadadae			
Magicicada cassini	6.8	31.8	Shade-seeking
		25.0	Leave shade
Endotherms			
Sphingidae			
Celerio lineata	2.9 – 3.2	38.0	Cessation of shivering
		37.7	Shade-seeking
		34.8	Resumption of shivering
Saturniidae			
Rothschildia jacobae	~4	36	Cessation of shivering
		~32	Resumption of shivering

Table 3. Set Points of Behavioral Temperature Regulation in Two Closely Related Ectotherms

Animal (habitat)	Panting (°C)	High temp. burrow- ing (°C)	Shade seeking (°C)	Area change (°C)	Leave shade (°C)	Head-up burrowing (°C)
Phrynosoma coronatum (coastal grassland)	43.2	40.5	37.7	37.4	34.2 NS*	35.3 NS
P. platyrhinos (desert)	44.1	41.0	39.1	38.9	35.7 NS	36.9 NS

* NS = P > 0.5

reception seems relatively unimportant in controlling regulatory behavior. These patterns also show the same detector-to-effector relationships, on-off, proportional, and rate controls, that are found in mammals (Heath, 1965).

Among tropical reptiles such as the green iguana (Bogert, 1959) or shade-selecting anoles (Ruibal, 1961) responses to prevent overheating are well developed. Because of the warmth of their habitat they do not need elaborate responses to cold. Very likely, the early terrestrial vertebrates also possessed only evaporative cooling, vasomotion, and a few behavioral patterns to regulate temperature (Cowles, 1958, a and b).

One major line in the evolution of thermoregulation has been an elaboration of behavioral mechanisms as adaptation to severe and more "temperate" habitats. Figure 2 demonstrates the complexity achieved by some modern reptiles.

Although the receptor sites for temperature and many of the effector mechanisms of temperature regulation are common between ectothermic and endothermic vertebrates (Hammel et al., 1967), the regulated internal temperature is rather constant in birds and mammals; but it regularly fluctuates in reptiles through a 3–5°C range. Is the endothermic integrative system derivable from that of ectotherms?

ORIGIN OF THERMAL REGULATION IN MAMMALS

The origins of mammals from reptilian stock are well known in their general aspects. Paleontologists, familiar with the mammal-like appearance of therapsid remains from Triassic beds, tend to favor the idea that these animals were progressing rapidly toward homeothermy. By convention, the loss of the reptilian jaw suspension and making of the dentary–squamosal joint separate the therapsids from true mammals (Simpson, 1960). However, many mammalian characteristics may have developed either before or after the acquisition of the mammalian jaw suspension (Brink, 1955). Indeed, Crompton (1958) described an intermediate animal, *Diarthrognathus,* which had a double articulation involving both the reptilian and the mammalian jaw suspension.

Brink (1955) listed several mammalian characteristics of therapsids. He found evidence of a diaphragm and development of ethmoturbinal bones for increased olfactory surface or warming and moistening inspired air. He also discussed the possible presence of vibrissae and sweat glands on the snout. The dentition of therapsids was differentiated, although it was mammal-like only in general aspects. At the same time the secondary palate developed, possibly to permit simultaneous mastication and respiration. These data led Brink to propose that some advanced therapsids were homeothermic; later (1959) he described a specimen of *Thrinaxodon liorhinus* discovered in a peculiarly mammal-like position. He suggested the position may have served to reduce heat loss. The animal was buried by a flood without disturbing its posture. It may have died during a hibernation period. This is a tempting explanation. Van Valen (1960) agreed that therapsids had some degree of homeothermy. Although all the mammal-like

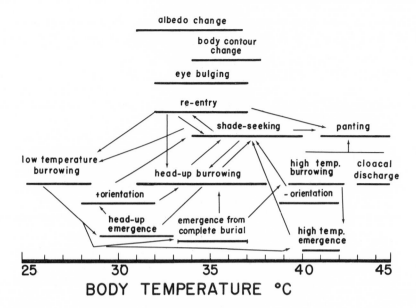

Fig. 2. Thermoregulatory ethogram of *Phrynosoma coronatum* (after Heath, 1965). The bars represent the range; arrows represent transitions. The sum of these activities results in regulation of body temperature to a prescribed range.

characteristics could be explained away—for example, the position of *Thrinaxodon* was accidental, or crocodilians have longer secondary palates than most mammals —the occurrence among therapsids of these mammalian facies when viewed in concert is impressive.

Therapsids possibly behaved more like mammals than like reptiles (Colbert, 1958). For example, the differentiated dentition of therapsids indicates that their feeding behavior was mammalian. On the other hand, the therapsid ear structure was still quite reptilian. Behavior associated with hearing was presumably also reptilian. Reed (1960) nevertheless proposed that therapsids be included in the class Mammalia. He argued that therapsids were homeothermic and that this was in part responsible for the changed posture and activity of therapsids.

I believe that most of the mammalian characteristics of therapsids can be traced not to "warm-bloodedness" but to a shift from the sprawling gait of pelycosaurs to the limb-supported posture of therapsids (Fig. 3). A diaphragm, secondary palate, differentiated teeth, even a moist nose, and expanded ethmoturbinal bones could be modifications to permit rapid respiration during high activity and rapid replacement of depleted energy stores. I believe that the shift in posture led not only to the development of mammalian temperature regulation but also to basic changes in the organization of the central nervous system.

During periods of rapid locomotion, therapsids must have experienced an increase in internal temperature above that of the surroundings, much like modern varanids. However, lizards produce insignificant quantities of heat at rest.

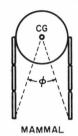

Fig. 3. Resting stance of a reptile and a mammal. The weight of the mammal is borne by the limbs; the reptile rests directly on the ground. CG, center of gravity; ø, angle of stability.

Very likely therapsids differed in this respect. The skeletal remains of therapsids suggest that they adopted the fixed pillar stance of modern mammals. This stance requires a great deal of activity in the muscles about the fixed joints, in the anti-gravity muscles of the back, and in the muscles of the pectoral girdle. Further, this posture demands more than increased muscular activity and tucking the limbs under the body. It requires sweeping changes in muscular organization from the action of muscle masses. (Vaughn, 1956) to the activity of the postural motor unit.

Among amphibians and to a lesser extent living reptiles, the muscles receive a double innervation—large nerve fibers with few endings on the muscle and smaller fibers with many endings. Stimulation of the large fibers produces an all-or-none twitch in the muscle. Stimulation of small fibers produces a graded local contraction within some motor units (Kuffler and Gerard, 1947). Muscular tone in the frog is produced by summing many small graded contractions. This is largely the case in reptiles as well (Zhukov, 1965). Mammals do not possess the graded contractile mechanism in skeletal postural muscles at all. Rather the postural motor unit responds in an all-or-none fashion. A steady pull upon a muscle's tendon is produced by summing the random twitch contractions of many motor units. The mammalian mechanism is simpler and perhaps offers greater control than the amphibian system of the magnitude of tension produced about the joint (Ruch and Patton, 1965). The tension in a mammalian muscle can change rapidly and with less delay than can frog or tortoise muscle (Zhukov, 1965). As a result of a shift in posture, then, mammal-like reptiles probably acquired *accidentally* a system to provide heat even at rest.

Among modern mammals, the tonic mechanism provides about 30 per cent of the heat production at basal levels (Jansky, 1962). The contractile mechanism accounts for 60 per cent of the response of rats to cold (Davis and Mayer, 1955b). Jansky (1962) obtained similar figures but included the basal metabolism of muscles to arrive at 73 per cent of the response to cold. Davis and Mayer (1955a) found a smooth transition from tonic activity in rats to full shivering. This smooth transition suggests that shivering is closely related to maintenance of tone and may have evolved from the tonic mechanism.

Noncontractile thermogenesis was probably elaborated later in mammalian evolution. Maher (1965) found increased metabolism after thyroid treatment of lizards. This response is sensitive to temperature and occurred only when the body temperature of the lizard was high (over 30°C). Increased sensitivity to thyroid hormones and a high body temperature may account for part of the difference between the basal metabolic rates of mammals and reptiles.

A high internal heat production requires an effective transport system to provide adequate nutrients and remove wastes. A four-chambered heart and reorganized vascular tree could have developed in response to a high oxygen demand resulting from exercise in therapsids. Tucker (1966) suggested that differences in the physiological properties of mammalian and reptilian circulation can be related in part to the high respiratory demand of mammals during exercise.

Adoption of a new posture required changes in the central nervous system to handle increased sensory input and to produce finer muscular control. There is a progressive increase in the size of the cranial vault among therapsids (Van Valen, 1960) which probably reflects the increasing role of the forebrain in sensory analysis and integration. Although endocranial casts of Jurassic and early Cretaceous mammals show only conspicuous increases in the size of the olfactory bulbs, by late Cretaceous, major alterations in the structure of the tectum indicate the culmination of a long trend toward reorganization of acoustic and visual input (Edinger, 1964). Both lines of modern mammals have somatotopically organized sensory projections into the forebrain (Lende, 1964), while most modern reptiles (Kruger and Berkowitz, 1960) and birds (Northcutt, 1966) have only diffuse projection. The parallelism between monotremes, and marsupial and placental mammals, suggests that these trends began with therapsid reptiles. The therapsid forebrain must have had localized and specific areas for sensory projection, which implies that the neocortex had begun to differentiate from the general cortex of earlier reptiles. Although the olfactory sense may have been accentuated at first (Edinger, 1964), the primary projection of olfaction is not to neocortex in any case. Further, modern reptiles which rely upon olfactory senses have not extended the size or importance of general cortex (Ariens-Kappers et al., 1936). More likely, a greater significance of visual input to motor coordination in rapidly moving therapsids compared to slowly moving reptiles increased tectocerebral interaction. In a more general way, Westoll (1963) suggested that the shift in posture from the reptilian to the mammalian stance presented therapsids with more information about the environment and began a trend toward greater intelligence.

There is evidence of changes in motor coordination as well. Amphibians possess the beginnings of the cortically originated extrapyramidal motor system (COEPS) of mammals (Herrick, 1948). In modern mammals the extrapyramidal system is concerned with gross postural control (Patton, 1965). It is connected through basal and midbrain nuclei to lower motor centers. It is at least partially somatotopically organized in placental mammals, but its condition in monotremes is not known. The COEPS is absent in lizards, crocodilians, and probably birds (Northcutt, 1966). It probably underwent modification during the initial changes in therapsid posture. However, the extrapyramidal system must have proved inadequate to control locomotion in therapsids.

Mammals have a second motor system absent in all other living vertebrates. This system projects directly from neocortex to both the red nucleus of the pons and to spinal motor centers. It is concerned with fine motor control. The pyramidal system originates in somatotopically organized cortex in marsupials, placentals, and monotremes (Lende, 1964). This suggests it originated with therapsids. The pyramidal system is evident in the gross anatomy of the brain and spinal cord, where it shows as cerebral peduncles, pons, and pyramids. Edinger (1962) doubted that any of these structures existed in therapsids. However, Olson (1944) described a pons in several therapsids. The existence of a pons correlates with an increase in cerebellar size, which signaled the beginning of the neocerebellum of mammals. Therapsids may have possessed the short feedback circuit of mammals which operates in locomotor integration. The appearance of a pons may also indicate changes in respiratory control of therapsids, perhaps involving a diaphragm. The origin of all mammalian brain specializations may have begun in response to the locomotor shift of therapsids.

I now hope to piece together the information available to outline a possible history of mammalian thermal regulation. Although Reed (1960) suggested that sphenacodonts might have been endothermic, there seems little to support his view. Therapsids must have possessed some vasomotor control of temperature and effective panting. Their small, reptile-like forebrain suggests that their behavior was highly stereotyped. Support of their bodies above the ground implies some basic shifts in the postural mechanism, especially a more active tonic mechanism intermediate between reptiles and mammals. This change in muscle activity proceeded simultaneously with the development of a diaphragm to provide ventilation of the lungs largely in response to exercise. The first therapsids probably possessed only white or fast muscle; "slow" or red postural muscles developed later. The red muscle system would grant greater stability. Its development might parallel the reduction in tail size among late therapsids.

Body temperature probably depended upon a combination of physiological mechanisms and selection of suitable environment. The central nervous integration of temperature remained reptilian. Therapsids probably experienced fluctuations in body temperature with activity but restricted the fluctuations to within a regulated range of temperature. The position of *Thrinaxodon,* referred to earlier, might suggest that it could arouse from low body temperature by increased tone in the skeletal muscle. However, the undisturbed repose of this animal suggests its arousal mechanism was limited. Therapsids, in general, probably lacked a complete shivering mechanism. Large therapsids may have had consistently high, but variable, body temperatures because of poor dissipation of heat.

For several million years therapsids remained the largest terrestrial carnivores. Their rapid locomotion might have forced contemporary sauropsids to develop more rapid running ability. By late Triassic, sauropsids developed a bipedal gait and possibly as great a speed as therapsids, at lower metabolic cost. In any case the therapsids disappeared, leaving the large carnivore niche to bipedal dinosaurs. The limb-supported posture and short tail of Cretaceous ceratopsians suggest a parallel with the mammal-like reptiles of several tens of millions of years before.

The successors to therapsids were much smaller animals. The brain of these early mammals continues the trend toward greater utilization of peripheral sensing. If the Jurassic and Cretaceous mammals resulted from capitalization upon internal heat production to exploit small size, then certain limitations of small "warm-blooded" animals may suggest something of their biology. These small mammals may not have maintained a high body temperature during inactive periods. Perhaps they conserved energy by undergoing daily torpor like modern bats or murine opossums (Morrison and McNab, 1962). The full exploitation of small size required development of a shivering mechanism in order to permit rapid warming from torpor to activity independent of surrounding temperature. Such activities also require effective insulation. If these small mammals underwent frequent torpor, there would be little advantage in refinement of the regulatory control inherited from therapsids.

The final stage in the development of mammalian temperature regulation began in late Cretaceous and Eocene times with elaboration of neocortex and full utilization of peripheral sensing. Mammals in these periods became larger and could no longer afford major fluctuations in internal temperature (Johansen, 1962). Peripheral receptors gradually modified the role of hypothalamic receptors of temperature in the control circuits of thermal regulation. The hypothalamic centers of modern mammals still require large changes ($\sim 2°C$) in brain temperature to stimulate thermoregulatory responses. However, such large changes do not occur frequently in nature. Instead, there seem to be two independent set points, one for cold and one for warm responses, just as in reptiles (Table 4). Each set point is variable and at least partially determined by ambient conditions (Hammel, 1965). Although the set points may completely overlap in modern mammals, under fixed ambient conditions, there is a surprisingly reptilian aspect to the temperature sensitivity of the hypothalamus. The modern mammalian thermoregulatory system anticipates changes in heat flux of the body by peripheral receptors and thereby avoids fluctuation of body temperature.

The chronology set forth is hypothetical. It does correspond to changes in size and adaptive trends in the phylogenetic lines leading to modern mammals.

Table 4. Set Points of Temperature Regulation in the Dog
  From Hammel, 1965.

Ambient temperature	Hypothalamic Temperature		
	Thermogenesis	*Panting*	*Range*
(°C)	(°C)	(°C)	
13.5	38.8	41	2.2
23.0	36.8	38.8	2.0

THE ORIGIN OF THE THERMOREGULATION OF BIRDS

The development of thermoregulation in birds followed a different course than in mammals. Although the general aspects of avian thermoregulation have been well studied, the details of the mechanisms have not received the intense inspection given to mammals. In addition, the fossil record of birds is fragmentary. However, the close morphological relationship of birds to reptiles and their analogy with insects give clues to the development of avian thermoregulation.

The impressions of *Archeopteryx* in the Jurassic beds clearly show that this bird-like reptile possessed aerodynamic feathers. A long, feathered tail means these animals belong to the class of stable fliers. They could glide from perch to perch, but they had not developed the musculature for flapping flight. Cowles (1946) suggested that the evolution of insulative materials must precede large heat production. The development of feathers prior to the acquisition of flight musculature in birds supports this contention.

The next fossils are found in Cretaceous strata, but by that time birds were fully developed. Clearly, the fossil record is inadequate to detail the early evolution of birds. However, if heat production is the primary difference between reptilian and avian thermoregulation, we can trace, by analogy from insects, some of the events leading to avian homeothermy.

Powered flight is an energetic process. Since muscle is not a perfect machine, a great deal of heat is produced incidental to flight. For example, Church (1960) found that the desert locust *Schistocerca gregaria* produces a heat excess of 6°C during flight. An excess of 4°C is found among periodical cicadas (Heath, unpublished). Whether a heat excess is ecologically important in insects can be documented only by field studies. In June 1965, while studying cicadas in Ohio, I had such a rare opportunity. One morning began with a heavy overcast. Male cicadas, *Magicicada septendecim,* sat about on prominent twigs in basking positions waiting for the sun to break through the overcast. Body temperatures of these animals were all within a fraction of 19°C. Although they can fly at this temperature, they will not do so voluntarily. Yet a few individuals were flying and actively singing. Body temperatures of these animals were 22–24°C. Since the flying cicadas could not have reached those temperatures by basking, they must have begun flying for one reason or another, and had warmed sufficiently to reach temperatures of normal activity. I verified this by simply knocking quiet males from their perches. The disturbed animals spread their wings and flew about awkwardly. Within a few moments, they began alternately flying and singing in cicada fashion. They were then captured and their body temperatures measured. They had reached 22–24°C. Meanwhile, inactive basking animals remained at 19°C. The few active individuals gained two to three hours of activity that morning over their quiescent comrades. Even small and incidental increases in body temperature may occasionally extend the activity period significantly. The cicadas probably do not encounter conditions like those I described often enough to develop behavioral patterns to capitalize on this heat production. Further, *Magicicada* is gregarious, and mating is not dependent upon the performance of any individual male. Among solitary species, for example *Tibicen canicularis*, more active males might have an advantage. The example illustrates what could be called incipient behavioral thermogenesis.

Among other insect groups, selection has operated differently so that much larger temperature excesses are produced, and body temperature is maintained to a narrow temperature range.

There is little doubt that heat production and regulation among birds evolved along similar lines. "Warm-bloodedness" in birds and in moths resulted from capitalization upon the incidental heat produced in flight. Many of the refinements in avian respiratory and circulatory anatomy and physiology probably evolved, as with mammals, in response to the metabolic demands of exercise.

Similarly, pterosaurs were endothermic to some extent (Romer, 1945). These flying reptiles were not strictly gliders. At least one group of pterosaurs, Pterodactyloids, developed unstable, powered flight. Further, some pterodactyls possessed hair-like structures (Romer, 1945). However, these may have served only tactile functions.

Further discussion of the evolution of avian temperature regulation is hampered by insufficient data. The general response of birds to cold is shivering. Nonshivering thermogenesis may exist in some birds (Freeman, 1966), but it may still involve the contractile tissue. What is the nature of tonus in birds? Is there a graded tonic response like that of reptiles, or have birds independently developed the mammalian, all-or-none motor unit? If there was a shift to twitch tonus, did this begin with the shift to bipedal posture in ancient reptiles? Since crocodilians are near the stem of thecodont reptiles, similar questions might be posed of these animals.

Birds have largely eliminated the cerebral cortex. Extrapyramidal motor control probably does not exist in birds (Northcutt, 1967). What then, is the nature of the central nervous tonic circuitry? Since the bird forebrain continues a trend begun in reptiles to striatal development and suppression of cortex, does this indicate that birds have retained an essentially reptilian perception of the thermal environment?

Birds normally undergo large fluctuations of body temperature especially in response to activity. Such fluctuations might mean the hypothalamus of birds still functions as the absolute sensor of body temperature and that it utilizes a minimum of peripheral sensory information. Are there anticipatory mechanisms other than vasomotion in birds? Dawson (1962) suggested that the central nervous integration required for thermoregulation of birds was probably present in ancestral reptiles. Is the bipartite behavioral temperature control of reptiles still discernible in the responses of birds? Without answers to these and many other questions, the problem of the origin of avian thermoregulation must remain very sketchy. However, when the details of avian thermal reception and integration are worked out, they need not mirror the mammalian system. Rather, they may reflect the independent development of thermoregulation by birds.

SUGGESTIONS FOR FURTHER WORK

The speculations made here cannot be fully explored without comparative investigations of the muscular mechanisms of tonus and its central nervous circuitry among higher vertebrates. Much more must be known of the control of temperature in reptiles, birds, and mammals. However, the crucial evidence of evolution always lies in the fossil record.

We need information on the angle of stability of the bodies of fossil reptiles (Fig. 3), on the distribution of weight upon the limbs, and on the size of postural muscles. With these data we can calculate the stresses and forces about supporting joints. The heat production of muscles supporting the joints and maintaining posture can then be estimated. We can also estimate the temperature excesses produced by activity. We would then be in a better position to speculate upon the time of appearance and the extent of endothermy among fossil reptiles. We can continue to hope to discover imprints of hair associated with the bones and trackways of fossils as a further clue.

Progressive refinement of locomotion and increased receptivity to sensation are associated with changes in the size and external features of the brain. Our interpretation of these changes depends upon a better knowledge of the neuroanatomy of living forms. With this knowledge in hand, we will be better able to interpret the endocranial casts made of fossil forms.

CONCLUSIONS

Thermoregulation developed in higher vertebrates and insects probably to withstand the rapid fluctuations of temperature in the terrestrial environment. The differences in temperature responses among each of the groups, although superficially very striking, are few. The most significant is the independent development of high internal heat production by birds, mammals, and some insects to oppose cold stress.

Endotherms appear to regulate body temperature to a single set point, whereas ectotherms have both high and low points separated by several degrees centigrade. Endothermic insects have clearly retained the bipartite regulatory mechanism, while mammals and perhaps birds have obscured the two ectothermic set points by increasing the role of peripheral temperature receptors. Ectotherms commonly undergo fluctuations in temperature and can rely upon a rigid internal receptor or receptors. Endotherms cannot afford the large losses or gains in heat content required to produce deviations of internal temperature. They rely heavily upon externally sensed "anticipatory" responses to thermal stress. This hypothesis opposes the generally held view, but it is consistent with the trend among mammals toward increased peripheral sensitivity.

Endothermy probably developed several times among Mesozoic animals. Early birds, several groups of insects, and possibly pterodactyls capitalized upon the high energy production in flight to arrive at varying degrees of endothermy. Among mammal-like reptiles, a shift to limb-supported posture required refinements in the musculature which ultimately led to control of internal heat for temperature regulation. The development of endothermy in each group accompanied or proceeded from experimentation with new locomotor patterns.

Acknowledgments. I thank J. S. Willis and R. G. Northcutt for critically reading the manuscript and for their penetrating comments which helped immeasurably in the formulation of the ideas presented here. Many refinements of my speculations resulted from conversations with B. C. Abbott, P. A. Adams, R. B. Cowles, W. R. Dawson, M. S. Gordon, H. S. McDonald, and C. L. Prosser. This work was supported by National Science Foundation Grant GB-3702.

REFERENCES

Adams, P. A., and J. E. Heath, 1964a. An evaporative cooling mechanism in *Pholus achemon* (Sphingidae). *J. Res. Lepidoptera*, 3(2): 69–72.

——, 1964b. Temperature regulation in the sphinx moth, *Celerio lineata. Nature*, 201: 20–22.

Ariens-Kappers, C. U., B. C. Huber, and E. C. Crosby, 1936. *The Comparative Anatomy of the Nervous System of Vertebrates Including Man*, reprinted 1960. Hafner, New York.

Ashby, W. R., 1956. *An Introduction to Cybernetics.* Chapman & Hall, London.

Bartholomew, G. A., and V. A. Tucker, 1963. Control of changes in body temperature, metabolism, and circulation by the agamid lizard. *Amphibolurus barbatus. Physiol. Zool.*, 36(3): 199–218.

——, 1964. Size, body temperature, thermal conductance, oxygen consumption and heart rate in Australian varanid lizards. *Physiol. Zool.*, 37(4): 341–54.

Bartholomew, G. A., T. R. Howell, and T. J. Cade, 1957. Torpidity in the White-throated Swift, Anna Hummingbird and Poor-will. *Condor,* 59: 145–55.

Benedict, F. G., 1936. *Physiology of the Elephant.* Rept. No. 474, Carnegie Inst., Washington.

Benzinger, T. H., C. Kitzinger, and A. W. Pratt, 1963. The human thermostat. In *Temperature—its measurement and control in science and industry*, J. D. Hardy, ed., pt. 3, Biology and Medicine. Reinhold, New York, p. 637–65.

Bogert, C. M., 1959. How reptiles regulate their body temperature. *Sci. American, 200:* 105–20.

Brink, A. S., 1955. Speculations on some advanced mammalian characteristics in the higher mammal-like reptiles. *Palaeontologia Africana, 4:* 77–96.

———, 1959. Note on a new skeleton of *Thrinaxodon liorhinus, Palaeontologia Africana,* 6: 15–22.

Church, N. S., 1960. Heat loss and the body temperature of flying insects. Parts I and II. *J. Exp. Biol., 37* (1): 171–212.

Colbert, E. H., 1958. Morphology and behavior. In *Behavior and Evolution,* A. Roe and G. G. Simpson, eds. Yale Univ. Press, New Haven, p. 27–47.

Colbert, E. H., R. B. Cowles, and C. M. Bogert, 1946. Temperature tolerances in the American alligator and their bearing on the habits, evolution and extinction of the dinosaurs. *Bull. Am. Mus. Nat. Hist., 86:* 327–74.

Cowles, R. B., 1946. Fur or feathers; A result of high temperatures? *Science, 103:* 74–75.

———, 1958a. Additional notes on the origin of the tetrapods. *Evolution, 12:* 419–21.

———, 1958b. Possible origin of dermal temperature regulation. *Evolution, 12* (3): 347–57.

———, 1962. Semantics in biothermal studies. *Science, 135:* 270.

Crompton, A. W., 1958. The cranial morphology of a new genus and species of ictidosaurian. *Proc. Zool. Soc. London, 130:* 183–216.

Davis, T. R. A., and S. Mayer, 1955a. Nature of the physiological stimulus for shivering. *Am. J. Physiol., 181:* 669–74.

———, 1955b. Demonstration and quantitative determination of the contributions of physical and chemical thermogenesis on acute exposure to cold. *Am. J. Physiol., 181:* 675–78.

Dawson, W. R., 1962. The evolution of avian temperature regulation. In *Comparative Physiology of Temperature Regulation,* J. P. Hannon and E. Viereck, eds. Arctic Aeromedical Lab., Ft. Wainwright, Alaska, p. 45–72.

Dorsett, D. A., 1962. Preparation for flight by hawk-moths. *J. Exp. Biol., 39:* 579–88.

Dotterweich, H., 1928. Beiträge zur Nervenphysiologie der Insekten. *Zool. Jahrb. Physiol., 44:* 399–450.

Edinger, T., 1964. Midbrain exposure and overlap in mammals. *Am. Zool., 4:* 5–20.

Edney, E. B., and R. Barrass, 1962. The body temperature of the tsetse fly *Glossina morsitans* Westwood (Diptera, Muscidae). *J. Insect. Physiol., 8:* 469–81.

Freeman, B. M., 1966. The effect of cold, noradrenaline and adrenaline upon the oxygen consumption and carbohydrate metabolism of the young fowl (*Gallus domesticus*). *Comp. Biochem. Physiol., 18:* 369–82.

Hammel, H. T., 1965. Neurons and temperature regulation. In *Physiological Controls and Regulations,* W. S. Yamamoto and J. R. Brobeck, eds. Saunders, Philadelphia, p. 71–98.

Hammel, H. T., F. T. Caldwell, and R. M. Abrams, 1967. Regulation of body temperature in the blue-tongued lizard. *Science, 156:* 1260–62.

Hardy, J. D., 1961. Physiology of temperature regulation. *Physiol. Rev., 41* (3): 521–606.

———, 1965. The "set-point" concept in physiological temperature regulation. In *Physiological Controls and Regulations,* W. S. Yamamoto and J. R. Brobeck, eds. Saunders, Philadelphia, p. 98–116.

Heath, J. E., 1964a. Head-body temperature differences in horned lizards. *Physiol. Zool., 37* (3): 273–79.

——, 1964b. Reptilian thermoregulation: An evaluation of field studies. *Science, 146:* 784–85.

——, 1965. Temperature regulation and diurnal activity in horned lizards. *Univ. California Publ. Zool., 64*(3): 97–136.

——, 1967. Temperature responses of the periodical "17 year" cicada, *Magicicada cassini* (Homoptera, Cicadidae). *Am. Midland Naturalist, 77* (1): 64–76.

Heath, J. E., and P. A. Adams, 1965. Temperature regulation in the sphinx moth during flight. *Nature, 205:* 309–10.

Herrick, C. J., 1948. *The Brain of the Tiger Salamander.* Univ. Chicago Press, 409 p.

Hutchinson, V. H., H. G. Dowling, and A. Vinegar, 1966. Thermoregulation in a brooding female Indian python, *Python moluris bivittatus. Science 151:* 694–96.

Jansky, L., 1962. Maximal metabolism and organ thermogenesis in mammals. In *Comparative Physiology of Temperature Regulation,* J. P. Hannon and E. Viereck, eds. Arctic Aeromedical Lab., Ft. Wainwright, Alaska, p. 133–74.

Johansen, K., 1962. The evolution of mammalian temperature regulation. In *Comparative Physiology of Temperature Regulation.* J. P. Hannon and E. Viereck, eds. Arctic Aeromedical Lab. Ft. Wainwright, Alaska, p. 73–131.

King, J. R., and S. D. Farner, 1961. Energy metabolism, thermoregulation, and body temperature. In *Biology and Comparative Physiology of Birds,* v. 2, A. S. Marshall, ed. Academic Press, New York.

Krogh, A., and E. Zeuthen, 1941. The mechanism of flight preparation in some insects. *J. Exp. Biol. 18:* 1–10.

Kruger, L., and E. C. Berkowitz, 1960. The main afferent connections of the reptilian telencephalon as determined by degeneration and electrophysiological methods. *J. Comp. Neurol. 115:* 125–41.

Kuffler, S. W., and R. W. Gerard, 1947. The small-nerve motor system to skeletal muscle. *J. Neurophysiol. 10:* 383–94.

Lasiewski, R. C., 1964. Body temperatures, heart and breathing rate, and evaporative water loss in hummingbirds. *Physiol. Zool. 37:* 212–23.

Lende, R. A., 1964. Representation in the cerebral cortex of a primitive mammal. Sensori-motor, visual, and auditory fields in the Echidna. *J. Neurophysiol., 27:* 37–48.

Maher, M. S., 1965. The role of the thyroid gland in the oxygen consumption of lizards. *Gen. Comp. Endocr., 5*(3): 320–25.

Morrison, P., and B. K. McNab, 1962. Daily torpor in a Brazilian murine opossum (Marmosa). *Comp. Biochem. Physiol., 6:* 57–68.

Morrison, P. R., F. A. Ryser, and A. R. Dawe, 1959. Studies on the physiology of the masked shrew *Sorex cinereus. Physiol. Zool., 32:* 256–71.

Northcutt, R. G., 1966. Analysis of reptilian cortical structure. *Nature, 210:* 848–50.

——, 1967. Architectonic studies of the telencephalon of *Iguana iguana. J. Comp. Neurol., 130:* 109–48.

Olson, E. C., 1944. Origin of mammals based upon cranial morphology of the therapsid suborders. *Geol. Soc. Am. Spec. Paper 55:* 1–136.

Oosthuizen, M. J., 1939. The body temperature of *Samia cecropia* (Lepidoptera, Saturniidae) as influenced by muscular activity. *J. Entomol. Soc. S. Africa, 2:* 63–73.

Patton, H. D., 1965. Reflex regulation of movement and posture. In *Physiology and*

Biophysics, T. C. Ruch and H. D. Patton, eds. Saunders, Philadelphia, p. 181–206.

Pearson, O. P., 1950. The metabolism of humming birds. *Condor, 52:* 145–52.

———, 1960. Torpidity in birds. In *Mammalian Hibernation,* C. P. Lyman and A. R. Dawe, eds. *Bull. Mus. Comp. Zool., 124:* 93–105.

Prosser, C. L., 1960. Comparative physiology in relation to evolutionary theory. In *Evolution after Darwin,* v. 1, S. Tax, ed. Univ. Chicago Press, p. 569–94.

Reed, C. A., 1960. Polyphyletic or monophyletic ancestry of mammals, or: What is a class? *Evolution, 14:* 314–22.

Rodbard, S., 1948. Body temperature, blood pressure, and hypothalamus. *Science, 108:* 413–15.

Rodbard, S., F. Sampson, and D. Furguson, 1950. Thermosensitivity of the turtle brain as manifested by blood pressure changes. *Am. J. Physiol., 160:* 402–09.

Romer, A. S., 1945. *Vertebrate Paleontology.* Univ. Chicago Press, 687 p.

Ruch, T. C., and H. D. Patton, 1965. *Physiology and Biophysics.* Saunders, Philadelphia. 1242 p.

Ruibal, R., 1961. Thermal relations of five species of tropical lizards. *Evolution, 15:* 98–111.

Satinoff, E., 1964. Behavioral thermoregulation in response to local cooling of the rat brain. *Am. J. Physiol., 206*(6): 1389–94.

Scholander, P. F., R. Hock, V. Walters, F. Johnson, and L. Irving, 1950. Heat regulation in some arctic and tropical mammals and birds. *Biol. Bull. 99:* 237–58.

Simpson, G. G., 1960. Diagnosis of the classes Reptilia and Mammalia. *Evolution, 14:* 388–92.

Tucker, V. A., 1966. Oxygen transport by the circulatory system of the green iguana (*Iguana iguana*) at different body temperatures. *J. Exp. Biol., 44:* 77–92.

Van Valen, L., 1960. Therapsids as mammals. *Evolution, 14:* 304–13.

Vaughn, P. P., 1956. The phylogenetic migrations of the ambiens muscle. *J. Elisha Mitchell Scient. Soc., 72:* 243–62.

Waites, G. M. H., 1961. Polypnoea evoked by heating the scrotum of the ram. *Nature, 190:* 172–73.

———, 1962. The effect of heating the scrotum of the ram on respiration and body temperature. *Quart. J. Exp. Physiol., 47*(4): 314–23.

Waites, G. M. H., and J. K. Voglmayr, 1963. The functional activity and control of the apocrine sweat glands of the scrotum of the ram. *Australian J. Agric. Res., 14*(6): 839–51.

Warburg, M. R., 1965. The influence of ambient temperature and humidity on body temperature and water loss from two Australian lizards, *Tiligua rugosa* and *Amphibolurus barbatus. Australian J. Zool., 13*(2): 331–50.

Westoll, T. S., 1963. The functional approach to paleontological problems. *Proc. XVI Internat. Cong. of Zool., 3:* 273–77.

Yamamoto, W. S., 1965. Homeostasis, continuity, and feedback. In *Physiological Controls and Regulations,* W. S. Yamamoto, and J. R. Brobeck. Saunders, Philadelphia, p. 14–32.

Zhukov, Ye. K., 1965. Evolution of physiological mechanisms of tonus. In *Essays on Physiological Evolution,* T. M. Turpayev, ed. Pergamon Press, London, p. 339–49.

Stanley D. Beck

9. ENVIRONMENTAL PHOTOPERIOD AND THE PROGRAMMING OF INSECT DEVELOPMENT[1]

An immature insect follows a developmental sequence that is predictable, at least theoretically, because it is genetically determined. As the insect advances through a series of embryonic and larval stages, the pupal stage, and finally attains the adult form, the developmental program followed has involved successive transpositions of coded genetic information into the form of the living system. The prevalent concept is that the larval, pupal, and adult developmental processes are determined by different parts of the total genetic complement. Thus Wigglesworth (1961) has referred to genetic complements that direct "larval synthesis" and to other sets of genes that are involved in "adult synthesis," as if the one individual organism were, from the standpoint of coded genetic information, potentially two—a larval and an imaginal insect. Certainly we do not, at the present time, understand the specific factors determining which genetic code is to be read and translated into the form of the living organism.

Many insects are polymorphic; that is, the body forms manifested may be different under different circumstances, particularly under different environmental conditions of temperature, moisture, day length, and population density. Through these factors the environment reaches into the organism and influences the programming of growth. Perhaps the simplest view of these phenomena is that some alternative pathways of growth and differentiation are possible in such polymorphic species, and that the genetic programming of development includes a degree of freedom in respect to which differentiation program is to be followed. At specific points in the insect's development, "decisions" must be made about which program is to be followed, and such decisions are controlled by an information input from the organism's environmental situation. This concept lies at the foun-

1. Approved for publication by the director of the Wisconsin Agricultural Experiment Station. This study was supported in part by Research Grant GM–07557 from the National Institutes of Health of the U.S. Public Health Service.

dation of Lees' (1961, 1966) accounts of polymorphism in aphids. Lees visualized form determination as involving a series of alternative pathways in which successive decisions were reached during embryonic development as to the sex, mode of reproduction, and wing condition of the adult aphid. Not all alternatives were open to all individuals in every generation. That the so-called decisions concern the choice between developmental *programs* is clearly indicated by the fact that form determination occurs during embryonic development, but the form so determined is not manifested until the insect reaches the adult stage. In such cases the effect of environmental factors is that of influencing the decision as to which of the two or more genetically possible programs is to be followed—not that of modifying the course of a program already being followed.

All insects except the most primitive—the Ametabola—are polymorphic in that they go through several immature stages before attaining the imaginal stage. Certainly, those that display larval and pupal forms that are quite different morphologically from the adult condition can be said to be polymorphic. And when we recall that the number of larval instars may, in many species, vary, we realize that larval and pupal forms may sometimes constitute developmental alternatives. Most frequently there are no alternatives, and as a larva is programmed for a molting cycle, it can be only that of another larval stage or of the pupal stage. In many species, however, temperature, nutritional state, and social environment (as in the case of termites) may influence the developmental programming, so that the immature insect may differentiate in a limited number of alternative directions. The injection or application of juvenile hormone to a last-stage immature insect also may cause local or entire programming for further larval synthesis (see review by Wigglesworth, 1964). In the several cases enumerated, either internal or external information input can be said to have influenced the direction of development, and therefore the programming of development among the genetically possible alternatives.

The problem to be discussed in the present paper is how an environmental factor such as photoperiod might influence the programming of development. The approach that will be taken involves some assumptions concerning the physiology of insect growth and differentiation. These simple assumptions are quite fundamental to the discussion, but they do not represent any significant departures from the well-established concepts that have been developed on the basis of a great body of experimental research by many other workers.

First, it is assumed that the fundamental processes of growth and differentiation do not vary under different environmental conditions. Factors such as temperature and photoperiod may influence the timing of growth and may influence the determination of developmental alternatives followed by the growing organism. But they do not evoke basically different biochemical or physiological mechanisms underlying the growth process.

The second assumption is that insect growth is entirely determined. Recognizing the logical limitations of the concept of determinism, we must assume that growth processes are determined within that conceptual framework. Modification by mutation, for example, cannot lessen the determinism but may of course alter the direction of differentiation. The assumption of determinism really means only that we must not explain a developmental phenomenon in terms of its being "spontaneous" or "inherent." It also means that the so-called decisions between developmental alternatives are determined and do not include any implication of an anthropocentric use of the term.

The third and final assumption concerns the input of information into the biological system. The genetic complement of an organism or a cell is generally regarded as a form of stored coded information. The growth and differentiation of an insect larva must involve sequential retrieval and implementation of such genetic information; indeed, this is what is meant by developmental programming. In polymorphism, however, the cellular or nuclear mechanisms by which the genetic code is read must be susceptible to the action of factors controlling the determination of the programming alternative to be followed. The assumption here is that these determining factors may also be regarded as forms of biological information influencing the determination of the developmental program. This would include the identity and concentrations of hormones and major metabolites, the equilibria within feedback control systems, and the temporal state of circadian rhythmic systems. The last factor may well be an integral part of the other factors mentioned. Although such information must ultimately exert its influence at the molecular level in the cell, its origin may be traceable to the action of environmental factors. Such extrinsic informational input may come as sensory stimuli, temperature conditions, nutritional intake, and daily rhythmic signals such as sunrise and sunset. Daily photoperiodic signals of sunrise and sunset might properly be classed with other sensory stimuli, but they are considered separately here because of our uncertainty about the receptor system, if any, and also because of their special importance to the temporal organization of the insect.

There are at least two reasons for considering the problem of photoperiodic control of diapause to be of basic biological importance. First, photoperiod represents a source of temporal information that is being fed into the organism. Because photoperiod can be controlled experimentally with great precision, it offers the research biologist an opportunity to investigate an important avenue by which environmental time factors actually influence the working processes of the living organism at the genetic, cellular, tissue, and total organism levels. In addition, the ecological adaptations of the organism may be closely tied in with its photoperiodic responses. Among the insects, photoperiodic adaptations appear to be evolved very rapidly, so that geographical populations of a given species may differ quite widely in this respect. This has been found to be the case even with species that have been introduced into new territories within relatively recent times. The European corn borer *Ostrinia nubilalis* can be taken as an example; it was introduced into North America in about 1912, and in a 1961 study of geographical populations, the existence of highly significant differences in photoperiodism and developmental adaptations was demonstrated (Beck and Apple, 1961).

Diapause represents a developmental alternative in the life cycle of insects of the many species displaying facultative diapause. Among species in which it never occurs, or in those in which it is obligatory, it does not represent an alternative, of course. Diapause is most usually defined as a period of arrested development, but this is an oversimplification. It is more accurately represented as a condition of greatly suppressed metabolic and developmental rates. An insect in diapause develops at a low rate, ranging from only slightly less than the nondiapause rate to a severely suppressed rate, as in diapauses of great intensity. The suppression of growth rate does not involve an alternative in respect to direction of differentiation, however, and the diapausing insect seldom differs significantly from the nondiapause in morphology. In some cases, however, minor differences in form and pigmentation appear to be associated with the diapausing individuals of a given species (Müller, 1957, 1960). Insofar as diapause is a developmental alternative, it generally represents a physiological rather than a morphological manifestation of the phenomenon of polymorphism.

The hypothesis that facultative diapause represents a developmental alternative having the characteristics of a type of polymorphism requires some explanation. Diapause is almost invariably stage-specific; that is, it can occur at only one (rarely two) stages in the life cycle of the insect. Among different species, diapause occurs at different developmental stages—egg, larva, pupa, adult. In any one species, however, diapause will occur at only a well-defined stage in the insect's development. The insect's anatomical and physiological condition at the beginning of diapause are precisely definable, as though diapause is a definite developmental stage that is attained by the insect at a precise point in its growth. This characteristic distinguishes diapause from all nonspecific randomly occurring responses such as cold torpor and various tactic responses. Diapause is genetically determined and programmed and is a physiological adaptation with very high survival value to the species. Although under ultimately genetic control, the manifestation of diapause is induced by specific environmental factors. In most species, photoperiod appears to be the major environmental cause. Determination of diapause may precede its manifestation by as much as one generation.

Because of the several characteristics discussed above, diapause cannot be explained as the insect's response to the direct action of photoperiod as a physical force on the insect as a reacting biochemical system. One of the earliest hypotheses concerning the action of photoperiod in the induction of diapause was that some unidentified "diapause factor" was synthesized during the scotophase and was degraded or otherwise neutralized during the photophase. If the photoperiodic cycle had a longer night than day, the diapause factor would increase in concentration until its titer exceeded a critical level, causing the insect to go into the diapause state. In the case of the so-called short-day insects, such as the commercial silkworm, the sequence was reversed, and the diapause factor was thought to be synthesized under the influence of light and degraded in the dark. Time and experimentation have not supported this general theory, since no good evidence of such a diapause factor has been forthcoming. Williams (1946) demonstrated that the pupal diapause of *Hyalophora cecropia* was not maintained by the presence of a diapause hormone that prevented adult differentiation. Similarly, parabiosis, hemolymph transfusion, and endocrine organ transplants have yielded results indicating that diapause is not induced or maintained by a diapause hormone (see reviews by Harvey, 1962, and Wigglesworth, 1964).

An apparent exception to this generalization is the "diapause hormone" of the silkworm moth *Bombyx mori*, investigated by Fukuda (1951, 1953) and Hasegawa (1952, 1957, 1965). This supposed exception actually lends the best possible support to the main point of this discussion, and therefore it merits some further examination. Whether the silkworm moth deposits eggs that will develop without diapause or eggs that undergo a long period of diapause is determined by the environmental photoperiod. But this photoperiodic determination occurs in response to the photoperiods experienced by the female moth during its late embryonic development. In other words, there is a full generation between the determination and the manifestation of diapause. The diapause hormone in the moth is a neurosecretory product, from the subesophageal ganglion, that influences the ovarioles and developing oocytes so that the eggs produced are committed to an embryonic diapause. The effect of photoperiod on the silkworm embryo has the effect of determining the developmental program to be followed by that insect all the way into the adult reproductive stage. The diapause hormone is not produced in a two-step light phase–dark phase synthesis but is a result of a prior determination between developmental alternatives.

The photoperiods experienced by early larval stages will, in a great many species, determine whether or not diapause is to occur in the pupal or adult stage. The action of photoperiod in such cases cannot be a direct suppression of either growth rate or hormone production, because the insects will pass through several successive molting cycles and growth stages before diapause occurs. And the diapause will occur long after the determining photoperiods. The action of photoperiod would appear, once again, to influence the determination of developmental alternatives and to program subsequent growth processes.

How does photoperiod influence diapause determination? The hypothesis under consideration here is that photoperiod exerts its influence via the rhythmic "time-measurement" systems within the organism. By this view, photoperiodic signals (light-on and light-off stimuli) act as phase-setting stimuli; and so—by the time elapsing between signals—they affect the temporal organization of the living system (Pittendrigh, 1961). This action of photoperiod may be viewed as a form of information input contributing to the "decision" between developmental alternatives and the determination of the programming of development, including diapause.

The view that diapause is one developmental alternative in a polymorphic system, and that photoperiod acts as an input of environmental information via its effects on the organism's temporal organization, opens some interesting possibilities for experimentation on growth processes which my co-workers and I have been exploring. Although our work is still rather preliminary and our conclusions

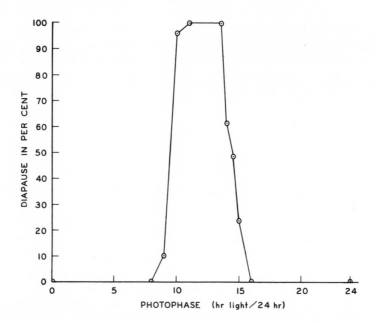

Fig. 1. Effect of day length on the incidence of diapause in the European corn borer *Ostrinia nubilalis*.

remain tentative, we believe that our approach to the problem has considerable promise.

Our experimentation has been almost exclusively on the European corn borer *Ostrinia nubilalis*. This lepidopterous species has a facultative diapause that is induced in response to short-day photoperiods. Artificial day lengths of 8 or fewer hours of light or continuous darkness do not result in diapause. Day lengths between 10 and 14 hours cause virtually all the insects to enter diapause, whereas 16 or more hours of light per day produce no diapause (Fig. 1). The corn borer diapauses as an early prepupa, that is, as a mature nonfeeding larva in which some prepupal biochemical and histological differentiation toward the pupal stage has begun.

Under our standard rearing conditions of 30° C and a meridic dietary medium, larval growth is rapid. When reared in continuous darkness or under any of the photoperiods that do not induce diapause, the borers begin to pupate on about day 13 of age; all will have pupated by the day 20 (Fig. 2). When reared under the influence of a diapause-inducing short-day photoperiod consisting of 12 hours of light and 12 hours of dark per day (12L:12D), few if any pupate prior to about day 75 (Fig. 2), although they advance through the larval instars, reach larval maturity, and cease feeding according to the same developmental time schedule as do the nondiapause-committed individuals. In our rearing experiments, larvae that had not pupated by the age of 21 days were considered to be in diapause and

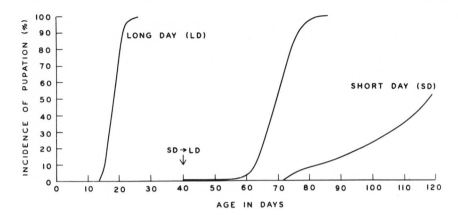

Fig. 2. Rates of pupation among nondiapause and diapause-committed European corn borer *Ostrinia nubilalis*

to remain in diapause until pupation occurred. Although pupation has been taken as the practical end of diapause, it must be realized that pupation is a post-diapause event. In most of our work on the effects of photoperiod and other factors on the induction and termination of diapause, we have dealt with populations of borers. The effectiveness of a treatment was assessed in terms of the incidence of diapause within the experimental population, or the average time required for pupation of the members of the treatment groups. Diapause in the corn borer can be terminated by exposing the insects to long-day photoperiods (16L:8D) for several weeks. Under these conditions the most precocious individuals will pupate about 18 days after the beginning of the long-day treatment, and 50 per cent will have attained the pupal stage by about the day 30 (Fig. 2).

If we regard diapause or nondiapause as developmental alternatives and the role of photoperiod as that of a determinant, we must ask about the developmental stage at which diapause determination takes place. Under our laboratory conditions and with the particular strain of borers we use, diapause determination occurs between days 11 and 12 of larval age, which is early in the final (fifth) larval stadium. This can be demonstrated by transfer of borer larvae from short-day to long-day conditions at different larval ages. When borer larvae are reared under short-day conditions for 9, 10, 11, or more days before being transferred to long-day conditions, the average time required to reach the pupal stage can be regarded as an indication of when diapause determination occurred. Experiments of this kind have shown that diapause was determined on about day 11 (Table 1), because transfer of the larvae to long-day photoperiods on or before day 11 of age resulted in very little delay in pupation. Transfer to long day lengths after day 11 of age resulted in a delay of pupation that was identical with that observed with diapausing borers of 20 or more days of age. It was apparent, then, that short-day-reared larvae reached a point of no return on about day 11, beyond

Table 1. Effect of Transfer from Short-Day to Long-Day Rearing Conditions on Duration of Diapause and Time of Pupation in the European Corn Borer Ostrinia nubilalis

Larval age when transferred	Average larval age at pupation	Average time from transfer to pupation
(days)	(days)	(days)
9	18	9
10	19	10
11	21	10
12	40	28
13	41	29
16	48	32
20	52	32

which they were committed to a diapause state that required the full 30-day long-day treatment for its termination.

Experiments have also been run in which the converse conditions were used, and larvae were reared under long-day photoperiods for 9, 10, 11, or more days before being transferred to short-day conditions. These transfers, however, did not lead to the induction of diapause. The results suggested that either the commitment to a nondiapause developmental program was made earlier than the last larval stadium or that long-day effects were less easily reversed than were short-day effects. Transfer of corn borer larvae from long-day to short-day rearing conditions resulted in diapause induction in 50 per cent or more of the insects only when the transfers were effected earlier than the latter part of the third larval stadium. These and earlier experiments (Beck et al., 1963) showed that long-day photoperiods experienced early in larval life (second instar) influenced the incidence of diapause in experimental populations. A number of other investigators, working with a variety of insect species, also reported that short-day effects are much more readily reversed than are long-day effects.

From experimental results such as these, it is apparent that diapause determination is not effected solely by the photoperiods experienced by the insect on day 11 or 12 of larval life. Determination of the developmental program to be followed is probably based on the temporal organization of the larva at that point in its developmental history. Its temporal organization would be the resultant of the interactions among internal rhythmic functions, some of which would be entrained by the environmental photoperiod. In other words, the entire development history of the larva would contribute to the determination of the developmental program, with photoperiod playing a major role.

In addition to diapause determination, other physiological changes occur in the European corn borer between 11 and 12 days of age. The larvae cease to feed, and the deposition of fat is accelerated. The ileal epithelium begins to change from an assimilative to a secretory function at this time (Beck et al., 1965b). The hemolymph protein pattern also undergoes both quantitative and qualitative changes at this point in the insect's development (Chippendale and

Beck, 1966). These observations have led us to the conclusion that the borers begin to switch from larval to prepupal physiology and differentiation at an age of
about 11 days. The changeover is effected prior to the onset of diapause. It seems
most likely that the larval-to-prepupal transition is the critical time at which diapause or nondiapause developmental alternatives are determined.

The finding that the corn borer, like a great many other insects, responds to
photoperiod in regard to diapause determination, would lead us to believe that
the insect possesses the ability to distinguish time differences among different
photoperiodic regimes. The insect must therefore possess a time-measuring system, or biological clock. It was postulated in the above discussion that such time-
measurement is carried out in terms of the effect of photoperiodic signals on the
temporal organization of the insect's internal functions. It is now appropriate that
we examine this concept in some detail.

Many workers have postulated that biological time-measurement is effected
by endogenous circadian rhythms that may be photoperiodically entrained (see
review by Bünning, 1963). An approximately 24-hour periodicity (circadian) has
been postulated because the diel photoperiod is a 24-hour cycle of daylight and
darkness and because many easily observed overt behavioral rhythms occur on a
regular daily basis. In respect to diapause determination, however, experimentation with a wide range of natural and unnatural photoperiods has shown that diapause induction is not necessarily dependent upon a 24-hour photoperiodic cycle.
Photoperiodic cycles of from 18 to 60 hours may be effective in the determination
of diapause, provided that the absolute duration of either the photophase or scotophase is of an appropriate number of hours. Most frequently, the scotophase duration is the more critical; if the scotophase is of the optimum duration for diapause
induction, the photophase may be varied experimentally within a wide range
without appreciably diminishing the effectiveness of the photoperiod in diapause
induction. The European corn borer, for example, is diapause-determined by a
12-hour scotophase whether combined with a photophase as short as 5 hours or as
long as 30 hours (Beck, 1962). Many other species studied also display a comparable relationship between scotophase duration and diapause determination. No
evidence has been obtained that diapause induction is ever dependent on a strictly
24-hour photoperiodic schedule. The effects of photoperiod on the determination
of diapause do not support the hypothesis that a circadian time-measurement system is involved.

An alternative to the circadian biological clock is one that works on an hourglass or interval-timer principle. This kind of time-measurement would depend
on a light-reaction system and a dark-reaction system, with the photoperiodic response being the result of the equilibrium between the two. This immediately calls
to mind the "diapause factor" hypothesis discussed earlier, and the interval-timer
theory of time measurement displays some of the same shortcomings as that hypothesis. Some, but far from all, of the effects of noncircadian photoperiods might
be explained on the basis of the interval-timer system. However, under constant
conditions of either light or darkness, this system would fail to function because

the environment would offer no interval to be timed. The interval-timer hypothesis breaks down at this point, as it is inadequate to account for any endogenous rhythms, that is, rhythmic functions that continue to be manifested under constant nonphotoperiodic conditions. Various rhythmic functions have been demonstrated in insects. In the European corn borer these include respiratory rate, neurosecretory cell activity, and secretory activity in the proctodone-producing cells of the hindgut (Beck et al., 1963; Beck, 1964; Beck et al., 1965a). Daily rhythms in the cells of the corpora allata, prothoracic glands, fat body, integument, and in metabolic process of detoxication have been demonstrated in a number of species (Beck, 1963; Rensing, 1964; Bull and Lindquist, 1965; Neville, 1965). These several physiological rhythms have been shown to be regulated by photoperiod and may be either an integral part of the insect's time-measurement system or may be entrained to a still unidentified clock system. Some of these rhythmic functions have been shown to be endogenous, as they will continue to be manifested under conditions of continuous darkness.

We have obtained experimental evidence that endogenous rhythmic functions are involved in the photoperiodic control of diapause termination in the European corn borer. The data indicated that photoperiodically regulated internal functions continued to operate endogenously when the borers were maintained under continuous darkness. In these experiments, diapausing corn borers that were 22 days of age were exposed to long-day photoperiods (16L:8D) for 10 days. They were then exposed to different photoperiodic regimes for an additional 10 days, after which they were held in one of the photoperiodic conditions and observed for pupation. The results (Table 2) showed that the developmental patterns were influenced by photoperiods and that the effect of a given photoperiod was maintained during prolonged periods of continuous darkness. When the diapausing borers were held in a long day throughout the experiment, the average time to pupation was 31 days (Schedule A). Continuous darkness during either the post-treatment holding period (Schedule B), during the second 10-day treatment

Table 2. *Effect of Different Photoperiods on Termination of Diapause in the European Corn Borer* Ostrinia nubilalis
All larvae were reared in a short-day photoperiod and were 22 days of age at the beginning of the experiment (based on data of Beck and Alexander, 1964).

Schedule	Photoperiodic treatments		Post-treatment photoperiod	Average time to pupation
	1st 10 days	*2d 10 days*		
				(days)
A	long-day	long-day	long-day	31
B	long-day	long-day	darkness	27
C	long-day	darkness	long-day	29
D	long-day	darkness	darkness	30
E	long-day	short-day	long-day	42
F	long-day	short-day	darkness	>50
G	long-day	short-day	short-day	>50

(Schedule C), or both (Schedule D) did not alter the rate at which diapause was completed. The rate of development that had been established during the long-day treatment was not changed during the subsequent continuous darkness. Under Schedule E, however, 10 days of long-day photoperiods were followed by 10 days of short-day photoperiods, after which the larvae were held under the long-day regime. The development of the borers was delayed in proportion to the time spent under the influence of the short day length. Borers that were exposed to long days followed by short days, and then transferred to continuous darkness (Schedule F), developed very slowly, as was also the case when the final holding condition was a continuation of the short-day photoperiod (Schedule G). Continuous darkness was again found to maintain the developmental pattern established by the previously experienced photoperiod. Such results strongly suggest that photoperiodically regulated endogenous rhythms are involved in diapause of the European corn borer.

Some of the relationships between time-measurement and diapause determination have been studied by means of "light-break" experiments in which the long scotophase of a short-day photoperiod is interrupted by short periods of light. In our work with the European corn borer we have used a 7L:17D photoperiod with 1-hour light breaks falling at different times during the scotophase. The insects' response was measured in terms of the incidence of diapause in the treated populations (Fig. 3). The uninterrupted photoperiod induced virtually no diapause,

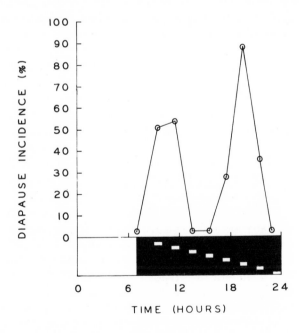

Fig. 3. Effect of 1-hour light breaks on the induction of diapause in the European corn borer *Ostrinia nubilalis* (based on data of Beck, 1962).

but light breaks occurring at either hour 11 or 19 caused an appreciable incidence of diapause. Two points are of particular interest. (1) A light break at hour 11 was followed by 12 hours of uninterrupted darkness, and a light break at hour 19 was preceded by 12 hours of uninterrupted darkness. These results again indicated the importance of a 12-hour scotophase in diapause determination in this species. (2) There is an apparent 8-hour difference between the 11-hour and 19-hour maxima of diapause determination.

The 8-hour difference between the two diapause determination maxima is of particular interest because of its possible similarity to other 8-hour effects detected in the rhythmic relationships of the corn borer. The day length–diapause incidence response curve (Fig. 1) shows that diapause determination is confined entirely to day lengths lying between 8 and 16 hours of light per day; this range is an 8-hour span of time. The physiological rhythms of the borer have been found to display 8-hour periodicities. Oxygen consumption was found to be rhythmic, with maxima occurring at 8-hour intervals (Beck, 1964). The lateral neurosecretory cell activity rhythm was also found to have an 8-hour period (Beck, 1964). The secretory rhythm in the proctodone-producing cells of the ileum was also observed to follow an 8-hour cyclic pattern (Beck, 1964; Beck et al., 1965a). In view of these 8-hour physiological rhythms, the 8-hour effects associated with diapause determination suggest that underlying rhythmic functions are indeed involved in the photoperiodic control of diapause.

The European corn borer is not the only insect in which physiological rhythms with relatively short periodicity have been described. Rhythms with periods of 6, 8, and 12 hours have been found in oxygen consumption, neurosecretory activity, and metabolic detoxication in a number of different species. Such rhythms are noncircadian, because they run at a frequency higher than one cycle per 24 hours. They are, nevertheless, phase-regulated by photoperiod and might easily function as components of a time-measurement system. A relationship between diapause determination and noncircadian rhythms is suggested in the case of the pink bollworm *Pectinophora gossypiella*. Light-break experiments of Adkisson (1964) showed results quite similar to those described above for the European corn borer, except that with the pink bollworm, the maxima of diapause determination were spaced about 6 hours apart. The detoxication of certain insecticides by the boll weevil *Anthonomus grandis* occurred rhythmically in a pattern indicating a 6-hour periodicity in metabolic process (Cole and Adkisson, 1964).

Although the experimental evidence cannot be considered conclusive, the present data strongly suggest that endogenous rhythmic functions are involved in the photoperiodic responses of insects. Neither the hourglass nor the circadian clock hypothesis is adequate to explain the experimental results. Photoperiodic determination of diapause is probably caused by the effects of photoperiodic signals on the phase relationships of continuously operating endogenous rhythms, but the rhythms are of subcircadian periodicity. Such high-frequency internal rhythms may function efficiently in time measurement under the diel periodicity of the natural environment. Under such conditions they would be subjected to phase adjustment by either dawn or sunset, or both, once each day; during the rest of the 24-hour day they would run on an undisturbed endogenous basis.

As was discussed earlier, diapause determination in the European corn borer was found to be closely dependent on a 12-hour scotophase. Such a scotophase is 1.5 times the period of the insect's 8-hour physiological rhythms. If it is assumed that some physiological rhythms are phase-set by the beginning of darkness (light-off stimulus) and others are phase-set by the onset of light (light-on stimulus), the phase relationships between the two types of rhythms would be determined by the photoperiod. With a scotophase of 12 hours' duration, an 8-hour rhythm that was sensitive to the light-off stimulus would be maintained in an out-of-phase relationship to an 8-hour rhythm that was sensitive to the light-on stimulus. With an 8- or 16-hour scotophase, the rhythms would run in phase with each other. Diapause in the corn borer is associated with a 12-hour scotophase, suggesting that diapause is determined by "out-of-phase" physiological functions. Two physiological rhythms meeting the postulated requirements have been detected: (1) the lateral neurosecretory cells of the corn borer's brain display an 8-hour secretory rhythm that is apparently phase-set by the light-on signal; (2) the proctodone-producing cells of the borer's hindgut show a secretory rhythm that has an 8-hour period and is phase-set by the light-off signal (Beck, 1964). Because the function of proctodone is thought to be the stimulation of the neuroendocrine system of the brain (Beck and Alexander, 1964), these phase relationships may be of considerable influence on the development of the borer larva.

A rather simple hypothesis of time measurement by phase relationships of light-set and dark-set rhythms, in which the duration of the scotophase determines the phase relationships maintained, is shown in Figure 4. According to this model the light-off stimulus sets the phase of the "dark" rhythm, and the light-on stimulus sets the phase of the "light" rhythm, both of which are endogenous with. an 8-hour periodicity. Upon the light-on signal, the light rhythm is not only phase-set but it is also entrained to the dark rhythm. When the dark rhythm is phase-set by the light-off signal, the light rhythm is also adjusted to maintain the entrainment set by the previous light-on stimulus. Such a mechanism would result in the apparent importance of scotophase duration that has been demonstrated experimentally. It would also account for the experimental results obtained by "light-break" experiments and experiments in which unnatural nondiel photoperiods were employed. The hypothetical time-measurement system has not been demonstrated by direct experiment, however, and probably represents an oversimplification of the actual biological system.

Diapause in the European corn borer is a condition in which developmental rates have been suppressed. Based on the time required for the termination of diapause under different conditions, Beck and Alexander (1964) calculated that under short-day photoperiods the developmental rate during diapause was only 20 per cent of that occurring under long-day conditions. Rate differences of such magnitude might result from differences in phase relationships of interacting physiological rhythms. Transfer of the diapausing borers from the diapause-main-

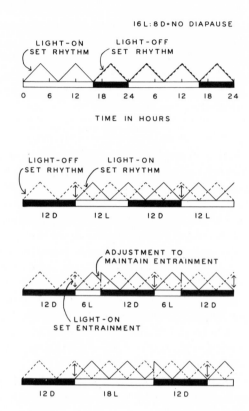

Fig. 4. Hypothetical noncircadian time-measurement system involving light-set and dark-set rhythms.

taining short-day photoperiod to a long-day photoperiod causes the physiological rhythms to be readjusted, and they reach a phase relationship that promotes a higher developmental rate. As was shown by the data of Table 2, 10 days of long day length followed by darkness was sufficient to terminate diapause. Previous studies have also shown that about 10 days are required for the diapausing borers to adjust to a long-day photoperiod after having been reared in short-day conditions (McLeod and Beck, 1963; Beck et al., 1965a). Superficially, it would appear that no developmental reprogramming is involved in the termination of diapause; diapause is terminated and active development is resumed as soon as the phase relationships of the physiological rhythms are favorable. However, if we consider the time characteristics reflected by the experimental data of Table 1, we will see that such a hypothesis is not supported. Borer larvae that were reared under a short-day photoperiod were, it may be assumed, fully adjusted to that photoperiod. If they were then transferred to long-day conditions at 10 or 11 days of age, they adjusted to the new photoperiod within about 10 days, at the end of which time they pupated. If the transfer to long day length was made after the critical time for diapause determination, that is, on the day 12 or later, we would again expect about 10 days to be required for phase regulation. But in this case the borers did not pupate at the end of the 10-day adjustment period; about 20 additional days were required. Once committed to diapause, the insect's developmental program cannot be returned to the nondiapause state by the action of photoperiod alone; additional requirements must be met. We do not know the exact nature of these latter requirements, but we have obtained some experimental evidence that they can be dealt with separately from the insect's photoperiodic requirements.

Termination of diapause and subsequent pupation of corn borer larvae may be accelerated by experimental means. Injection of relatively massive doses of ammonium ions (usually as ammonium acetate) will result in an average time for pupation of from 10 to 12 days after treatment, provided that the treated larvae were held under a long-day photoperiod (Beck and Alexander, 1964). If the treated borers were held in continuous darkness, there was little or no reaction to the ammonium ion treatment. It is apparent that the ammonium ions stimulated the developmental processes that would normally be rate-limiting after the insect's adjustment to long-day photoperiods was completed. In the absence of rhythmic resynchronization, the ammonium ions had little or no effect on diapause. Similarly, we have found that the physiological water balance has a strong influence on the post-photoperiodic phases of diapause termination but does not influence the insect's ability to make the adjustment from a short-day to a long-day photoperiod (Beck, 1967).

Diapause in any postembryonic stage is usually considered to be caused by the absence of the growth-promoting hormones of the retrocerebral system. Indeed, it has been well established that the growth-limiting factor in pupal diapause is the brain's failure to produce prothoracotropic hormone. In the larval diapause of the European corn borer, however, the inability of the brain and its associated organs to produce hormones does not seem to be the primary cause of diapause. To be sure, the borer is unable to pupate until the proper hormones have been secreted, but the diapause state appears to involve rate-limiting factors that precede the action of the prothoracotropic hormone.

The role of the brain, and presumably its neuroendocrine system, in the termination of diapause was investigated through experiments involving the exchange of brains between two lepidopterous species (Table 3). Diapausing European corn borers and mature nonfeeding larvae of the greater wax moth *Galleria mellonella* were used. The latter species was selected because it does not display a diapause and, as far as is known, its growth is not influenced by photoperiod. The brains were removed from large numbers of wax moth larvae and diapausing borers. Brains of one or the other species were then implanted into the operated larvae. The insects were then held under continuous darkness in the case of the wax moth larvae, or under a photoperiod in the case of borers.

Implanting wax moth brains into brainless wax moth larvae resulted in pupation (Table 3, Series A), as would be expected on the basis that neither brain nor body was in diapause. Wax moth larvae also pupated normally when receiving

Table 3. Effect of Reciprocal Brain Transplants Between Diapausing European Corn Borers and Early Prepupal Greater Wax Moths

Series	Brain donor	Brain recipient	Post-treatment conditions	Survivors	Pupation	
				(no.)	(no.)	(%)
A	WM*	WM	darkness	10	10	100
B	DCB†	WM	darkness	20	19	95.0
C	DCB	DCB	long-day	12	11	91.7
D	DCB	DCB	short-day	18	14	77.8
E	WM	DCB	long-day	52	36	69.2
F	WM	DCB	short-day	50	1	2.0

* Early prepupa (mature, nonfeeding larva) of the greater wax moth *Galleria mellonella*.
† Diapausing European corn borer *Ostrinia nubilalis*.

brains from diapausing corn borers (Series B). This effect should not be expected if the diapausing borer brains were inactive from the standpoint of hormone production. One possible explanation of the apparent endocrine activity of the diapausing borer brain is that the brain was reactivated by the surgical manipulations involved in extirpation and reimplantation. This interpretation is supported by the results of Series C and D, in which diapausing borer brains were implanted into brainless diapausing borers. Whether held under a long-day or a short-day photoperiod, the recipient larvae pupated. When this effect was originally reported (Cloutier et al., 1962), the hypothesis was advanced that perhaps the surgical procedures destroyed a barrier to metabolite exchange between the brain and the hemolymph. As long as such a "brain barrier" was functional, the insect remained in diapause. Once the barrier was broken—via photoperiodic responses under natural conditions or via surgical damage—the developmental rate was elevated and diapause was terminated. No direct experimental evidence has been obtained, however, that would lend support to the brain barrier hypothesis.

The brains of mature wax moth larvae were also implanted into brainless diapausing corn borers (Table 3, Series E and F). The recipient larvae were held under either short-day or long-day photoperiods. Those maintained under short-day conditions remained in diapause, whereas those that were held under long-day photoperiods terminated diapause and pupated. These experimental results are quite inconsistent with the hypothesis that diapause is caused by a shutdown of the insect's neuroendocrine system. It would seem that diapause in the European corn borer involves more of the cells, organs, and physiological functions than only the neuroendocrine system. Diapause may or may not be terminated by the implantation of a brain system, depending on the characteristics of the implanted brain. The essential characteristic of the implanted brain does not appear to depend on whether or not it came from a diapausing donor.

The termination of diapause may be accelerated by experimental means, but some caution must be exercised in the interpretation of such effects. For example, the diapausing insect may respond to ecdysone injection or to endocrine organ implantations, but this response does not prove that the diapause state was caused by the simple absence of such hormones. If such proof were acceptable,we could claim that diapause in the European corn borer is caused by an ammonium deficiency, because administration of ammonium ions was found to stimulate the termination of diapause. Obviously, the situation cannot be assessed in such limited terms. Many workers have insisted upon regarding diapause as a pathological condition resulting from a biochemical defect in the organism. Such a concept of diapause would appear to be too narrow and to fail to take into account much of what is known about the characteristics of diapause in regard to both its induction and termination. Regarding diapause as a developmental alternative in a polymorphic system would appear to be a more promising approach to the problem. This hypothesis does not diminish the importance of research into the biochemistry and physiology of the diapause state. It has the very great advantage, however, of casting the problem within a broader biological framework in which modern knowledge and techniques related to control mechanisms and information storage and utilization may be applied.

REFERENCES

Adkisson, P.L., 1964. Action of photoperiod in controlling insect diapause. *Am. Naturalist, 98:* 357–74.

Beck, S. D., 1962. Photoperiodic induction of diapause in an insect. *Biol. Bull., Woods Hole, 122:* 1–12.

——, 1963. Physiology and ecology of photoperiodism. *Bull. Entomol. Soc. Am., 9:* 8–16.

——, 1964. Time-measurement in insect photoperiodism. *Am. Naturalist, 98:* 329–46.

——, 1967. The role of water in diapause development of the European corn borer, *Ostrinia nubilalis. J. Insect Physiol., 13:* 739–50.

Beck, S. D., and N. Alexander, 1964. Chemically and photoperiodically induced diapause development in the European corn borer, *Ostrinia nubilalis. Biol. Bull., Woods Hole, 126:* 175–84.

——, 1964. Proctodone, an insect developmental hormone. *Biol. Bull., Woods Hole, 126:* 185–98.

Beck, S. D., and J. W. Apple, 1961. Effects of temperature and photoperiod on voltinism of geographical populations of the European corn borer, *Pyrausta nubilalis. J. Econ. Entomol., 54:* 550–58.

Beck, S. D., E. J. Cloutier, and D. G. R. McLeod, 1963. Photoperiod and insect development. *Proc. 23rd Biol. Colloq., Oregon State Univ. 1962,* p. 43–64.

Beck, S. D., I. B. Colvin, and D. E. Swinton, 1965a. Photoperiodic control of a physiological rhythm. *Biol. Bull., Woods Hole, 128:* 177–88.

Beck, S. D., J. L. Shane, and I. B. Colvin, 1965b. Proctodone production in the European corn borer, *Ostrinia nubilalis. J. Insect Physiol., 11:* 297–303.

Bull, D. L., and D. A. Lindquist, 1965. A comparative study of insecticide metabolism in photoperiod-entrained and unentrained bollworm larvae *Heliothis zea* (Boddie). *Comp. Biochem. Physiol., 16:* 321–25.

Bünning, E., 1963. *The Physiological Clock*. Academic Press, New York.

Chippendale, G. M., and S. D. Beck, 1966. Hemolymph proteins of *Ostrinia nubilalis* during diapause and prepupal morphogenesis. *J. Insect Physiol., 12:* 1629–38.

Cloutier, E. J., S. D. Beck, D. G. R. McLeod, and D. L. Silhacek, 1962. Neural transplants and insect diapause. *Nature, 195:* 1222–24.

Cole, C. L., and P. L. Adkisson, 1964. Daily rhythm in the susceptibility of an insect to a toxic agent. *Science, 144:* 1148–49.

Fukuda, S., 1951. The production of the diapause eggs by transplanting the suboesophageal ganglion in the silkworm. *Proc. Imper. Acad. Japan, 27:* 672–77.

———, 1953. Alteration of voltinism in the silkworm following transection of pupal oesophageal connectives. *Proc. Imper. Acad. Japan, 29:* 389–91.

Harvey, W. R., 1962. Metabolic aspects of insect diapause. *Ann. Rev. Entomol., 7:* 57–80.

Hasegawa, K., 1952. Studies on the voltinism of the silkworm, *Bombyx mori* L., with special reference to the organs concerning determination of voltinism. *J. Fac. Agric., Tottori Univ., 1:* 83–124.

———, 1957. The diapause hormone of the silkworm, *Bombyx mori*. *Nature, 179:* 1300–01.

Hasegawa, K., and O. Yamashita, 1965. Studies on the mode of action of the diapause hormone in the silkworm, *Bombyx mori* L. VI. The target organ of the diapause hormone. *J. Exp. Biol. 43:* 271–77.

Lees, A. D., 1961. Clonal polymorphism in aphids. *Proc. Roy. Entomol. Soc. London, Symposium no. 1,* p. 68–79.

———, 1966. The control of polymorphism in aphids. *Advanc. Insect Physiol., 3:* 207–77.

McLeod, D. G. R., and S. D. Beck, 1963. Photoperiodic termination of diapause in an insect. *Biol. Bull., Woods Hole, 124:* 84–96.

Müller, H. J., 1957. Die Wirkung exogener Faktoren auf die zyklische Formenbildung der Insekten, insbesondere der Gattung *Euscelis*. *Zool. Jahrb., 85:* 317–430.

———, 1960. Die Bedeutung der Photoperiode im Lebensablauf der Insekten. *Zt. angew. Entomol., 47:* 7–24.

Neville, A. C., 1965. Circadian organization of chitin in some insect skeletons, *Quart. J. Microscop. Sci., 106:* 315–25.

Pittendrigh, C. S., 1961. On temporal organization in living systems, *Harvey Lect., 56:* 93–125.

Rensing, L., 1964. Daily rhythmicity of corpus allatum and neurosecretory cells in *Drosophila melanogaster*. *Science, 144:* 1586–87.

Wigglesworth, V. B., 1961. Polymorphism—A tentative hypothesis. *Proc. Roy. Entomol. Soc. London, Symposium no. 1,* p. 103–113.

———, 1964. The hormonal regulation of growth and reproduction in insects. *Adv. Insect Physiol., 2:* 247–336.

Williams, C. M., 1946. Physiology of insect diapause: The role of the brain in the production and termination of pupal dormancy in the giant silkworm, *Platysamia cecropia*. *Biol. Bull., Woods Hole, 90:* 234–43.

Kenneth S. Norris

10. THE EVOLUTION OF ACOUSTIC MECHANISMS IN ODONTOCETE CETACEANS

The most important factor in the evolution of acoustic mechanisms in odontocete cetaceans is that while density differences between the bone and soft tissue of a terrestrial animal and air are on the order of 10^4, they reach a maximum of about $8\times$ for an animal submerged in water, and are usually much less. Hickling (1962) points out that for this reason we may expect environmental sounds to induce little vibration in terrestrial animals except at very localized points, while much vibration will be induced in aquatic organisms by environmental sounds, and at a large variety of loci. For the most part, this paper concerns an attempt to trace the effects of submergence of the terrestrial ancestor of odontocetes (toothed whales) in terms of these density differences and the structures that have evolved as a result. In my opinion, the results probably have been a profound modification of the skull and lower jaw, the middle ear, and the sound-sending and -receiving equipment of the animal. These changes may have been of such a degree that modern odontocetes have partitioned sound generation between two or more loci, which may or may not include the larynx, and perhaps they no longer use their external auditory meatus for most sound reception but instead have substituted the lower jaw and loci on the forehead for reception of a major portion of sound energy eventually reaching the cochlea (Fig. 1). The documentation for these rather far-reaching speculations lies to a considerable extent in the fossil record.

Fortunately, even though the fossil record of odontocetes is highly incomplete, there are several aspects of available material that seem acoustically related and can thus be traced generally through time, if not with any accuracy regarding exact paths of change. The skeletal features that might be related to the evolution of acoustic mechanisms in cetaceans follow. (1) The "telescoping" of the skull, or the sliding of the maxillary and premaxillary bones in particular, over other skull bones, as the nostrils moved from terminal position on the snout to a dorsal position (Miller, 1923); associated with this evolution has been the devel-

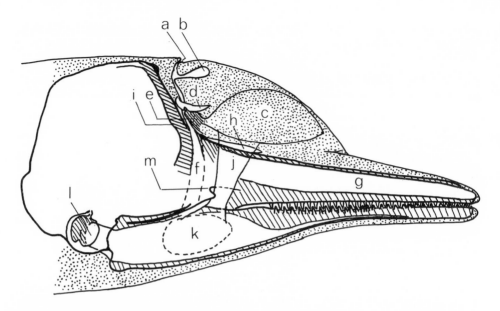

Fig. 1. Structures in the delphinid odontocete head: a, blowhole; b, vestibular sac; c, melon; d, tubular sac; e, nasal valve with lip entering tubular sac; f, internal nares; g, mesorostral (or ethmoid) cartilage; h, premaxillary nasal sac; i, cribriform plate; j, proposed wave guide from melon to outer tissue of mandible, passing anterior to antorbital notches; k, acoustic window in mandible, and the site of overlying fatty window; l, attachment point of mandibular wave guide onto bulla; m, antorbital notch.

opment of some remarkable species-specific asymmetry in the anterodorsal quadrant of the skull, and this too, I suspect, is related to acoustic factors. (2) The development of a cartilage-filled mesorostral canal, lined dorsally on both sides by unusually dense premaxillary bone and below by the vomer to form a long subcylindrical channel, running from the median mesethmoid division of the bony nares to the tip of the rostrum. (3) The excavation of a variety of air sinuses in the head, whose major functions may be to isolate acoustically certain structures from self-produced signals, and to channel sound in various ways. (4) The thinning of the posterior portion of the mandible forming a thin pan of translucent homogeneous bone. (5) Certain modifications of the tympanic bulla and ossicular chain, in particular the suspension of the bulla, modifications of the shape and leverage of the ossicles, and the existence of a bony ankylosed extension of the malleus (the processus gracilis), that attaches to the bulla.

ACOUSTIC MECHANISMS IN MODERN ODONTOCETES

In order to appraise what has happened evolutionarily to odontocete acoustic systems it is necessary to describe briefly the acoustic attributes of modern forms. First, as almost everyone is aware, some porpoise species, and perhaps all, are acoustic animals *par excellence*. I suspect that their acoustic attributes are in general quite the equal of the better-understood bats, and in one sense perhaps more intricate. Porpoises not only echolocate, as do bats, but they also live in tightly organized schools, many of whose integrative signals are sounds. Whistle-like cries and echolocation clicks are often emitted simultaneously by the same animal (Lilly and Miller, 1961; Evans and Prescott, 1962), implying the ability of the animal to use two domains of sound at once, perhaps much as we might use two separate but related senses like smell and taste.

The sound emissions of modern odontocetes have received considerable attention, both observational and experimental, and the details of their projection and reception are beginning to emerge (see for example Kellogg et al., 1953; Evans and Prescott, 1962; Norris, 1964; Schevill, 1964; and Evans, in press.) Echolocation is seemingly widespread, and perhaps universal, among odontocetes. It is accomplished by trains of brief (0.7-24 msec), extremely broad-band clicks. It is becoming increasingly evident that these signals are projected forward in structured sound fields that are highly directional. For instance, the clicks of the rough-tooth porpoise *Steno bredanensis* are restricted to a narrow field with little energy beyond 20° to either side of the midline of the animal's rostrum. The highest frequencies, which may exceed 200 kHz, are recorded only directly ahead of the animal (Norris and Evans, 1967). Field recording and observation of school position show that this phenomenon is widespread in odontocetes. (For example, strong directionality seems to occur in the Hawaiian spinner porpoise *Stenella* sp., the Pacific spotted porpoise *Stenella attenuata*, the bottlenose porpoise *Tursiops* sp., and the false killer whale *Pseudorca crassidens;* personal observation.) Schevill and Watkins (1966) report similar directionality in the relatively low-frequency screams of the killer whale *Orcinus orca*.

When porpoises are observed during echolocation behavior they are usually moving their heads about in jerky more-or-less circular paths. Thus the projected sound beam is moved about, much like the beam from a miner's headlamp, as the animal moves its head. Echolocation is typically exhibited during active swimming, particularly while the animal is engaged in searching or inspection behavior.

Surprisingly little is known about sound generation in odontocetes. Sounds are known to issue from somewhere on the forehead of porpoises, above the level of the mouth (Norris et al., 1961), and this is perhaps related to the existence of structures in the nasal diverticula that could act as sound generators, suggesting that the entire process occurs in this area (Evans and Prescott, 1962; Norris, 1964). Concurrence with this view is not complete, as some workers consider the larynx to be the sound source, even though vocal cords are absent (Purves, 1966). Question is cast on this view because sound-pressure measurements made outside the animal in the region of the larynx during emission of echolocation signals are much lower than those adjacent to the forehead (W. E. Evans, personal communication).

The aryteno-epiglottid extension of the larynx could be a source of sound, and since this structure normally lies within the ventral base of the bony nares where it rests upon the pterygoid hamulae, which are excavated by the pterygoid air sac, it is presumably acoustically isolated from below, and sounds produced there should not project a strong ventrally directed field.

Click emission, at least superficially like that involved in echolocation under-water, has been observed in porpoises vocalizing in air with the blowhole open. In this case the sounds were accompanied by a sputtering of water over the lateral corners of the nasal plugs, a pair of heavily muscularized valves which could be seen below the blowhole.

Sounds produced in this region would have to pass through the fatty porpoise forehead or melon (Fig. 1), or through the rostrum itself to reach the water, and not the mouth, which remains closed during sound emission. In the case of the pygmy sperm whale (*Kogia* sp.) the peculiar spermaceti case, filled with liquid spermaceti oil in life, is interposed between the supposed sound generator and the water ahead of the animal on top of the bony upper jaws. Musculature is present that could deform these structures, and in the beluga (*Delphinapterus leucas*) the animal is capable of considerable deformation of the melon. This feature adds interest when one considers the idea, first suggested to me by Forrest Wood, III, that the melon and case may be sound transducers assisting in the projection of sound into the water.

Another controversy exists with regard to sound reception. The majority of present-day workers suggest the area of the external auditory meatus as the site of sound reception (Fraser and Purves, 1960; Reysenbach de Haan, 1957), while Norris (1964) has suggested that the peculiar fat-filled lower jaw might act as a wave guide passively transmitting sound to the tympanic bulla, to which the fat body is attached.

Very recently two of my colleagues, working as part of a team with a group of Japanese neurophysiologists (Yanagisawa et al., 1966), provided the best evidence to date that the lower jaw wave guide may indeed function when they were able to lower electrodes into the colliculus (a tertiary auditory center in the brain) of living anesthetized porpoises (*Stenella*, *Steno*, and *Tursiops*) and to record electrical potentials when the animals were stimulated with sounds of various frequencies at various loci over their heads.

For high-frequency signals (95 kHz) these workers found that in the region of the lower jaw directly over the pellucid bone covering the mandibular fat body the porpoise was six times as sensitive as over its external auditory meatus. They then drew a topographic map of sensitivity to sound over the entire head of the porpoise and found, surprisingly, that in addition to the most sensitive areas on the lower jaws two additional areas of nearly equal sensitivity exist on either side of the fatty forehead or melon. Thus for high-frequency sounds at least, the animal has four reception points, none of which is the external auditory meatus, and during auditory scanning in which the animal moves its head in a more-or-less rotary fashion, it is effectively scanning the echo field across four points of reception, each in a different transverse quadrant of the head. As the experimenters reduced frequency, the sharp sensitivity points became less prominent. Hence it seems that at least part of sound reception does not follow the normal reception channels used by terrestrial mammals.

The possible function of the auricular muscles and cartilages, which lie buried in the tissue overlying the greatly modified tympanic membrane, is also controversial. Fraser and Purves (1960) and Purves (1966) suggest that these structures are functional and that their mobility may serve to move the distal extremity of the auricular cartilages in and out of the sound shadow of adjacent air sacs, thus assisting in audio direction finding. Reysenbach de Haan (1957) suggests that these structures are functionless.

Scattered throughout the head of odontocetes are several paired or single air sacs (Fraser and Purves, 1960). These include the peribullary sinus, which almost completely isolates the cochlea-bearing periotic bone from the adjacent skull, and the pterygoid sinus and its associated ramifications, which extend within the posterior bones of the palate (pterygoid hamulae) and lateroposteriorly. In some species such as the common dolphin (*Delphinus delphis*) these sacs also extend forward nearly to the tip of the rostrum.

Various functions have been ascribed to these sacs, and doubtless they have more than a single function. They have been called reservoirs for the storage of air to provide an air bubble about the ossicles during the pressure changes associated with diving, and devices for production of sound shadows (Purves, 1966). I have suggested that they might channel or reflect sound during emission (Norris, 1964). We will return to this matter later.

Diverticula of the nasal passages also exist. These are concentrated on the forehead, and generally consist of a pair of premaxillary sinuses, lying directly on the dorsal surface of the rostrum, running anteriorly from the nasal passages; a pair of cowhorn-shaped tubular sacs lying in the middle of the soft tissue of the forehead; and a superficial pair of vestibular sacs (see Fig. 1) lying just beneath the skin surface adjacent to the blowhole (Lawrence and Schevill, 1956).

These nasal diverticula have also been implicated in various functions; for example in capture of inhaled water (Lawrence and Schevill, 1956), in recovery of fresh water (Coulomb et al., 1965), and in beaming of emitted signals (Norris, 1964).

Great differences exist between the typical terrestrial middle and inner ear and that found in cetaceans. The leverage relationships of the ossicles are profoundly different from those of terrestrial mammals, and their massiveness is increased. The tympanic membrane has been altered into a very thin pars flaccida that is scarcely noticeable in dissection, and a massive fibrous part that has been altered into a tough triangular ligament retaining its attachment to the malleus. The malleus has a bony strut that is ankylosed to a special prominence of the bulla, the sigmoid process or flexure. Fraser and Purves (1960) have carried out extensive experiments indicating that the approximately 36 dB acoustic impedance mismatch that exists for a submerged terrestrial mammal has been compensated by adjustments of ossicular leverages and anchorage points. As we shall see later, while such adjustment has obviously been achieved, there is some uncertainty about how it has been accomplished.

EVOLUTIONARY PATHWAYS AND SOUND

Various terrestrial ancestors have been suggested for cetaceans. Some authors consider odontocetes and mysticetes to have had separate terrestrial origins. From anatomical examination of modern forms Slijper (1966) suggests that cetaceans are most closely allied to artiodactyl ungulates. Boyden and Gemeroy (1950) arrive at a similar conclusion on the basis of extensive studies of blood proteins. The cetacean fossil record begins in the lower Eocene (Kellogg, 1928). Students of these fossils have suggested a variety of ancestral types as well, ranging from creodonts (Romer, 1947) to condylarths (Van Valen, 1966).

Whatever type of mammal was ancestral, the initial invasion or invasions occurred early in the radiation of mammals, perhaps in the Paleocene, or even in the Cretaceous as Flower (1883) has suggested, since archaeocetes, which were presumably an offshoot group, are found in the lower Eocene. They were then so well differentiated that their antecedents are obscure. The first unquestioned odontocetes are known from the upper Eocene (or possibly lower Oligocene) in the form of *Agorophius pygmaeus* (True, 1907). Whatever the origins of cetaceans were, it seems certain that initially they had terrestrial acoustic mechanims, probably of a reasonably sophisticated sort. Long before, during the Mesozoic establishment of mammals, the basic format of three middle ear ossicles and associated structures had been established (Tumarkin, 1955). Obviously by the Paleocene, when mammalian adaptive radiation reached a peak, most features that we consider modern and mammalian were present, because they are spread throughout the various living orders of mammals. They include pinnae, auricular musculature, the ossicular chain and its muscles and ligaments, and increased complexity of the cochlea. It is instructive to look at these features in more detail, as a baseline against which aquatic adaptation must have taken place.

By considering only features that are of general occurrence throughout modern mammals and not specializations within restricted groups, we will remain close to the cetacean ancestral condition. First, the cetacean's hearing of airborne sounds was probably acute, as is the case with most mammals, but there is no reason to suppose that it had echolocation. Since odontocetes may generate and clearly do project echolocation sounds from somewhere in structures that are obviously aquatic adaptive complexes (nasal diverticula, the melon, or the spermaceti case) and not in more generally occurring mammalian structures, we can say with some assurance that modern cetacean echolocation has developed during the course of aquatic adaptation wholly within the odontocete line. As an aside, there is no evidence that any mysticete actively echolocates, unless the peculiar 20-Hz signals of finback whales (Schevill et al., 1964) or the cries and moans of other baleen whales are considered to serve this purpose.

More likely, hearing and sound emission were of modest frequency range such as is used by most modern mammals in the avoidance of predators, sensing prey, or in a variety of communications functions. Sounds were probably at least partly produced in the vocal cords, and modulated and directed by the resonating tube of the airway, though snorts or sibilances and whistles originating at the lips or nostrils may also have been used; certainly they are common enough in a variety of modern mammals, including ungulates. Most of these sounds probably were produced with a loss of air. To judge from the buried remnants of auricular cartilages and associated muscles found in the modern cetacean, it had functional pinnae that could be moved to localize sound sources. In addition, these pinnae likely served to amplify sound and to produce time delays useful in determining the direction of sound sources (Batteau, 1964).

It seems reasonable to assume that the ancestral type had middle and external ears whose general features were typical of mammals in general. That is, the pinnae led directly into a meatal tube, at the bottom of which lay a typical tympanic membrane which was thus mechanically protected and humidified. The meatal tube may have had a geometry such that it acted roughly like an organ pipe tuned to the general band of frequencies of special importance to the animal, and perhaps corresponding to its frequency of greatest acuity. Inside lay the middle ear ossicles within an air bubble where acoustic impedance matching was achieved. Except at the ears, environmental sounds were not absorbed in important amount by the animal, save for its own signals which may have traveled rather widely within the animal by bone and tissue conduction (Békésy, 1962).

What did such an ancestral form face upon reentering the aquatic world? Briefly, nearly every acoustic structure or relationship so hard won in the subaerial world became maladapted. Subaerial ears incur about a 36 dB loss when submerged (Van Bergeijk, 1966), yet, as we have seen, much ambient sound will enter the body directly at other points with little loss and is transmitted through paths not intended for it. The pinnae are useless, both as tuned amplifiers and as time-delay devices for, with sounds in water traveling nearly five times as fast as in air, all wavelength relationships are distorted by that amount. Likewise the tuned cavity of the throat, mouth, and larynx is seriously affected. The normal mode of sound production in which air is expelled is essentially unworkable. Not only does water rush in with each vocalization but directionality patterns for propagated sound are greatly altered, and coupling difficulties are encountered. With water about 800 times as dense as air, even short dives cause great changes in the shapes of resonating cavities since pressure-compensating mechanisms adjusted to water pressure do not exist. Furthermore, many features of sound propagation in water differ markedly from similar propagation in air. Such features as scattering, attenuation, and production of echoes are unlike their counterparts in air. Just as environmental sound enters the body of a submerged animal at many points, it enters environmental objects as well, and many will resonate sufficiently to act as sound sources. Thus environmental data reaching the ears are different.

Even with all these difficulties considered, the animal has entered an environment in which sound carries information for longer distances than does light, and more reliably. The raw materials for evolution are there but, figuratively speaking, when our terrestrial cetacean ancestor first submerges most of its body in

water on the road to the evolution of a modern porpoise, there is much evolutionary work to do, and most of it for the second time.

Early Beginnings

Among wild animals, repeated sounds from any source tend to assume informational value to a variety of listeners. Thus organisms may mask, direct, or even
ventriloquize their sounds protectively, or emit them from relatively impregnable
positions, like a mockingbird on a treetop. Adventitious sounds may carry un-
solicited meaning, or they may be utilized through selection in a developing behavioral matrix (Emlen, 1960). Such a fortuitous circumstance may have marked
the beginning of underwater acoustic behavior in the ancestral cetacean. Perhaps
sometime during the development of amphibiousness, the ancestral type developed a propensity for making airborne sound signals while largely submerged.
Such signals would propagate an underwater component that could be picked up
by species members whose ears were wholly submerged. Two observations have
impressed me in this regard. First, according to my colleague, William E. Evans
(personal communication), the California sea lion (*Zalophus californianus*) exhibits just such behavior. Barks normally heard on land are also generated by
the animal while it is swimming and do propagate into the water, presumably
from the tissues surrounding the larynx. The sea lion goes one step farther and
generates a number of sounds when it is wholly submerged, with its mouth closed
(Evans, 1967). Second, I was impressed to hear the peculiar cries of humpback
whales (*Megaptera novaeangliae*) while I was swimming off Maui Island in
Hawaii, with my own submerged and thus highly inefficient ears, even though the
whales were an estimated mile away and could be seen playing on the surface
(Norris, in press). This situation is not unlike that faced by the hypothetical ancestor, in that while the listener's ears incurred a serious loss of sensitivity, the
sender's voice was likely well coupled to the surrounding water, even if fortuitously.

Most aquatic vertebrates have developed valvular nostrils allowing exclusion
of water. For example, we see such nostrils in seals, crocodilians, and even in
sand-dwelling lizards. The porpoise ancestor was probably no exception. In the
odontocetes it takes but little imagination to picture the nasal plugs of modern
forms as the paired valvular nostrils of ancestral forms. Not only do they resemble such valves but they reside in the tissue just above the paired bony nares.

Sounds are produced by some modern animals by forcing air through the
partly closed nostrils, for example, the sibilant whistles of a frightened antelope.
Sounds produced in this way may have been part of the repertoire of the porpoise ancestor, and this seems particularly likely since the nasal plugs have been
implicated in the sound production of delphinids (Evans and Prescott, 1962).
Loss of air during such sound production, that limits not only depth but time
available for a dive, is a serious problem in a diving animal. Further, such air as
there is in a lungful came through time to serve a variety of purposes, some of
which could not well undergo fluctuations in air supply. Air probably was needed

in the middle ear, and became increasingly useful for acoustic reflection in the air sacs and to improve the signal-to-noise ratio for the animal between sounds it must produce and those it must hear (Békésy, 1962), and it was likely essential for sound production.

Thus, a recycling system for air used in phonation became a crucial requirement for extended stays underwater. I look upon the upper complex of sacs above the nasal plugs and the blowhole itself as an evolutionary development serving this purpose (Norris, 1964). Even though underwater communication had been achieved early and a variety of avenues for adaptation lay open, many problems remained. Not only were external pinnae probably useless underwater but they must have been hydrodynamic nuisances. The auricular cartilages, the associated muscles, and the tiny, sometimes occluded meatal tube that remain in living porpoises are buried beneath the smooth surface of the body. Whether these structures are true vestiges, as is suggested by some (Reysenbach de Haan, 1957), or have become modified and are functional (Fraser and Purves, 1960) is a matter of debate. Can we expect structures to change adaptively that are instantly five times undersized with regard to their sound localization function when submerged, or can we expect other structures in the multiple sound paths entering the animal to assume such a function? The same question faces us with regard to the tuned amplification function of the pinna and meatal tube. To be sure, during the course of evolution odontocetes came to use high frequencies that could conceivably have reinstated such resonance relationship, but the shape of the structure makes it seem impossible that it could amplify sound. I will leave this controversy where I found it—an unsolved question in need of further experimental data.

The acoustic impedance mismatch of the submerged terrestrial ear is, of course, another serious problem. I find it instructive to consider this problem from the viewpoint of Van Bergeijk (1966), who likens the middle ear cavity to a resonating air bubble contained within rigid walls except at the tympanic membrane. In his view, the middle ear mechanism, and this bubble in particular, serve to match airborne sound pressures from the environment and fluid-borne displacements in the cochlea. Briefly, this match for the cetacean terrestrial ancestor would have been achieved in the following way. When sound passes through the tympanum it causes resonations of this bubble, which in turn cause excursions of the tympanic membrane. The ossicular chain, attached at one end to the membrane and at the other resting against the fluid-backed oval window, is set in motion. Because the bubble is contained by rigid tissue except at the tympanum, displacement is amplified at that surface, by a factor of A/a, where A equals the surface area of the middle ear bubble and a equals the area of the tympanum. The pressure involved in this tympanic displacement may be further amplified by the leverages of the middle ear ossicles until the approximately 36 dB hearing loss of air–water transition is compensated. Since the bubble is a resonator to outside sound reaching it, it produces both a near-field of displacement waves and a far-field of pressure waves. This bubble acts much like the gas bladder of an os-

tariophysan fish and, like that gas bladder, is connected to a displacement receptor (the cochlea in the porpoise) by a chain of small bones (Van Bergeijk, 1966).

A curious partitioning and modification of the tympanic membrane have occurred, and the greatly modified ossicular chain was produced, apparently quite early in cetacean history (Eocene archaeocetes had well-developed aquatic ear bone complexes). The malleus was tightly adherent or even fused to the bulla in very early forms (for example in the Eocene Zeuglodont *Protocetus;* Kellogg, 1928). In view of the widespread occurrence of this feature in terrestrial mammals, it may have existed in the terrestrial ancestor itself. Thus utilization of a channel of adventitious information through the malleolar strut in place of the badly mismatched terrestrial channel via the tympanum may have occurred. Such an event is suggested by the recent experimental results that suggest hearing through the mandible (Yanagisawa et al., 1966), since this channel leads directly to the bulla to which the malleus attaches, as will be discussed in detail later.

The directional nature of environmental sounds would have been lost to a submerged terrestrial animal not only because the pinnae lost their time-delay function but also because the individual ears were no longer independent receivers able to funnel a discrete portion of the ambient sound field to each cochlea. Sounds would have come from a variety of sources through tissue and bone to both ears, in particular from the animal's own underwater signals. It is therefore interesting to find that by the time most modern groups had appeared in the Miocene, a variety of sound-reflecting air sacs had appeared. The periotic bone, containing the cochlea, had become nearly isolated within such a sac—the peribullary sinus—particularly completely in delphinids (Fraser and Purves, 1960). A large pterygoid sinus spreads between the ear complex and the suspected locus of click production on the forehead. Thus if my inference is correct that these sacs function, in part at least, to reflect self-generated sound signals away from the ears and to channel emitted sound signals into discrete sound beams, we can expect that these Miocene forms produced sounds much as modern forms do. Some of the Miocene forms are essentially modern in most respects, as for instance *Delphinodon dividum* (True, 1912), and traces of all sinuses as well as the premaxillary nasal sacs exist. Since modern forms varying from physeterids through ziphiids and platanistids to delphinids already existed by middle Miocene, and most by the lower Miocene, and since all have a complement of sacs, it is a reasonable inference that the ancestral odontocete stock from which they mutually arose had sacs as well. Thus with some confidence we may expect that sacs arose early in the evolution of odontocetes. How early, I cannot guess (see Fraser and Purves, 1960). The fossil of the earliest odontocete *Agorophius* has been lost, and the plates are not revealing in this respect.

Likely correlated with this development of nasal diverticula, and probably the fat or oil accumulations of the melon and spermaceti case, was the telescoping of the skull. This feature has been carefully traced through fossil forms (Miller, 1923; Raven and Gregory, 1933; Kellogg, 1928) and has proceeded upon fundamentally different plans in the odontocetes and mysticetes. In the odontocetes it has resulted in the backward migration of the nostrils and the formation of the upswept and usually markedly asymmetrical forehead we see in modern forms. It is within this scoop-shaped forehead that the putative sound generators lie, the nasal diverticula are found, and the melon or case is located. Some degree of telescoping is found in all fossil odontocetes, but is absent in the zeuglodonts of the Eocene. It is complete by the Miocene.

While the peribullary air sinus acoustically isolated the periotic bone with an air barrier, the bulla is not isolated. The outer surfaces of this bone are tightly adherent to tissues, mostly those of the mandibular fat body. Since the lower jaw is now implicated in odontocete hearing, we should consider the possibility that a wave guide is present, perhaps representing an evolutionary elaboration upon an originally extraneous sound source.

Wave Guides

Fat especially is closely impedance-matched to seawater (castor oil $= 1.45 \times 10^5$ gm/sec/cm^2, while seawater at 35 ppt salinity, standard temperature and pressure, $= 1.54 \times 10^5$ gm/sec/cm^2). Both Reysenbach de Haan (1957) and Purves (1966) discuss the acoustic impedance correspondence of fat and seawater. Further, Purves reports some interesting tests using a pointed acoustic probe and pickup which allowed measurement of sound attenuation and transmission through various porpoise tissues. He reports:

> During these experiments I found that sound conductivity from one type of soft structure to another, and from soft tissue to bone, was relatively poor. For instance, blubber, though an extremely good conductor, does not readily transmit sound to the underlying muscles. I found that the attenuation through 60 cm of blubber alone was less than through 2 cm of blubber plus 1 cm of subadjacent muscle. . . . These differences in transmission had nothing to do with the presence of air bubbles in the tissues, but depended upon the inherent variability of the molecular arrangements of the structures involved. This fact was demonstrated by passing the same frequencies through my own limbs, which, presumably, contained no gas bubbles. The transmission could be made to vary through 15 dB by merely changing the tension and attitude of my muscles. Moreover, the óscilloscope display showed that the original pure tone underwent considerable modification within the various structures, some wave trains arriving at the receiving end several degrees out of phase with others.

If blubber was early developed, it must have transmitted sounds wherever it ran beneath thin skin. Deeper fatty deposits invading the blubber could have directed sound into unexpected places in the internal anatomy. On the other side of the ledger, air spaces, wherever they may have occurred, acted as very efficient sound mirrors (Fig. 2). The higher the frequency of the sound involved, the more minor tissue interfaces tend to reflect. Hence we can say that our ancestral creature, once submerged, developed a new "internal sound anatomy" that had

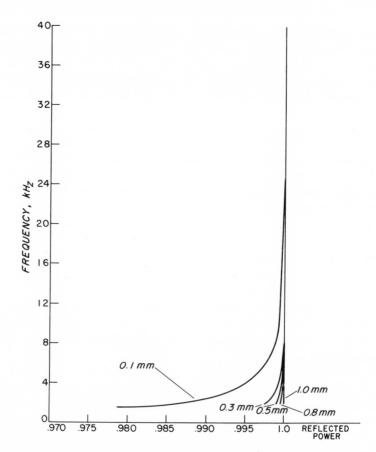

Fig. 2. Reflected power of films of air surrounded on either side by seawater. Note that even a film 0.1 mm thick is essentially a perfect reflector to all but the longest wavelengths of sound.

been all but lacking while it remained on land, except for the internal propagations of its own signals. In my view, selection has acted upon this initially unwanted complex of sound transmission patterns to produce several features of the uniquely adapted acoustic animal we are just beginning to understand today.

In the spring of 1959, while walking down a lonely beach bordering the Gulf of California in Mexico, I came upon the skeleton of a bottlenose porpoise (*Tursiops gilli*). I puzzled over its odd features, and in particular over the strange lower jaw. The mandibular canal, which bears blood vessels and the mandibular branch of the trigeminal and facial nerves, had been massively excavated until the posterior jaw was nothing but a thin hollow shell of homogeneous bone, so thin on its outer aspect that light shone easily through the bone in a large oval area (Fig. 3). Later I found that in some species such as *Kogia breviceps* it is even thinner (Table 1). Anteriorly the canal tapered abruptly and pierced the jaw in a number of places where nerve twigs and blood vessels led to the sur-

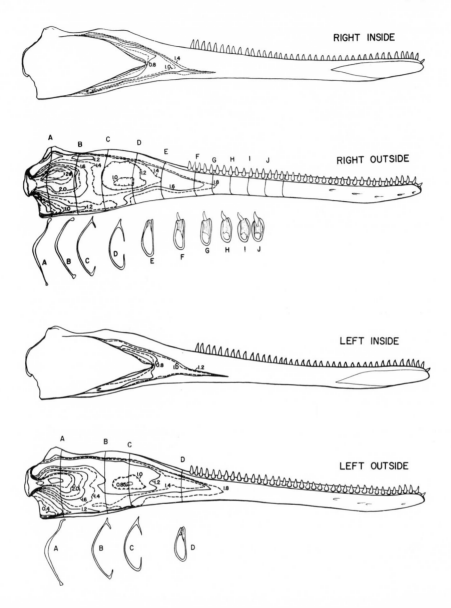

Fig. 3. Topograph of the lower jaw of the Hawaiian spotted porpoise *Stenella attenuata*. Measurements are in millimeters of thickness. The toothed line indicates that thicknesses less than the bounding measurement lie within. Cross sections were made at listed points and are also shown. Note the conformance of the margin of the inner bony shelf with the thinnest part of the exterior bone.

Table 1. Some Characteristics of the Posterior Mandible in Various Cetaceans

Species	Dimensions of internal opening* of fossa (cm)	Dimensions of thinnest area† (cm)	Locality and shapes‡	Extremes of thickness§ (mm)
Grampus griseus	16.5 × 9	9.5 × 2.3 (1.0)	Near dorsal margin; elongate ovoid	0.9–1.9
Steno bredanensis	12.0 × 8	4.1 × 4.2 (1.9)	Middle anterior near angle of fossa; subcircular	1.5–3.6
Sousa sp.	13.0 × 6.5	8.5 × 2.3 3 × 1.5 (2.5)	Two, divided by heavy midlongitudinal ridge; neither pronounced; elongate oval (ventral)	1.42–4.03
Delphinapterus leucas	16.5 × 9.5	15.5 × 2.5 (3.0)	Narrow area along ventral margin of fossa	1.5–3.65
Kogia breviceps	22.5 × 10.5	12.5 × 7.5 (1.0)	Pronounced in large ovoid area below dorsal margin	0.4–1.55
Kogia simus	7 × 3.7	7 × 3.7 (0.54)	Entire area of fossa extremely thin, particularly post. edge, normally fragmenting in dissection	0.20–0.54
Berardius bairdi	21.5 × 10.5	12 × 9 (2.5)	Anteriorly pointed chevron-shaped area divided by jaw art.; thinnest at post. margin	0.69–3.6
Mesoplodon europaeus	24 × 10	21.5 × 10 (1.5)	Large area incl. entire post. ⅓ narrowing to upper ½ ant.	0.38–2.08
Pontoporia blainvillei	10 × 5.5	10 × 5.5 (0.9)	Entire fossa area very thin, particularly post. margin	0.19–0.9
Platanista gangetica	8.8 × 9.9	8.8 × 9.9 (1.07)	Entire fossa area thin	0.2–1.07
Globicephala melaena	15 × 9.5	7 × 6 (1.5)	Thinnest area ant. in middle of fossa	1.1–3.8

* Longest measurements across width and length of mandibular fossa.
† Arbitrarily, a thickness contour was chosen (in parens, mm) and its approximate dimensions noted.
‡ The approximate shape of arbitrarily chosen contour is described.
§ Excepting area of buttress of jaw articulation

face of the lower jaw. The articulation of the jaw was distal and just anterior to the tympanoperiotic complex which houses the middle and inner ears. (Fig. 4). I knew that the mandibular canal in life is filled with a unique oil-rich fat, once so valuable for fine oil that porpoises were fished for this purpose (True, 1890).

The pattern of lower jaw structure in odontocetes is quite constant from species to species, and even from family to family, with regard to certain features. In all odontocetes the jaws become broadened dorsoventrally in the posterior third to half, and the interior of the jaw is greatly excavated. The outer bone over this broadened section exhibits a topography of thinness, with a relatively discrete central oval area usually being thinnest of all (Table 1).

In all species that I have examined (*Stenella attenuata* and *Stenella* sp., *Tursiops gilli, Kogia breviceps, K. simus, Delphinus bairdi,* and *Inia geoffrensis*), in the soft tissue overlying the lateral border of the lower jaw there is an oval fatty

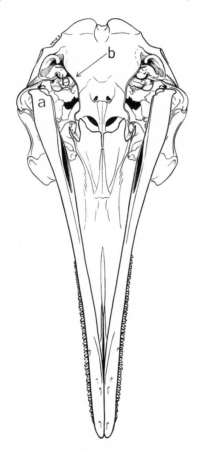

Fig. 4. Ventral view of the skull of *Stenella* sp. (Oahu, Hawaii), the Hawaiian spinner porpoise, showing the close juxtaposition of the mandibular articulation (a) with the tympanoperiotic complex (b) to which the mandibular fat body attaches.

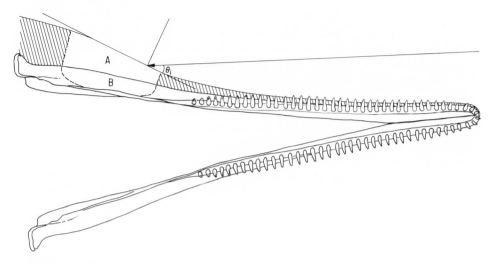

Fig. 5. Delphinid lower jaw, showing the tissue overlying the jaw with its fatty "acoustic window," and the angle of incidence (θ) of sound coming from directly ahead of the animal.

area that corresponds closely in outline to the region of minimum bone thickness (Fig. 5). It is probably an "acoustic window" allowing sound to reach the jawbone relatively unimpeded. In *Kogia simus*, which because of the shape of its jaws has a thick mass of tissue over the posterior mandibles, this plug of material is especially evident as a thick, prominent region of liquid spermaceti (melting point ca. 80°F) lightly contained in connective tissue, oval in cross section, penetrating from the epidermis to the bone, and located between adjacent muscle masses and darker-colored fat. Muscle fibers are absent in the window whereas they are prominent in adjacent tissue. Within the jaw one finds that the region of minimum bony thickness is also demarcated in adjacent internal tissue. In both species of *Kogia* it appears as an ovoid area of spermaceti that descends into the soft fatty tissue filling the fossa. This cylinder slants posteriorly as a sharply demarcated channel and terminates over the smooth surface of the bulla. The thin lateral bony window of the jaw, or pan bone as the whalers called it, is typically composed of hard, translucent, very homogeneous bone. The inner wall of the jaw is usually incomplete, with the posterior margin of the bony shelf corresponding with some fidelity to the anterior margin of the thin outer bony window, directly adjacent to it (Fig. 3).

If one views the entire lower jaw of various odontocete species, some regularities emerge. When viewed from above, the two bodies of the lower jaw typically form a V, with its apex at the symphysis (Fig. 5), or a Y in such genera as *Inia, Kogia, Platanista,* and *Physeter,* where the two solid mandibular bodies join at the symphysis for a considerable length and then flare. The entire intramandibular fat body is contained within the diverging arms of the Y in these forms, with only a narrow channel extending forward into the dense cancellate bone of the symphysis. In forms whose lower jaws form a V, the fat body still lies in the posterior half of each jaw body but is apt to taper less abruptly into the narrow anterior channel. Figures for various thicknesses are given in Table 1; the topography of the lower jaw is shown in Figure 3.

The delphinid bulla is often extremely thin (0.4–0.5 mm in *Stenella*) where the fat body adheres to it. Elsewhere it is greatly thickened, particularly on its medial margins where it contacts the periotic bone.

In the Amazon River porpoise *Inia geoffrensis*, the jaw fat body is especially well defined and in life is composed of liquid oil suspended in a mesh of connective tissue. It does not contact the bulla in the same way it does in delphinids, but instead the oil channel curls around its anterior aspect and touches the bulla in a small area at the anterior edge of the sigmoid flexure, interestingly enough, directly over the ankylosed malleus. The bulla of this species is very thick except where the oil touches it.

How might such a complex structure function as a wave guide, as it seems to do? If it functions as a passive pickup and conductor of sound, tracing a possible sound path will be revealing. The simplest case is that in which a plane wave arrives normal to the jaw surface. There it encounters the variety of tissues overlying the jaw. It will pass most easily into the oval area of fat or liquid oil over the flared posterior end of the jaw. Once within this fatty or oily "window" it will be largely contained by reflection from surrounding structures until the jawbone itself is reached. At first glance the jawbone seems to be an impenetrable barrier, but such is not the case. In fact, this thin bone is transparent to the sounds used by porpoises in its thinnest region and is selectively less transparent as thicker surrounding bone is reached. The highest frequencies are affected most strongly by these thickness differences; low frequency sounds are less affected (Fig. 6). This relationship is expressed in a formula for transmission of sound through three media at normal incidence (Kinsler and Frey, 1962).

$$P_{t_{1-3}} = \frac{\dfrac{4\rho_1 c_1}{\rho_3 c_3}}{\left(\dfrac{\rho_1 c_1}{\rho_3 c_3} + 1\right)^2 \cos kl + \left(\dfrac{\rho_1 c_1}{\rho_2 c_2} + \dfrac{\rho_2 c_2}{\rho_3 c_3}\right)^2 \sin^2 kl} \qquad (1)$$

where

l = length of medium 2 in cm
$k = 2\pi/\lambda$
λ = wavelength in medium 2 in cm
P_t = power transmitted
ρc = acoustic impedance in appropriate material
and

$$P_{r_{1-3}} = P_{t_{1-3}} - 1 \qquad (2)$$

where.

P_r = power reflected.

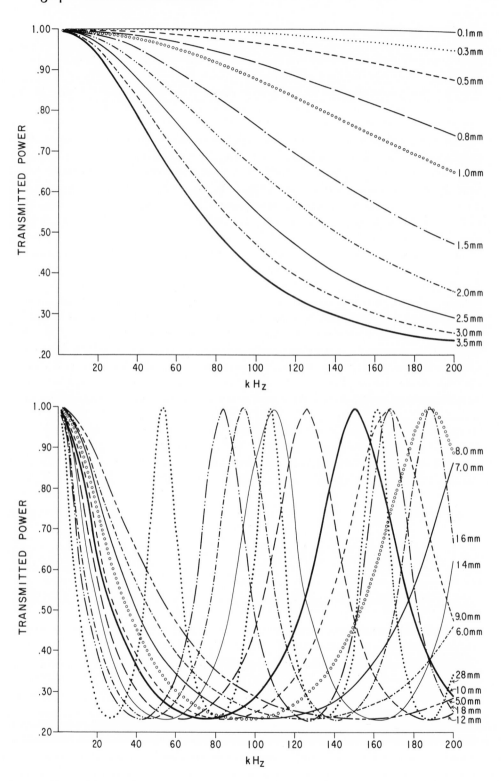

Figures for the acoustic impedance of specific materials involved in the case we are studying here have not been developed, but the existing condition can be closely approximated by using values for similar materials. Thus, curves for transmission in bone bounded on two sides by seawater are given in Figure 6. At all wavelengths conceivably of use to a porpoise or whale, the thin pan bone lying over the mandibular fat body is transparent to normally incident sound.

The function of thickness topography of the pan bone would seem to be important because most sounds, particularly echoes of the animal's own sounds, usually do not hit the jaw or its fatty covering tissue at normal incidence but at a considerable angle instead. Further, the animal scans by movements of its head (Kellogg, 1960; Norris et al., 1961) and thus alters this angle of incidence constantly. Thus it is important to know what happens to sound transmission when the angle of incidence is changed.

The effect of angular change upon transmission from water into oil is profound and probably provides the porpoise with a very sensitive means of angular discrimination. No figures are available for these changes from water to bone. Kinsler and Frey (1962) present data for transmission of sound from water to oil as well as the refracted angles involved (Table 2). These figures represent a reasonable approximation for the transmission characteristics of sound entering the oily window lying over a porpoise jaw. Note that at the tangential angle of 90° no transmission occurs but that, within a 9° change, transmission has risen to 63 per cent and rises to nearly perfect transmission at an angle of 28.8° from the plane of longitudinal axis of the body. Thus it becomes important to know the angle of the external surface of the jaw over the fat body in relation to the longitudinal axis of the animal, and similar angles for the receptive surface of the melon. Some measured angles are presented in Table 3. Note that several hover around a point at which transmission is essentially perfect for sounds arriving from directly ahead, but very close to the angle at which transmission would drop precipitously with a small change in angle. In the case of the common dolphin *Delphinus*

Fig. 6. The transmission of sound through three media: seawater–ivory–seawater. Ivory was used as the closest available approximation of petrous or jaw bone (speed of sound, 3,013 mps), while the use of sea water (1,500 mps) approximates transmission through fat or oil.

Upper: Transmitted sound power through thin sheets of bone (ivory) at normal incidence. Since echoes of a porpoises's own signals will arrive at a variety of angles varying from tangential incidence to normal, the effective thickness will vary accordingly. Thin bones, for example those 0.5 mm or less in thickness, will affect sound transmission least by angular change.

Lower: Transmitted sound power through thicker sheets of bone bounded by seawater at normal incidence. As thickness increases, fluctuating transmission relationships enter. Peak transmission occurs at 0.5 wavelength intervals, calculated for the speed of sound in the specific material, in this case, bone (ivory). Changes in angle of incidence from normality will effectively thicken the bone with regard to incident sound and thus shift the wavelength of the peak transmission point.

Table 2. Transmission of Sound from Water to Oil Modified from Kinsler and Frey, 1962.

Incident angle in degrees* O_i (water)	Refracted angle in degrees O_t (oil)	Sound transmission coefficient (t)
90.0	0	0.986
55.2	30	0.979
35.2	45	0.953
28.8	50	0.935
21.0	55	0.885
9.0	60	0.63
0.0	61.4	0.00

* Angles relative to longitudinal axis of animal.

Table 3. Surface Angles of Some Species of Odontocetes, Relative to Longitudinal Axis*

Species	Sex	Locality	Melon L	Melon R	Mandible L	Mandible R
Kogia breviceps	♂	Playa del Rey, Calif.		25°		28°
Delphinus bairdi	♀	San Pedro Channel, Calif.		28°		18°
Stenella microps	♂	Central America	27°	25°	20°	15°
Stenella graffmanni	♀	Central America	24°	25°	15°	17°
Tursiops truncatus	♂	Florida		30°		28°

* Taken over presumed sound receptor areas. These angles are approximations only because of varying contours of jaws and melon.

bairdi, the lower jaws lie at an angle that would fall on the region of rapid change in transmission, while the melon lies at an angle allowing nearly all sound to enter, but, once again, near the break point where small angular changes produce important reductions in transmission.

With bilateral loci of reception, the porpoise is thus able to shut down one pair of reception points while, by small movements of its head, increasing the reception of the other pair. Further, since these surfaces do not all lie in the vertical plane, complex angular discrimination for targets above and below the longitudinal axis is to be expected. Thus, rotary head scanning, as has been noted by several authors, will provide crucial information to the porpoise relating to location of an echo source or of an animal that is signaling.

Once sound has entered the "acoustic window" over the jaw and has penetrated the thin bone of the posterior mandible, the mandibular fat body is encountered. In dissection, this body is usually very well differentiated from surrounding tissues and leads directly to the bulla. The mechanics of sound-ducting, once sounds reach the wave guide of the mandibular fat body, are obscure, but it is assumed that the tissue interfaces channel the sound toward the bulla by relationships such as that discussed for refraction and reflection of sound from water–oil interfaces. Experimentation is needed.

Since submergence of the terrestrial cetacean ancestor made the amplification of sound by the pinna inoperative, it is interesting to see whether these proposed mandibular sound channels might not serve the same function. The relationship should be found in the ratio between the area of the fatty window over the jaw and the area of the mandibular fat body attaching to the bulla. This has been measured for some species (Table 4). To what extent this relationship compensates for energy loss to surrounding tissues and contributes to actual sound amplification at the middle ear can be determined only by direct experiment. At any rate, structures are present that could achieve a considerable amplification.

When sound arrives at the bulla, once again it is impossible to predict with any accuracy what happens to the incident energy. No firm evidence exists about the state of the middle ear air bubble for a diving animal, particularly in relation to the pressure change as the animal dives and surfaces, when volume changes as great as a hundred times may be expected (in the sperm whale). It is probably retained in some form. As Purves (1966) points out, the middle ear cavity is lined with a complicated vascular mucous membrane that is continuous with the lining of the peribullary sinus, plus a mass of cavernous tissue (the corpus cavernosum tympanicum). Both may contribute to pressure compensation through blood engorgement. Their effects in sound processing must be assessed before sound paths in the middle ear can be understood.

The problem of what happens to sound reaching the bulla can at this stage only be solved, or even understood, by direct experiment. The mathematics are not available that will allow acoustic analysis of such a peculiarly shaped structure as the bulla and its contained structures. However, it is instructive to look at what is known about ensonified spheres of various wall thicknesses that contain either air or water (Hickling, 1962; Diercks and Hickling, 1966). First, if the sphere is water-filled, as its walls are thinned it ceases to return echoes in relation to wave-

Table 4. Comparison of Surface Areas in Proposed Mandibular Wave Guide

Species	Area of acoustic window over mandible* (sq cm)	Area of fat body on tympanic bulla* (sq cm)	Amplification factor
Kogia breviceps (Playa del Rey, Calif.)	90	4.83	18.7×
Inia geoffrensis	88	7.4	11.9×
Delphinus bairdi	32	3.32	9.7×

* These areas are approximations because of tissue irregularities and indefinite borders between tissues.

length, low frequencies first (long wavelengths) progressing to short wave-lengths. Thus, as we have already seen for the case of the jaw wall, the thin-walled portion of this water- (or blood-) filled bulla would clearly transmit sound into the middle ear without significant reflection loss. A reflection of part of the wavelengths would occur at the opposite wall, because the periotic bone is thick and dense. Except where the bulla is thick this echo would be transmitted back down the jaw wave guide. If the bulla was air-filled, or even if it maintained only a thin film of air, a variety of complicated events could be expected to occur. In air-filled metal spheres whose walls are thinner than the ensonifying wavelengths, flexural waves are propagated around the sphere (Hickling, 1964), and perhaps this is what happens in the bulla, with sounds reaching the ossicular chain through the processus gracilis of the malleus.

Fraser and Purves (1960) describe experiments with a mechanical model of the middle ear in which they conclude that sound must enter the middle ear ossicular chain via the tympanic ligament and that it cannot arrive via resonant vibrations of the bulla. However, their simulation of the attachment of the malleus to the sigmoid process of the bulla ("a thin flexible plastic junction," Purves, 1966) seems inappropriate and may have led to spurious results. The attachment is actually very firm and quite rigid. Further, the actual excursions of the middle ear bones in an aquatic animal are so slight, even during perception of loud sounds, that interpretation of leverages in a model such as this seems suspect. For instance, while excursion of the human tympanic membrane at threshold levels are on the order of the diameter of a hydrogen atom (10^{-9} cm), they are from two to three times smaller for waterborne vibrations (Van Bergeijk et al., 1960). Even close to pain thresholds, excursions are relatively slight, and one wonders if the model was not thrown into excessive vibration that could change its essential pattern. For example, at high sound-energy levels the human ossicular chain apparently protects the inner ear mechanism against excessive sound by abruptly developing an entirely different mode of vibration in which application of addi-tional energy to the tympanum does not produce greater and greater excursions of the footplate (Békésy, 1960). At any rate, in view of the facts and speculation presented here I believe that we must reappraise Purves' (1966) conclusion that "resonant vibrations of the bulla play no part in cetacean hearing."

So far, the emphasis has been upon the proposed wave guide in the lower jaw. Other possibilities exist above the jaw line. It has already been noted that sounds produced in the nasal passages above the bony nares would have to pass through the fatty melon which comprises most of the soft tissue of the delphinid forehead anterior to the blowhole. Dissection of the melon of the Pacific common dolphin (*Delphinus bairdi*) shows that this organ, which is roughly cylindrical in cross section, swings to the right side as it passes caudad toward the level of the nasal plugs, and finally enters the tissue of the right nasal plug. This plug is approximately twice the size of the left plug. Its distal edge terminates in a lip-like tip that Evans and Prescott (1962) have suggested is a sound generator. Another interesting relationship is found in the Amazon River porpoise (*Inia geoffrensis*). While handling a captive specimen in an oceanarium, I noted that the forehead was extremely flaccid, and assumed that I was feeling an air sac. Later, dissection of a frozen specimen showed that the species has a "case" filled with liquid oil in life. When this structure was followed caudad, it was found to enter the tissue of both nasal plugs.

Dissection of both species of pygmy sperm whales (*Kogia simus, K. breviceps*) showed that the spermaceti organ of both extends caudad as a cylindrical oil-filled channel that finally rises dorsally in a twisting "spout" to enter the lips of the *museau du singe*, a structure that gives every appearance of being a sound generator, as was suggested to me several years ago by Forrest Wood, III. Its hardened striated lips top an extension of the right naris (see Kernan and Schulte, 1918), which is much the smaller of the two nares in these species.

Thus the melon or the spermaceti case, in combination with the supposed noisemakers of the nasal plugs or the *museau du singe,* looks suggestively like sound-generation and beaming apparatus. Caution against making any firm interpretation of this sort is provided by the sperm whale *Physeter catodon,* in which the *museau du singe* is located at the tip of the snout beneath locally very thin blubber, where an air sac, the distal sac, lies at the anterior end of the spermaceti case, not behind it, as in *Kogia,* while the nasal plugs occupy their normal position at the posterior end of the case.

It is especially suggestive of the involvement of these structures in sound processing to find the fat or oil of the melon or case penetrating into the lips of the proposed sound generators, since this arrangement would produce optimum transduction of sound produced by air in an aquatic animal (Fig. 1). In this situation we should not think so much of transmission of sounds produced into air sacs as of the vibrations of the tissues of the generating organs which are allowed to occur because the air column passing through the generator has someplace to go (the sac into which the generator empties). Thus a tissue-to-tissue transduction can occur, a much more efficient arrangement than an air–tissue transduction and, for sharp signals like clicks, one not involved with the resonations of an air cavity. The anatomy mentioned here allows such sounds to be guided away from the generator through what is probably the most efficient sound pipe or wave guide in the body—fat or oil—to the surface of the body where it is closely coupled, impedance-wise, to the seawater outside.

The studies of Yanagisawa et al. (1966) show that sound is received at the melon in addition to other suggestions that it is generated in that region. Anatomy that could support this is obscure, but the prime inference seems to be that a tissue wave guide may lead over the edge of the rostrum into the tissue of the fatty window of the lower jaw, passing just anterior to the antorbital notches, anterior to the eye.

Finally, two additional structures should be considered as possible sound processors. In delphinids, and also in most other odontocetes, the mesorostral cartilage and canal should receive experimental attention. This cartilage (the ethmoid cartilage; see Lawrence and Schevill, 1956) is contained within a subcylindrical canal in the rostrum, bounded dorsolaterally by the premaxillary and maxillary bones, and below by the vomer (Fig. 1). The premaxillary bone surrounding the canal is usually very dense and ivory-like, in sharp distinction to other bones of the rostrum and forehead. The canal opens directly at the tip of the upper jaw, and the contained cartilage extends as a rounded protrusion a few millimeters beyond the bone, ending under thin skin from which the blubber layer is absent, within a millimeter or two of the surface skin. Following the canal caudad we find that it characteristically has an open slit-like area facing upward at about or anterior to the midlength of the rostrum, where the premaxillary bones do not close over the canal. The shape and location of this opening is species-specific. Posterior to this the canal typically closes over the contained cartilage to the point of the narial septum, where the cartilage is confluent with the cartilaginous septum between the two nares. It is especially suggestive that the median borders of the nasal plugs are tightly attached to this median septum and actually hinge upon it during their movement (Lawrence and Schevill, 1956). It is also suggestive that in some delphinids (*Delphinus*, for example) a rostral extension of the pterygoid air sac system extends nearly to the tip of the rostrum along the length of this cartilage. The cartilage is thus optimally situated to serve as a wave guide. It is tightly adherent to the proposed sound generators, and it is acoustically isolated by materials widely variant from water as far as impedance is concerned (the air sacs and ivory-like bone). Experiments of course are needed to solidify or reject this proposal. If correct, the sound field should emanate as a narrow beam from the tip of the rostrum (present experiments suggest this but are not precise enough), and a component of the field might be generated away from the dorsal surface of the rostrum in a distinct peak of sound pressure through the characteristic opening found there.

How closely matched acoustically to water this cartilage might be is not known, but, because of its low density and richness in water, it surely is not badly mismatched, particularly compared to surrounding materials.

A mesorostral groove appears to have been present in the earliest known odontocete (*Agorophius;* True, 1907). Since sound reception seems to involve the odontocete forehead, the marked asymmetries of the scooped forehead in many species might conceivably have come to function in the assessment of directionality in place of the lost pinnae. The forehead probably represents the proper increase in size (about $5\times$) of dimensions needed in water as compared to air. Further, as Gregory Bateson pointed out to me, the fact that these asymmetries increase with age is not unlike the situation one finds in the pinnae, in which a human can learn to compensate for a damaged pinna or can even learn quickly to use models of someone else's pinna.

It is an intriguing possibility that the evolution of sophisticated sound production structures on the forehead of odontocetes may have contributed to the reduction and final loss of the sense of smell in these animals. The facts that suggest this possibility are several. First, during odontocete evolution there was a gradual closure of the foramina of the olfactory nerves passing forward from the olfactory bulbs of the brain. Olfactory structures were evident in Eocene zeuglodonts and persisted into the Miocene, where they existed in restricted form in the squalodonts and in such forms as the platanistid ancestor *Zarhachis flagellator*. The foramina are completely closed in most modern toothed whales, except fetuses (Kellogg, 1928). The cribriform plate, through which the olfactory nerves pass in mammals, has become altered in modern forms (Fig. 1). The mesethmoid and ectethmoid bones have fused and overspread the nasal bones on the posterior surfaces of the nasal passage, thus effectively blocking the olfactory nerve completely. The barrier between the nasal passage and the brain in the modern *Stenella attenuata* is composed of very thick bone (varying in thickness from 8 to 11 mm). The proposed site of sound production at the nasal plugs directly overlies these bones.

The clicks of modern odontocetes, in general, might be expected to cause difficulties, and perhaps even tissue destruction, at the termination of the nerves or by passage through the nerve foramina directly into the brain behind. As noted, these sounds are often extremely intense (calculated at 124 dB at 1 m from the source, rel. 0.0002 dyne/cm^2; *Steno bredanensis*; Norris and Evans, 1967).

Obviously, much of what has been presented here is speculative and in need of experimental testing, but enough is known to show that the great reduction of density differential between animal tissue and environment, once the odontocete ancestor became submerged, has been a potent force in the evolution of acoustic mechanisms in the group.

In summary, the evolutionary sequence proposed here for odontocete acoustic mechanisms is as follows.

1. During the early Cenozoic the ancestral form became amphibious, and communication by the partly submerged animal developed, propagating an underwater component that then became used in intraspecific communication.

2. Sounds came to enter and leave by many adventitious channels, some of which provided the raw materials for adaptation.

3. Nasal valves, which are represented today by the nasal plugs, were developed and may have been used for sound production very early in odontocete history.

4. Air recycling developed to conserve air during diving, and the structures involved are seen today as the blowhole and upper nasal sacs.

5. Occurring concurrently were the development of acoustic barriers and reflectors in the form of air sacs; the telescoping of the skull, possibly implicated in direction-finding; the thinning of the mandible, which is now a reception point; and the reorganization of the middle ear mechanism.

6. Fat, oil, and cartilage may all have been used to produce acoustic wave guides with low transmission and transduction loss characteristics.

7. No mention has been made of the alterations of the cochlea or central nervous mechanisms that surely must also have occurred.

Acknowledgments. Building a speculative framework such as this requires bringing together information from diverse fields, and many people have helped me learn about underwater acoustics, hearing theory, cetacean anatomy, and cetacean history. I thank all who helped for their patience with me, and especially Georg von Békésy, W. van Bergeijk, Scott Johnson, and William Evans. Even though my ideas about function often run counter to theirs, I maintain the highest regard for the anatomical studies of porpoises conducted by F. C. Fraser and P. E. Purves, and I thank them for suggestions in conversation. Barbara Lawrence and William Schevill have successfully counteracted my tendency to feel that we know more than we actually do about sources of sounds in odontocetes. Mrs. Barbara Mooney, Midori Brown, and Miss Eda Bloom have helped with illustrations and the preparation of the manuscript. Finally, I am grateful for the support of the National Institute of Neurological Diseases and Blindness in my studies of cetacean acoustics.

REFERENCES

Batteau, D. W., 1964. The role of the pinna in human localization. Report for U.S. Naval Ord. Test Sta. (mimeo.), 30 p.

Békésy, G. V., 1960. The gap between the hearing of external and internal sounds. *Symposia Soc. Exp. Biol., 16:* 267–88.

Boyden, A., and D. Gemeroy, 1950. The relative position of the Cetacea among the orders of Mammalia as indicated by precipitin tests. *Zoologica, 35:* 145–51.

Coulomb, H. N., S. H. Ridgeway, and W. E. Evans, 1965. Respiratory water exchange in two species of porpoise. *Science, 149:* 86–88.

Diercks, K. J., and R. Hickling, 1966. Echoes from hollow aluminum spheres in water. *U.S. Naval Ord. Test Sta. Rept. 122.2,* p. 1–18.

Emlen, J. T., Jr., 1960. *Introduction to Animal Sounds and Communication,* W. E. Lanyon and W. N. Tavolga, eds. Publ. 7 AIBS, Washington D.C., 443 p.

Evans, W. E., 1967. Vocalization among marine mammals. In *Proceedings of 2nd Conference on Marine Bio-Acoustics,* W. N. Tavolga, ed. Am. Mus. Nat. Hist., 1966. New York.

Evans, W. E., and J. H. Prescott, 1962. Observations of the sound production capabilities of the bottlenose porpoise: A study of whistles and clicks. *Zoologica, 47:* 121–28.

Flower, W. H., 1883. On the characters and divisions of the family Delphinidae. *Proc. Zool. Soc. London,* p. 466–513.

Fraser, F. C., and P. E. Purves, 1960. Hearing in cetaceans. *Bull. Brit. Mus. (Natur. Hist.), 7:* 1–140.

Hickling, R., 1962. Analysis of echoes from a solid elastic sphere in water. *J. Acoust. Soc. Am.,* 34(10): 1582–92.

——, 1964. Analysis of echoes from a hollow metallic sphere in water. *J. Acoust. Soc. Am.,* 36(6): 1124–37.

Kellogg, R., 1928. The history of whales: Their adaptation to life in the water. *Quart. Rev. Biol., 3:* 174–208.

Kellogg, W. N., 1960. Auditory scanning in the dolphin. *Psych. Rev., 10:* 25–27.

Kellogg, W. N., R. Kohler, and H. N. Morris., 1953. Porpoise sounds as sonar signals. *Science, 117:* 239–43.

Kernan, J. D., and H. W. Schulte, 1918. Memoranda upon the anatomy of the respiratory tract, foregut, and thoracic viscera of a foetal *Kogia breviceps. Bull. Am. Mus. Nat. Hist., 38:* 231–67.

Kinsler, L. E., and A. R. Frey, 1962. *Fundamentals of Acoustics,* 2d ed. Wiley, New York, 524 p.

Lawrence, B. A., and W. E. Schevill, 1956. The functional anatomy of the delphinid nose. *Bull. Mus. Comp. Zool., 114:* 103–51.

Lilly, J. C., and Alice Miller, 1961. Sounds emitted by the bottlenose dolphin. *Science, 133:* 1689–93.

Miller, G. S., 1923. The telescoping of the cetacean skull. *Smithsonian Misc. Coll. 76:* 1–71.

Norris, K. S., 1964. Some problems of echolocation in cetaceans. In *Marine Bio-acoustics,* W. N. Tavolga, ed. Pergamon Press, New York, 413 p.

———, in press. Some observations on the migration and orientation of marine mammals. *Oregon State Univ. Colloq.,* 1966.

Norris, K. S., and W. E. Evans, 1967. Directionality of echolocation clicks in the rough-tooth porpoise *Steno bredanensis* (Lesson). In *Proceedings of 2nd Conference on Marine Bio-acoustics,* Am. Mus. of Nat. Hist., 1966, W. N. Tavolga, ed. New York.

Norris, K. S., J. H. Prescott, P. V. Asa-Dorian, and Paul Perkins, 1961. An experimental demonstration of echolocation behavior in the porpoise, *Tursiops truncatus* (Montagu). *Biol. Bull., 120:* 163–76.

Purves, P. E., 1966. Anatomy and physiology of the outer and middle ear in cetaceans. In *Whales, Dolphins and Porpoises,* K. S. Norris, ed. Univ. Calif. Press, 789 p.

Raven, H., and W. K. Gregory, 1933. The spermaceti organ and nasal passages of the sperm whale (*Physeter catodon*) and other odontocetes. *Am. Mus. Nat. Hist. Novitates,* no. 677, p. 1–18.

Reysenbach de Haan, F. W., 1957. Hearing in whales. *Acta Otolaryngol., Suppl., 134:* 1–14.

Romer, A. S., 1947. *Man and the Vertebrates,* 3d ed. Univ. Chicago Press, p. 168–70.

Schevill, W. E., 1964. Underwater sounds of cetaceans. In *Marine Bio-acoustics.,* W. N. Tavolga, ed. Pergamon Press, New York, 413 p.

Schevill, W. E., and W. A. Watkins, 1966. Sound structure and directionality in *Orcinus* (killer whale). *Zoologica, 51*(2): 71–76.

Schevill, W. E., W. A. Watkins, and R. H. Backus, 1964. The 20-cycle signals and *Balaenoptera* (fin whales). In Marine Bio-acoustics, W. N. Tavolga, ed. Pergamon Press, New York.

Slijper, E. J., 1966. Functional morphology of the reproductive system in Cetacea. In *Whales, Dolphins and Porpoises,* K. S. Norris, ed. Univ. Calif. Press.

True, F. W., 1890. Observations on the life history of the bottlenose porpoise. *Proc. U.S. Nat Mus., 13:* 197–203.

———, 1907. Remarks on the type of the fossil cetacean *Agorophius pygmaeus* (Müller). *Smithson. Inst. Spec. Publ.,* no. 1694 p. 1–8.

———, 1912. Description of a new fossil porpoise of the genus *Delphinodon* from the Miocene formation of Maryland. *Proc. Acad. Nat. Sci. Philadelphia,* 2d ser., *15:* 165–94.

Tumarkin, A., 1955. On the evolution of the auditory conducting apparatus: A theory based on functional considerations. *Evolution,* 9(3): 221–43.

Van Bergeijk, W., 1966. Evolution of the sense of hearing in vertebrates. *Am. Zool.,* 6(3): 371–77.

Van Bergeijk, W., J. R. Pierce, and E. E. David, Jr., 1960. *Waves and the Ear.* Double-day, Garden City, 235 p.

Van Valen, L., 1966. Delpatheridia, a new order of mammals. *Am. Mus. Nat. Hist. Bull.* 32(1): 90–93.

Yanagisawa, K., O. Sato, M. Nomoto, Y. Katsuki, E. Ikezona, A. D. Grinnell, and T. H. Bullock, 1966. Auditory evoked potentials from brain stem in cetaceans. *Fed. Proc. Physiol.* (abstr. 1539).

Richard Levins

11. TOWARD AN EVOLUTIONARY THEORY OF THE NICHE

The notion of the ecological niche has long been used heuristically in biology to indicate that species differ in what they require from the environment (e.g. Grinnell, 1922) or its position in the food chain (Elton, 1927), and biogeographers have been concerned with vacant niches (indicating that a new species could successfully invade a biota) or with niche equivalence (e.g. the niche equivalence of placental and marsupial carnivores as accounting for their similar appearance). But it is largely due to the work and inspiration of G. E. Hutchinson that a rigorous theory is now being developed.

A satisfactory theory of the niche must first of all give a specific meaning to the vague idea of niche breadth as an inverse measure of specialization, and to niche overlap or distance between niches as a measure of competition. Once these measures are defined we can ask questions about the differences among species' niches—What are the causes and the consequences of different niche breadths? How is the environment divided into niches? How similar can the niches of species be and yet allow coexistence? From there, the theory should account for the relative abundance of species in a community, the numbers of species of different kinds or in different situations (e.g. temperature vs. tropical zones), the coevolution of the niches of species in contact, and the circumstances that permit the sudden change or expansion of niches.

Hutchinson (1965) defines the niche as a volume in a hyperspace the axes of which are the relevant variables in the life of a species. Thus each point represents a combination of factors (environment) that permit the species to survive, and the set of all such points is the fundamental niche. But not all such environments actually occur or are available. The set of environment actually used is designated the realized niche.

There is a certain ambiguity in the geometric representation, since any volume can be turned into a point. Suppose that species 1 can exist from 20° to 28°C, and that species 2 can exist from 26° to 30°C. On a single temperature axis the niches of the two species are intervals that overlap. But if we use two axes to represent the lower and upper temperature limits respectively, the species are

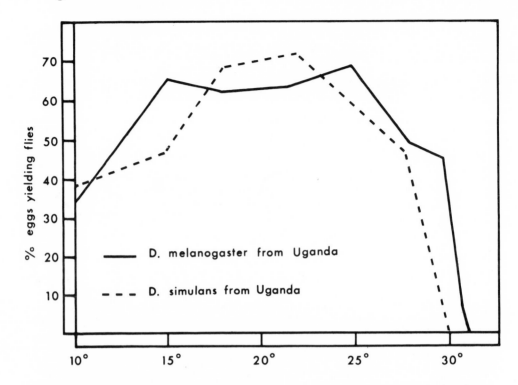

Fig. 1. Niche breadth of *Drosophila* eggs. The ordinate is per cent survival, the abscissa is temperature (after Tantawy and Mallah, 1961).

represented by the distinct points 20, 28 and 26, 30. The similarity of the species appears in the first case as overlap, in the second as distance. Both methods have their uses. Until such time as a single procedure demonstrates its superiority and becomes an accepted convention, we can use either one.

Two further qualifications are required. First, different combinations of environmental factors may not support the species equally well. Second, the behavioral pattern may result in a habitat or food preference which can separate species even if their ranges of potential survival coincide. Thus, corresponding to each point in the environmental hyperplane there is a measure of the probability of survival and reproduction in that environment, and a measure of the relative preference for that environment. Finally we come to our definition of the niche as *a fitness measure on an environment space.*

It is often possible to measure the shape of the fundamental niche with respect to some factor such as temperature. Thus Tantawy and Mallah (1961) compared the survival of egg batches of *Drosophila melanogaster* and *D. simulans* over a wide range of temperatures. As we can see from Figure 1 the former species has the broader niche. It would be possible to measure niche breadth as the length of the interval over which viability is at least 50 per cent of the maximum viability but, for reasons of consistency with other aspects of the niche, other measures will be used.

Maldonado and Levins (1966) set twenty traps for *Drosophila* in a small area of a coffee grove, and the collection from each trap were classified separately. There clearly were significant differences among species in their distribution over the microsites. Further, some species seemed to occur in almost all traps equally, while others were more concentrated in a few. We could not arrange the traps along any axis indicative of environmental factors; there were simply different microhabitats. Nonetheless, it was possible to measure the niche breadth.

Any niche breadth measure must satisfy the following requirements: (1) a species that utilizes equally K of a set of n alternative resources has niche breadth K; (2) a species that uses two resources, but unequally, has a niche breadth between (1) and (2).

Two measures of niche breadth which have been proposed are

$$\text{Log } B = -\Sigma P_i \log P_i$$

and

$$B = 1/\Sigma P_i^2$$

where P_i is the proportion of the total collection of that species which is taken on resource i. Both measures satisfy our minimum requirements, and either may be used until we have good reason to establish one of them. The niche breadth for *Drosophila* species is shown in Table 1. Since we were unable to observe any interspecific aggressive behavior around feeding sites, these data are a direct measure of habitat preference and hence of the fundamental niche. In contrast, the observed frequencies of species at different seasons or of littoral snails at different tidal levels are the result both of inanimate environment and species interactions and therefore represent the realized niche.

The realized niche can change rather quickly as a result of environmental change, demographic change, or individual learning. The fundamental niche is

Table 1. Niche Breadths of Drosophila *Species**

Species	Food breadth	Microhabitat	Season
D. melanogaster	0.65	0.31	0.52
D. latifasciaeformis	.60	.74	.67
D. willistoni group	.60	.65	.41
D. dunni	.73	.52	.76
D. ananassae	.78	.34	.37
D. tristriata		.30	.20
D. repleta			
D. paramediostriata			.21
D. nebulosa	.73		.22

* The numbers are the proportion of total niche space occupied.

modifiable by way of natural selection. We now turn to consideration of factors that determine the direction of this natural selection.

The rate of increase of a population in the absence of competitors can be expressed by

$$dx/dt = rx\,(K\text{-}x)/K$$

where x is the population size, r is the intrinsic rate of increase, and K is the carrying capacity of the environment for this population. It is irrelevant to our present discussion that the age composition and recent history may affect both r and K.

It follows from the equation that if K is the same for all genotypes, differences in fitness are differences in r. This will also be true even when the K's differ, if the population is usually much below K (that is, if there is wide, rapid fluctuation of population size). On the other hand, as x approaches K, differences in K become more important, and if a population is at its maximum, as MacArthur has shown, selection will maximize K and hence population size. Thus, depending on the demographic situation, intrapopulation selection maximizes either r or K.

We will now prove our major results, which relate niche breadth to environmental uncertainty. Since any mathematical model of a complex system requires simplification, there is always the danger that a particular result is an artifact of the model rather than a property of nature. Therefore, we attempt to derive the same results, using quite different models. The conclusions common to several models are considered to be robust theorems reflecting properties independent of the details of methodology.

MODEL I (Levins, 1962)

Consider an environment consisting of two alternatives (habitats or temperatures, or resources). Then any phenotype has a fitness (average number of offspring) in each environment which can be represented by a point on a graph whose axes are W_1 and W_2. There is one phenotype which does best in each environment and many which are of intermediate fitness in both. The set of all points representing possible phenotypes is designated the *fitness set* and is shown in Figure 2. Any mixed population will be represented by a point on the straight line joining the fitness points of the component phenotypes. Thus all possible mixed populations lie on the smallest convex set that contains the fitness set. If the original fitness set is convex, then mixed populations add no new possibilities that cannot be achieved by monomorphic populations.

The optimal population is one that maximizes fitness, which will be some monotonic increasing function of the fitness in the two environments separately. But the form of the fitness function depends on the pattern of the environment.

Case I. The environment is uniformly either 1 or 2 at any given time (over a whole generation) but varies from generation to generation. Then the rate of increase is the product of the fitness in each generation. Therefore the optimal

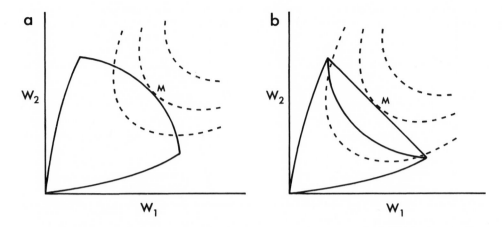

Fig. 2. Fitness set model for temporal variation. The point M corresponds to the population that maximizes $W_1^p W_2^{1-p}$. Diagram a optimizes on a convex set; diagram b on a concave set.

population is the one that maximizes $W_1^p W_2^{1-P}$ where p is the frequency of environment 1, as shown in Figure 2. If the fitness set is convex, the optimum is monomorphic population which is of intermediate fitness in both habitats; if the fitness set is concave it will be polymorphic, a mixture of specialized types. In either case the population as a whole will have a broad niche and survive well in both environments.

Case II. The environment is uniform in time but heterogeneous in space. The heterogeneity is fine-grained; that is, each individual is exposed to many units of environment (or eats many units of resource). If the probability of surviving through a period of length t is $1-\lambda(t)\Delta t$, then as Δt decreases toward zero the probability of survival is $1 - \int \lambda(t)dt$. Thus in a fine-grained environment the diversity affects fitness additively. Therefore the optimal population is the one that maximizes $pW_1 + (1-p)W_2$. This is shown by the straight lines in Figure 3. The result is that in a spatially heterogeneous fine-grained environment, the optimal population is monomorphic. If the fitness set is convex, it will be intermediately adapted to the two environments; if it is concave, the population will be specialized to one of the environments.

Since it can be shown that when the two environments are quite similar the fitness set will be convex, and when the environments are very different compared to tolerance of an individual phenotype the fitness set is concave, the foregoing analysis leads to the conclusion that a species' niche will span a range of similar environments. If the environments are too different, however, fine-grained spatial heterogeneity leads to specialization, whereas temporal variation leads to polymorphism and a broad niche. In the 1962 paper cited I did not recognize the distinction between fine- and coarse-grained environments, so that case II was described merely as spatial heterogeneity.

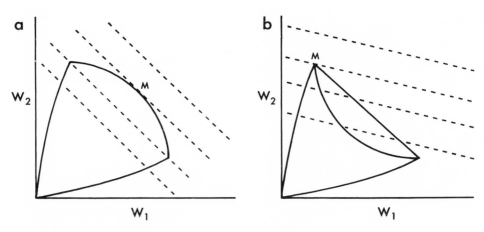

Fig. 3. Fitness set model for fine-grained spatial heterogeneity.

MODEL II

Suppose now a continuum of possible environments S with a frequency distribution $P(S)$. We want to maximize fitness, subject to the restriction

$$\int W(S)\, dS = C$$

that is, that the total area under the fitness curve $W(S)$ is constant but that otherwise it can be freely allocated among the environments. (Alternative restrictions give qualitatively similar results.) Then, in case I (temporal variation) the optimal population maximizes $\int \log W(S)P(S)dS$ subject to the restriction. This gives

$$W(S) = CP(S)$$

so that fitness is assigned to different environments proportional to their frequency. Hence the greater the environmental variability, the broader the niche. At optimum, the log rate of increase is

$$\log C + \int \log P(S)P(S)dS = \log C - U$$

where U is the measure of environmental uncertainty. In model I we can also measure the fitness loss at the optimum from the graph. In case II (fine-grained spatial heterogeneity) we must maximize $\int W(S)P(S)dS$ subject to the same restriction. The answer $W(S)$ is the greatest possible value for the most frequent environment, and zero elsewhere; this corresponds to the specialized monomorphic solution of model I.

Models I and II differ in several important ways. In model I, $W(S)$ is close to $W(S+\Delta S)$. The similarity of environments is therefore taken into consideration. Further, individual phenotypes are recognized, and polymorphism is distinguished from monomorphic populations. Finally, only discretely different environments are considered. Model II allows a continuum of environments but considers each environment to be totally different, so that any fitness assigned to environment S is unavailable in environment S'. Fitness is assigned in terms

of the population as a whole rather than individual phenotypes. This can be corrected for, however, by placing an upper limit on niche breadth of a single phenotype. If the optimum niche is broader, polymorphism is required.

Despite these differences in the models, they agree on the three major conclusions: (1) the optimal niche will be specialized to a narrow range of environments in a fine-grained, spatially heterogeneous environment; (2) for a tem-
porally fluctuating environment, the niche must be broader (its breadth increases
with the environmental variability); (3) the fitness of an optimal population in a
fluctuating environment is less than it would be in a constant environment
(there is an inevitable loss of fitness due to environmental uncertainty, and if this
uncertainty is too great the population cannot maintain itself).

We will now compare the results of these purely ecological arguments to a
model which considers the facts of genetics. On the same graph whose axes are
fitnesses in two alternative environments, let the points AA, AA', $A'A'$ represent
the fitness of the three genotypes at a single locus with two alleles as in Figure 4.
Since the frequencies of the genotypes depend on the gene frequency X, the
fitness of any population lies on the curve that joins the two homozygous points
and approaches halfway to the heterozygous fitness point.

Selection in a fine-grained stable environment will maximize the rate of increase $pW_1 + (1 - p)W_2$ and will therefore lead to a population represented by
the point M in the graph which is tangent to one of the straight lines. Polymorphism
is possible only if there is average heterosis. In that case, the optimum would still
be a monomorphic population which is all heterozygous, but polymorphism is
imposed by Mendelian laws.

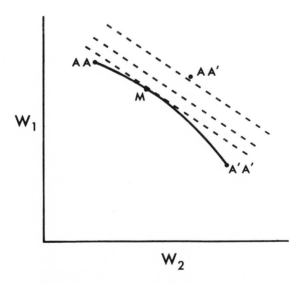

Fig. 4. Selection in a fine-grained environment. AA, AA', $A'A'$ are fitness points for a
single locus with two alleles. Mendelian populations all lie on the curve (AA, $A'A'$).
Axes are fitness in environments 1 and 2.

Table 2. Model for Selection in a Two-phase Environment

Genotype	Frequency	Fitness in I	Fitness in II
AA	X^2	M	L
$A'A$	$2X(1-x)$	$\dfrac{M+L}{2}+h$	$\dfrac{M+L}{2}+h$
$A'A'$	$(1-x)^2$	L	M

Assume a symmetric genetic situation with the fitnesses as shown in Table 2. The heterozygote is superior to the average homozygote in both environments by an amount h. M is the fitness of a genotype in the environment where it is best, L where it is poorest. Then total fitness is

$$\overline{W} = 2X^2h + 2X[h + (M-L)\,(\tfrac{1}{2}-p)] + (1-p)\,M$$

where p is the frequency of resource or environment 1; the equilibrium gene frequency is

$$\hat{X} = \tfrac{1}{2} + \tfrac{1}{2n}\,(M-L)\,(\tfrac{1}{2}-p)$$

which lies between 0 and 1 if and only if

$$\tfrac{1}{2} - \frac{h}{M-L} < P < \tfrac{1}{2} + \frac{h}{M-L}$$

Therefore, in addition to the requirement of marginal heterosis, each environment must be sufficiently common. Otherwise the population will specialize to the more abundant environment. The threshold p depends on the degree of heterosis. If $h > \tfrac{1}{2}(M-L)$, the heterozygote is superior to each homozygote in both habitats, and there will always be polymorphism. But a homozygote whose phenotype corresponds to that of the heterozygote would be even better. For a fixed h, $M-L$ increases as the two environments become increasingly different. Then (provided $p = \tfrac{1}{2}$) a point is reached beyond which a polymorphic broad-niched strategy can no longer be sustained. The difference $M-L$ depends on the breadth of niche for the individual genotypes. Thus our result corresponds to model I: in a fine-grained stable environment of two alternative habitats, if the environments are similar enough there will be an intermediate population doing fairly well in each, but if the environments are too different a specialized population will result. However, there is one new result: for similar environments model I does not recognize a threshold abundance of either habitat as necessary for an intermediate (non-specialized) adaptation.

Any mixture of specialized species would be represented in Figure 4 by a fitness point on the straight line joining the homozygous points. Therefore it would be below the point for a polymorphic broad-niched species. Hence (in the absence of habitat selection) the population established by intrapopulation selection would also outcompete specialists which are subject to the same constraints. Nonetheless, fitness has been lost as a result of environmental heterogeneity. A species which had fitness M on both resources, or a mixture of specialists each using only its preferred resource, would be represented by the point P and would therefore eliminate the broad-niched population.

We now introduce the coarse-grained environment. Here each individual spends his whole life in either environment I or environment II, except for pan-mictic mating of the whole population and random assortment among the environments. This model was studied by Levene (1953), Li (1955), and Levins and MacArthur (1966). Here the environments are presented to individuals not as averages but as alternatives, and it can readily be shown that natural selection maximizes the average Log $(\overline{W}_i)$ over habitats i. Thus in the graph in Figure 5 the equilibrium population is represented by the point that maximizes $P \log W_1 + (1 - p) \log W_2$. It is no longer necessary to have average heterosis for polymorphism to exist. If we use the same model of Table 2, a sufficient condition for selection to push a population from the near homozygous condition toward a polymorphic equilibrium is (transcribed from Levene's notation), setting $h = 0$,

$$\frac{M}{M+L} > p > \frac{L}{M+L}$$

For different values of h this will of course change. But we still have a threshold situation. As the environments become more similar, L approaches M and it becomes increasingly restrictive on p. But for any difference between M and L, polymorphism is possible, even for the extreme case $L = 0$. The polymorphism

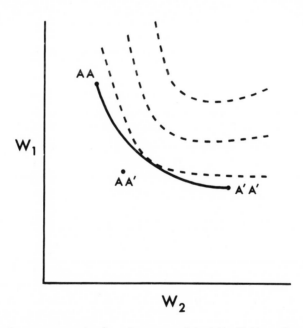

Fig. 5. Selection in a coarse-grained environment. AA, AA', $A'A'$ are fitness points for the three genotypes at one locus with two alleles. Mendelian populations lie on the curve $(AA, A'A')$. Axes are fitnesses in the two environments.

that occurs in this coarse-grained case is different from the previous one in that it does not depend on heterosis. A new homozygous genotype whose phenotype corresponds to that of the heterozygote would be inferior, and the polymorphism is a true mixed strategy of the sort we found in model I with temporal variation. The results of models I and II can now be restated to replace environmental variation in time by environmental uncertainty.

Although, when neither resource is too rare, selection results in the establishment of a broad-niched polymorphism, the fitness lost due to environmental heterogeneity is greater than in the fine-grained case. Further, a mixture of specialized species will now be represented by a point on the line joining the homozygotes, which is above that of the polymorphic population. We now have the surprising result that, while intrapopulation selection moves toward extending the niche breadth, interpopulation competition may eliminate populations which so evolve. The reason for this is that although a broad niche may increase K, it is reduced in each habitat. The fitness loss can be shown to be proportional (to a first approximation) to the variance in equilibrium frequencies for the habitats taken separately. The equation for genetic change,

$$\Delta x = x(1-x)\, \Delta x = \tfrac{1}{2}x(1-x)\, \sum p_i\, \frac{\delta \overline{W}_i}{\delta x} \bigg/ \overline{W}_i$$

weights the fitnesses in such a way that the fitness of each genotype is dependent on gene frequency. Thus Fisher's theorem no longer holds. Finally we note that here too a single specialized competitor can reduce p below threshold, resulting in the displacement of the population to specialization in a narrower range of environments. So far we have treated the environment as given, as if the temporal and spatial variability were meteorological facts. But animals and plants live in only part of the environment. Dormant stages and habitat preferences can bypass some of the more extreme stresses. It is clear that the evolution of niche breadth in the sense of viabilities in different environments depends on the effective environmental variation, not on the meteorological pattern, and that habitat selectivity will depend on the viability niche breadth. We must therefore study their joint evolution.

One way to measure the environmental pattern is through the components of species diversity. Within a collection of animals or plants the measure of diversity is the familiar

$$D_{A+B} = \frac{D_A + D_B}{2} + D^*$$

where D^* is the diversity due to the different conditions separating collections A and B. Such measurements were made on *Drosophila* collections differing in season, bait, microhabitat, site, and geographic region. These are shown in Table 3. Of special interest are the observations that for *Drosophila* the diversity measure is quite uniform from place to place, and that the seasonal component accounts for some 30 per cent of the diversity in Austin, Texas, 22 per cent in subtropical Puerto Rico, and 15 per cent for Brazil (all sites combined) but only 3 per cent in

Table 3. Components of Diversity in Drosophila

Source	Within-bait	Among baits	Total
Puerto Rico	0.42	0.09	0.51
Brazil (Dobzhansky & Pavan)	.43	.14	.57
	Within season	*Among seasons*	
Puerto Rico	0.56	0.16	0.72
Texas (Patterson)	.52	.22	.74
Brazil (Dobzhansky & Pavan)	.67	.12	.79
	Within microsites	*Among microsites*	
Puerto Rico	0.28	0.25	0.53

Belem. Thus we can measure the relative importance of temporal variation in the environment from the fly's point of view.

The evolution of habitat selection can be viewed as follows. Suppose that an animal is searching for an appropriate site (say for oviposition). There are very favorable sites scattered about, within which fitness is W_1. Suppose that the probability of finding such a site in the interval dt is $q\,dt$. Then the probability of not finding any in time t is e^{-qt} and the total fitness is

$$\overline{W} = (1 - e^{-qt})\,W_1$$

Now suppose there is another environment available in which fitness is lower, W_2. It is available at a relative frequency r. Then

$$\overline{W} = (1 - e^{-(q + r)t})\,[W_1q + W_2r]\,/\,(r + q)$$

which is

$$\overline{W} = (1 - e^{-(q + r)t})\,[W_1 - \frac{r}{q + r}\,D]$$

where D is $W_1 - W_2$, the difference in viability in the two habitats. Habitat selection results in the reduction of r. This increases the danger of not finding any site but increases fitness if a site is found. Clearly, if D is very small, only the first term above matters, and there is no reason for selectivity. On the other hand if qt is large enough, the danger of not finding any site nearly vanishes, and selectivity is advantageous. Thus a broad tolerance (D small) favors broad-niched behavior, whereas a high productivity in the environment (low uncertainty of finding the favored habitat) favors specialization. The derivative of W with respect to r will be negative if greater selectivity is favored, positive if less selectivity is favored. This is

$$\frac{\partial \overline{W}}{\partial r} = te^{-(q + r)t}\,W_1 + \frac{D}{(q + r)^2}\left\{ [e^{-(q + r)t} - 1]q - tr\,(q + r) \right\}$$

The coefficient of D is negative. Thus when D is sufficiently large, $\partial \overline{W}/\partial r$ will be negative and selection will strengthen habitat preference, whereas for $D = 0$,

$\partial \overline{W}/\partial r$ is positive. Call C_2 the threshold value of D below which no selectivity is advantageous. C_2 will be a large number if the environment is very productive and falls with reduced productivity (or the ability to find the better resource).

The joint evolution of niche breadth and selectivity is shown in Figure 6, a and b. In each case, if D is less than some threshold, C_2 (in the symmetric fine-grain case this was $\frac{1}{2} - h/[M - L]$), no selectivity will evolve, and p will remain at its original P_0. As D increases, habitat selectivity will increase too, and p will approach o or 1 when D reaches C_1. Thus p will move toward the solid line in the figures 6a and 6b which shows p as a function of D.

D is the difference in fitness of the whole population in the two environments. At some value of p ($p = 0.5$ for the symmetric model), the gene frequency will be such that $D = 0$ (in the symmetric case, at $X = 0.5$). But if $p < C_3$ or greater than $1 - C_3$, the population remains homozygous and $D = M - L$. Thus D evolves toward the broken line in Figure 6.

In Figure 6a, $M - L > C_1$. Then the equilibrium where the D and p lines cross is a saddle point, and the final result is specialization, monomorphism, and extreme selectivity. This would occur when the productivity of the environment is low, when the environments are very different, or when the time available is short. In Figure 6b, $C_1 > M - L$. The productivity is high, and selectivity is less easy to establish. The final result will be the establishment of an intermediate degree of selectivity, a broad niche, and a polymorphic population.

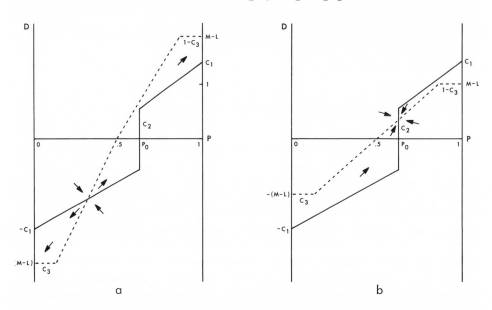

Fig. 6, a and b. The joint evolution of niche breadth and habitat selection. The solid line is the value toward which p (habitat frequency) evolves as a function of D. The broken line is the value toward which D changes as a function of p. The arrows indicate the direction of selection.

In a coarse-grained environment, the absolute habitat selectivity predicted in Figure 6a would be modified by density effects. As density increases in environment 1, W_1 is reduced whereas W_2 is unchanged. Eventually D falls below C_2, and selection will now favor expanding the niche (MacArthur's K maximization; MacArthur, 1962). Furthermore, since linkage disequilibrium is a common feature of complex genetic systems, it is likely that the genes favoring use of environment 2 will be associated with those increasing viability in that environment so that the broad-niched result will be somewhat better than predicted. But if density fluctuates, the specialization may persist.

Another kind of habitat selection occurs by way of dormant stages. We refer back to model I, where we have to maximize $\int \log W(S) P(S) dS$ subject to the restriction $\int W(S)dS = C$. At the optimum, $W(S) = CP(S)$ and overall fitness was $\log \overline{W} = \log C - U$, where U is the uncertainty of the environment. If there are N equally abundant alternative environments, this is $\log C - \log N$. Suppose now that an organism accepts only K of these environments, that it has optimum fitness allocation over these and is otherwise dormant without loss of viability. In these K environments its rate of increase is $\log C - \log K$, but the waiting time is N/K so that the total rate of increase is $(\log C - \log K)(K/N)$. This can be maximized as a function of K to give $\log K = \log C - 1$ and $K = C/e$. Thus the rate of increase will be C/Ne.

We see once again that fitness is reduced by the environmental uncertainty. The niche breadth is increased by C, the potential reproductive rate. This model was designed for the tardigrades. Cohen (1965) has given a more general treatment of the problem of delayed reproduction.

A similar analysis could be applied to diapause strategy in insects. We have now examined the evolution of niche breadth by means of several different models. Despite differences in the specific assumptions and the form of the results, several conclusions seem to be common to them.

1. Insofar as the same phenotype is not optimal in all environments, niche spread involves some fitness loss in each habitat. In a completely certain stable environment narrow specialization would evolve.

2. It is the uncertainty of the environment that creates the selective pressures toward a broad niche. This uncertainty may arise from: (1) temporal variability of the environment; (2) a coarse-grained habitat, so that the environment faced by any given individual is uncertain; (3) low productivity, so that the probability of finding a suitable resource is low. Under these conditions we can say roughly that the final niche breadth that evolves will be an increasing function of the uncertainty.

3. In an uncertain environment there is a loss of fitness at the optimum niche structure. This loss of fitness is roughly proportional to the uncertainty of the environment. It may be so great as to make the species inviable or outcompeted by combinations of specialists. This negative relation between niche breadth and peak fitness may be quite a general one. Sacher (1966) suggests that the cost of the feedback systems which permit broad tolerance reduces the peak. From this

he predicts that life-cycle stages which are less subject to environmental uncertainty will show tall, narrow peaks. Some evidence is offered for this in the comparison of larval stages of insects with pupae and eggs.

4. When the uncertainty of the environment exceeds the upper limit of niche breadth, habitat selection can reduce the uncertainty. Thus both the lower and upper limits to the niche breadth depend on the uncertainty of the environment compared to the tolerance of the individual.

It is at this point that evolutionary theory is held back by a lack of physiological and developmental knowledge, especially with regard to the components of individual tolerance and acclimation.

A mathematical model is not a hypothesis. As a simplification of reality it is necessarily wrong in the sense that it omits additional aspects and possibilities. Yet almost any plausible model is true in that it identifies some real processes of nature. The issue then becomes not whether the model is true or false, but whether it has really isolated sufficiently significant aspects of reality to matter. The justification for a model is then not to be sought in a single crucial experiment as in physics, but in the generation of many specific, testable hypotheses giving a cumulative support to the approach.

I now propose a number of hypotheses to test the approach here presented.

1. Since the broadening of the niche results in a loss of fitness, a negative relation is suggested between the rate of increase in the best environment and the breadth of niche or population size. This would be manifested in the frequent occurrence, among groups of similar species, of a dominant species which outcompetes the others in the best environments but cannot invade the marginal situations where these others, with broader niches, survive. One can of course easily cite anecdotal evidence for cases of this kind, but what is required is a statistical study over many taxa.

2. Since it is possible to measure niche breadth and at least some components of environmental uncertainty, these can be compared over many regions and groups. It is proposed that the number of *Drosophila* species increases with spatial heterogeneity and certainty.

3. Natural-selection experiments in the laboratory could impose different patterns of environmental uncertainty. For instance, temperature fluctuation every few hours simulates a fine-grained environment as against a random separation of a population into two bottles raised for a whole generation at different temperatures (coarse-grained). In habitat-selection experiments, a clue such as an aromatic scent in some foodcups of a population cage would be needed.

4. The qualitative argument about dormancy can be made more precise and applied to those species, such as the corn borer, which are best known. From developmental rate and meteorological studies it should be possible to calculate, for each geographic area, the probability of completion of a generation started on a given date, and the average number of eggs laid. The threshold for diapause should be the date on which the probability of completion of a new generation times the average number of offspring, falls below 1. The northern limit of multi-

voltinism should occur where this figure is always less than 1 after the first generation. And the relative roles of day length and temperature should be related to their predictive power. My guess is that temperature would be more important in regions where it is mostly indicative of topography (that is, the year-to-year variance for a given day is small at each site) and less important when the year-to-year fluctuations are great.

5. Different stages of the life cycle, different structures, and different physiological processes face quite different environmental patterns. Sacher (1966) has pointed out that whereas insect larvae are able to seek favorable microhabitats, because the eggs and pupae are sessile they must survive whatever comes their way. This is somewhat mitigated by selection of oviposition and pupation sites. Therefore we would predict much broader niches for these sessile stages than for larvae and adults, but that this difference would be reduced by narrow niches for egg-laying or pupation sites.

Similarly, the environment of plant roots, especially forest plants, is more stable with respect to short-term fluctuations than are the aerial parts and should therefore be narrower-niched with respect to them.

The differential buffering of different tissues in the mammalian body with respect to oxygen should also result in different-shaped efficiency curves.

All of these arguments refer to the realm of microevolution. The optimum adaptations can arise by calibration of the constants of generally fixed developmental systems. But, as distinct from game theory, in evolution the difference between adapting a strategy within the game and changing the game itself is only a matter of time scale.

Thus, the fitness set argument of model I specified the shape of the set, the set of possible phenotypes. But it is possible for an innovation to change that shape drastically. If for example, a fixed surface–volume relation determined heat loss, each body shape would have its own fixed fitness set with respect to temperature. But if an animal could roll into a ball under cold conditions and stretch out in the heat, this plasticity would in effect make the fitness set much more convex.

A new increase in plasticity may arise from a quite small genetic change. It is well known that the properties of a complex feedback network are radically altered by unit changes which open or close loops or alter time lags or other constants across some threshold values. Such changes in the adaptive system will, however, impose a cost on the system. This cost comes from several sources: (1) the formation of any additional substances or structures; (2) the stresses imposed on other parts of the system which have already evolved in relation to the old form; (3) the lack of initial buffering in the new adaptive system (its own functioning will be more prone to error, and these errors may be quite drastic).

Therefore it is not enough for a new adaptation to arise in order for it to be selected—its advantage must exceed some threshold. Thus the appearance of what is usually regarded as a "general advance" in evolution need not be attributed to the chance occurrence at that time of the appropriate mutation. Rather, we could suspect that it may have arisen many times but had been selected only when the threshold was achieved in some special environment. Once established, it would of course interact in the selection of the rest of the genotype, cost would go down, and it could spread even into environments where the gain was less. Thus, in origin, even the broadest adaptations are adaptations to particular environments.

The alternative views, that the macroevolutionary breakthroughs depend on the occurrence of very rare mutations or of unique environments, can be distinguished experimentally. The methods of genetic assimilation (Waddington, 1961) permit selection even for traits that do not normally vary within a species. It would then be possible to measure the ease of selection for different aspects of the phenotype, the correlated changes (indicative of the tightness of coupling of different subsystems both developmentally and in terms of fitness), and the cost of the adaptations. Then a developmental theory of adaptation could complement the population level analysis in an integrated evolutionary theory of the niche.

REFERENCES

Bradshaw, A. D., 1965. Evolutionary significance of phenotypic plasticity in plants. *Adv. Genet.*, *13*: 115–55.

Cohen, D., 1965. "Optimizing reproduction in a risky environment with communication." USPHS Grant Technical Report no. 4.

Dobzhansky, T., and C. Pavan, 1950. Local and seasonal variation in relative frequencies of species of *Drosophila* in Brazil. *J. Animal Ecol.*, *19* (1): 1–14.

Elton, C. S., 1927. *Animal Ecology*. Sidgwick & Jackson, London.

Grinnell, J., 1922. The trend of avian populations in California. *Science*, n.s. *56*: 671–76.

Hutchinson, G. E., 1965. *The Ecological Theatre and the Evolutionary Play*. Yale Univ. Press, New Haven.

Levene, H., 1953. Genetic equilibrium when more than one ecological niche is available. *Am. Naturalist*, *87*: 311.

Levins, R., 1962. Theory of fitness in a heterogeneous environment. I. The fitness set and adaptive function. *Am. Naturalist*, *96*: 361–73.

Levins, R., and R. MacArthur, 1966. The maintenance of genetic polymorphism in a spatially heterogeneous environment: Variations on a theme by Howard Levene. *Am. Naturalist*, *100*: 585–90.

Li, C. C., 1955. The stability of an equilibrium and the average fitness of a population. *Am. Naturalist*, *89*: 281–95.

MacArthur, R. H., 1962. Some generalized theorems of natural selection. *Proc. Nat. Acad. Sci.*, *48*(11): 1893–97.

Maldonado, C., and R. Levins, in preparation. Ecology and genetics of Puerto Rican *Drosophila*, III. Microhabitat segregation of sympatric species.

Patterson, J. T., 1943. *The Drosophilidae of the Southwest*. Univ. Texas Publ. no. 4313.

Sacher, George A., 1966. "The complementarity of entropy terms for the temperature-dependence of development and aging" (unpubl. MS.).

Tantawy, A. O., and G. S. Mallah, 1961. Studies on natural populations of *Drosophila*, I. Heat resistance and geographical variation in *Drosophila melanogaster* and *D. simulans*. *Evolution*, *15*: 1–14.

Waddington, C. H. Genetic assimilation. *Adv. Genet.*, *10*: 257–93.

J. M. Rendel

12. THE CONTROL OF DEVELOPMENTAL
PROCESSES

The precision with which a developmental process is carried out is of the greatest significance to the fitness of an organism, and failure of precision results in monsters which are familiar enough in all species including our own. It is clear that abnormalities less extreme than anencephaly and spina bifida or acromegaly and achondroplasia would be of considerable evolutionary significance; any loss of fine control during development may well have consequences which are to some extent to the disadvantage of the organism. It is quite likely that at any one moment in the existence of a population most, if not all, characters have an optimum, the level of expression which is optimum depending to a large extent on the level at which other processes are going forward. There are large numbers of examples that could be cited from *Neurospora,* of which the best known is possibly the case of the strain that requires sulfonamide for normal growth. This strain can be combined with one requiring *p*-aminobenzoic acid to produce a heterokaryon that grows on minimal medium. The need for sulfonamide comes from the sensitivity of the strain to overproduction of *p*-aminobenzoic acid, the natural production of which is suppressed by sulfonamide (Emerson, 1947). It is now known that the idiocy of humans who excrete phenylpyruvic acid can be much improved if the amino acid phenylalanine is kept out of the diet before it has had time to do permanent brain damage, for it is excess of this amino acid which is primarily responsible for the damage; the phenylpyruvic excretors are incapable of metabolizing phenylalanine, which therefore reaches damagingly high concentrations. It has been shown that heterozygotes are less tolerant of phenylalanine than are individuals homozygous for wild type (Hsia et al., 1956). These are two examples of the toxic nature of essential substances such as *p*-aminobenzoic acid and phenylalanine in excess. It is a general observation established in the early 1900s and published in the early volumes of *Biometrika* that extremes in a population are less viable than the modes; groups of young individuals drawn from a population are more variable than groups of older individuals, not only because the course taken to reach adult conformation is not uniform but because on the whole those individuals that die are more extreme than those that live. The level at which a developmental process goes forward is of evolutionary significance; thus it is important to show how rates of development are genetically fixed at a given level and how natural selection might operate to change the level.

I shall mention two lines of work which bear on this point. One line concerns the control of enzyme synthesis in bacteria, and this, though quite recent, is so well known that I shall deal with it only briefly. The second is in a sense a corollary. The control of the rate of enzyme synthesis turns out to operate through control of the major structural gene. If genes are precisely controlled with reference to the processes they regulate, we can expect some rather constant characters, which indeed we find. My second topic concerns the effect of selection on some constant and variable characters and arrives at the conclusion that genes expressed in higher organisms as morphological traits are also controlled through rate of action of the major gene. This conclusion has led me to speculate upon the evolution of dominance as well as the wider issue of the evolution of mechanisms controlling gene expression.

The control of enzyme synthesis in bacteria has been shown to consist of the following elements (Jacob and Monod, 1961). There is a structural gene, the sequence of base pairs in which determines the nature of the messenger RNA it makes. Mutations in the DNA of the structural gene, which may be changes in the sequence of base pairs through substitution, deletion, or addition, are reflected in the RNA of the messenger put out by the structural gene. The messenger determines the sequence of amino acids in the proteins which are made by the combined action of messenger and ribosome. A mutation in DNA results in a change in messenger which in turn results in the production of an abnormal protein. The production of a protein by the joint action of messenger and ribosome is mediated by transfer RNA. A transfer RNA is a molecule, one end of which fits the code on the messenger RNA; the other end picks up a specific amino acid. Wherever a messenger has a sequence UUU, say, it will attract transfer RNA molecules with the complementary code, all of which carry phenylalanine at the other end, so phenylalanine always corresponds to UUU. Mutations that alter transfer RNA may result in the production of transfer RNA molecules carrying the wrong amino acid, so UUU would then attract, for example, valine instead of phenylalanine. This results in apparent simultaneous mutation in hundreds of genes as a result of a change that can be isolated to one locus. This series of links between gene and protein operates in a medium containing substrate and energy source, and no doubt the rate of action of the process will be influenced by the availability of substrate and energy as well as by temperature, pH, and other conditions of the reaction. But there are two overriding controls, one initiating gene action and one stopping it. In the reactions studied most, the initiator is substrate of the enzyme which eventually results from the action of the gene—the gene whose initiation results in changes in the enzyme B. Galactosidase is initiated by lactose and some related molecules. The regulators that shut the gene off are produced by one or more genes which are themselves initiated by some substance which it is presumed is a product of the gene or of a gene product. Through this chain of reactions the rate at which a gene acts can be very closely controlled and with reference to the progress of the developmental process initiated by the major gene. Clearly here, through gene control, there is a mechanism that might help to maintain fine control over development.

In recent years experiments have been undertaken to show to what extent development in higher organisms is under fine control; they provide good prima facie evidence for supposing that control is exercised through the major gene in much the same way as in bacterial syntheses. The experiments extend a body of earlier work on developmental genetics.

The experiments of Waddington (1952) with the posterior crossveins in *Drosophila melanogaster* are the starting point. Waddington sought to show that much genotypic variation is not expressed in a wild-type individual. He demonstrated that a small fraction of a population which had been exposed to a heat shock during the pupal stage developed into images with more or less complete absence of the posterior crossvein. When he bred from individuals which had abnormal veins as a result of treatment, and treated their progeny the same way, he found that the fraction of the population which developed wings without crossveins increased. Eventually some flies emerged without crossveins even after development at normal temperature. He concluded that the treatment had exposed genetic variation in the response to heat shock, that selection could accumulate a genotype extremely sensitive to heat shock in the direction of absence of crossvein, and that this genotype was in fact one which tended to have no crossvein in all circumstances. Waddington was most interested to show how genetic variation responsible for differences in sensitivity to heat shock could be used to breed flies which genetically lacked crossveins as a particular example of the more general phenomenon he calls genetic assimilation. But the experiment shows that much genotypic variation goes unexpressed and raises the question how this is brought about. Either there is a threshold beyond which excess production is not used by the developing organism, or there is control such that production is turned off when it has done enough or reached the proper rate. The experiment is an extension of earlier work on developmental genetics, notably by Stern and Goldschmidt, who also showed that dominance modifiers and other modifiers are really the same; the modifiers all act to affect the expression of the major gene in whatever form it is present and to reinforce environmental effects, but beyond a certain threshold further additions not only of modifiers but also of major gene loci have no effect on gene expression.

The next two experiments make a clear step forward. Both were carried out in my laboratory, one by Dun and Fraser (1959) and one by myself (Rendel, 1959a, 1959b). If modifiers affect all genotypes, what is selected in one genotype should have its effect in another. If the constancy of developmental response to genotype is a control built in by evolution and is not a simple threshold, it should be possible to override it by sufficient effort. In fact Schultz showed in 1935 that this could be done with the character *shaven*. He showed $+^{sh}+^{sh}+^{sh}$ to have an occasional extra bristle. Our experiments, carried out in mice and *Drosophila* respectively, were designed to select for animals most closely approaching wild type in a segregating population. I selected for increased bristle number in a population of flies segregating for the mutant *scute*. Selection was applied to the mutants and the response followed in their wild-type sibs. Response to selection was immediate in the *sc* genotypes but not in the wild-type ones. By the end of twenty-five generations however, the bristle number had increased in flies with wild-type genotypes, flies with five and six scutellar bristles instead of the customary four beginning to appear. The mouse experiment ran on parallel lines. The point was made that the wild type is affected by genes selected for their effect on mutants and that constancy of phenotype is due to control and is not the result of a threshold beyond which nothing further happens; there is an area of gene activity within which gene activity comes under control so as to produce a fixed phenotype, and control can be transcended by selection that enhances the effect of the major gene.

If you now compare our findings in mice and flies with the control outlined for microorganisms you will see we have isolated a major gene which by analogy would be expected to make a specific messenger. We have shown that it is controlled at a given level, but we have added a new set of genes, the modifiers which when selected move the total activity of the whole system, major gene plus modifiers, up the genetic scale. This element is not present in the usual microorganism model. We now have to consider whether we really are dealing with gene control and, if so, what is controlled and how. Control might be jointly of the activity of both major and minor genes or only of one or of the other. In order to settle this point, gene dosage experiments were carried out at several different levels of gene activity (Rendel et al., 1965). Three lines were available, one in which bristle numbers are very large, one in which they are average, and one in which they are low. Extra + and *sc* genes were introduced by adding the tip of the X chromosome to the Y, an operation performed for me by Prof. M. M. Green, and these extra *scute* alleles were added to the high, the low, and the medium line on the Y chromosome. These lines differ by the modifying genes which have been selected into them. If it is the modifying genes that are controlled, introduction of an extra *sc* allele into the line will have the same effect in all lines. It will add its piece. If it is the major gene that is controlled, the added extra locus will come under the control exercised over the normal locus; it will have little effect when bristle number is high, since its activity will be shut off, but a strong effect when it is low. We have to sort out also the possibility that control of the major gene could be with reference to the major gene's own activity only, or to the combined effect of major and minor genes; and if control is through modifiers, the possibility must be examined that control is with reference to modifier activity only.

It turns out that control is almost certainly on the major gene only, but that it is triggered by the total activity present. The fact that mutant *scute* genotypes can be selected up to the point where many of them have four or even five bristles enables one to see that in *scute* as in wild-type genotypes, control is at a phenotype of four bristles. So one can say that the major gene's activity is cut down as soon as total activity of major gene plus modifiers is enough for four bristles. Control takes account of and responds to the whole genotype. If this were not so, there would be no reason why bristle number should be constant at four in mutant genotypes. If control were with respect to the major gene only, one would expect mutants to show no signs of control at four bristles because in them the higher numbers of bristles are due to modifiers. That the major gene is the one controlled is shown first by the fact that strength of control is proportional to potential activity of the major gene. The more there is to turn off or down, the wider the range of genotypes that can be controlled. It is also indicated by the fact that extra loci added to the genotype have a much bigger effect when added to low than to high lines, but that variability is greater in high lines which are so high that no flies have as few as four bristles. At this point the major gene is cut off all the time, and variation of minor genes has full play.

The picture that we now have of a developmental process is that it starts with the activation of a major gene, and the major gene is supported by a halo of minor genes. The sum total activity of both triggers a control which acts to damp down the major genes but has no effect on the minor genes. The parallel to the microorganism is getting closer. The minor genes are an extra, and the substrate which activates the major gene has not been located but is certainly endogenous.

Something more definite can be said about the control mechanism. The information comes from experiments in which selection was for control of scutellar bristle number at two bristles instead of four (Rendel et al., 1960, 1966). This was achieved by fifty generations of selection during which the population responded in two bursts. For the first 18 generations there was no response, thereafter response was linear for 12 generations, followed by another 10 or 12 generations of no response, followed by 12 of linear response. Thereafter a slow increase in control has accumulated over a further 150 generations or so. The stock now has a "two" class which covers some four probits. That is to say, 97 per cent of the population regularly has two bristles. In the original population with a mean of two, the range was from zero to four with about 30 per cent in the "two" class.

So control can be built in by selection. The number of genes concerned is not known. Enzyme synthesis in microorganisms appears to be controlled by one or two regulator genes. It is possible that the number controlling *scute* is small, selection operating on modifying genes which increase the effectiveness of the regulators. There is some evidence that selection for control has operated on the major gene too: whereas back mutation from *sc* to + is normally very rare, in the LV (low variance) line it has crept up to as much as 1 in 5,000. This does not appear to have been brought about by an overall increase in back mutation. It is possible that the process of building in a new control is one in which selection operates on both major gene and regulators to fit one to the other.

The final picture then is of a developmental process initiated by the activation of a major gene which is controlled, assisted by modifying genes which are not controlled, control being exercised by regulator genes which are themselves activated with respect to both major and modifying gene activity. Selection can

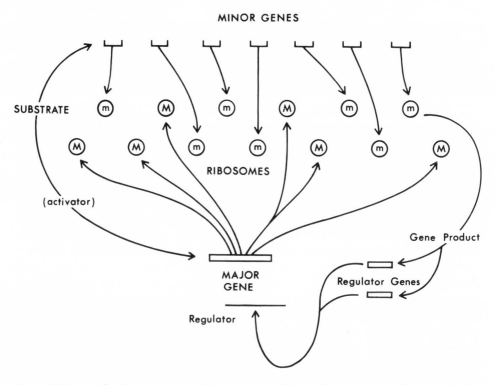

Fig. 1. Major and minor genes are shown activated by substrate or, in the case of the major gene, some product of substrate. The messenger RNA's of major and minor genes compete for the center circles, perhaps ribosomes, which represent the opportunity for gene action. The degree to which the major gene is successful determines how many of the circles are occupied by major gene messenger. The phenotype is finally adjusted by regulation of the major gene, which can cut out or leave in all activity, represented by the circles occupied by M. Variables upon which selection can act are: the number and activity of the minor genes; the number, activity, and configuration of the regulator genes; the activity and configuration of the major gene; the availability of substrate, which will usually be endogenous; and possibly the number of circles, which may turn out to represent ribosomes.

operate in three ways: (1) to change mean gene activity; (2) to control gene activity at a definite level; (3) to change the level at which control acts. If gene activity is increased or decreased too far, it will escape from the buffering affect of control through the major gene. There will either be too little activity to reach the normal phenotypic level or so much that, even when the major gene is shut off to the maximum extent, the whole overshoots. On the other hand, selection for or against control can increase or decrease the degree of control so that a response which was linear may become highly plateaued, and one which was plateaued may become linear. The distinction between selection that changes total gene activity and selection that operates on control mechanisms is important when one considers such problems as the evolution of dominance. Most work on the evolution of dominance has shown that by increasing or decreasing the potency of the genes controlling a developmental system, the mean of a population may come to lie nearer to a threshold below which dominance is no longer complete. Fisher supposed minor modifying genes would act in this way as a result of selecting heterozygotes toward normal. Haldane believed that in addition, different alleles at the major gene locus would also push the mean up or down the scale of gene action. Of course both agents will do this as well as suitable environmental agents, but no amount of pushing total gene activity up and down the scale will result in dominance if the proper gene dose–phenotype response curve is not already there. Wright assumed that this curve was a characteristic feature of the enzyme produced by the gene. But if we are correct, it is the result of the reaction between major gene and regulator which fixes the gene dose–phenotype relationship. One can of course regard selection which pushes the mean gene dose up and down the scale, in and out of the influence of regulator control, as selection for dominance. Personally I prefer to regard selection which introduces the control and fixes the level at which regulators control the major gene as the primary agent in evolution of dominance. Fisher's own experiments with poultry (Fisher, 1935) bear out this way of looking at things. He outcrossed dominants of the Silky which he believed had been made dominant by human selection, since they were the disadvantageous form and could not have been dominant by natural selection; he found that the heterozygote of the outcross had about the same expression as the old homozygote but that the homozygote was now far more extreme, demonstrating that selection had reduced the homozygote to the level of the heterozygote rather than the other way around.

The hypothesis put forward here has many gaps and uncertainties. We do not know precisely how the modifying genes, the selection of which tends to increase or decrease the expression of a character, play their part. It has been assumed that they do the same thing as the major gene, adding directly to the store of product which the major gene makes by some other route and eventually helping to activate the regulator genes which will close down on the major gene. But it could be that they act through the major gene by making circumstances favorable for its action and for the action of its product. It could be that in the presence of a deletion the modifying genes will have no effect at all. If this were so, a developmental process could be regarded as a process initiated by activation of a major gene, whose action would be controlled by one or more regulator genes with reference to the level of activity reached; the major gene would be assisted more or less by modifying genes to bring its own output up to this level.

Another major uncertainty is the relationship between selection to alter the mutant and selection to alter the wild type; that is, the extent to which selection of *sc* flies affects + and the extent to which selection of + affects *sc*. In the early stages of selection and in many lines, the two go hand in hand, but there is a growing body of evidence to show that selection on one genotype brings about an effect which is not necessarily the same in both genotypes. This favors somewhat the idea that modifiers are acting through their effect on the major genes, but it could also be explained by supposing that more than one developmental process may be concerned in the measurement used to characterize the one in question. Where it is found that + is more affected by selection on + than is *sc*, it could also be supposed that selection had reduced control over the major gene, a reduction which would be more effective when done to the more active gene. This remains to be sorted out.

Yet another doubtful point is the way in which selection brings about control of the major gene. While selecting to control *scute* at two bristles, we found that the back mutation rate from *sc* to + had changed from a negligible rate to the rate of 1 in 5,000 chromosomes. This is more like a crossover rate than a mutation rate. It suggests that at least part of the process of selecting a regulating system is the selection of alleles of the major gene that can be regulated, as well as the selection of regulators that affect the major gene.

These points and others remain to be cleared up before the hypothesis can be considered established. If it is eventually established, it will introduce into evolutionary thinking the idea of a controlled developmental process which natural selection has brought under control at a particular level. As dominance of the wild type, according to the hypothesis, is one manifestation of a controlled system, the number of such processes can be judged from the number of loci at which a good dominant of the wild type is known. In well-established species this is a very large number. We can expect fewer clear-cut dominants in a newer, more plastic species. The level at which a phenotype is controlled will be fixed at what is the optimum for the time being, and this optimum will have to take account of the relationship between one developmental process and another. It will be as important for a developmental process to match its fellows as it will be for it to fit the animal for its external environment. When one considers that there may be hundreds of such processes, all rigidly controlled to suit each other, one can understand how selection in one direction so often brings with it in the first instance a lack of fitness. And it becomes easier to account for the uniformity of design that runs through individuals of a species (and indeed related species of a genus or even an order) than to account for the plasticity that enables species to adapt to the external environment.

When a canalized character is to be changed and recanalized, which at least in the laboratory is a far more tedious operation, the unfitness introduced when the fine adjustment between developmental processes is destroyed will always be counteracting directional selection. Until a new adjustment is attained by recanalizing whole sets of characters at a new level of expression, directional selection must introduce unfitness. This antagonism between fitness and directional selection will have to be taken into account in interpreting outbursts of evolutionary change followed by long stability, failure of species to adapt to a change in their habitat, and changes which appear to have no relevance to adaptation and which in the end may even be detrimental to the species. Evolution is at least two-faced—it makes what is for the moment the perfect organism, to judge from internal criteria only, and it answers the question, "How well does this piece of mechanism work?" It also makes the animal most suited to a particular way of life. If the hypothesis I have outlined of the developmental process is true, it will often be difficult and time-consuming to reconcile the two.

REFERENCES

Dun, R. B., and A. S. Fraser, 1959. Selection for an invariant character, vibrissae number in the house mouse. *Australian J. Biol. Sci., 12:* 506–23.

Emerson, S., 1947. Growth responses of a sulphonamide-requiring mutant strain of Neurospora. *J. Bacteriol., 54:* 195–207.

Fisher, R. A., 1935. Dominance in poultry. *Phil. Trans. Roy. Soc. B., 225:* 195–226.

Hsia, D. Y.–Y., K. W. Driscoll, W. Troll, and W. E. Knox, 1956. Detection of phenylalanine tolerance tests of heterozygous carriers of phenylketonuria. *Nature, 178:* 1239–40.

Jacob, F., and J. Monod, 1961. Genetic regulatory mechanisms in the synthesis of proteins. *J. Molec. Biol., 3:* 318–56.

Rendel, J. M., 1959a. Variation and dominance at the scute locus in *Drosophila melanogaster. Australian J. Biol. Sci., 12:* 524–33.

———, 1959b. Canalization of the scute phenotype of *Drosophila. Evolution, 13:* 425–39.

Rendel, J. M., and B. L. Sheldon, 1960. Selection for canalization of the scute phenotype in *Drosophila melanogaster. Australian J. Biol. Sci., 13:* 36–47.

Rendel, J. M., B. L. Sheldon, and D. E. Finlay, 1965. Canalization of development of scutellar bristles in *Drosophila* by control of the scute locus. *Genetics, 52:* 1137–51.

———, 1966. Selection for canalization of the scute phenotype. Part II. *Am. Naturalist, 100:* 13–32.

Schultz, J., 1935. Aspects of the relation between genes and development in *Drosophila. Am. Naturalist, 69:* 30–54.

Waddington, C. H., 1952. Selection of the genetic basis for an acquired character. *Nature, 169:* 278.

Bryan C. Clarke

13. BALANCED POLYMORPHISM
AND REGIONAL DIFFERENTIATION
IN LAND SNAILS

It is now a commonplace that genes interact. The classic experiments of Morgan (1929), Nabours (1929, analyzed by Fisher, 1939), and Dobzhansky (1954), among many others, have shown how genic interactions may influence the fitness of individual organisms. In the field of evolutionary studies these interactions raise many interesting problems, not the least of which concerns the relative importance of the genetic environment, compared with the external environment, in determining the spread or decline of particular alleles.

When we are faced with spatial or temporal changes of gene frequency we tend to adopt two explanations. If the changes can be related to variations in the environment we may attribute them to the direct action of natural selection. If they can not we may, under suitable conditions, attribute them to random genetic drift. The two categories, however, are not exclusive, and the battle between the champions of selection and drift has been long and hard. In the heat of strife we have perhaps neglected a third explanation, that changes of gene frequency can sometimes be due to alterations in the genetic background. In these circumstances the patterns of gene frequencies, because they are second-order effects, may not precisely correspond to variations in the environment.

Mayr (1954) has powerfully argued the importance of a changed genetic environment in the evolution of peripherally isolated populations. In this paper I shall consider some recent observations on natural populations of land snails, observations that seem to demand an extension of Mayr's hypothesis, and that lead to conclusions which may be of general evolutionary interest.

Among the land gastropods there are many species polymorphic for shell color and pattern. Some of them provide almost ideal material for studies of the genetics of natural populations. They are easy to collect, to follow, to mark, and to score. Members of two genera, *Cepaea* and *Partula,* have received the greatest share of attention.

In the following discussion I shall first review the patterns of genetic variation in *Cepaea*. I shall hope to show that although some of these patterns can be attributed to the direct selective effect of the external environment, there are others for which we have no satisfactory explanation except in terms of selection by the genetic environment. I shall then consider some studies of *Partula* that lead to the same conclusion. Finally I shall attempt a hypothesis applicable to similar patterns of variation in other organisms.

Two closely related species of *Cepaea* occur in the British Isles. Both *Cepaea nemoralis* (L.) and *C. hortensis* (Mull.) are polymorphic for shell color and pattern, and their polymorphisms appear to be homologous. In crosses between them, at least some of the genes concerned behave as alleles (Lang, 1908). Most of the variants found in nature are known to be inherited. The environment appears to have little or no direct effect on the ornamentation of the shell (Lang 1912; Lamotte, 1954; Cain and Sheppard, 1957; Cain et al., 1960; Murray, 1963). The two species are almost identical in form, show a similar range of phenotypes, and seem to share the same predators and parasites. Mixed populations are not uncommon.

Cain and Sheppard (1954), working with *C. nemoralis,* have found that in the region of Oxford the frequencies of various phenotypes in a colony can be related to the nature of the habitat. The commonest phenotypes are those that most closely match their background. In beechwoods, which have a ground cover of dark leaf litter, pink and brown unbanded shells are common. Grasslands and rough herbage, on the other hand, harbor a high proportion of yellow shells. Visually uniform habitats often support a high frequency of "effectively unbanded" shells (a category that includes all shells lacking the two uppermost bands on each whorl), but in habitats with a mixed or striped background, five-banded shells are common (see Fig. 1). Cain and Sheppard explain these relations in terms of selective visual predation, which has been demonstrated by Sheppard (1951). Song thrushes, the predators studied by Sheppard, apparently kill a larger proportion of snails whose color or pattern stands out against the visual background, and a smaller proportion of those whose color or pattern more nearly resembles it.

Since *C. nemoralis* and *C. hortensis* are very similar, we might expect that in mixed colonies they would show parallel variations. As Lamotte (1951) pointed out, they do not. Lamotte considered that this apparent lack of correlation argued against the importance of natural selection in determining the distribution of morphs.

A study of *C. hortensis* (Clarke, 1960) has shown that in the Oxford region this species, like *nemoralis*, responds to the nature of the habitat. However, despite an apparently homologous polymorphism, it does so in a very different way (Figs. 2, 3). In beechwoods it shows a high proportion, not of browns or pinks, but of yellows. The yellows are almost all banded, with many of the bands fused together to give the shells an overall brown appearance (except at the edges of the whorls, where the yellow color shows through). In mixed herbage there are many banded yellow shells without fusions, and in uniform green grass the proportion

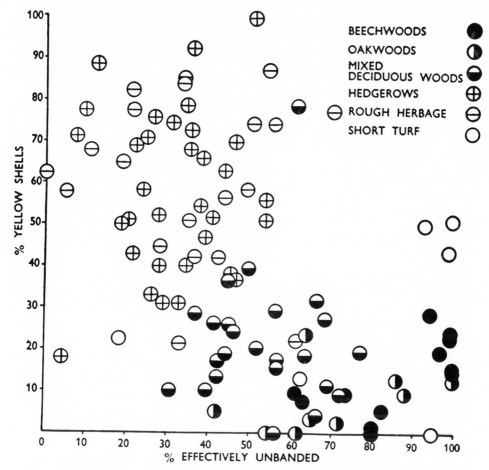

Fig. 1. *Cepaea nemoralis* in the Oxford region. A scatter-diagram of the relation between the percentage of yellow shells, the percentage of "effectively unbanded" shells, and the nature of the habitat (after Cain and Sheppard, 1954).

of yellow unbanded shells is usually relatively high. Contrary to the views of Lamotte, these results again suggest the importance of visual selection (at least in the Oxford region).

The divergence of genetic response between *nemoralis* and *hortensis* occurs in mixed colonies as well as in colonies of one species only (Clarke, 1962a). Although the two snails differ in behavior (Sedlmair, 1956; Clarke, 1962a) they are not found on appreciably different backgrounds within the same mixed colony. Thus, even when they are subject to the same or closely similar visual selective forces, they react in clearly dissimilar (but nevertheless appropriate) ways. We must find a "nonvisual" explanation for the relative deficiency of pinks and browns in the *hortensis* of the Oxford region. The simplest hypothesis is that the

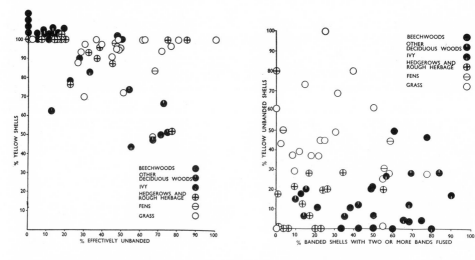

Fig. 2. *Cepaea hortensis* in the Oxford region. A scatter-diagram like Figure 1, showing the different distribution of phenotypes in this species (from Clarke, 1960).

Fig. 3. *Cepaea hortensis* in the Oxford region. A scatter-diagram of the relation between the percentage of yellow unbanded shells, the percentage of banded shells with fused bands, and the nature of the habitat. The proportions on the horizontal axis are expressed as percentages of the numbers of shells with two or more adjacent bands (from Clarke, 1960).

genes for pink and brown are less advantageous against the local genetic background of this species. It may be possible to invent an explanation that does not require genic interaction, but we would be forced to introduce hypotheses of greater complexity.

We have, then, some indirect evidence that the genetic environment plays a role in determining differences in gene frequencies between species. When we come to consider differences within species (first of *Cepaea,* then of *Partula*), the evidence is more compelling.

Various studies of *Cepaea* have shown that the type of variation found in the Oxford region, although occurring elsewhere (Currey et al., 1964), is by no means universal. On some sand dunes (Diver, 1932; Clarke and Murray, 1962; Clarke, Diver, and Murray, unpublished), on the Wiltshire Downs (Cain and Currey, 1963a, 1963b), the Berkshire Downs (Cain and Currey, 1963a; Carter, 1965), in eastern Scotland (Jones, 1966), and elsewhere, we find that both *nemoralis* and *hortensis* may show the preponderance of a few morphs, apparently regardless of habitat or background, over wide areas. Between such areas, the morph frequencies may change violently within distances of 200 m or less, often in apparently uniform environments. An example is given on Figure 4.

Cain and Currey (1963a) suggest that these "area effects" may be due to cryptic environmental differences that produce sharp changes of selective forces over short distances. They argue that random genetic drift cannot be the present

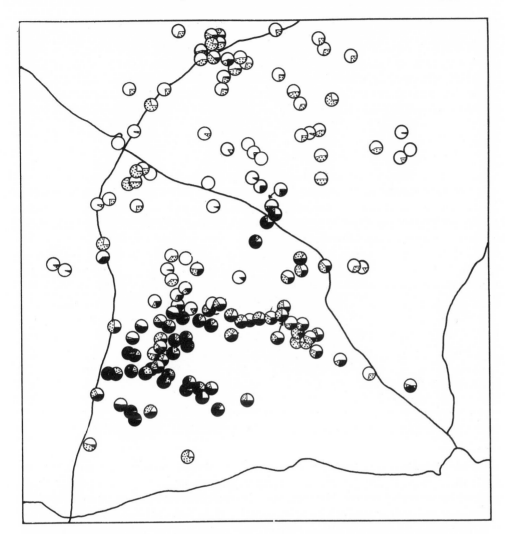

Fig. 4. *Cepaea nemoralis* on the Marlborough Downs. The "area effects" in the proportions of yellow, pink, and brown shells (browns, black; pinks, stippled; yellows, white). The map covers an area of about 70 sq km (from Cain and Currey, 1963a).

cause of the pattern since the areas are too large (very much larger than a panmictic population). They also provide evidence that there have been no recent "bottlenecks" in the numbers of *Cepaea* on the Marlborough Downs. Their collections of subfossil shells suggest that the area effects may have persisted in this region for several thousand years.

Goodhart (1963) argues that the differences between areas are due to the "founder principle" of Mayr (1954; see also Diver, 1939). He suggests that the first groups of snails that arrived in the region were small populations differing by chance from each other. Initial differences between these populations then persisted because of the evolution of balanced gene complexes. When the groups expanded and came together, interpenetration was prevented by the relative inviability of hybrids between the balanced systems, and clines became established along the lines of contact. Such clines, he argues, could be maintained indefinitely in a state of dynamic equilibrium. Wright (1965) has put forward a similar argument.

Cain and Currey (1963c), replying to Goodhart, suggest that different balanced gene complexes would not be equally successful and that one group would be expected eventually to replace the others, unless each was best suited to its own particular area. Thus their argument once more appeals to differential selection. They also point out that the geography of the clines is difficult to reconcile with the view that they are "hybrid zones."

If the conflict over area effects is finally to be resolved, we must find answers to the following questions. (1) To what extent do the areas reflect differences in the external environment? (2) Is there coadaptation within areas? In other words, are the changes of gene frequencies between areas partly or completely the result of changes in the genetic environment? (3) If coadaptation exists, is it necessarily the result of chance differences between founders? At the present time we can suggest tentative answers to these questions. Since they lead us to conclusions that involve larger issues than the population genetics of snails, let us consider each question in turn.

(1) THE RELATION OF AREA EFFECTS TO THE
EXTERNAL ENVIRONMENT

I have said that area effects bear no apparent relation to habitat or background. We must examine this assertion more carefully. Cain and Currey (1963a), in their study of *nemoralis* on the Marlborough Downs (Wiltshire), have suggested that the occurrence of areas with high frequencies of brown shells might be related to topography and climate. They point out that in this region *hortensis* predominates in the valleys and on the low plain at the foot of the chalk scarp, while *nemoralis* is widespread on the uplands. They argue that since *hortensis* is found much farther north than *nemoralis*, it is probably better able to withstand cold conditions, which may be expected to have a greater effect on the snails in summer when they are active. The range of *nemoralis* extends into central Scotland, and its northern limit roughly corresponds to the summer isotherms. They point out that local differences in climate can be produced by cold air draining down from higher land on still, clear nights, forming pools and rivers covering the bottoms of nearby valleys. This observation could explain the distribution of the two species on the Marlborough region.

Cain and Currey draw a parallel between the factors governing the distribution of species and those governing the distribution of brown shells. They suggest that, since browns seem to be commoner in northern Europe than they are farther south, the brown gene may confer an increased resistance to cold. In the Marlborough region, high frequencies of browns are associated with the short and low-lying valleys opening into the Kennet Valley, or with the lower ends of the larger valleys running down from near the scarp face. The correlation with topography is, however, by no means perfect.

Later studies have cast some doubt on the general validity of this ingenious hypothesis. Although Carter (1965), working on the Berkshire Downs, obtained a high proportion of samples containing brown shells on or near the chalk scarp, and a lower proportion elsewhere, in other regions the distribution of browns does not seem to be clearly related to topography (Cain and Currey, 1963b; Jones, 1966). In Kincardineshire (Scotland), where *nemoralis* reaches its northern limit and where we would expect the climatic conditions to be stringent, we find area effects similar to those on the Marlborough Downs, with the crucial exception that browns are rare or absent (Jones, 1966).

There have been many other attempts to relate area effects in *nemoralis* and *hortensis* to a wide range of environmental factors (including altitude, aspect, topography, rainfall, temperature, geology, flora, and background). Without exception they have failed (unpublished material of Diver, of Carter, and of Clarke, in addition to the references quoted above). There is, of course, always the possibility that these studies have overlooked some cryptic environmental factor. Indeed we should expect that any two areas will differ, on the average, in *some* aspect of the external environment. Such an observation by itself would not support a belief in the selective importance of the external environment unless it could be shown that similar environments in different regions give rise to similar area effects, or that the borders of areas correspond to environmental discontinuities. With the doubtful exception of brown *nemoralis* on the Wiltshire and Berkshire Downs, no such relations have been found. The weight of negative evidence is now great enough to warrant a search for other explanations. We must consider the possible importance of coadaptation.

(2) THE RELATION OF AREA EFFECTS TO THE GENETIC ENVIRONMENT

Cepaea itself provides no direct evidence of coadaptation within areas, but it is not the only genus of land snails that shows area effects. Similar phenomena have been observed in *Bradybaena* (Komai and Emura, 1955), *Cerion* (Mayr and Rosen, 1956), *Bulimulus* (Clarke and Heatwole, unpublished), and *Partula* (Crampton, 1916, 1932; Clarke and Murray, unpublished). Some recent work on the last-named genus throws light on the problem.

Several species of *Partula* occur on the island of Moorea in French Polynesia. They were studied in great detail by Crampton (1932), who considered the varieties of shell color and pattern among these snails to be "indifferent characters" unaffected by selection. To account for their spread he invoked the processes of recurrent mutation and migration. Since then they have been discussed as a possible example of random variation resulting from genetic drift (Huxley, 1942).

These possibilities cannot be confirmed or denied on the basis of Crampton's data alone. Each of his collections represented a large area, often several square kilometers. Such samples might well obscure the selective effects of localized habitats, and we have recently found that significant changes of phenotype frequency can take place over distances less than 20 m (see below).

Crampton made several visits to Moorea between 1907 and 1924. Because successive collections in the same area differed from each other he concluded that evolution had taken place during the intervening periods. This conclusion is no longer tenable, since the changes may have been due to his collecting in slightly different places at different times.

With J. J. Murray, Jr., I visited Moorea in 1962 to resurvey its populations of *Partula*.[1] Among other things, we studied the distribution of phenotypes in *Partula taeniata* Mörch, which is the commonest species on Moorea. We concentrated our efforts on the northwest corner of the island because only one other species of *Partula* (*P. suturalis* Pfeiffer) is found there. Elsewhere the situation is complicated by the occurrence of several sympatric species.

The *taeniata* of northwest Moorea, members of the "subspecies" *nucleola* (Crampton, 1932), are polymorphic for shell banding and color. Figure 5 shows the proportions of banded shells in localized random samples from the region, and Figure 6 shows the proportions of "purple" shells (the shells are actually purplish-brown in color, and come into the categories $N3$ and $N4$ of Murray and Clarke, 1966). These phenotypes are known to be inherited, and it seems that the environment has little or no direct effect on their ontogeny. All forms of banding appear to be dominant to the unbanded condition. Purple shells are dominant to yellow ($Y1$ and $Y2$) and white (W), but their relation to brown shells ($N1$ and $N2$) is uncertain. There is some evidence of linkage between the loci for color and banding, although the details of the situation are not yet clear (Murray and Clarke, 1966).

It can be seen from Figure 5 that the proportions of banded shells are generally low. In the far west two samples show frequencies above 20 per cent. In the north center there is a small area where the frequencies reach 10 per cent. In the southeast there is a similar area. Elsewhere the frequencies vary between 0 and 5 per cent (but see below).

The proportion of purple shells varies more widely. There is an irregularly shaped area in the east central part of the region where the frequencies exceed 30 per cent. At the edge of this area they fall rapidly, in some places to zero. There are some local increases in the northwest.

We have attempted to relate the distribution of banding and color to various factors in the environment. We could find no correlation with altitude and topog-

---

1. I am particularly grateful to Dr. Murray for allowing me to report some of our unpublished work. He is not, however, responsible for the views I shall express.

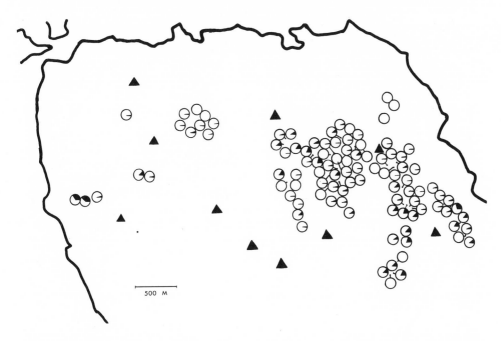

Fig. 5. *Partula taeniata* in northwest Moorea, showing the distribution of banded shells. Six degrees of arc represent 1 per cent. Triangles show mountain peaks.

raphy (which largely determine temperature and rainfall) nor with the color and pattern of the background. We could find none with the distribution of other species of snails (*Partula suturalis* Pfeiffer, *Bradybaena similaris* Ferrussac, *Trochomorpha pallens* Pease, *Subulina octona* Bruguiere, and *Succinea pudorina* Gould).

We carried out a floral survey of the sampling localities, in which we plotted the distribution of 109 species of plants. Of these, only 20 were common enough for detailed analysis, but we hoped that some of them might act as indicators of otherwise cryptic environmental factors. During our survey we found several significant associations between one plant species and another, but none between any individual species (or any combination of them) and color or banding in *taeniata*.

Because *taeniata* is arboreal, and climbs no higher than about 5 m, the snail is obvious and easy to collect. Our samples therefore constituted a large proportion (between 50 and 90 per cent), of the population. This was confirmed by mark, release, and recapture. The sizes of samples thus provide rough estimates of population density. We could find no relation between the estimated densities and the proportions of banded or purple shells.

Nor could we relate the distribution of phenotypes to the occurrence or activity of predators. Most of the indigenous birds of the Society Islands are now extinct, and the introduced species do not generally penetrate into the forests where *Partula* is found. Possible predators are the native kingfisher *Halcyon venerata*

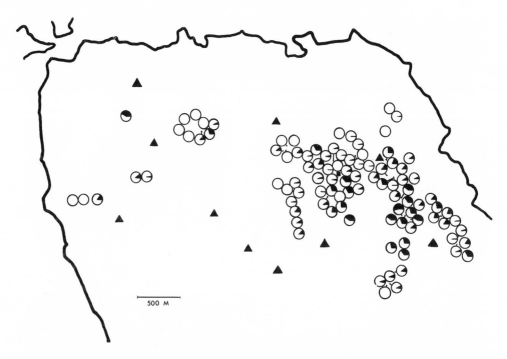

Fig. 6. *Partula taeniata* in northwest Moorea. The distribution of "purple" shells (actually purple-brown: the N3 + N4 category of Murray and Clarke, 1966). Four degrees of arc represent 1 per cent. Triangles show mountain peaks; the small black square gives the position of the center of the transect (see text). The map covers an area of about 25 sq km.

(Gmelin), which is rare, and the feral jungle fowl, rat, and pig. None of them, with the possible exception of the color-blind rat, seems to be an important enemy of *Partula*.

In mixed colonies of *taeniata* and *suturalis*, we could find no correlation between the geographical Distributions of phenotypes in the two species, nor between the phenotypes of one species and the estimated density of the other. The former observation contradicts my reanalysis of Crampton's data (Clarke, 1962b). The disagreement is probably due to the fact that his samples represent whole valleys rather than localized populations.

The "high purple" area extends over a wide range of habitats, stretching from one valley to the next over a high mountain ridge. It encompasses a change of 500 m in altitude—a transition from lowland forest to montane scrub—yet its limits do not appear to be related to any environmental discontinuity.

Despite these negative results, we have reason to believe that strong selection is at work. In crosses between individuals heterozygous for banding we find significant deficiencies of banded young ($p < 0.01$). The average ratio of banded to unbanded offspring is almost exactly 2/1, suggesting that homozygous banded individuals are subvital or lethal (Murray and Clarke, 1966). If this is true of natural populations, the maintenance of banding polymorphism would necessitate, in the southeastern part of the region, a 5 per cent advantage of the heterozygote over the unbanded homozygote, and in the extreme western part of the region a 14 per cent advantage. We do not yet know if homozygous purples are similarly subvital or lethal. Our first cross has given a ratio of 27 purples to 12 yellows.

The evidence for selection in the laboratory, when considered in relation to the lack of evidence for selective agents in the field, suggests that internal factors may be important in determining morph frequencies. In order to investigate this question we took a transect across the border of the "high purple" area. It stretched 200 m (northeast and southwest) between a colony with 37 per cent purple shells and a colony with none. The center of the transect is marked by the small black square on Figure 6. Twenty samples from 10-m squares were taken along the transect.

Figure 7 shows the percentage of purples (solid line) and bandeds (dashed line) in the samples. The boxes below the graph give the numbers of snails collected. It can be seen that clear (and significant) changes of phenotype frequency take place over distances less than 20 m. Although there are four adjacent samples in which *taeniata* is rare or absent, we find the greatest changes of frequency where it is common. The changes do not therefore seem to be caused by any external barrier to the movement of snails. The most striking feature of the

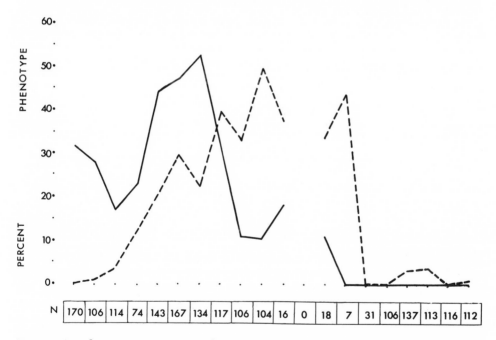

Fig. 7. *Partula taeniata* transect. The percentages of purple shells (solid line) and banded shells (dashed line) in samples from twenty adjacent 10-m squares. The boxes give the numbers of adult snails collected.

transect is the phenomenal increase of banded shells at the center. They reach a level of 50 per cent, far higher than in any other sample from northwest Moorea. This totally unexpected result cannot be explained in terms of any obvious peculiarity of the environment since the habitats along the transect seem to be relatively homogeneous. It can, however, be explained in terms of coadaptation if we assume that the increase in banding is due to the special conditions of the genetic environment produced by "hybridization" between two different coadapted gene complexes. This interpretation is strengthened by the fact that the expression of banding is unusual. Banded shells are normally quite distinct from unbanded, but in the transect various intermediates occur between them, a situation reminiscent of the breakdown of dominance in crosses between isolated races of *Triphaena*

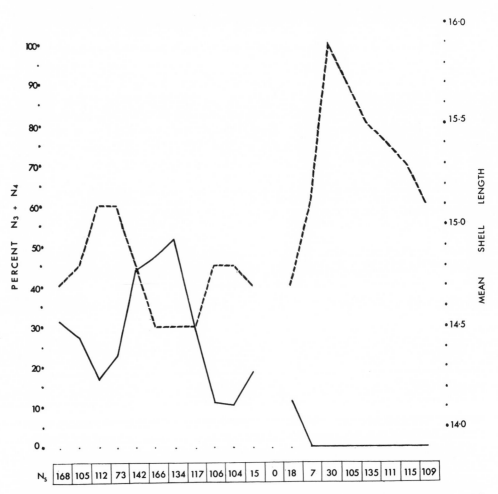

Fig. 8. *Partula taeniata* transect. The percentage of purple shells (= N3 + N4, solid line) and the mean shell length in millimeters (dashed line) in samples from twenty adjacent 10-m squares. The boxes give the numbers of adult snails measured.

comes (Ford, 1965). It will clearly be of great interest to study the genetics of banding at this locality.

If the transect covers a zone of hybridization between two coadapted gene complexes, we might expect to find correlated changes in other characters. On Figure 8 the dashed line shows the mean shell length (in millimeters) for each sample. The boxes below the graph give the numbers of shells measured, and Figure 9 shows the 95 per cent limits of the means. There is a sharp and significant increase of size as one passes from high purple to low purple. Within samples, however, there is no relation between size and color, although banded shells are significantly smaller ($p < 0.01$).

Over the whole region of northwest Moorea the mean shell length is negatively correlated with altitude ($p < 0.01$), but the proportion of purple shells varies independently of both variables. In general, the mean shell length decreases at

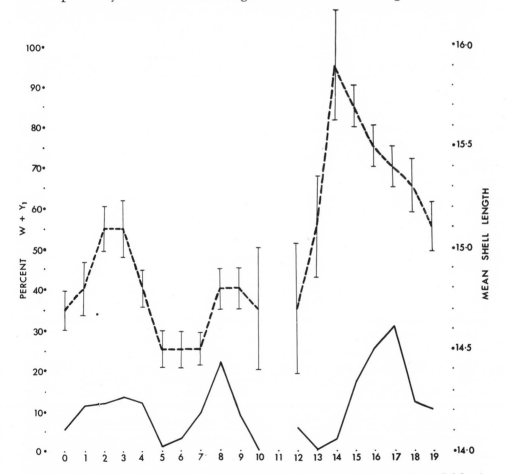

Fig. 9. *Partula taeniata* transect. The percentage of pale shells ($= W + Y_1$, solid line) and the mean shell length in millimeters (dashed line) in samples from twenty adjacent 10-m squares. The vertical lines indicate ± 2 standard errors.

a rate of about 0.5 mm per 100 m of altitude. Within the transect, the average rate is about 1.5 mm per 100 m. At present we cannot assign a probability to this difference, but it seems to be clear-cut.

Partula is an ovoviviparous hermaphrodite in which the eggshell is resorbed by the mother before birth. It is therefore possible to discover the breeding condition of any individual by dissecting out its uterine contents. The dashed line on Figure 10 gives the average number of uterine eggs and young per adult *taeniata* in the transect samples. The boxes show the numbers of adults dissected. There is a significant increase in the average numbers of eggs and young as one passes from high purple to low purple. Unfortunately, it is difficult to compare changes within the transect with changes elsewhere, because the number of uterine eggs

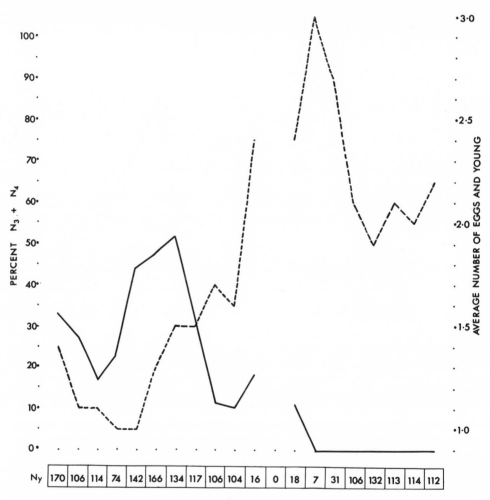

Fig. 10. *Partula taeniata* transect. The percentage of purple shells (= N3 + N4, solid line) and the average number of intrauterine eggs and young (dashed line) in samples from twenty adjacent 10-m squares. The boxes give the numbers of adult snails dissected.

and young is related to the date of collection. As yet we have insufficient data to carry out a complete analysis by partial regression. Outside the transect there is no evident relation between the average contents and the proportion of purple shells among samples collected at approximately the same time, nor is there any significant relation with altitude. Within samples from other localities, larger individuals tend to contain more eggs and young ($p < 0.01$). However, our data indicate that this effect is not strong enough to account by itself for the change along the transect. It seems that the trend in average contents is not merely a secondary effect of shell size.

Thus our study of the border between the high purple and low purple areas has shown that there are gross disturbances in the frequency and expression of banding and that there are concomitant changes of size and breeding condition. These observations are difficult to explain in terms of direct selection by the environment but easy to explain if the area effects represent different coadapted gene complexes. The evidence collected supports the view that the genetic environment has an important role in determining the distribution of morph frequencies in *Partula* and, by extrapolation, in *Cepaea*. If we accept this hypothesis, we must inquire how coadaptation has come about.

(3) THE ORIGIN OF COADAPTATION

It is tempting to regard the area effects of *Cepaea* and *Partula* as semispecies, and the borders between them as hybrid zones. We can then imagine their origin through the classic cycle of geographic isolation and genetic differentiation followed by some degree of hybrid inviability or reduced fertility. There are, however, difficulties in this view. The area effects are defined in terms of variations at only one locus. At the borders of an area there may be steep changes in several characters but, apart from the characters that define the areas, the total *amount* of change may be greater within areas than between them. This seems to be true, for example, of shell length in *P. taeniata*.

Within one species, area effects for different loci may not geographically correspond. For instance, among the *C. nemoralis* on the Marlborough Downs there are steep changes of banding within the color areas, and steep changes of color within the banding areas (Cain and Currey, 1963a). If these changes represent hybrid zones, the area effect must be a larger category than the semispecies (yet smaller than the species!). In fact, of course, it is not a taxonomic category in any useful sense.

As Cain and Currey (1963c) have pointed out, any satisfactory explanation must take into account these curious geographic arrangements. Their pattern and constancy make them difficult to reconcile with Goodhart's (1963) hypothesis of fortuitously different founders in an effectively uniform external environment. No such difficulties arise if we assume that the external environment is, even to some slight degree, selectively heterogeneous. It is then no longer necessary to postulate different founder populations.

Let us imagine a large region, such as the Marlborough Downs, inhabited by a series of identical polymorphic populations. Local environments will differ from place to place, and some alleles will be favored in one part of the region but not in another. Migration will produce morph-ratio clines between the different parts. In areas or regions where a particular allele is common, selection will favor other genes that are compatible with it. The spread of these "modifier" genes may further increase the frequency of the orginal allele. By a process analogous to embryonic differentiation, an originally uniform series of populations may become differentiated into a series of separate coadapted gene complexes. Migration between populations may tend to resist this differentiation but will not necessarily overcome it. It will, however, often result in nearby populations tending toward the same coadaptive equilibrium.

An algebraic analysis of this system (Clarke, 1966) supports the conclusion that there may be an evolutionary trend toward the steepening of morph-ratio clines, and toward the formation of one or more sharp steps within them. The position of the steps need not correspond to any discontinuity in the external environment. In two dimensions this process could give rise to regions of comparatively uniform morph frequency, separated from other such regions by narrow zones of transition. In other words it could give rise to area effects.

Different morph-ratio clines may have few modifiers in common. This would allow the possibility of area effects for different loci to occur independently of each other. At the same time a zone of transition might involve changes in a large number of genes, and in some places the disturbance due to "hybridization" may be sufficient to produce genetic or developmental instabilities, which apparently happens in the *taeniata* transect.

Thus we have a hypothesis that satisfactorily explains some puzzling patterns of variation in polymorphic land snails. It may well be applicable to similar phenomena in other organisms, such as the unexplained geographic variation in the flower color of *Linanthus parryae* (Epling and Dobzhansky, 1942; Wright, 1943; Epling et al., 1960). It may also throw light on the problem of the distribution of human blood groups. Nijenhuis (1965) has recently argued for the importance of the genetic environment in determining blood-group frequencies. Cavalli-Sforza (1966) has noted an increased variance of blood-group frequencies among small, isolated human populations. He also found that a classification of human races according to the proportions of several blood groups agrees well with classifications based on other characters. These observations led him to minimize the importance of selection by the external environment and to favor an explanation in terms of random genetic drift. His results can more easily be explained if we assume that the frequencies of blood-group (and other) genes are influenced by the genetic background. Small isolated populations are likely to have somewhat different genetic backgrounds (as well as different external environments) and therefore to differ slightly in the proportions of their blood groups. On a larger scale, related races are likely to have generally similar genetic backgrounds, and therefore to have similar *gross* proportions of blood groups.

I should perhaps point out, as a postcript to this paper about the history and geography of genes, that the museums of the world enshrine (or entomb) vast stores of untapped information about the past and present distributions of genetic variants. Much of this information is germane to the problems discussed here. Museum zoologists have already made enormous contributions to the study of evolutionary processes at the population level, but perhaps there are greater triumphs yet to come.

Acknowledgments. These studies would have been impossible without the generous support of the Royal Society, the National Science Foundation, the Carnegie Trust for the Universities of Scotland, the Science Research Council, the Percy Sladen Trust, and the universities of Edinburgh and Virginia. Dr. M. A. Carter has very kindly allowed me to quote some of his unpublished work on *Cepaea*, and I am grateful to him for critically reading the manuscript. Professor A. J. Cain, Captain C. Diver, C.B., C.B.E., and Professor P. M. Sheppard, F.R.S., have given generously of their help and encouragement.

REFERENCES

Cain, A. J., and J. D. Currey, 1963a. Area effects in *Cepaea. Phil. Trans. Roy. Soc. B.,* 246: 1–81.

———, 1963b. Area effects in *Cepaea* on the Larkhill artillery ranges, Salisbury Plain. *J. Linn. Soc. (Zool.),* 45: 1–15.

———, 1963c. The causes of area effects. *Heredity,* 18: 467–71.

Cain, A. J., and P. M. Sheppard, 1954. Natural selection in *Cepaea. Genetics,* 39: 89–116.

———, 1957. Some breeding experiments with *Cepaea nemoralis* L. *J. Genet.,* 55: 195–99.

Cain, A. J., J. M. B. King, and P. M. Sheppard, 1960. New data on the genetics of polymorphism in the snail *Cepaea nemoralis* L. *Genetics,* 45: 393–411.

Carter, M. A., 1965. "An investigation of the area effect in *Cepaea.*" Thesis submitted for the degree of D.Phil. at the Univ. of Oxford.

Cavalli-Sforza, L. L., 1966. Population structure and human evolution. *Proc. Roy. Soc. B., 164:* 362–79.

Clarke, B., 1960. Divergent effects of natural selection on two closely-related polymorphic snails. *Heredity, 14:* 423–43.

———, 1961. "Some factors affecting shell colour polymorphism in *Cepaea.*" Thesis submitted for the degree of D. Phil. at the Univ. of Oxford.

———, 1962a. Natural selection in mixed populations of two polymorphic snails. *Heredity, 17:* 319–45.

———, 1962b. Balanced polymorphism and the diversity of sympatric species. In *Taxonomy and Geography,* D. Nichols, ed. Systematics Assn., Oxford.

———, 1966. The evolution of morph-ratio clines. *Am. Naturalist, 100:* 389–402.

Clarke, B., and J. Murray, 1962. Changes of gene-frequency in *Cepaea nemoralis. Heredity, 17:* 445–65.

Crampton, H. E., 1916. Studies on the variation, distribution and evolution of the genus *Partula.* The species inhabiting Tahiti. *Carneg. Inst. Publ., 228:* 1–311.

———, 1932. Studies on the variation, distribution and evolution of the genus *Partula.* The species inhabiting Moorea. *Carneg. Inst. Publ., 410:* 1–335.

Currey, J. D., R. W. Arnold, and M. A. Carter, 1964. Further examples of variation of populations of *Cepaea nemoralis* with habitat. *Evolution, 18:* 111–17.

Diver, C., 1932. Mollusc genetics. *Proc. 6th Internatl. Cong. of Genetics, 2:* 236.

———, 1939. Aspects of the study of variation in snails. *J. Conchol.*, *21:* 91–141.

Dobzhansky, T., 1954. Evolution as a creative process. *Proc. 9th Internatl. Cong. of Genetics, 1:* 435–49.

Epling, C., and T. Dobzhansky, 1942. Microgeographic races in *Linanthus parryae*. *Genetics, 27:* 317–32.

Epling, C., H. Lewis, and F. M. Ball, 1960. The breeding group and seed storage: A study in population dynamics. *Evolution, 14:* 238–55.

Fisher, R. A., 1939. Selective forces in wild populations of *Paratettix texanus*. *Ann. Eugenics, 9:* 109–22.

Ford, E. B., 1965. *Ecological Genetics.* Methuen, London.

Goodhart, C. B. 1963. "Area effects" and non-adaptive variation between populations of *Cepaea* (Mollusca). *Heredity, 18:* 459–65.

Huxley, J. S., 1942. *Evolution, The Modern Synthesis.* Allen & Unwin, London.

Jones, J. S., 1966. "Two studies relating to the area effect in *Cepaea*." Thesis submitted for the degree of B.Sc. at the Univ. of Edinburgh.

Komai, T., and S. Emura, 1955. Study of population genetics on the polymorphic land snail *Bradybaena similaris*. *Evolution, 9:* 400–18.

Lamotte, M., 1951. Recherches sur la structure génétique des populations naturelles de *Cepaea nemoralis* L. *Bull. Biol. Suppl., 35:* 1–239.

———, 1954. Sur la déterminisme génétique du polymorphisme chez *Cepaea nemoralis* L. *Compt. Rend. Acad. Sci., 239:* 365–67.

Lang, A., 1908. Ueber die Bastarde von *Helix hortensis* Müller und *Helix nemoralis* L. *Festschrift, Univ. Jena,* 1–120.

———, 1912. Vererbungswissenschaftliche Miszellen. *Z. indukt. Abstamm.–u. Vererb-Lehre, 8:* 233–83.

Mayr, E., 1954. Change of genetic environment and evolution. In *Evolution as a Process*, J. Huxley, A. C. Hardy, and E. B. Ford, eds. Allen & Unwin, London.

———, 1963. *Animal Species and Evolution*, Harvard Univ. Press, Cambridge.

Mayr, E., and C. E. Rosen, 1956. Geographic variation and hybridization in populations of Bahama snails (*Cerion*). *Am. Mus. Nat. Hist. Novitates, 1806:* 1–48.

Morgan, T. H., 1929. Variability of *Eyeless*. *Carnegie Inst. Publ., 399:* 139.

Murray, J., 1963. The inheritance of some characters in *Cepaea hortensis* and *Cepaea nemoralis* (Gastropoda). *Genetics, 48:* 605–15.

Murray, J. and B. Clarke, 1966. The inheritance of polymorphic shell characters in *Partula* (Gastropoda). *Genetics, 54:* 1261–77.

Nabours, R. K., 1929. The genetics of the Tettigidae (Grouse Locusts). *Bibliog. Genet., 5:* 27–104.

Nijenhuis, L. E., 1965. Blood groups and natural selection by genetical environment. *Genetica, 36:* 208–28.

Sedlmair, H., 1956. Verhaltens–, Resistenz– und Gehauseunterschiede bei den polymorphen Bänderschnecken *Cepaea hortensis* Mull., und *Cepaea nemoralis* L. *Biol. Zbl., 75:* 281–313.

Sheppard, P. M., 1951. Fluctuations in the selective value of certain phenotypes in the polymorphic land snail *Cepaea nemoralis* L. *Heredity, 5:* 125–34.

Wright, S., 1943. An analysis of local variability of flower colour in *Linanthus parryae*. *Genetics, 28:* 139–56.

———, 1965. Factor interaction and linkage in evolution *Proc. Roy. Soc. B., 162:* 80–104.

Frank C. Vasek

14. OUTCROSSING IN NATURAL POPULATIONS: A COMPARISON OF OUTCROSSING ESTIMATION METHODS[1]

In species that are not obligate outcrossers or obligate self-pollinators, the frequency of cross fertilization obviously may vary between 0 and 100 per cent. Rough estimates of the cross-fertilization frequency may be deduced from observations of pollinator behavior and from knowledge of flower structure. Protandry and long, exserted styles obviously promote outcrossing, and proximity of receptive stigmas to mature anthers promotes self-pollination.

However, in self-compatible outcrossing species, flower-to-flower cross pollination on an individual plant may result in a small amount of self-fertilization. Furthermore, in many self-pollinating species, the stigma of a given plant may be receptive for several hours, and pollen from other plants of the population may be introduced before or as self-pollination occurs. Consequently, deductions concerning outcrossing frequency, based on flower structure or natural history observations, may be somewhat misleading.

For example, in *Clarkia exilis*, the receptive stigma usually comes in contact with pollen of the same flower the first day the flower opens. Moreover, plants isolated in an insect-free greenhouse and left to their own devices produce full seed sets in capsule after capsule. On this basis, *C. exilis* may be judged to be a self-fertilizing species. However, dominant offspring in progenies of recessive wild plants indicate that some outcrossing does occur, and, with genetic methods, the frequency of cross fertilization is estimated at about 45 per cent (Vasek 1964, 1965, 1967). Therefore, quantitative estimates of outcrossing provide more information about the breeding system than qualitative judgments based on flower structure. Accordingly, it is appropriate to examine several methods of estimating outcrossing frequency. However, the accuracy and reliability of quantitative estimates depend upon the assumptions made in obtaining the estimates. Therefore,

---

1. This article is the fourth of a series (the others have Roman numerals before the subtitle) by the author on estimation of outcrossing in natural populations.

an attempt to evaluate each method of estimation will be made on the basis of whether the necessary assumptions are reasonable or not.

Data from a natural population of *C. exilis* (Rancheria Road, Kern County, Calif.; see Vasek 1958) will be used as an example in each of the several methods of estimation. Most methods require a single gene marker, and this population is particularly useful in that it is polymorphic for two single gene traits: (1) petal color, of which pink is dominant to white; (2) a dark purplish spot on the petal, the presence of which is dominant to the absence.

The population area was marked off into squares by locating stakes at 10-m intervals. At flowering time the plants in each square were counted and scored for phenotype. Many flowering plants in thirty randomly selected areas of about 1 sq m each were tagged with a note of their location and phenotype. Later, ripe seeds were collected from the tagged plants and progenies were grown in a University of California greenhouse in Riverside. The population was scored during the spring of 1962, and progenies were grown during the winter and spring of 1963–64 and 1964–65. Usable seed samples were derived from 341 wild plants.

The Rancheria Road population occupies about 3,000 sq m, at an elevation of about 2,100 feet, on a north-facing slope with several boulders and rock outcrops, numerous thickets of *Ribes quercetorum,* and occasional trees of *Quercus wislizenii, Q. douglasii,* and *Aesculus californica.* The *Clarkia* plants occur in patches of varying size among the grasses and other herbs in clearings between shrub thickets and/or boulders.

The population is highly heterogeneous with regard to both plant density and phenotype distribution. Inspection of Figure 1 reveals that plant density ranges from 1 to 739 flowering plants per 10-m square.

Phenotypic frequencies are also highly variable. Excluding those few squares with very low plant densities, the phenotypic frequencies range from essentially zero to 0.402, 0.972, and 0.995 respectively for pink spot, pink, and white. The white and white-spotted phenotypes are difficult to distinguish under field conditions and are therefore combined in the white phenotype category. Occasionally a wild plant was scored as white, but then produced all white-spotted progeny in the greenhouse. Consequently, a precise determination of the number of white and white-spotted phenotypes in each 10-m square, and of their distribution in the population, was not feasible. Rather, the proportion of white to white-spotted phenotypes among the wild plants sampled was determined from progeny tests and utilized to estimate the relative phenotypic frequencies for the entire population. Outcrossing data for and from this population are presented in Table 1.

METHODS OF ESTIMATION

All the methods of estimating outcrossing which are discussed below require the growing of experimental progenies to test for heterozygosity and/or to obtain the several outcrossing estimators. Consequently, all methods assume equal survival of zygotes and equal seed germination in experimental plots. The necessary as-

col1	col2	col3	col4	col5	col6	col7	col8	col9	col10
			208 0.019 0.972 0.009						
		189 0.402 0.249 0.349	317 0.050 0.924 0.026	739 0.093 0.836 0.071	113 0.319 0.549 0.132	168 0.119 0.262 0.619	132 0.242 0.197 0.561	99 0.222 0.333 0.445	
39 0.000 0.974 0.026	29 0.034 0.241 0.725	500 0.292 0.184 0.524	531 0.120 0.665 0.215	432 0.155 0.690 0.155	77 0.221 0.506 0.273	310 0.139 0.539 0.322	113 0.283 0.336 0.381	444 0.344 0.475 0.181	
1 0.000 1.000 0.000	66 0.136 0.728 0.136	217 0.046 0.774 0.180	271 0.122 0.697 0.181	42 0.309 0.524 0.167	206 0.204 0.204 0.592	154 0.370 0.214 0.416	131 0.275 0.206 0.519	197 0.173 0.472 0.355	77 0.156 0.143 0.701
118 0.000 0.271 0.729	8 0.000 1.000 0.000								
175 0.005 0.000 0.995									

Fig. 1. Plant density and phenotype distribution in the Rancheria Road population of *Clarkia exilis*. Each square represents a 10-m square area of the population. The first number in each square refers to the number of plants in flower on May 3, 1962. The next three numbers in each square refer to the phenotypic frequencies of plants with pink-spotted, pink-nonspotted, and white (both spotted and nonspotted) petals respectively.

sumption of monogenic inheritance for the markers utilized has been tested and found valid for these markers in other populations of *C. exilis* (Vasek 1964, 1967) and is assumed to be valid for this population as well. Additional assumptions differ from one method to the next and will be indicated in the description of each method of estimation.

Equilibrium Method

This method is based on frequencies expected according to Wright's equilibrium,

$$\underset{p^2 + pqF}{D} + \underset{2pq - 2pqF}{H} + \underset{q^2 + pqF}{R} = 1$$

where the expected frequencies of homozygous dominants, heterozygotes, and recessives in the population are expressed in terms of the inbreeding coefficient (F) and the dominant (p) and recessive (q) gene frequencies, and where $p + q = 1$. The outcrossing frequency (λ) relates to F in that, at equilibrium and in the absence of selection, $\lambda = (1 - F)/(1 + F)$ and $F = (1 - \lambda)/(1 + \lambda)$ (Nei and Syakudo 1958). By this method the observed zygotic frequencies, D, H, and R are determined by counting phenotypes in the population and then by progeny-testing dominant phenotypes to determine the proportion of homozygotes to heterozygotes.

Two of the expected frequencies of the equilibrium are set equal to the observed frequencies,

$$H = 2pq - 2pqF \tag{1}$$

and

$$R = q^2 + pqF \tag{2}$$

and the two equations are simultaneously solved for F and p.

The solutions are $p = D + \frac{1}{2}H$, and $F = [(4D \times R) - H^2]/(2D + H)(H + 2R)$.

This method assumes that the population is in equilibrium and there is no

Table 1. Data used in Estimating Outcrossing Frequency in the Rancheria Road
    Population of Clarkia exilis.*

A. Phenotype Frequencies

Phenotype	PS	P	WS	W	Total
No.	1,045	3,242	1,180	636	6,103
Freq.	0.171	0.531	0.193	0.105	1.000

B. Phenotype, Zygote, and Gene Frequencies

Marker	Phenotypes		Wild plants No. tested		Zygotic frequency			Dominant gene frequency
	Dom.	Rec.	Dom.	Het.	D	H	R	p
Pink	0.702	0.298	135	97	0.409	0.293	0.298	0.556
Spot	0.364	0.636	71	90	0.161	0.203	0.636	0.263

C. Progenies from Wild Plants

Marker	Dominant			Heterozygous				Recessive			
	No.	d	r	No.	d	r	RH	No.	d	r	DR
Pink	135	12,433		97	6,922	2,051	0.229	109	1,335	10,265	0.115
Spot	71	6,739		90	6,223	2,500	0.287	180	1,931	15,613	0.110
Pink on spot	31	2,556		60	3,900	1,287	0.244	70	841	6,788	0.110
Pink on nonspot	104	9,877		37	2,932	764	0.207	39	494	3,477	0.124
Spot on pink	29	2,060		62	4,065	1,708	0.296	141	1,505	12,068	0.111
Spot on white	42	4,679		28	2,158	792	0.268	39	426	3,545	0.107

* Dominant offspring, d; recessive offspring, r.

selection, and that cross fertilization is at random with respect to the several genotypes.

In applying the equilibrium method to the *Clarkia* example, the data presented in Table 1B yield outcrossing estimates of $\lambda = 0.422$ and $\lambda = 0.355$ for the pink and spot markers respectively (Table 2).

Allard Method

This method of estimation, employed extensively by Professor R. W. Allard and his students (e.g. Harding and Tucker, 1964; Imam and Allard, 1965; Allard and Workman, 1963; and Jain and Allard, 1960), utilizes the observed frequency of dominants in progenies of naturally pollinated recessives. These dominant offspring have obviously resulted from cross fertilization and are heterozygous. The expected frequency of dominants in progenies of wild recessives is a function of the dominant gene frequency (p) in the pollen pool and the frequency of cross fertilization (λ). Setting the observed frequency (DR) equal to the expected frequency (λp) gives

$$DR = \lambda p \qquad (3)$$

The dominant gene frequency is estimated from zygotic proportions, as in the equilibrium method, substituted for p, and the equation is solved for λ. This method has the advantage of simple and direct calculation. Its major assumption is that the gene frequency in the pollen pool is the same as in the zygotes that

Table 2. Comparison of Several Outcrossing Estimates

Method	Estimators		Pink		Spot	
			λ	P	λ	P
Equilibrium	H	R	0.422	0.556	0.355	0.263
Fyfe & Bailey	DR	RH	0.146	0.788	0.368	0.299
Combination	H	DR	*	*	0.264	0.417
	H	RH	0.437	0.596	0.336	0.280
	R	DR	0.183	0.630	0.441	0.249
	R	RH	*	*	0.320	0.269
Allard	p	DR	0.207 ⎫ 0.556		0.418 ⎫ 0.263	
	p	RH	0.750 ⎭		0.312 ⎭	
Double-recessive†	p′	H	0.514 ⎫		0.345 ⎫	
	p′	R	* ⎪ 0.315		0.303 ⎪ 0.272	
	p′	DR	0.397 ⎪		0.397 ⎪	
	p′	RH	* ⎭		0.325 ⎭	
Average (N)			0.382(8)	0.577(5)	0.380(12)	0.293(7)

* Impossible solution.

† Estimate of p from double recessives, p′.

produced the pollen grains. In addition, the resulting outcrossing estimate is assumed to apply equally to all genotypes in the population.

Applying the Allard method to the *Clarkia* example, DR from Table 1C and p from Table 1B yield estimates of $\lambda = 0.207$ and $\lambda = 0.418$ for the pink and spot markers respectively.

Fyfe and Bailey (1951) Method

Rather than any estimates based on zygotic frequencies, this method utilizes the progenies from naturally pollinated recessives and naturally pollinated heterozygotes. The frequency of dominants in the progenies of wild recessives is the same estimator (DR) used in the Allard method. The second estimator is the frequency of recessives observed in the progenies of wild heterozygotes (RH). The latter is expected in the frequency of $(1/4)(1 - \lambda) + (1/2)\lambda q$ (Vasek, 1964) or $(1 + \lambda - 2\lambda p)/4$. Setting the observed frequency equal to the expected frequency gives

$$RH = (1 + \lambda - 2\lambda p)/4 \qquad (4)$$

Equations 3 and 4 are solved simultaneously for estimates of λ and p. The major assumption is that recessives and heterozygotes have the same outcrossing frequency. This is basically the same assumption as that made in applying estimates derived by the Allard method, but in this case made before, not after, outcrossing is estimated. No assumption is made concerning zygotic or gene frequencies. However, a major disadvantage of this method is that RH is an unreliable estimator, as will be discussed in a later section.

By applying the Fyfe and Bailey method to the *Clarkia* example, DR and RH from Table 1C yield outcrossing estimates of $\lambda = 0.146$ and $\lambda = 0.368$ for the pink and spot markers respectively.

Double-Recessive Method

In populations where two markers are available, an estimate of dominant gene frequencies in the outcrossing fraction of the pollen pool may be obtained for each marker and utilized to solve equation 3 for an estimate of λ. In progenies of double recessives, the proportion of dominants for one marker among dominants for the other marker provides a direct estimate of p in the outcrossing fraction of the pollen pool. For example, the frequency of pink-spotted phenotypes among all the spotted (pink and white) progeny of double recessives (Table 4) is $0.034/(0.034 + 0.074) = 0.315$. Similarly, the frequency of spotted phenotypes among all the pink offspring is $0.034/(0.034 + 0.091) = 0.272$. Since only known outcrosses were scored, $\lambda = 1$, and 0.315 and 0.272 are direct estimates of p for the pink and spot markers respectively. By substituting into equation 3, the resulting estimate of λ is 0.397 for both markers.

This method assumes that the frequency of dominants for one marker among dominants for the second marker is the same as the frequency of dominants for the first marker among recessives for the second marker. In other words, independent association of the two markers is assumed.

In the example at hand, a 2×2 table indicates that the phenotypes of the two markers (Table 1A) are not randomly associated. The chi square of 901.2, with one degree of freedom, is highly significant. An excess of pink, nonspot and white, spot phenotypes, together with a corresponding deficiency of pink, spot and white, nonspot phenotypes, indicates a nonrandom association in repulsion phase.

The occurrence of this disequilibrium in itself is an interesting aspect of the population and merits further study. A disequilibrium could be maintained with or without linkage by certain selective forces such as pollinator preference, and general breeding experience with the two markers in question suggests that linkage is probably not a factor. Although the principal assumption of this method is invalidated by the nonrandom association, the magnitude of error in estimates obtained, however difficult to assess, may not be large. For example, if the progeny of each wild phenotype are scored separately (Table 1C), outcrossing estimates for each marker against a background of each phenotype of the other marker are obtained, by the Fyfe and Bailey method, as follows:

for pink on spot $\qquad \lambda = 0.166, p = 0.663$
for pink on nonspot $\qquad \lambda = 0.076, p = 1.632$
for spot on pink $\qquad \lambda = 0.396, p = 0.280$
for spot on white $\qquad \lambda = 0.286, p = 0.374$

These estimates are moderately close to the comparable total estimates for each marker (Table 2), except for the inordinately high gene frequency estimated for pink on a nonspot background. The latter phenotype, of course, comprises over half the population.

Combination Methods

Since the four equations describe the expected frequencies for four independent observed sets of data, any two of the equations may be solved simultaneously for λ and p. In addition to the simultaneous solution of equations 1 and 2 (equilibrium method) and equations 3 and 4 (Fyfe and Bailey method), four additional estimates of λ and p may be obtained from the simultaneous solution of the following pairs of equations: 1 and 3; 1 and 4; 2 and 3; 2 and 4.

Additionally, since all expectations are expressed in terms convertible to the two unknown components, λ and p, other estimates of λ may be obtained by estimating p, substituting, and solving all the equations for λ. This is merely extending the Allard method to equation 4 and the double-recessive method to equations 1, 2, and 4. Needless to say, this compounds the assumptions made for the individual methods.

From the several described methods and the combination methods, a total of fourteen outcrossing estimates is possible. However, two of the estimates, those derived from p and equations 1 and 2, are equivalent to the equilibrium method. The remaining twelve estimates for each marker are listed in Table 2.

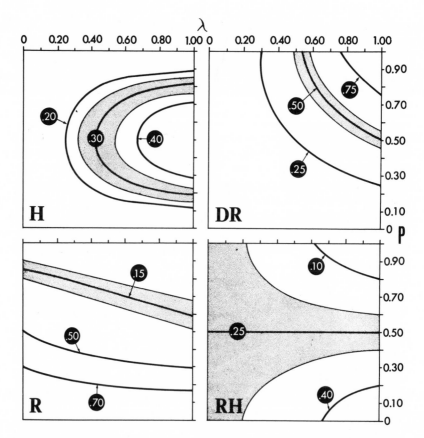

Fig. 2. Properties of the curves for *H, R, DR*, and *RH*. Several hypothetical values (circled numbers) for each estimator are plotted against λ (horizontal axis) and *p* (vertical axis). The shaded areas indicate the area of possible solution if a 5 per cent error in observed value were assumed.

Reliability of Estimators

Each of the four basic estimators, *H, R, DR*, and *RH* as defined by equations 1 to 4, can be expressed in terms of the component frequencies *p* and λ. Thus a curve for each estimator can be plotted against the two components by assigning a series of arbitrary values from 0.00 to 1.0 to one component and then solving the appropriate equation for the other component. A series of such curves for several hypothetical observed values is shown in Figure 2. On each square one curve shows, by the extent of the shaded area, the magnitude of error in estimation of λ and *p*, when a 5 per cent error in the observed value is assumed.

Quite clearly, errors of estimation are large for *H* and exceedingly large for *RH*. Especially for *RH*, errors of estimation are inordinately large if *p* happens to approach 0.50 or if λ happens to be low. In contrast, *R* and *DR* yield acceptably small errors of estimation with an assumed 5 per cent error in observed value.

Furthermore, R and DR are both directly observed without depending upon vagaries of segregation from heterozygotes. Thus fewer opportunities for errors occur, and these estimators hence are much more efficient and accurate than H and RH.

Note that in R, small changes in p may result in large changes in λ, whereas in DR, p and λ mostly change in about the same proportion. The properties of the curves indicate, then, that DR is the most efficient estimator, with R an acceptable second best estimator, and H a third best estimator. Unless gene frequencies are quite high or quite low, and outcrossing frequencies are quite high, RH is an inefficient and unreliable estimator.

Population Structure

Clarkia populations are highly complex in structure. They are characterized by marked heterogeneity in phenotype distribution, genotype distribution, and plant density, as described earlier (here and Vasek, 1967). In addition, DR and RH are exceedingly variable. Data for both these estimators are highly heterogeneous, whether from different subgroups within a population or from adjacent plants within a population subgroup (Vasek, 1967). Extrapolation leads to the prediction (Vasek, 1967) that data derived from different flowers on the same plant would be about as variable and heterogeneous as plant-to-plant or group-to-group comparisons. This prediction was tested by a small experiment which is reported in Table 3.

In this experiment, observed values of DR for individual flowers ranged from 0.000 to 0.667. For two plants, all 18 flowers sampled yielded observed values of $DR = 0.000$, which, of course, is a homogeneous array of data. However, in each of the other seven plants tested the minimum DR was 0.000, but the maximum ranged from 0.214 to 0.667. The flower-to-flower data for these seven plants are highly heterogeneous, as indicated by the fact that the observed chi square exceeds the chi square expected at the 5 per cent level of probability by approximately 50 to over 250 per cent. Similarly, if the 77 flowers from all nine plants are treated as a single sample, the observed chi square is about 350 per cent greater than the chi square for 5 per cent.

Observed values of RH were less variable, ranging from 0.200 to 0.565. The three plants sampled each yielded variable but not significantly heterogeneous (Table 3) arrays of data. However, if the 19 flowers from the three plants are considered as a single sample, the observed chi square does become significant at the 5 per cent level of probability. This suggests that, for RH, plant-to-plant variation is greater than flower-to-flower variation on the same plant.

Variation in RH is limited by the fact that outcrossing can be detected in progeny derived from, at most, only a statistical 50 per cent of the ovules. Thus, less variation and hence greater homogeneity in RH, as compared with DR, might be expected. The plant-to-plant differences in RH probably relate to the frequency of the recessive gene in the general population area in which the test heterozygotes were located. However, the population consisted of only 203 plants in the year this experiment was conducted, rather than the approximately 4,000 plants observed in an earlier season. Whether the pattern of plant-to-plant differences would pertain under conditions of higher plant densities is problematical.

Incidentally, the complex structure of populations, particularly with regard to heterogeneity of plant density, is extended to the dimension of time by drastic fluctuation in population size from one season to another.

Because of the complex population structure, resulting from the high degree of heterogeneity in the parameters discussed above, very large samples are necessary for reasonably accurate outcrossing estimates, and even then considerable statistical and sampling errors are likely to occur. Thus, any one estimate may be inaccurate and misleading. Consequently, the employment of several estimation methods is desirable as a partial control against errors and inefficient estimators and as a partial test of the assumptions made for each method.

DISCUSSION AND EVALUATION

The twelve possible outcrossing estimates (Table 2) are in moderately good agreement for the spot marker, ranging from $\lambda = 0.264$ to $\lambda = 0.441$, with a mean of $\lambda = 0.380$. But the several outcrossing estimates for the pink marker are notably

Table 3. Chi Square Test for Flower-to-Flower Heterogeneity of DR and RH in a population of Clarkia exilis at Deer Creek, Tulare Co., California.*

Recessive plant	No. fls.	Minimum DR	N	Maximum DR	N	Total plant DR	N	Chi square OBS.	Exp.	d.f.	
1	8	0.000	42	0.000	9	0.000	192	0.00	14.07	7	Not signif.
2	10	0.000	61	0.000	16	0.000	402	0.00	16.92	9	Not signif.
3	11	0.000	35	0.214	42	0.101	326	24.24	18.31	10	Heterog.
4	3	0.000	14	0.278	18	0.111	45	8.44	5.99	2	Heterog.
5	12	0.000	64	0.667	15	0.147	443	36.16	19.68	11	Heterog.
6	8	0.000	27	0.414	29	0.125	232	37.77	14.07	7	Heterog.
7	12	0.000	25	0.306	36	0.130	370	33.76	19.68	11	Heterog.
8	5	0.000	22	0.419	31	0.158	152	25.20	9.49	4	Heterog.
9	8	0.000	57	0.348	23	0.074	269	37.34	14.07	7	Heterog.
Total	77					0.092	2431	344.92	97.35	76	Heterog.

Heterozygous plant		RH	N	RH	N	RH	N				
1	4	0.200	10	0.478	23	0.379	66	2.47	7.81	3	Not signif.
2	7	0.333	24	0.565	23	0.443	158	6.40	12.59	6	Not signif.
3	8	0.136	22	0.409	22	0.282	294	8.70	14.07	7	Not signif.
Total	19					0.344	518	34.88	28.86	18	Heterog.

* Progenies were grown in the spring of 1966 from wild seed samples of June 1965.

diverse (Table 2), ranging from $\lambda = 0.146$ to $\lambda = 0.750$, and four of the potential solutions were impossible. The variance for the eight estimates obtained is 0.041, which is about twenty times greater than the variance of the twelve estimates for the spot marker ($S^2 = 0.0023$).

The relative diversity of outcrossing estimates for the two markers is shown graphically in Figure 3. For the spot.marker, the simultaneous solutions, as indicated by the points where two curves intersect, are well clustered. One minor exception concerns the curves DR and H which intersect at an acute angle at about $\lambda = 0.26$. The deviation of this point from the main cluster is well within an experimental error of 5 per cent or even 1 per cent. Of particular interest is the near coincidence of the dominant gene frequency estimated from zygotic frequencies and that estimated in the pollen pool by the double-recessive method. This close agreement suggests that for the spot marker the gene frequency in the outcrossing fraction of the pollen pool is the same as in the zygotes producing that pollen. The clustering of solutions further suggests that the same gene frequencies apply more or less equally to all the other four estimators. Thus for the spot marker the assumptions all appear to be rather reasonable. Whatever small errors occur tend to cancel each other out so that the average of the several estimates is a reasonable overall estimate of outcrossing for the spot marker.

On the other hand, for the pink marker the several common solutions are well scattered. The diversity of the common solutions suggests that the same outcrossing frequencies and/or the same gene frequencies do not apply equally to the several estimators. Furthermore, two pairs of curves, those for estimators R and RH, and for H and DR, do not intersect at all, indicating that these estimators have impossible algebraic solutions.

The impossible solutions suggest that the same gene frequencies and/or the same outcrossing frequencies do not apply equally to the several genotypes. Thus the diversity of estimates indicates that the assumptions made in obtaining those estimates are, by and large, not reasonable.

Of particular interest, the gene frequency in the outcrossing fraction of the pollen pool (Fig. 3) is much lower than in the population of zygotes producing that pollen. Quite clearly, then, there is selection against the dominant pink gene, at least as far as outcrossing to double recessives is concerned. This selection could be accounted for by pollinator preference such that white $\times$ white or pink $\times$ pink cross matings are effected in preference to white $\times$ pink cross pollinations. With white $\times$ pink crosses being discriminated against, the observed frequency of DR is lower than would be expected under conditions of nonselection. If DR were about twice as great, its curve (Fig. 3) would pass approximately at the equilibrium estimate, and again there would be a fairly close clustering of estimates. R and RH would still not intersect, but one could rationalize here that experimental error or the inefficiency of RH was sufficient to account for the discrepancies.

The selection against pink accounts for a large part of the scattering of common solutions. Selection by pollinator preference invalidates the assumptions of:

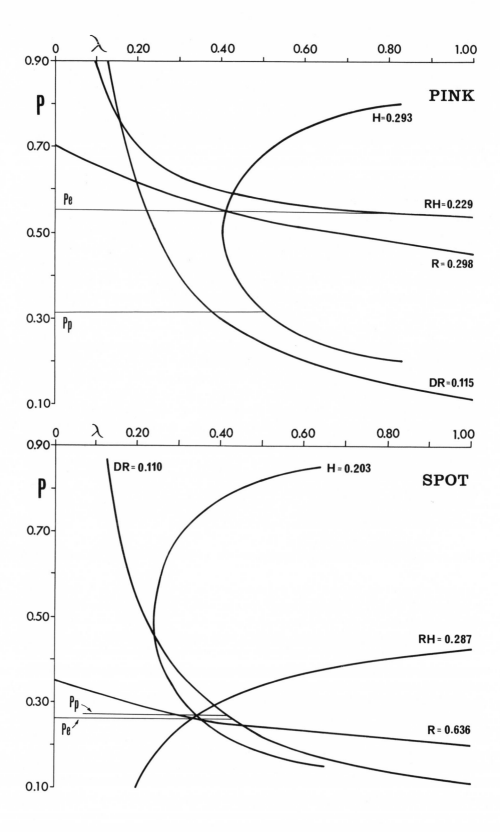

(1) equilibrium and no selection; (2) equality of genotypes with respect to out-crossing frequency; (3) equal gene frequency in the pollen pool and in the zy-gotes producing the pollen; (4) random or independent association of the gene markers. Thus in all methods of estimation at least one major assumption is considered invalid.

Nevertheless, the average of the several estimates is practically the same as the average outcrossing estimate for the spot marker. This close coincidence suggests that for the pink marker, too, the assumptions err in different directions and that, upon averaging the several estimates, the errors tend to cancel each other out. Since the important basic assumptions are difficult, if not impossible, to test independently, the utilization of several estimates, rather than only one, becomes critical. The use of only one estimate could be quite misleading. For example, with the two best estimators DR and R, estimates of $\lambda = 0.18$ and 0.45 are obtained for the pink and the spot marker respectively. If perchance only the former estimate had been obtained, without the partial control of other estimates, a somewhat erroneous conclusion would be reached concerning outcrossing frequency. Therefore several estimates of outcrossing are necessary.

However, even an average estimate based on a dozen individual estimates should not be taken as a constant outcrossing frequency, for Harding and Tucker (1964) found that, in addition to differences between genotypes and geographical location, outcrossing frequency in lima beans sometimes also differed from year to year. Similar variation was observed by Imam and Allard (1965) in wild populations of *Avena fatua* and by Allard (1954) and Allard and Workman (1963) in lima beans.

It follows that breeding systems are somewhat variable and that several estimates provide only an indication of the approximate average frequency of cross fertilization.

PROUT'S DIGENIC OUTCROSSING MODEL

The necessity for making major assumptions in all the estimation methods described earlier has prompted consideration of possible outcrossing models that incorporate a minimum of assumptions. One such model, suggested and developed by Professor Timothy Prout, is presented here for general consideration. At this writing the model has not yet been perfected or tested. However, even a preliminary presentation of the basic general idea is a logical sequel to earlier discussion.

With two gene markers considered together, four phenotypes can be recognized visually, and nine genotypes can be identified from a combination of the phenotype and the segregation pattern in the progeny. Four different gametic geno-

---

Fig. 3. Curves for the outcrossing estimators H, R, DR, and RH. Observed values for the pink and for the spot markers are plotted against λ and p. The horizontal lines represent estimates of p by the equilibrium method (pe) and by the double-recessive method (p_p).

Table 4. Progenies from Plants of Known Genotype for Two Loci

Wild parents sampled			Total	Phenotypic freq. in progeny				Freq. in population		
Phenotype	Genotype	No.	progeny	PS	P	WS	W	Zygotic	p (pink)	p (spot)
PS	PPSS	12	780	1.000				0.022	0.022	0.022
I	PPSs	19	1,776	0.699	0.301			0.036	0.036	0.018
II	PpSS	17	1,280	0.744		0.256		0.032	0.016	0.032
III	PpSs	43	3,997	0.536	0.224	0.170	0.070	0.081	0.040	0.040
P IV	PPss	104	9,877	0.107	0.893			0.392	0.392	
V	Ppss	37	3,696	0.089	0.704	0.031	0.176	0.139	0.070	
WS VI	ppSS	42	4,679	0.094		0.906		0.116		0.116
VII	ppSs	28	2,950	0.114	0.022	0.617	0.247	0.077		0.039
W VIII	ppss	39	3,971	0.034	0.091	0.074	0.801	0.105		
Total		341	33,006					1.000	0.576	0.267

Table 5. *Phenotypic Frequencies Expected in Progenies of Wild Genotypes According to the Digenic Outcrossing Model*

Parent genotype	Equation number	Observed frequency	Expected frequency
PPSs	1	I dd =	$\frac{3}{4}(1-\lambda_1) + \lambda_1 w + \frac{1}{2}\lambda_1 x + \lambda_1 y + \frac{1}{2}\lambda_1 z$
	2	I dr =	$\frac{1}{4}(1-\lambda_1) + \frac{1}{2}\lambda_1 x + \frac{1}{2}\lambda_1 z$
PpSS	3	II dd =	$\frac{3}{4}(1-\lambda_1) + \lambda_1 w + \lambda_1 x + \frac{1}{2}\lambda_1 y + \frac{1}{2}\lambda_1 z$
	4	II rd =	$\frac{1}{4}(1-\lambda_1) + \frac{1}{2}\lambda_1 y + \frac{1}{2}\lambda_1 z$
PpSs	5	III dd =	$\frac{9}{16}(1-\lambda_1) + \lambda_1 w + \frac{1}{2}\lambda_1 x + \frac{1}{2}\lambda_1 y + \frac{1}{4}\lambda_1 z$
	6	III dr =	$\frac{3}{16}(1-\lambda_1) + \frac{1}{2}\lambda_1 x + \frac{1}{4}\lambda_1 z$
	7	III rd =	$\frac{3}{16}(1-\lambda_1) + \frac{1}{2}\lambda_1 y + \frac{1}{4}\lambda_1 z$
	8	III rr =	$\frac{1}{16}(1-\lambda_1) + \frac{1}{4}\lambda_1 z$
PPss	9	IV dd =	$\lambda_2 w + \lambda_2 y$
	10	IV dr =	$(1-\lambda_2) + \lambda_2 x + \lambda_2 z$
Ppss	11	V dd =	$\lambda_2 w + \frac{1}{2}\lambda_2 y$
	12	V dr =	$\frac{3}{4}(1-\lambda_2) + \lambda_2 x + \frac{1}{2}\lambda_2 z$
	13	V rd =	$\frac{1}{2}\lambda_2 y$
	14	V rr =	$\frac{1}{4}(1-\lambda_2) + \frac{1}{2}\lambda_2 z$
ppSS	15	VI dd =	$\lambda_3 w + \lambda_3 x$
	16	VI rd =	$(1-\lambda_3) + \lambda_3 y + \lambda_3 z$
ppSs	17	VII dd =	$\lambda_3 w + \frac{1}{2}\lambda_3 x$
	18	VII dr =	$\frac{1}{2}\lambda_3 x$
	19	VII rd =	$\frac{3}{4}(1-\lambda_3) + \lambda_3 y + \frac{1}{2}\lambda_3 z$
	20	VII rr =	$\frac{1}{4}(1-\lambda_3) + \frac{1}{2}\lambda_3 z$
ppss	21	VIII dd =	$\lambda_4 w$
	22	VIII dr =	$\lambda_4 x$
	23	VIII rd =	$\lambda_4 y$
	24	VIII rr =	$(1-\lambda_4) + \lambda_4 z$

types occur, with each gamete containing one allele of each marker. With the nomenclature of the *Clarkia* example at hand, the gametic genotypes are *PS*, *Ps*, *pS*, and *ps*, and they occur in the frequencies *w*, *x*, *y*, and *z* respectively. The model is therefore concerned immediately with gamete frequencies, rather than gene frequencies. Obviously, however, $p_{pink} = w + x$, and $p_{spot} = w + y$.

For each genotype, the expected phenotypic frequencies in the progeny are described in terms of outcrossing and gamete frequencies in the same way that *DR* and *RH* were earlier described in terms of λ and p. However, useful information is derived from the progenies of only eight of the nine genotypes (Table 4), the homozygous double dominant being the exception. The expected frequencies (Table 5) are set equal to observed frequencies (Table 4) to obtain solutions of maximum likelihood.

Outcrossing is estimated separately for each phenotype. Thus the parameters to estimate are λ_1, λ_2, λ_3, λ_4, *w*, *x*, *y*, and *z*. With 24 equations and 16 degrees of freedom, these estimates should be possible. Theoretically the excess of degrees of freedom should permit a chi-squared test for goodness of fit.

On the surface, this model shows promise of being quite useful. No assumptions need be made concerning selection or equilibrium. The model itself tests whether different phenotypes have different outcrossing frequencies. And the assumptions of equality between gene frequencies in the pollen pool and in the zygotes producing that pollen pool are obviated since the model considers only the pollen pool. The model does assume that pollinators cannot distinguish between homozygous and heterozygous dominants.

The model still requires a thorough search to uncover implicit assumptions and possible errors of logic. There remains to develop a program for the maximum likelihood estimates by means of the 24 equations of Table 5 and the data of Table 4.

Considerable caution will have to be exercised in testing and evaluating this model, because it relies heavily on segregations from heterozygotes. In view of the relative inefficiency of *RH*, as discussed earlier, the dependence on heterozygote segregation may be an unfortunate weakness. If so, a major point is underscored concerning the difficulty of avoiding errors and assumptions in dealing with breeding systems, and this in turn underscores the exceedingly great complexity of natural populations.

Acknowledgments. I am most grateful to Professor Timothy Prout for his ideas about an outcrossing model and for many suggestions relating to theory, statistics, and the manuscript. Financial support was provided by the National Science Foundation.

REFERENCES

Allard, R. W., 1954. Natural hybridization in lima beans in California. *Am. Soc. Hort. Sci., 64:* 410–16.

Allard, R. W., and P. L. Workman, 1963. Population studies in predominantly self-pollinated species. IV. Seasonal fluctuations in estimated values of genetic parameters in lima bean populations. *Evolution, 17:* 470–80.

Fyfe, J. L., and N. T. J. Bailey, 1951. Plant breeding studies in leguminous forage crops. I. Natural cross breeding in winter beans. *J. Agric, Sci., 41:* 371–78.

Harding, J., and C. L. Tucker, 1964. Quantitative studies on mating systems. I. Evidence for the nonrandomness of outcrossing in *Phaseolus lunatus. Heredity, 19:* 369–81.

Imam, A. G., and R. W. Allard, 1965. Population studies in predominantly self-pollinated species. VI. Genetic variability between and within natural populations of wild oats from differing habitats in California. *Genetics 51:* 49–62.

Jain, S. K., and R. W. Allard, 1960. Population studies in predominantly self-pollinated species. I. Evidence for heterozygote advantage in a closed population of barley. *Proc. Nat. Acad. Sci. U.S.A., 46:* 1371–77.

Nei, M., and K. Syakudo, 1958. The estimation of outcrossing in natural populations. *Jap. J. Genet., 33:* 46–51.

Vasek, F. C., 1958. The relationship of *Clarkia exilis* to *Clarkia unguiculata. Am. J. Bot., 45:* 150–62.

———, 1964. Outcrossing in natural populations. I. The Breckinridge Mountain population of *Clarkia exilis. Evolution, 18:* 213–18.

———, 1965. An estimate of outcrossing frequency in *Clarkia exilis. Am. J. Bot. 56*(6), Part 2: 648 (abstr.).

———, 1967. Outcrossing in natural populations. III. The Deer Creek population of *Clarkia exilis. Evolution, 21:* 241–48.

Douglas E. Yen

15. NATURAL AND HUMAN SELECTION
IN THE PACIFIC SWEET POTATO

Since 1957 the collection of clonal varieties of sweet potato *Ipomoea batatas* (L.) Lam. has been progressively augmented[1] until it numbers 580, representing varieties grown in America, Polynesia, Melanesia, and Southeast Asia. The growing of a live collection under uniform experiment-field conditions has allowed varietal comparisons and cytological analysis too difficult to carry out in field expeditions. Some features of the resultant data follow in summary form:

1. The South American varietal complex exhibits the most extensive range of variation in most of the morphological and physiological characters studied.

2. The comparable ranges in Polynesian, Melanesian, and Southeast Asian varieties are surprisingly wide and, in three cases, must be considered transgressive to those found in the American collection.

3. In the 33 characters studied, including the "physiological" such as flowering and edible-root production under New Zealand conditions, and reaction to cold and to three disease pathogens, continuous variation inferring genetic control by many genes is the order.

4. The patterns of variation in the areal populations of varieties do not conform with a single-stream transfer model from America across the Pacific in that there is no general trend of variation loss in any direction other than that shown by the comparison of the American population with the remainder. The tripartite hypothesis of Barrau (1957) to account for sweet potato distribution would seem to be upheld.

5. Preliminary work has shown that there is no evidence for genetic isolation between varieties from different regional sources. Breeding experiments have resulted in fertile seed production from crosses among Peruvian, Fijian, New Guinean, and Asian varieties.

6. No clear differentiations of local races based on morphological traits have been recognized.

1. All Pacific field collections were supported by The Rockefeller Foundation, New York, with Grants GA. AGR. 5750, 6275, and 63142.

7. The cytological survey (Wheeler and Yen, unpublished data) of representative varieties from all study areas has revealed no divergence from the complement of $2n = 90$ assigned to the species (Ting and Kehr, 1953). The study of chromosome pairing in meiosis, however, does not agree with the observations of Ting et al. (1957) that only secondary association is involved. More recently Jones (1965), working with North American breeding material, has recorded the additional incidence of multivalent configurations, and such has been the case throughout the Pacific varieties.

Some of these points have already been made in a preliminary report of the material (Yen, 1963a), which has been subsequently added to by a numerically stronger collection from all areas except South America, and the consideration of a greater number of plant characters. In the following discussion, the topic of directions of diffusion of the plant is not included. Attention will be focused instead on the Pacific populations of sweet potato varieties as the result of interaction of the genetic background of the introductions, natural selection, and the adaptive procedures of man. For although it seems that little significant evolutionary progress has been achieved in the plant, there may be interest in the component factors that have produced a largely negative result.

THE GENETIC BACKGROUND

Although knowledge of the genetics of sweet potato has not attained the level of that in other crop plants, the exigencies of increasing interest in the breeding of this plant have stimulated the accretion of some information in the last decade. Poole (1955) was able to analyze the inheritance of selected plant characters with the use of the progeny of a comparatively rare self-fertilizing plant. In categorizing those characters to fit relatively simple Mendelian ratios there was an obvious necessity to involve the action of genetic modifiers in most of the characters to account for continuous variations. The variable nature of the species had been underscored, however, and in comparison with wild *Ipomoea* species (van Ooststroom, 1954) the variability and consequent difficulty in assigning unqualified taxa is probably approached only by *I. trifida* (Nishiyama and Teramura, 1962). The sexual reproductive system of the plant has probably claimed the most attention (review by Martin, 1965), for the general outbreeding habit is complicated by the occurrence of an incompatibility system which is seen as a barrier to breeding progress. While Martin suggests that there may be geographic differentiation of incompatibility groups, on the basis of the data of Wang (1964), which have no representation of American varieties in two of the six groups to which Asian varieties were assigned, the most recent work of Hernandez and Miller (1964) suggests that all groups are covered within American material. It is notable that only two species of *Ipomoea*, *batatas* and *trifida*, are known to hybridize freely, according to Nishiyama (summary, 1963) and associates, where common features are chromosome number and an incompatibility group.

The long-standing controversy on the geographic center of origin, the nexus of argument for hypothetical views on directions of transfer of sweet potato by humans, has benefited little from botanical evidence. It can be said, in fact, that all of these views have been founded botanically on historical recordings of the plant and deduction from distribution of allied species in taxonomic work (e.g. House, 1908; van Ooststroom, 1954). The strength of the alliances has been tested in some cases, but the claims of Tioutine (1938) of fertile hybridizations of sweet potato with *Ipomoea* species of different chromosome numbers have not been repeated (Ting et al., 1957; Nishiyama, 1959). Regardless of the validity of Nishiyama's interpretation of the relationship of *I. trifida* to *I. batatas,* the common hexaploid chromosome number $2n = 90$, their cross-ability and partially common incompatibility systems, with their common distribution in America, constitute the strongest of arguments for American origin or, at least, domestication. On cytological grounds, it is uncertain whether allopolyploidy alone is responsible for the structure of the species, but the general association of allopolyploidy with outcrossing breeding systems in perennial or vegetatively propagated plants, as pointed out by Grant (1956) and Gustafsson (1947), would seem to be the basis for the preservation of variation and heterozygosity in the plant's distribution.

From what we know it is a fairly safe surmise that the sweet potato populations, in their pan-Pacific distribution including America and Southeast Asia, are at the same general stage in evolution.

BREEDING SYSTEM AND CULTIVATION

The sweet potato plant is structured as a facultative reproductive unit with the ability of sexual and asexual reproduction (Hayward, 1938). The outbreeding nature and the heterozygous genotype of the species together present opportunities for variation and selection which are restricted by the alternative form to the incidence of chance mutations, whose incidence in themselves appears to be genetically controlled (Hernandez et al., 1964). Stebbins (1950) has classified asexual reproduction as a form of apomixis, one of the most conservative forms of plant reproductive behavior, in which evolutionary progress is slow. The sweet potato must be one of the easiest plants to propagate since all stem nodes have the ability to develop root systems; the swollen storage roots may produce hundreds of vegetative shoots for planting, and small roots can be used for planting (e.g. as the New Zealand Maoris did; Berridge, 1913). As well, cut flesh of the roots may produce shoots after callus formation (Uewada, 1965). Thus although the plant has so many alternative means of survival, it has not been found in the wild state disassociated from agricultural activity. A primary activity of man that influences selection and possible courses of evolution in the plant is then the exercise of choice in the breeding system. In the Pacific, this "choice" is probably more a reflection of agricultural practices in the other staple plants.

Field observations of true seed production made earlier (Yen, 1960) have shown that sexual reproduction, under cultivation based on the alternative, is operative nevertheless. Between the latitudes 30° North and South, spontaneous incidence of seed has been found in the Ryukyu Islands, the Philippines, Timor, New Guinea, the Solomons, New Hebrides, New Caledonia, Fiji, Tonga, the Marquesas Islands, Easter Island, and Peru. No correlations of this incidence can be made with environment. Seeds have been collected in rainforests and arid areas, and from near sea level up to 7,000 feet. The inference is that the genotypes were not restrictive enough to preclude the clonal interbreeding that would be the case if only one variety, or varieties of the same incompatibility group, were introduced.

Although indigenous cultivators are sometimes puzzled by questions about sweet potato seed, the identification of it with the flower of the plant is universal in the tropics; but no purposive raising of seed has been recorded except in Peru. Thus the raising of seedling varieties in such contexts must be assigned to chance survival in fields rather than to selection or conservation. Although large numbers of seeds are produced, there are considerable limits on their successful propagation. The impermeability of the seed, which requires chemical or physical treatment to ensure germination in reasonable time (Steinbauer, 1935) for modern breeding purposes, and the weeding out of seedlings that is generally practiced in cultivations, tend to be eliminative factors before any action of selection can occur. Nevertheless, accounts of discoveries of new varieties have now been recorded from many areas, which, although connected circumstantially with seedling propagation, in some cases could have been vegetal mutants.

Strong evidence has recently been recorded in the Philippines. In Mindoro, a Hanunóo informant was not only able to recount circumstances of the finding of new varieties, but he pencil-drew such seedlings with cotyledon and true leaves differentiated in shape (Fig. 1.). Ifugao informants of Conklin (1967) in his Luzon Mountain Province studies, while observing that the seed is a part of the flower and claiming that it was of no use, were able to find, on prompting, seedling varieties in a new swidden cultivation of sweet potato. The finding of such plants had apparently not been connected hitherto with the high incidence of seed in the region, but among the large number of varieties there (over 100 varietal names) several were claimed to have been discovered in this way. In Malaita (Solomon Islands), available informants said that seedlings found in cultivations would be weeded out. Bulmer (1965, in press) has described in detail the comments of New Guinea Highlanders in two areas, concerning their observation and selection of new varieties. What is more, his informants related the appearance of new varieties to the intermediary action of birds whose ingestion of seed could fulfil requirements of scarification and transport (Yen, 1960).

The alternative forms of reproduction must be considered as concurrent opposing forces in the expression of variations—the conservative agricultural asexual form and the variation-producing accidental sexual. The persistence of the dominant agricultural practice in all areas of sweet potato distribution, however, acts to perpetuate desirable variations. The general effects of human intervention in the breeding system thus are the preservation of the species from extinction as one aspect of evolution and the retarding of the rate of evolutionary progress that may be typified by such a phenomenon as imperfect chromosome diploidization.

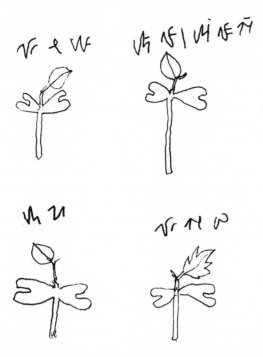

Fig. 1. Hanunóo drawings of sweet potato seedlings found after burning of new swidden in Mindoro, Philippine Islands. The pair of notched cotyledon leaves is clearly defined, while true leaf differences illustrate varietal differences.

THE DISTRIBUTION OF SWEET POTATO IN THE PACIFIC

The present-day distribution of sweet potato in the Pacific Islands does not show close correlations with ecological factors, since, with the exception of the Tuamotuan atolls, the plant may be collected universally. Even in some seemingly unfavorable edaphic environments such as the sandy or coral-derived soils of coastal New Hebrides and northern New Caledonia, the plant may be found in generally unthrifty house gardens. Barrau (1958, 1961) has indicated the areas where sweet potato attains major status and secondary role in agriculture. The plant occupies (or did occupy) the status of a major cultigen in areas which are marginal or near-marginal for the cultivation of the other Pacific starch staples—coconut, taro, breadfruit, yam. In Polynesia, at time of contact, the plant was the major agricultural subsistence in Easter Island and New Zealand and was probably secondary but important in Hawaii. The twentieth-century discovery of the New Guinea Highlands, whose peoples are dependent on the sweet potato, has prompted considerable speculation on the plant's antiquity there (Damm, 1961) and therefore in Melanesia, but the emergence of the plant as the dominant cultigen in near-equatorial but relatively cool conditions which limit the cultivation of the crops of the lowlanders and islanders, stands out as a fact that demands an explanation of differential adaptation by human processes. Rice is the dominant crop of South-east Asia, but in some areas, notably the high regions of the Philippines and Taiwan, the sweet potato, while ritually insignificant, has a place of economic importance second only to rice and in some communities may be used in greater quantity in the daily diet.

To account for this distribution, the most obvious correlates might be temperature and the edaphic factors included in Thomas' classification (1963) of island types. On low islands of carbonate rock and those of elevated reef rock, the plant is of minor importance; but the sweet potato attains major status in the volcanic Hawaiian Islands and Easter Island and in islands containing "continental" rocks such as New Guinea, New Zealand, and the Philippines. With Hawaii as the exception, it can be said that the favorable temperature is typified by altitude in the tropic zones, and by latitude in nontropic regions. This cannot, of course, be taken to mean that the sweet potato is a plant of cool temperature adaptation alone, since its distribution belies this, but the indication is that its range of adaptation to both soil and climatic requirements confers on the sweet potato relatively more adjustability to lower temperatures and broader soil types than other Pacific crop plants are capable of. In the introduction of crop plants, then, the sweet potato exhibits a flexibility that allows its cultivation in varied ecological contexts.

The minor importance of the sweet potato in central Polynesia has been the subject of some speculation, since it is in this area that landfalls of South American plants were probably made. While Brown (1935) has considered that the plant is a survivor of an agricultural pattern superseded by breadfruit and other plants in the eastern areas, there is little cultural evidence to support this contention. Nor on present-day evidence can it be suggested that edaphic factors limit plant growth, as Brown has also suggested, since in the Marquesas and Society Islands, the Cook Group, and Tonga the plant produces, in its secondary agricultural role, as well as it does anywhere.

The possibility that the plant was absent from the western reaches and was of post-European introduction was indicated by Dixon (1932) in his survey of early settlement sources. However, it must be considered that the well-adapted yam and taro complex, introduced from Melanesia, successfully concealed the secondary plants or those used in secondary agriculture. This "competitive" effect of older crop plants (manifest in technological development of cultivation practices in taro and yam, pit storage of breadfruit in eastern Polynesia, and ritual storage of yam in Melanesia and western Polynesia) may well have resulted in emphasis of the more stable, cyclic aspects of the agricultural systems, to the neglect of the seemingly casual swidden portions to which the sweet potato is well adapted. The value of the crop for slope cultivation is obvious in the exploitation of soil resources that are otherwise unusable or limited, and in some areas the expansion of such practice may well have produced a negative effect of erosion or the degeneration of endemic flora, as hypothesized by Robbins (1963) for the New Guinea Highlands.

Sweet potato distribution is not, however, restricted to sloping swidden cultivation, for in some naturally flat topographies it is a major crop. The most conspicuous Melanesian example is on Frederik Hendrik Island where Serpenti (1965) contrasts the yam agriculture in the north with sweet potato culture in the south. He believes the sweet potato has taken over the main agricultural role not only as a food staple but in the main ritual activity of *nambu*, because of its better adaptation to soils of the region.

The addition of the sweet potato to the agricultural patterns of Asia is generally accepted now as recent (Ho, 1955), and this is no better documented anywhere than in the Ryukyu Islands where political circumstances made its seventeenth-century introduction an outstanding event. Kerr (1959) has recounted the adoption of a new plant, surmounting the formidable barrier of traditional rice agriculture, as a social action stemming from economic pressure.

The ability of a plant to grow in a given environment must be considered the first selective factor in any sequence of crop introduction. Its adoption in an agricultural system, however, is the result of an intermediate stage of adaptation by experiment, which already may be seen as a response to the requirements of agricultural man. Plant selection at a subspecies level is one measure of experimental adaptation, and its progress is influenced by the confluent modification of environment which establishes agricultural procedure. From a study of the variations of the relatively recently introduced sweet potato, we seek to divine the possible influence of man in adjusting the plant to the natural environment and to that altered by his own activities.

VARIETAL POPULATIONS OF THE PACIFIC

In his commentary on biological evolution in island environments, Dobzhansky (1963) has emphasized the essence of its action as the "random process of sampling from the gene pool of a Mendelian population." Thus the proposition that the genetic variations of Pacific populations of sweet potato were derived from three separate introductions may well account for the differences in distribution of characters that are seen in the populations. The original American immigrants are seen as random samplings of the genotype in its variability from at or about the means of the American populations, and thus may well account for the resemblances rather than differences between the Pacific groups (Yen, 1963a). The difficulties presented by navigation of prehistoric native seacraft, and indeed sailing vessels of the early era of Pacific discovery, would support the model of small populations, both varietal and plant number, at first introduction. Thus the first principle in the functioning of "random genetic drift" of Sewall Wright (1931) or the "founder principle" of Mayr (1942) would seem to be attained. The examination of data has not revealed the extensive possibilities of the loss of genes of nonadaptive characters that might have been expected. The subsequent expansion of population depended to a great degree on the agricultural uses to which the plant was put. Superficially, therefore, evolutionary progress might be expected in the areas of greatest use of the plant, e.g. New Guinea Highlands, Philippine Islands, marginal Polynesia.

However, the contemporary or even historic importance of the plant in the study areas may not reflect the population levels in the past. Fluctuation of population numbers in time has been emphasized by Ford (1964) as an agent for acceleration of evolutionary rates in wild populations. In the case of the sweet potato in nuclear Polynesia, it is probable that earlier populations were higher numerically and allowed for the possibility of selection after periods of increase when the possibility for recombinations and mutations was highest. Given that populations of central Polynesia never reached the levels of those current in the montane Philippines and New Guinea, the opportunities for variation *in time* may equate with the numerical advantages in the latter if we accept the introduction of the sweet potato into Polynesia at around A.D. 1000 and the earliest into the Western Pacific at after 1500. The latter date is of particular importance, for it spelled the end to the "relative" isolation in the Pacific and the beginning of constant European contact (Sharp, 1960).

In Polynesia the subsequent opportunities for the reintroduction of the sweet potato may be inferred from Melville's reference (1847) to the Tombez (Peru) potato; and the efforts of missionaries, settlers, and agriculturists terminated the genetic isolation and its evolutionary consequences that might have produced geographic races or at least characteristic groups of varieties. The gradual early diffusion of the plant within Polynesia that resulted in its becoming well known throughout, by accidental or purposeful voyages, perhaps took the plant even beyond the western limits—cf. the plant word *kumala* in Fiji (Guppy, 1896) and New Caledonia (Hollyman, 1959)—which might have allowed a pattern of variation revealing more closely the directions of transfer. The new "immigrations," with their dispersal of random introductions from American sources, as well as subsequent introductions within and between areas, probably contributed to the confusing pattern of variation that now exists in the Pacific. Any directions of allopatric evolution tended to be disguised by the reinfusion of genotype and by the opportunity for recombinations of areal segregants that were originally from one source.

Some features of the Pacific sweet potato collection, however, are worthy of examination despite the limitations described. These may be grouped into the very tentative categories of nonadaptive and adaptive. Nonadaptive characters are those for which no obvious correlates have been found in the way of natural factors of climate or soil, and of altitude or topography; and also for which no claims can be construed for favor, or selection within their ranges, by cultivators. They are, however, known by them, being used for taxonomic recognition at the varietal level. Thus characters like purpling, root color, leaf shape, hairiness, etc., are generally very similar to our own varietal classifications (e.g. Thompson and Beattie, 1922).

Figure 2 summarizes the data of variation in specific gravity of edible roots and hairiness of the reproductive organs—ovary and filaments. The lowest figure for specific gravity was recorded in a variety from the Marquesas Islands; nearly glabrous reproductive organs were recorded from Melanesia and Thailand.

Two characters of taxonomic use by native cultivators are leaf form and root

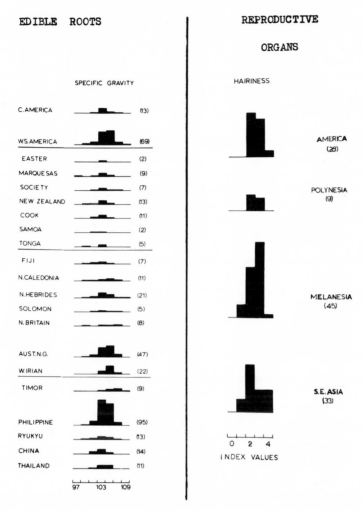

Fig. 2. Frequency distributions of specific gravity measures of edible roots and hairiness of reproductive organs (the added indices of scorings of ovary and filament hairiness: o = glabrous, 4 = very hirsute).

color. Figure 3 shows the variation range of the former; Table 1 shows that in the distribution over the four major population areas, the extremes of diversity of the lower pair are confined to Melanesia. Type C of II-V is found only in the area of continental New Guinea and is lacking in the islands of Biak, the Solomons, New Britain, New Caledonia, New Hebrides, Fiji, and elsewhere in the Pacific. The familiar purpling of the flesh of the edible root is a character of low frequency in Polynesia, and this is illustrated in Figure 4, where the population is contrasted with the American. The three Polynesian varieties having the purpling characteristic were collected in the Cook Islands (one variety) and New Zealand (two).

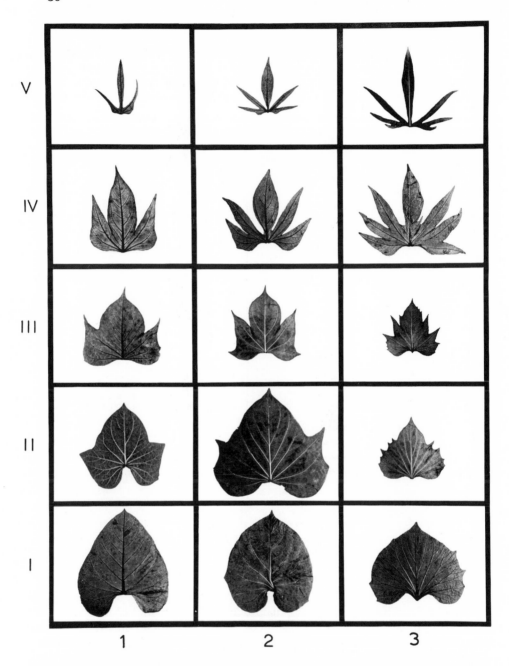

Fig. 3. Variation of leaf dissection in sweet potato. Vertical scale I–V represents degree of dissection of apical lobe, with horizontal 1–3 the degree of dissection of lower paired-lobes.

The latter are derived from European introductions in 1846 from Rarotonga, according to information collected by Berridge (1913). According to Handy (1940) there were several purple-fleshed varieties among the ancient Hawaiian varieties. In samples too small for statistical significance, it seems that the frequency of this character in the four main collections may differ somewhat.

These data can be taken only as rather tenuous examples of evolutionary trends in populations in relative isolation. They are the result of random introduction from the original American gene pool and reflect the deviations from the average that must occur in some plant characters from such introduction. The extension of variation beyond the range of the American population may be a reflection of the skewness of the original representation of the genotype—an effect similar to intensive selection in quantitative characters toward one end of the range; also, there is the additional prerequisite that the concentration of these genes was possible because the early varietal forms carrying them were from different incompatibility groups—i.e. crossable. Thus we return to the nature of the "founder" populations. The phenomenon of "drift" with its loss of genes affecting a character may be viewed as possible only in the case of specific gravity and internal purpling of roots in the Polynesian populations, for high values are lacking in the former and rare in the latter. The maintenance of the purpling character in a New Zealand commercial variety is the subject of constant selection of roots, without which stocks may degenerate. It may thus be suggested that, with

Table 1. The Distribution of Leaf Types in American, Polynesian, Melanesian, and Southeast Asian Populations of Sweet Potato*

	America				Polynesia		
V	1	3	0	V	1	9	0
IV	8	7	0	IV	3	11	0
III	9	11	0	III	14	10	0
II	22	2	0	II	19	0	0
I	32	16	5	I	29	3	1
	a	b	c		a	b	c

	Melanesia				Southeast Asia		
V	0	1	2	V	0	3	0
IV	3	15	5	IV	4	17	0
III	9	21	6	III	13	9	0
II	33	11	1	II	63	9	0
I	68	13	1	I	40	17	0
	a	b	c		a	b	c

* See Figure 3.

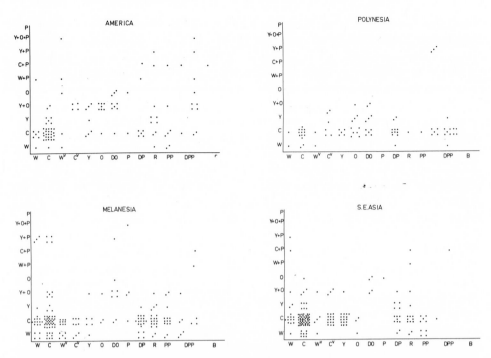

Fig. 4. Comparison of sweet potato populations of America, Polynesia, Melanesia, and Southeast Asia in the purpling characteristic of the edible roots. W + P to P on vertical scale indicates presence of purpling in flesh. Horizontal scale denotes skin colors. (W, white; C, cream; ᵛ, with pink coloration; Y, yellow; O, orange; DO, dark orange; P to DPP, degrees of pink to dark purple; B, very dark purple.)

the apparent lack of preference of Pacific peoples for root colors, the loss of genes for purpling indicates that the lack of selection and therefore "degeneration" of the character has been going on longer in Polynesia than in other Pacific areas.

The function of mutation, however, has to be considered. The extremely dissected leaf forms, not found in areas other than New Guinea, may indicate a mutant form there, whose incidence in different varietal forms indicates interbreeding as well as diffusion within the continent.

Two "adaptive" characters appear to have undergone selection by humans, to account for their frequency distributions in some areas. Table 2 shows the reaction to cold, in a New Zealand experimental field, of varieties collected from various altitudes in America, Polynesia, Melanesia, and Southeast Asia. After 6° of frost (26°F) all varieties showed signs of cold damage, but while varieties from lower altitudes demonstrated it in varying degrees, those from higher than 5,000 feet above sea level were least affected by cold. Many of the Melanesian varieties were collected at low levels, but most of them came from the highlands (Yen, MS.). It is significant that the Melanesian varieties under symptom 3 were collected from New Britain and Fiji (two varieties). The Polynesian varieties, all collected from low altitudes, are interpreted to represent nonselection and are thus a reflection of the introduced genotype (cf. American varieties from low altitudes, breeding at random).

One of the most striking variations in *I. batatas* is its growth habit, for it ranges from a compact bush plant, little more than 2 feet across at maturity to a long sprawling vine plant in which individual stems have been measured at 15 feet. Figure 5 illustrates the extreme and intermediate forms. The wide use of the plant in mountain swidden contexts in Southeast Asia and Melanesia seems to be correlated with the distribution of plant growth types. Figure 6 shows that most of the varieties from these areas are of the intermediate type with their generally strong branching habits, and judged to be used most in slope agriculture where soil cover is desirable. The long-vined types investigated exhibit very slow growth in the early stages after planting and produce poor cover, as do the bush types. The Polynesian types, which again exhibit variation around the mean of the American, may thus reflect adaptation to generally flat-land cultivation, especially typified by the example from Tonga, where compact bush types are generally grown.

The summary of the observations of plant growth types (Fig. 6) indicates the shift of the mean, type 2 of the American and Polynesian populations, toward the intermediate type 3 in the areas where the plant is a major economic factor *and* is important in the high and steeper swidden agricultural systems of Melanesia and Asia—the Highlands of New Guinea and the Philippines. The smaller populations of the Melanesian islands present an interesting contrast to continental New Guinea, for they tend to be more similar to those of island Polynesia. This tendency in many of the other characters studied has suggested that

Table 2. *Reaction to Cold Temperature of Sweet Potato Varieties Collected from Various Altitudes and Grown in an Experimental Field at Otara, New Zealand, after 6° Ground Frost (26°F.), May 1963*

Source and number of varieties	Collection altitude (ft. above sea level)	Number of varieties showing symptoms				
		0	1	2	3	4
America	<1000		16	31	9	12
(106)	1—5,000		6	19	5	0
	>5,000		3	3	0	0
Polynesia	<1000		7	29	2	1
(39)						
Melanesia	<1000		35	19	3	0
(116)	1—5,000		5	7	0	0
	>5,000		30	17	0	0
Southeast Asia	<1000		8	16	7	1
(32)						

Fig. 5. Variation of growth habit in sweet potato. a. Type 1, Very compact bush. b. Type 2, Bush, tending to sprawl with age.

c, d. Type 3, Sprawling, large and small-leaved forms.

e, f. Type 4, Sprawling, similar to Type 3, tending to greater stem elongation with age.

g. Type 5, Elongated vine, with branching from crown. h. Type 6, Similar to Type 5, with less development of branching.

PLANT GROWTH

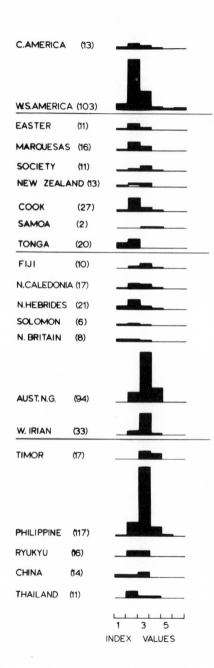

Fig. 6. Distribution of types of plant-growth habit (see Fig. 5) in Pacific populations of sweet potato.

the "founders" in these island areas have much in common and may be evidence of diffusion from Polynesia to Melanesia. With the linguistic evidence of comparatively recent contacts (or re-contacts?) it may well be that Polynesian immigrants brought genes which altered the complement that was originally introduced by European contact in the East Indies and diffusion into Melanesia from the West. The alternative, of course, is that the present Melanesian island populations more accurately reflect, at least in phenotype, the original genotypes on which selection was exercised in the New Guinea Highlands.

Apart from adaptation to the climatic environment, one is inclined toward the view that human selection measures have been exercised more on the plant form than on other plant characters. The selection of intermediate phenotypes suggested for some of the main areas of sweet potato cultivation has resulted in the conservation of genotypic variability. In recent and conflicting conclusions on the effect of such modal selection, the mathematical model of Curnow (1964) is borne out in the cotton-breeding experiments of Walker (1964), in which one of the results is this conservation. The elimination of extremes of the type range in highland Melanesian populations could be due to the more intense selection exercised on phenotype than occurs for example in the Philippines, where an established Ifugao mountain variety *qaggetqet* is of the extreme bush type.

THE INFLUENCE OF AGRICULTURAL PROCEDURES

Man's activities in the adaptation of the sweet potato plant is twofold and concurrent—indeed inseparable. In addition to selective effects, which in the sweet potato plant are not spectacular, the application of external modifications—agricultural procedures—may prove more effective. In some respects these procedures may prove adaptive beyond the genetic ability of the species; in other respects their success negates the necessity of intensive selection for existing inherent adaptive characteristics. Thus the selection process which leads to racial divergences may be arrested by the agricultural measures of man, which in themselves are the subject of change and development.

There has been some discussion of planting methods applied to sweet potato, especially in New Guinea where variations are considerable (Brookfield, 1962; Bowers, 1965). Regardless of the rationalizations for various cultivation practices, the one common effect, whether soil disturbance consists of excavating shallow or deep drains or raising small or large mounds, is the lowering of the water table from the proximity of forming roots. Such measures are universal and may be interpreted in low rainfall areas as precautionary against sudden and violent downpours. In lowland areas, e.g. Frederik Hendrik Island, Serpenti (1965) has reported the adaptation of "mounding" techniques where sweet potato has become an important though secondary crop to *Dioscorea* yam. The application of such procedures has enlarged the ecological range of the species whose natural requirements are inclined toward dry-field culture (Conklin, 1963; Barrau, 1965) and which may lack genetic flexibility in this regard. Similarly, the composting of large mounds as described by Bowers (1965) in the New Guinea Highlands and ground mulching by the Maori (Best, 1925) may be precautionary measures against the effect of cold.

A further feature common to native plantings is the mixed variety field, in many cases associated with mixed species as well. There are agronomic advantages in mixed plantings, where spread of maturity allows for partial harvests continuing over long periods, which are typical of swiddening systems. As well, the factor of groundcover may be better dealt with by mixing plants of different growth habit and rate.

The variability of reaction of clonal varieties to fungous diseases, which has been found in this collection, does not indicate a selection for resistance, and the mixed variety (and species) stands may actually help in reducing, while not suppressing, disease incidence. Plant diseases are broadly recognized by indigenous cultivators, often related to "sickness." The greater susceptibility of one Rarotongan variety, *manioka*, to the leaf disease caused by *Elsinoe* sp. is recognized. The positive step in disease control is not elimination of the variety but growing it by planting roots rather than stem cuttings. Although symptoms do appear on leaves and stems, the effect of the disease is delayed sufficiently for plants to produce useful crops.

Many Pacific agricultural systems are of the *partial* type (classification of Conklin, 1957), which show considerable variation in the proportion of permanent to shifting cultivation. Two instances of the importance of sweet potato in nonswidden contexts may be quoted. The Kakoli of the Kaugel Valley in the western Highlands of New Guinea occupy land rising from the river at 7,200 to 8,500 feet above sea level. Bowers (1965) in her fieldwork here has described the agricultural system in which swiddening and "quasi-permanent" mounded field techniques are employed in the low-flat and high-sloping areas of occupation. The sweet potato is the main staple in these cultivations, so even at these high altitudes where varieties appear to be selected for cold resistance, there is variability of topography which allows for variability of plant growth type. Although some varieties are categorized by Kaugel cultivators as "never planted" or "suited to" mountain gardens (Bowers, personal communication), no close correspondence between type and topography has been found. However, it may well be that two varieties collected by Bowers as introduced, and the only ones in the area of plant type 2, have been successful because of the comparatively recent adoption of the large-mound technique and its extension into mountain planting methods.

In the Mountain Province of Luzon in the Philippines, a common utilization of the permanent rice terraces among the Bontoc people is the alternation of wet-season rice with dry-season sweet potato, mounded in various patterns. Around this rotational field agriculture there is extensive slope swiddening in which sweet potato is again a main plant component. The direction of selection that was imposed by the earliest planting of sweet potato in swiddens may well have been diverted by the subsequent development of alternating cultivation practices. These appear to have spread, at least to some parts of neighboring Ifugao.

The temporal and spatial aspects of social determinants of specific forms of agriculture as outlined by Conklin (1961) are seen as fluctuating forces in selection. It is posited, however, that although the effect of increased populations is increased scope for selection, the often concomitant diversification of the role of a given plant in the agricultural system has a diffuse effect on the objectives of selection. The contrast with natural selection and directive evolution, stimulated by the action of man, is seen in the work of Kettlewell on polymorphism and industrial melanism in moths, summarized by Ford (1964).

The association of animal husbandry, particularly that of pigs, with sweet potato in agricultural systems is notable in the Pacific tropical region. Pospisil (1963) in his Kapaukuan studies suggests that four kilograms of sweet potato are fed per pig each day in addition to its own foraging and periodic grazing of harvested gardens. While pig husbandry in Melanesia may constitute an economic advantage by utilizing roots not edible to man (Vayda et al., 1960), large pig populations demand that crops be increased above human requirements. The pioneer investigations of R. and S. Bulmer (1964) of stratified archaeological rock shelter sites indicate fairly early occurrence of the pig in an "almost certainly agricultural phase" in the New Guinea Highlands. The exploration of settlement and agricultural sites should reveal changes in pig populations that may best indicate when sweet potato cultivation reached significant proportions in the sequence of highland agricultural development (Watson, 1965). The present survival of such plants as yam (Meggitt, 1958), taro, and *Pueraria* (Watson, 1964) at altitudes above 5,000 feet whose effect on these plants is generally an increase in time required for maturity after planting, implies a degree of sedentary agriculture with the development of adaptive cultivation techniques prior to sweet potato introduction. In the Philippine mountains, where there is less archaeological information, the pig has strong economic and ritual associations, and it may be suggested that a similar mutual, quantitative effect occurred after sweet potato introduction, in a contrastive agricultural sequence.

The selective advantage of the intermediate plant growth types in slope cultivation is extended to their use for pig fodder because of their branching stems and greater quantities of herbage. The regular harvesting of sweet potato greens for controlled feeding of pigs has become a feature of agriculture in many areas of Southeast Asia and New Guinea.

The adaptation of the sweet potato has not entailed the development of technologies markedly different from those applied to earlier Pacific subsistence plants. Cultivation and harvest techniques and the tools concerned did not require the modifications that would be entailed by the adoption of an annual grain plant as a staple starch producer. One characteristic of grain culture widely used in Melanesia in relation to harvested yams is storage (e.g. Malinowski, 1935). No general areal use of such a technique or its modification has been recorded for sweet potato, but two localized examples, found in the Kaugel Valley, western New Guinea Highlands and in Bontoc, Luzon, must be added to the New Zealand Maori example (Yen, 1961). During a field visit in the Kaugel Valley, an informant explained that small holes tunneled into a bank near a Kakoli house were places for storing sweet potato roots for consumption when visitors were expected. The holes, closed with turf plugs, were large enough to hold about twenty pounds of roots each. This technique was said to have originated in another part of the valley. A more widespread measure was to fill with roots the pits left in the large mounds after the harvest (Bowers, 1965) and to recover them with soil.

The Bontocs have adapted their wooden rice-storage structures (*alaŋ*) for the storage of sweet potato roots grown in the dry-season terrace cultivations, since the roots must be harvested completely to allow for succeeding rice crops. Thus rotation is practiced not only in terraced fields but also in the store houses. The neighboring Ifugao, who practice terrace cultivation of sweet potato to a lesser extent, have not adopted this practice.

There are two motivations for storage in these examples: a minor social adjustment of short duration and one of longer term to fit into an agricultural practice. While these differ from the interpretation for New Zealand of response to a cool and unfavorable environment, there are some features in common. In all three, the *sealing* of material for effective storage is recognized, and the Maori and Bontoc examples have converted a virtually perennial plant into an agricultural annual.

The effects of such practice on plant selection can only be extrapolated, for, in the example of the nonswidden, discontinuous type of harvest of the Bontoc, where faster-maturing types and perhaps monovarietal plantings may be more desirable, varieties are mixed and common to both swidden and terrace portions of the agricultural system. The negative impetus to selection of successful coping with the environment by technical means might be indicated by the fact that the four Maori varieties are not cold-resistant. Apart from speculation that the original founding stock may have narrowly represented the species genetically, and the opportunities for variation were probably less (Yen, 1963b), the plant at its ecological limit may not have produced any significant transformations by selection. In the New Guinea Highlands, however, the selection for cold resistance may have contributed more so far than agricultural adjustments to the species' survival. The sequence of agricultural development that might have produced more effective measures to ensure internal stability of food supplies is being diverted along other pathways.

CONCLUSIONS

While the vegetative reproduction of the sweet potato plant confers a conservative element on evolutionary progress, the alternative outbreeding method produces variability which reflects the heterozygous nature of the species. The vegetative propagation of new seedling variations, prompted by the horticultural instinct of preservation of novelty, endues material for selective adaptation to diverse environments, natural and man-influenced. The scope for such selection, however, is dependent on the genotype of the founder stocks, and the small differences in Pacific populations could be attributed solely to the random nature of introductions from American sources. The formation of recognizable phenotypic races, expected from the processes of random genetic drift or the directive selection of mutations or recombinants, may have been impeded merely by the combined function of shallow time-depth and the emphasis on vegetal plant reproduction. However, the preservation of variability in populations may have been further assisted by the summed effects of man's activities—reintroduction of the species, the differing objectives of selection in agricultural adaptation sequences in both space and time, modal selection in one important character, the "taxonomic" rather than "functional" roles of many of the visually distinguishable plant characters, and the relative success of external agricultural measures in plant adaptation.

With the exception of coconut, the traditional staple crop plants in Pacific subsistence patterns are vegetatively reproduced (Barrau, 1958, 1961) and are widely distributed in the Malaysian region (Burkill, 1935). Simmonds (1962) has outlined some of the characters in the banana which have been selected for by man, but neither in *Musa* nor the other plants have extensive intraspecific studies been made. Such studies may not prove to be quite the enigmatic proposition that the sweet potato seems to be, for the other species generally can be assumed to have had a considerably greater depth of time in which internal and external adaptations could be made. In some species, at least, the lack of interest of Europeans in transferring them eliminates the pervading suspicion of the variation observed from any area. As botanical markers there are some further advantages, for origin areas and directions of transfer, with their broad correspondence to movements of culture and language, may well give closer correlates than the sweet potato has done. The occurrence of wild relatives, at least in the western areas of the Pacific, may present opportunities for discovering the trends in evolution, for example by introgression, not found in the sweet potato. While basic cytogenetic information is still lacking in many species, sexual reproduction as an alternative to asexual is known, e.g. in taro and yam (Barrau, 1965). Moreover, in some of the main crop plants there are definitions of species based on cytology in bananas (Simmonds, 1962) and indications from the work on *Dioscorea* (Martin and Ortiz, 1963), especially from Africa and Asia, that similar differentiation of basic chromosome numbers and polyploidy may be a productive avenue for investigation of Pacific populations of the species. Recent chromosome counts on taro (Yen and Wheeler, MS.) indicate that in at least this character there has been a decline in variability from India toward the eastern Pacific.

The further detailed study of current agricultural situations, together with increasing activity of archaeologists in all Pacific regions, will not only provide the subsistence backgrounds for the diversity of social phenomena and their development but will also indicate the stimulus and mechanisms by which agricultural development, in its fullest sense including plant adaptation, has been achieved.

REFERENCES

Barrau, Jacques, 1957. L'Enigme de la patate douce en Oceanie. *Etudes d'Outre-Mer,* *40*(3): 83–87.

——, 1958. Subsistence agriculture in Melanesia. *B. P. Bishop Mus. Bull.,* 219, Honolulu.

——, 1961. Subsistence agriculture in Polynesia and Micronesia. *B. P. Bishop Mus. Bull.,* 223, Honolulu.

——, 1965. L'Humide et le sec. *J. Polynes. Soc., 74*(3): 329–46.

Berridge, W. C., 1913. Kumeras, or sweet potato. *New Zealand J. Agric., 7:* 415–19.

Best, Elsdon, 1925. Maori agriculture. *Dominion Mus. Bull.,* 9, Wellington.

Bowers, Nancy, 1965. "Agricultural practices and successional vegetation in the Upper Kaugel Valley, Western Highlands, Australian New Guinea." Paper read to Highland New Guinea Symposium, Northwest Anthropological Conf., Washington.

Brookfield, H. C., 1962. Local study and comparative method: An example from New Guinea. *Ann. Assoc. Am. Geographers, 52*(3): 242–54.

Brown, F. B. H., 1935. Flora of Southeastern Polynesia III. Dicotyledons. *B. P. Bishop Mus. Bull.,* 130, Honolulu.

Bulmer, Ralph, 1965. Beliefs concerning the propagation of new varieties of sweet potato in two New Guinea Highlands societies. *J. Polynes. Soc. 74*(2): 237–41.

——, 1966. Birds as possible agents in the propagation and dispersal of the sweet potato. *Emu, 65* (3): 165–182.

Bulmer, Susan, and Ralph Bulmer, 1964. The prehistory of the Australian New Guinea Highlands. *Am. Anthropologist, 66*(4), pt. 2, J. B. Watson, ed.

Burkill, I. H., 1935. *A Dictionary of the Economic Products of the Malay Peninsula,* 2 vols. Crown Agents for Colonies, London.

Conklin, Harold C., 1957. *Hanunóo Agriculture.* FAO Forestry Development, Paper 12, Rome.

——, 1961. The study of shifting cultivation. *Curr. Anthropol., 2*(1): 27–61.

——, 1963. The Oceanian-African hypotheses and the sweet potato. In *Plants and the Migrations of Pacific Peoples,* J. Barrau, ed. Bishop Mus. Press, Honolulu.

——, 1967. Some aspects of ethnographic research in Ifugao. *Trans. N.Y. Acad. Sci.,* 30(1).

Curnow, R. N., 1964. The effect of continued selection of phenotypic intermediates on gene frequency. *Genet. Res., 5:* 341–53.

Damm, Hans, 1961. Die Sübkartoffel (Batate) in Leben der Völker Neuguineas. *Z. Ethnol. 86*(2): 208–23.

Dixon, R. B., 1932. The problem of the sweet potato in Polynesia. *Amer. Anthropologist 34:* 40–66.

Dobzhansky, Theodosius, 1963. Biological evolution in island populations. *Man's Place in the Island Ecosystem,* F. R. Fosberg, ed. Bishop Mus. Press, Honolulu.

Ford, E. B., 1964. *Ecological Genetics.* Methuen, London.

Grant, Verne, 1956. The influence of breeding habit on the outcome of natural hybridisation in plants. *Am. Naturalist, 90*(854): 319–22.

Guppy, H. B., 1896. "The Polynesians and their plant names." Paper read to Victoria Institute, London.

Gustafsson, A., 1947. Apomixis in higher plants, III. Biotype and species formation. *Lunds Univ. Arsskr., 43*(2): 183–371. Quoted by Grant, 1956.

Handy, E. S. C., 1940. *The Hawaiian Planter,* vol. 1. *B. P. Bishop Mus. Bull.,* 161, Honolulu.

Hayward, Herman E., 1938. *The Structure of Economic Plants.* Macmillan, New York.

Hernandez, T. P., and J. C. Miller, 1964. Further studies on incompatibility in the sweet potato. *Proc. Am. Soc. Hort. Sci., 85:* 426–29.

Hernandez, T. P., T. Hernandez, and J. C. Miller, 1964. Frequency of somatic mutations in several sweet potato varieties. *Proc. Am. Soc. Hort. Sci., 85:* 430–33.

Ho, Ping-ti, 1955. The introduction of american food plants into China. *Am. Anthropologist, 57:* 191–201.

Hollyman, K. J., 1959. Polynesian influence in New Caledonia: The linguistic aspect. *J. Polynes. Soc., 68*(4): 356–89.

House, H. D., 1908. The North American species of the genus *Ipomoea. Ann. N.Y. Acad. Sci., 18*(6): 181–263.

Jones, Alfred, 1965. Cytological observations and fertility measurements of sweet potato (*Ipomoea batatas* (L.) Lam.). *Proc. Am. Soc. Hortic. Sci., 86:* 527–37.

Kerr, George H., 1959. *Okinawa.* Tuttle, Tokyo.

Malinowski, Bronislaw, 1935. *Coral Islands and Their Magic.* Allen & Unwin, London.

Martin, Franklin W., 1965. Incompatibility in the sweet potato. A review. *Econ. Bot., 19*(4): 406–15.

Martin, Franklin W., and Sonia Ortiz, 1963. Chromosome numbers and behavior in some species of *Dioscorea. Cytologia, 28*(1): 96–101.

Mayr, E., 1942. *Systematics and the Origin of Species.* Columbia Univ. Press, New York.

Meggitt, M. J., 1958. The Enga of the New Guinea Highlands: Some preliminary observations. *Oceania, 28*(4): 253–330.

Melville, Herman, 1847. *Omoo.* Grove, New York.

Nishiyama, Ichizo, 1959. Collecting the sweet potato and its allied species in U.S.A. and Mexico. *Jap. J. Breeding, 9:* 73–78.

———, 1963. The origin of the sweet potato plant. In *Plants and the Migrations of Pacific Peoples,* J. Barrau, ed. Bishop Mus. Press, Honolulu.

Nishiyama, Ichizo, and T. Teramura, 1962. Mexican wild forms of sweet potato. *Econ. Bot., 16*(4): 304–14.

Ooststroom, S. J. van, 1954. Convolvulaceae. In *Flora Malesiana* v. 7, p. 4. Noordhoff-Kolff N. V., Djarkata.

Poole, C. F., 1955. *Sweet Potato Genetic Studies.* Univ. Hawaii Agric. Exper. Sta. Tech. Bull., 17.

Pospisil, Leopold., 1963. *Kapauku Papuan Economy.* Yale Univ. Publ. Anthropol., 67, New Haven.

Robbins, R. G., 1963. The Anthropogenic grasslands of New Guinea. *Proc. UNESCO Symposium on Humid Tropics Vegetation, Goroka, 1960.* Govt. Print, Canberra.

Serpenti, L. M., 1965. *Cultivators in the Swamps.* Van Gorcum, Assen.

Sharp, Andrew, 1960. *The Discovery of the Pacific Islands.* Oxford Univ. Press, Oxford.

Simmonds, N. W., 1962. *The Evolution of the Bananas.* Longmans, London.

Stebbins, G. Ledyard, 1950. *Variation and Evolution in Plants.* Oxford Univ. Press, London.

Steinbauer, C. E., 1935. Methods of scarifying sweet potato seed. *Proc. Am. Soc. Hortic. Sci., 35:* 606–08.

Thomas, William L., Jr., 1963. The variety of physical environments among Pacific islands. In *Man's Place in the Island Ecosystem*, F. R. Fosberg ed., Bishop Mus. Press, Honolulu.

Thompson, H. C., and J. G. Beattie, 1922. *Group Classification and Varietal Descriptions of American Varieties of Sweet Potatoes*. U.S. Dept. Agric. Bull., 1021.

Ting, Y. C., and A. E. Kehr, 1953. Meiotic studies in the sweet potato. *J. Hered.*, 44(5): 207–11.

Ting, Y. C., A. E. Kehr, and J. C. Miller, 1957. A cytological study of the sweet potato plant *Ipomoea batatas* (L.) Lam. and its related species. *Am. Naturalist, 91* (858): 197–203.

Tioutine, M. G. 1935. Breeding and selection of sweet potatoes. *J. Hered.*, 26(1): 3–10.

Uewada, T., 1965. On the rooting and tuberization from cut fresh of the root tuber of sweet potato. *Proc. Crop. Sci. Soc. Jap.*, 34(2): 109–13.

Vayda, A. P., A. Leeds, and D. B. Smith, 1960. *"The place of pigs in Melanesian subsistence."* Paper read to VIth Internatl. Congr. of Anthropological and Ethnological Sciences, Paris.

Walker, J. T., 1964. Modal selection in upland cotton. *Heredity, 19*(4): 559–83.

Wang, Hsia, 1964. A study on the self- and cross-incompatibilities in the sweet potato in Taiwan (Formosa). *Proc. Am. Soc. Hort. Sci., 84*: 424–30.

Watson, James B. 1964. A Previously unreported root crop from the New Guinea Highlands. *Ethnology, 3*(1): 1–5.

———, 1965. The significance of a recent ecological change in the Central Highlands of New Guinea. *J. Polynes. Soc., 74*(4): 438–50.

Wheeler, Jocelyn M., and D. E. Yen. Unpublished data on sweet potato cytology.

Wright, Sewall, 1931. Evolution in Mendelian populations. *Genetics, 16*: 97–159.

Yen, D. E., 1960. The sweet potato in the pacific: The propagation of the plant in relation to its distribution. *J. Polynes. Soc., 69*(4): 368–75.

———, 1961. The adaptation of the sweet potato by the New Zealand Maori. *J. Polynes. Soc., 70*(3): 338–48.

———, 1963a. Sweet potato variation and its relation to human migration in the Pacific. In *Plants and the Migrations of Pacific Peoples*, J. Barrau, ed. Bishop Mus. Press, Honolulu.

———, 1963b. The New Zealand Kumara or sweet potato. *Econ. Bot., 17*(1): 31–45.

———, MS. *"The sweet potato in the Pacific."*

Yen, D. E., and J. M. Wheeler, Ms. "Introduction of taro into the Pacific: Indications of the chromosome numbers."

Harold C. Brookfield

16. NEW DIRECTIONS IN THE STUDY
OF AGRICULTURAL SYSTEMS
IN TROPICAL AREAS

In a symposium on ethnobotany, the contribution of a human geographer can take two forms. He can discuss the direct relations of his own field of study with cultivated plants. These would include the deductive and inductive reasoning on the migration of cultivated plants and their associated cultivation techniques that has been well developed in this country, as well as the detailed inquiries into plant utilization among primitive and peasant societies that have developed especially in the western Pacific. Alternatively, he can try to put the study of cultivated plants into the context of wider thinking in his own and related disciplines. His task would then be to discuss the field of agrarian geography—that is, the study of agriculture not only in relation to its use and manipulation of natural resources but also to land tenure, holding, and allocation, and to the social, economic, and political systems within which farming is carried on. I adopt the latter approach in this paper. Inevitably, such discussion cannot be bounded within the contributions of geographers, for anthropologists have worked in this field more extensively than we have, if with a somewhat different viewpoint. Some preliminary discussion of recent changes in both geography and anthropology may help explain this situation.

CULTURAL ECOLOGY, GEOGRAPHY, AND ANTHROPOLOGY

The convergence of interests between human geographers and social and cultural anthropologists over a wide field of common ground in their studies of tropical regions is a phenomenon mainly of the last decade. In geography there has been a growing awareness of social and cultural variables in their effect on the location and distribution of phenomena; in anthropology, observations which were once interpreted almost exclusively in terms of kinship, social organization, and customary law are now being thought of as reflecting the interplay of both social and natural factors. Cultural geographers and cultural anthropologists have drawn on each others' material for decades, especially in the United States. Some anthropologists, Gluckman for example (1941), rested their interpretation of particular social systems on environmental factors as far back as 1941. But for long, members of these two disciplines tended to hold each other at arm's length, each finding the use made by the other of his own material thoroughly unsatisfactory; their scale of work was quite different, and while the one felt himself to be concerned with people, the other felt sure that his primary concern was with land (Spate, 1953, p. 22). The change has come about largely through what one might describe as the "ecological revolution" occurring simultaneously in both disciplines. Conklin (1954) was perhaps the first to outline the new approach, which he elaborated in his study of Hanunóo agriculture on Mindoro, published in 1957. Bringing together social, cultural, demographic, agronomic, climatological, botanical, and zoological considerations, he opened up what he called the "ethnoecological approach," which soon came to be known, following Steward (1955) as "cultural ecology." In an important paper, Frake distinguished between the social system as "a network among persons of a social community" and the ecological system as "the network of the relationships between man, the other organisms of his biotic community, and the constituents of his physical environment." He went on to point out that "in both cases the net is woven of cultural threads, and the two networks are, of course, interwoven at many points" (Frake, 1962, p. 54). The year before Frake's paper appeared, Fosberg called together at the Pacific Science Congress his symposium on "Man's Place in the Island Ecosystem" in which he redefined the concept of the ecosystem as "a functioning, interacting system composed of one or more living organisms and their effective environment, both physical and biological" (Fosberg, 1963, p. 2). The participants of the symposium included five geographers and four anthropologists. By this time there had already been completed a number of works in which anthropologists and geographers had studied in collaboration, with varying success, and found, as two of us put it: "Our techniques are neither difficult nor complex: it is only their use in conjunction that is new. The manner in which the subsistence cultivators of the world [and we could have omitted the word subsistence] evaluate, use and allocate their land resources is . . . a matter of interest to both our disciplines. Further work in this field by anthropologists and geographers, together or separately, could do much to illuminate the relationship of land, its use, and social organization" (Brookfield and Brown 1963, p. 178).

Among human geographers, ennui with the long-standing and fruitless dispute whether the subject is concerned with man–land relationships, with man's effect on nature, or with the "areal differentiation" of phenomena on the earth's surface, led to an eager reception for Ackerman's proposition (1963) that our overriding concern is with the analysis of man–environment systems. It was argued that by study of the whole system evolved by man for the use of the earth, by concern with *how* patterns are formed, regions evolved, and phenomena located, we should escape the sterility of simple comparison or related patterns of areal differentiation. In the last few years a plethora of papers has appeared in our journals arguing that the ecosystem concept, by its monistic nature, "brings together environment, man, and the plant and animal worlds within a single framework" (Stoddart, 1965, p. 243). We still lack a single successful piece of work in *human* geography conceived and carried out entirely within such a framework, but in fact many of us have for some time been concerned with explaining the mechanisms by which distributions evolve, with the question How? rather than with the traditional questions Where? and Why? Much of this modern work, most especially in economic geography, is more properly described as locational analysis than as the study of man–environment systems. However, those of us who have worked away from sources of statistical data among the world's unlettered and largely unnumbered cultivators have found our most useful method is inquiry into the nature of whole systems, from the natural environment through its manipulation to the distribution of wholly man-generated phenomena such as social and political groupings (Blaut, 1959; Brookfield, 1964). Often we have found it necessary to work in depth at the level of the small community, that is, at the same level that seems most appropriate to the anthropologist. And in such work we have found reason to heed Conklin's precept (1957, p. 155) that "the first step should be the analysis of the structure and content of the particular agricultural systems involved." It is in this work that we, like the anthropologists, have become closely linked with the ethnobotanists.

This is the context in which this paper is written, and its main concern will be with recent work among agricultural peoples carried out both by geographers and anthropologists, and with the manner in which an analysis, or appreciation, of the man–environment system is leading to fruitful new lines of thought. Most of the work referred to has been carried out among people who traditionally, and generally also by Conklin's minimal definition,[1] would be described as shifting cultivators. Hence I propose to start by obeying Conklin's precept cited above, to "analyse the structure and content of the system," and will briefly return to the taxonomic or typonomic problem that has troubled writers on shifting cultivation for more than twenty years: How is this system to be defined and described?

TYPONOMY OF CULTIVATION SYSTEMS

Shifting, or swidden, cultivation as an ideal type is well enough understood. People clear a patch of bush by cutting and burning, plant a crop in the clearing, which is used for one year, perhaps two, and then relinquished to a wild fallow during which fertility is restored. Geertz (1963, p. 15–28) has described the system in ecological terms in relation to the tropical forest it replaces. Both are highly diverse systems, in which matter and energy pass rapidly through a plant-to-plant cycling system among the vegetation components and the surface soil. In swidden agriculture, the system that replaces the tropical forest is, like the forest,

---

1. "Any continuing agricultural system in which impermanent clearings are cropped for shorter periods in years than they are fallowed" (Conklin, 1961, p. 27).

highly generalized; ecological productivity is lower, but the yield to man is increased. Burning, to channel to the surface soil nutrients that are locked up in plants, is normally the crucial factor in determining the productivity of the swidden; indeed in one system described by West (1957) in an overwet area of western Colombia, seed is sown broadcast in the undergrowth which is then slashed without burning so that the crop grows directly in the mulch.

But all land use is, as Simmons has put it (1966, p. 63) the "manipulation of ecosystems to reach a desired end." Many land-rotational systems which employ natural regeneration to restore the nutrient supply also employ a very wide range of other means to create and maintain a specialized ecosystem for the cultivation of food plants. Even in some very simple systems, the ground is holed deeply for reception of the plant, and the resources of the subsoil are thereby tapped. To grow yams, the Abelam of northern New Guinea depend so much on the soil that the garden is swept clean before planting, and the sweepings, "containing much ash, are then put behind logs or around stumps or even thrown over the garden fence" (Lea, 1964, p. 83). In this and many similar systems, restoration of the nutrient supply may depend as much on the speedy renewal of tropical soils under rapid weathering on steep slopes as on the fallow cover, provided that erosion is not excessive. Other peoples control the fallow cover: in the New Guinea Highlands, casuarina seedlings are widely planted in gardens about to be left fallow (Brookfield, 1962), and similar practices are reported from Timor (Ormeling, 1956). Casuarinas protect the soil, add humus, shade out undesirable grasses, and also fix atmospheric nitrogen. The Sérères of West Africa propagate the Acacia *Faidherbia alba* through seeding by cattle; this tree sheds its leaves at the beginning of the rains, thus permitting cropping, but shades the soil during the dry season and at the same time provides cattle fodder (Baer, 1965). Similar practices, in which the fallow as well as the cultivation forms a "tame" rather than a "wild" ecosystem, are not uncommon.

Many land-rotational agriculturalists practice radical transformations of the environment, including ridging, tilling, mounding, ditch draining, and even terracing. The extensive irrigated taro terraces of New Caledonia were cultivated on a rotational cycle, including only one year of cropping to three or more of fallow (Barrau, 1956, p. 80). In Chimbu, one of the most densely peopled areas of the New Guinea Highlands, with densities rising locally to as much as 500 persons per square mile, most land is certainly left fallow for longer than it is cultivated. Yet the agricultural system here includes field drainage, tillage, some mulching, a planted fallow cover, some elements of crop rotation and crop-livestock rotation, and the formation of terracettes on steep slopes to control soil creep (Brookfield and Brown, 1963). This is open-field agriculture creating a tame ecosystem totally different from that of the wild vegetation, which has been entirely removed. In the Baliem Valley of West Irian, land is used rotationally with seemingly short cultivation periods, but here natural swamps have been reclaimed by deep ditching and high ridging, combined with extensive, but as yet unstudied, systems of district-wide drainage (field observation; and Veldkamp, 1958). Crops are planted in spoil thrown from the ditches onto the ridges, after clearing of a reedy fallow cover.

Faced with systems such as this, Brown and I questioned the continuing utility of the generalization that is "shifting agriculture." We suggested that "all these techniques found in association with land-rotational agriculture in various parts of the world can be grouped into erosion control, water control, and manurial or soil-nutrient control . . . we prefer to abandon attempts to refine an outworn classification and concentrate attention on the efficiency of the erosion, water and soil-nutrient control measures applied in any particular area. We would assess agriculture in any given locality from the point of view of its efficiency in producing food without damage to the resources available to future generations on the same land" (Brookfield and Brown 1963, p. 166–67). What we were asking for, in effect, was that the use of the crop–fallow time ratio as a single criterion be discontinued and that in its place we should move toward an *appreciation* of agricultural systems, based on their success in sustaining a maximum yield and ensuring that nutrients are not taken out of the ecosystem faster than they can be replaced.

This was a lot to ask. While I would sustain my view of 1963 that the exclusive use of the crop–fallow time ratio yields only a classification that contains more diversity within than between classes, I would now be less negative than I was then toward the problem of typonomy. Perhaps we should restrict the terms "swidden" and "shifting" cultivation to those relatively few systems in which there is no disturbance below the surface soil, and which hence operate mainly or almost entirely on a direct plant-to-plant cycling ecosystem? For the large remainder of *all* agriculture, the crop–fallow time ratio should then become a subsidiary, rather than the primary, criterion.

Tentatively, I would suggest that the primary description of agricultural systems should be based first on essentially agronomic considerations of farming technique and management, and second on the type of crop and crop combination. It is essential to what I say that this description be applied not to a whole people or region but to a particular tract of land used in a particular way. Soil management, rotational practices, water control, direct nutrient control, and erosion control or site-conservation measures are categories into which most technological variations could be placed.

Within *soil management* might be distinguished systems employing only partial tillage (e.g. holing or mounding of individual plants) and those in which the whole surface is disturbed by the transposition, by whatever means, of topsoil and subsoil. Spade-, hoe-, and plough-culture are means, varying in labor requirement, by which the effect is achieved. Within *rotational practices* there is greater basic variety, from no rotation of any kind (monoculture) at one extreme, to crop period separated by wild fallow at the other. Between are systems employing continuous cropping with regular rotation of crops, continuous cropping with changing crops in no regular rotation, crop and livestock rotations, crop periods separated by managed fallow, and also systems employing interculture. Within *water control* measures are systems with no water control, with field drainage, regional drainage, ponding of rainwater, and irrigation; flood-farming is a special type. *Direct nutrient control* measures are less easy to group. They include principally use of fire and its absence, mulching and manuring; other indirect methods are mostly consequential on rotation, soil management, water control, and the type of crop. Also partially distinct are *erosion control* measures, designed for the conservation of the site. Within this group, separation may be made between those systems with no such measures other than those elsewhere included in the methods of management, and those with special measures ranging from modifications of management—such as tilling on the contour—to protection by means of banks or fences, intercepting drains and terracettes, and terracing.

Cross-cutting and amplifying the information on a particular system derived from description on such lines as these is classification of the type of crop and crop combination. Here I follow the Polish Land Utilization Survey, which distinguishes among intensive crops, structure-forming crops, and exhaustive crops, each with distinctive agronomic requirements. As Kostrowicki puts it (1965, p. 15), their system is based on:

> agronomic foundations, that is on differences between particular crops in as far as their requirements are concerned with regard to the habitat, ways and means of cultivation and taking care, their part played in crop rotation and particularly the part they play as fore-crops, and last but not least—on the volume of input (intensity). This system of grouping divides crops into three sections: (1) intensifying or intensive crops, (2) structure forming or structure building crops and (3) a group which can be termed as exhaustive, extractive or soil depleting crops. In agreement with the premises accepted within the group of intensifying crops were included plants calling for greater input of labour and means, demanding more careful land cultivation and manuring so that they enrich the site and are beneficent for subsequent crops. The structure forming plants do not necessitate considerable inputs but owing to their provision of nitrogen into the soil they manage to keep its crumb structure and therefore are also a welcome fore-crop. The third group are the soil exhausting or depleting plants, the cultivation of which leaves soil in a state which calls for special action or a proper rotation in order to restore its fertility, otherwise soil tends to become degraded.

Kostrowicki goes on to observe that some crops change their class according to the way they are managed; this caveat applies with much greater force in tropical farming where some root crops and leguminous crops fall into the exhaustive class for a variety of reasons, including exposure of bare ground to sun, wind, and rain, and in some cases by taking time from a fallow period when nutrients would otherwise be directly restored. Such is the case, for example, with ground nuts in the savanna regions of West Africa. Perennial crops, which are mainly tree crops, permanent improved pasture, and permanent unimproved grazing, are further and separate categories. Classification of land-using crop and crop combinations needs care, but it would greatly improve understanding of agricultural systems and would also reflect the significance of ecological differences between different climatic, soil, and vegetational zones. Comparative use of technological and crop bases of classification would then make possible more meaningful use of parameters such as the crop–fallow time ratio; yield in terms of calories, grain equivalents, or other standard unit; and also intensity, in its true meaning of the number of cost inputs that are applied up to the economic margin.

To proceed along these descriptive lines would not immediately yield any simple system of classification, though it might in time lead to the recognition of a number of basic types of farming. It would, however, greatly facilitate both cross-cultural comparison and quantification. I do not imagine that the very tentative proposals outlined above would be acceptable in detail, and certainly they do not constitute a system of classification. The subjective element remains. What I have said is geared primarily to subsistence and peasant farming and would be hard to adapt to industrial systems; perhaps the structural organization of farming, and the proportion of the output that is consumed on-farm (or within the community) and off-farm (entering the market), should be overriding primary classifications of agricultural types. The Commission on Agricultural Typology of the International Geographical Union is considering these problems, and their first report reveals little or no agreement (International Geographical Union, 1966).

Audacious though it may seem to say so in the face of an immense mass of literature, I feel that an approach based on precise description of what is found in any agricultural system would better enable us to understand agriculture as the manipulation of ecosystems than would continued use of the shifting cultivation–permanent cultivation dichotomy. Barrau's threefold division of systems into "shifting cultivation," "long fallow cultivation," and "permanent cultivation" is more sensitive but still can yield more variety within than between classes. The basis of my argument is that crop–fallow time ratio is not the most significant criterion to use in describing a wide range of tropical farming types. In particular, an approach based on orderly description would avoid the evolutionary implications of transition from a lower, shifting, form toward a higher, permanent, form, which I submit should be set aside for want of evidence at this stage. While it is almost certainly true that the latter has in fact evolved from the former, it does not follow that a similar evolution can be traced in all areas: what is true of the whole is not necessarily true of the parts. In describing agriculture as we find it in any area, it can be positively misleading to classify systems along some sort of time-dependent continuum, especially when we often find a variety of systems currently in use on adjacent sites, by the same people.

It seems to me that we need a fresh start. I agree with Simmons (1966, p. 67) that in land-use studies the main task for research at present "seems to be the evolution of a workable union of economics and ecology which would combine the intelligent manipulation of ecosystems and a determination of their carrying capacity (that is, how much they can be cropped, essentially by and for man) with the analytical knowledge imparted by such techniques of economics as cost-benefit analysis." To do this, and provide the necessary quantified data for comparison, we must first evolve a typonomy of agricultural systems that can be discussed simultaneously in ecological and economic terms, including in the latter especially considerations of labor and capital input. Feasibility of cross-classification between intensity of method and type of crop or between land and capital and labor input, is a main object of the proposal outlined above. The necessity for such cross-classification and correlation may become more apparent as I go forward

SOME ASPECTS OF MEASUREMENT

Hand in hand with the ecological revolution in anthropology and geography has gone the quantifying revolution, in which economic geographers especially have played a leading part. From the simple propositions of central place theory and the work of location economists has evolved an elaborate set of constructs for network analysis, location and regional analysis, and a new appreciation of the importance of distance in the location of human activity. To agrarian and other cultural geographers much of this revolution seemed at first irrelevant, but it had its impact in that descriptive and qualitative statements increasingly failed to satisfy, and the task of measurement has absorbed the time and energies of an ever-growing number of field workers. In the more directly agronomic and ecological aspects of the study of tropical agriculture, measurement has received a major impetus from the work of Popenoe (1959), and the comprehensive survey by Nye and Greenland (1960), who brought together succinctly the whole body of data on the responses of soil to land-rotational agriculture as it stood at the end of the 1950s. Some recent work has thrown doubt on the concept of successional stages, at least insofar as they apply to the floristic composition of the successional vegetation, and on some other tenets of belief about the relationship of soil characteristics to successional vegetation (M. G. Kellman, personal communication), but this work has yet to be fully reported.

An early application of measurement to peasant agricultural systems was that of Allan, who derived a simple formula for the calculation of population capacity, using the acreage under cultivation per head, a "cultivation factor" which represents under any system the multiple in years of this figure required to complete the cycle, and the percentage of each land type within a given territory that is cultivable (Allan, 1949). The formula is simple, but the acquisition of data is not. Others have independently developed similar formulae, and I have used Allan's system with some refinements to measure not absolute population capacity but the effective capacity under a given farming system, with given appreciation of natural resources (Brookfield and Brown 1963, p. 108–22). Allan (1965) has since modified his own system and applied it to a range of African areas to show the scale of the African problem of rising population pressure on resources. Much could be said on this subject, but I must refrain from doing so at this point.

Far more precise data on the crop–fallow time ratio are now available for a large number of societies than were available a few years ago, even though the difficulty remains of collecting reliable information from informants with little sense of time measurement, and one is sometimes drawn to suspect that investigators are trying to measure a "cultivation cycle" where no such regularity exists. By repeated surveys over eight years in Chimbu, New Guinea, I had originally hoped to obtain precise data to substantiate or deny the 'early information on the cultivation cycle which I used as the basis for calculations in Brookfield and Brown (1963). However, no regular cycles have emerged and, furthermore, the agriculture of these people has been more and more changed as a result of the development of cash-cropping; so I have found myself studying not a traditional system but an agricultural revolution.

Through the same growth of measurement we are also getting better data on the area of land under cultivation per head in a whole range of agricultural systems. Allan (1965) has assembled such data for a large part of Africa. In the Pacific area modern work has in large measure confirmed the guesstimates quoted by Barrau (1958), who suggested that these root-crop agriculturalists used between 0.15 and 0.35 acre per head, in different areas. Some lower figures have been obtained, as low as 0.1 acre in some localities, and a few much higher figures. What is particularly interesting, and at present somewhat puzzling, is the growing realization that in a range of communities the acreage under cultivation per head varies within quite wide limits from year to year. This links up with the result of yield studies which show an unexplained surplus of production over consumption of food. It has been estimated for New Guinea from a small sample that over the whole country 11 pounds of food are produced per person per day (Bureau of Statistics 1963, p. 15), and this result receives confirmation from some local studies. With generous allowance made for underestimation of consumption, Lea (1964, p. 136) found an average daily surplus of 1.3 pounds of yams in a village where severe food shortages are said to occur. Variations in the size of an omnivorous livestock population, such as pigs, may be correlated with variations in the surplus, and so also may variations in the scale of ceremonial activity. But the data through which such variations may be explored scarcely exist, since from all but a few localities observations of acreage, yield, and consumption are made only at one, two, or at most three widely separated points in time.

The problem of yield determination is particularly difficult where crops are lifted from a garden plot over time, rather than in a single harvest. This is the case with most Pacific root-crop farmers, and with mixed gardens everywhere. Some studies have relied on informants bringing their crop to be weighed after lifting, instead of on sample liftings of whole plots, beds, or mounds. One of the most interesting of recent attempts is that of Lea, who was concerned to establish differences and similarities between two yam-growing communities in the Sepik district of New Guinea, which differed radically in population density, in the efficiency of cultivation and in the ecological equilibrium of the village territories. To test a hypothesis that yields per hole were in fact lower in village A than in village

B, it was necessary to weigh nearly 2,000 individual yams as soon as possible after these were lifted in the normal way for subsistence purposes, the weighings being dispersed as widely as possible among garden blocks in each village, and among distinguishable named varieties, of which 32 were included. Testing variance within and between varieties and villages, Lea found a significant difference between yields in the two villages, but this was not true of all varieties. He found a complex picture, with "variety, environment and agricultural techniques, seen as independent variables. While it is possible, for example, to compare the yield of any given variety grown by the same technique in two environments, or of two varieties grown by the same technique in the same environment, it is impossible to make any generalized statement . . . that does not need to be hedged around with qualifications regarding the other variables." (Lea 1964, p. 101–07 and 173–77; quotation at p. 107.)

These last remarks have been designed to outline some of the problems of measurement rather than to proclaim results. Often there is even the basic problem that gardens must be mapped de novo, population counted and located, and consumption and production measured, all from scratch, and usually on shoestring funds. Air photography has been found useful as an aid in field mapping by a number of workers, but photographs taken from high altitude rarely provide sufficient definition, even when enlarged. Provided there exists some triangulated base, a tolerable "do-it-yourself" job can be done by using war-surplus cameras either slung outboard from light aircraft, or, better, mounted on a rigid frame which will ensure a closer approximation to vertical photography. Runs taken from between 1,500 feet and 2,000 feet above ground level with such equipment have provided data on settlement and land-use distribution in a number of surveys far more cheaply and accurately than could be obtained by field-survey methods on the ground.

It is, of course, possible to do much more with air photography than this. Improved lenses and high resolution film make possible photographs taken from low and medium altitudes on which individual plants can be identified and counted. Use of true-color film is expensive, but its value in precise studies of tropical agriculture needs no elaboration, and it awaits experimentation by those fortunate enough to be able to lay hands on the necessary funds. By means of film sensitive to light of particular wavelengths, such as infrared film, minus-blue color film, and camouflage detection film, it is possible more readily to isolate particular crops and trees, crops at different stages of growth, soil disturbance, and some water conditions, though much experimental work is required before such tools can become a useful aid in fieldwork. Such methods will not replace, but rather will greatly enhance the work of the ground observer.

LANDHOLDING AND SOCIETY

Improvements in the quality of data are valuable in themselves, but their real significance lies in relation to other, and more theoretical, developments. The manner in which the "network among persons" is related to the "network of the relationships between man . . . and his physical environment" (Frake 1962, p. 54) has been explored in several interesting ways.

In 1961 Leach (p. 300–01, 305) showed how the continuity of the small Ceylon dry-zone community of Pul Eliya, a community that lacks any obvious kind of ongoing corporation, is not the society but the place—

> the village tank, the *gamgoda* area, the Old Field with its complex arrangement of [shares in tank water]. For . . . technical reasons . . . the arrangements of the Pul Eliya ground are difficult to alter. They are not immutable, but it is much simpler for the human beings to adapt themselves to the layout of the territory than to adapt the territory to the private whims of individual human beings. Thus . . . Pul Eliya is a society in which locality and not descent forms the basis of corporate grouping. . . . I want to insist that kinship systems have no "reality" at all except in relation to land and property. What the social anthropologist calls kinship structure is just a way of talking about property relations which can also be talked about in other ways.

These conclusions were reached by a meticulous examination of land tenure and water rights in the community; in essence the core of this community is the tank–field–village ecosystem, the relationships being demonstrated by precise and quantitative analysis. Biebuyck (1963, p. 2–15) had a little earlier expressed somewhat similar ideas in a review of African land tenure systems. He noted that the application of land rights may vary within the one society according to variations in the type of land use, and between societies with variations in population density and in agricultural systems, for Africa has a range of cultivation systems that runs parallel with but is wider than that we encounter in the Pacific. Recently, Colson has taken up the same line of argument (1966, p. 7). Noting that, while the rules of land tenure among the Valley Tonga of Zambia have remained the same during the past forty years, there are wide variations from time to time in the manner in which these rules are reflected in the actual pattern of landholding; this may be explained by the "interplay between a large number of social and natural factors, none of which are necessarily to be regarded as constants." Scudder (1962, p. 52–71) earlier pointed out the effect of a diminution of wild life, especially elephants, in permitting a spread of fields into the bush, with consequent variations in the application of the tenure rules.

Returning to the Pacific, Brown and I sought to interpret the Chimbu system of land tenure and of transfers of land (an important part of the system of reciprocity), in terms of their evaluation and varying use of land resources. A belted terrain with varied soils, plant cover, and "terrain climatology" (Geiger, 1965, p. 455) was so allocated through a process of land gift, new settlement, and conquest in minor warfare that, within a political federation comprising seventeen subgroups, each subgroup had access to parcels of land of varying types, including favored farmland, land used mainly for pig grazing, and land at different altitudes which were suited to different ranges of subsidiary crops (Brookfield and Brown,

1963). We found that the system of land transfers tended to perpetuate this distribution, and that some groups which were short of land had particular recourse to land loans and gifts from members of other better-off groups. Fixity of tenure, however, varied according to the type of land, and hence its intensity of use, rather than to land shortage. Meggitt, working among the Mae Enga, has argued that both fixity of tenure and rigid adherence to unilineal inheritance of land vary positively with population density (Meggitt, 1958, 1965). Chimbu data do not seem to support this argument, nor do data from some other Pacific societies, but Meggitt has gained support from data on a number of societal studies by anthropologists and also from the findings of Lea among the land-short Wosera (Lea, 1965, p. 198–99; 1966, p. 7). In order to resolve issues such as this, which have interesting theoretical implications, quantifiable data are required and are being accumulated.

The strip-like holdings on belted terrain, running up and down slope, which we found in Chimbu, are interestingly paralleled among the Kakoli of the Kaugel Valley (Bowers, 1965), and compare also with the wedge-shaped holdings running from the coast inland on small Pacific volcanic islands (Crocombe, 1964). Among the Kakoli and on small islands, more than among the Chimbu, different farming types are encountered in different ecological situations within a group territory, the different systems being interrelated. On the river flats at the bottom of her territorial strips, Bowers found what she called "quasi-permanent sweet potato mound fields," which are worked much as are many Chimbu gardens in the central belt: some plots seem almost continuously in use; others are rested haphazardly, with no notion of a regular rotation. In wet sites, she also found taro plots. In the same general location are "mixed vegetable gardens" with a definite cycle of cultivation and fallow; tillage is not practiced, but there is careful management of the fallow vegetation. Above this belt is a wide zone of *miscanthus* grassland, the main use for which is pig grazing, unimproved, but managed within fences. Above this belt, on the forest edge, is a zone of forest gardens, cut in the disturbed edge of the primary forest and prepared by slash-and-burn without tillage, except for a belt of sweet potato mounds made on the grassland edge to help keep out bush rats. The plot is recultivated after a fallow period of some years, this time being tilled and mounded, and goes on in this way through a number of crop–fallow rotation cycles. Ligneous vegetation is weeded out, so that the final result is an extension of the *miscanthus* grasslands.

JOHANN HEINRICH VON THÜNEN IN THE TROPICS

This kind of variable manipulation of the ecosystem for different purposes in different parts of a group territory or individual holding invites comparison with similar integrated methods of land-use management in other parts of the world, and with premodern European farming. Bowers provides only limited measurement data and does not discuss the spatial relationships of the different elements in Kakoli farming, though her material shows that almost all settlement is in the closely occupied belt at the bottom of each strip territory, where the livestock are also housed. The spatial distribution of land-use types within a farm and their relation to settlement and market have, however, become major objects of interest among some geographers in recent years, after a reawakening of interest in the theoretical systems of agricultural location developed initially by Thünen in 1826 (Hall, 1966) and later elaborated by Brinkmann (1935) and others. As with Ricardo, Thünen began with the premise that enterprises and farming systems are in competition for any plot of land, and that choice will go to the enterprise or system yielding the highest net return or rather the highest *rent*. He postulated an isolated state on a featureless, uniform plain, with no connections with the rest of the world, and a single city in the center of the plain. Then, using data obtained from his own estate over a five-year period, he calculated the rent accruing to each of a range of activities, at different distances from the city, and under different systems, taking account of the costs of production and transport and of prevailing market prices. He found that these activities would tend to fall in ordered rings around the city, commonly diminishing outward in intensity of input. There were exceptions, as where there was a large output per unit area despite low production cost, and low value but high transport cost. Such was the case of timber in Thünen's day, and he found this would be located close to the city.

In an extended discussion of distance as a factor affecting land use and settlement, Chisholm (1962, p. 47–49) argued that since a farmstead, hamlet, or village is the point of origin for all input applied on the land it controls, and also the point to or through which all produce from the land is normally brought, then each such unit can be regarded as an "isolated state," and be subjected to analysis of the distribution of activities around this central point. He goes on to glean data widely on yield per plot at varying distances from the farm, and finds quantitative evidence to show that both gross and net product normally decline with distance. Adjustments to the handicap imposed by distance may take the form of reduced intensity in the same enterprise or the substitution of enterprises demanding lower inputs. These same principles seem to apply in both European and African case studies. He writes (p. 71):

> Shifting cultivation displays in an extreme form a principle of widespread importance: while the further lands are unused or under-used, the nearer are exploited beyond the limits they are able to sustain indefinitely. In the case of shifting cultivation, the settlement traditionally moves before the results become serious . . . The point comes when it is worth while to remove the whole household to a new site, since the cost of resettling will be fully compensated by the saving in cultivation costs. Hence, the rational nature of shifting cultivation and the fact that it displays certain characteristics which are readily explicable in terms of location principles.

In Bowers' material, discussed above, we find the main concentration of intensive mounding close to the house sites and in the valley bottom. These sites are far from any wild source of timber for building and firewood; hence perhaps the intermingling in the same area of the less intensively worked mixed gardens, which provide such timber from the managed fallow. Pigs are farther out in the *miscanthus* grasslands upslope but are herded and fed each night in the settlement area. "In some settlement areas, homes and gardens are dense and leading pigs to their grazing grounds takes up much time. Here one sometimes finds the pig owner moving his residence to a more convenient locality, often upslope" (Bowers, 1965, p. 28). Beyond the pig-grazing area is the forest garden belt, at first sight a puzzling location. But a possible indication of the reason is found in Bowers' rather limited data on yields. She obtained a range between 22 and 68 pounds per mound from terrace fields in the valley, with a mean of 43 pounds per mound, i.e. about 9.35 tons per acre, which is probably rather high by New Guinea Highlands standards as a whole. From only a single mound on the forest edge she obtained 76 pounds (personal communication). If this single value were representative we would have an indication that higher soil fertility in these newer gardens raises the "economic rent" in terms of output gained from units of input to a level at which intensive agriculture becomes worthwhile at this distance from the settlement, even though the necessary high fertility is a wasting resource, and agriculture has to move constantly but slowly farther out. Land shortage has, it seems, not yet reached the stage when the Kakoli need to follow other highlanders and garden in the intermediate grassland, where they would obtain lower yields per unit of labor input.

Thünen analysis can thus be meaningfully applied to agricultural distributions in a society far removed in space, time, culture, and technology from the one within which it was conceived. Chisholm has applied this reasoning to De Schlippe's material on the Azande (De Schlippe, 1956, p. 101–16), showing how intensity of land use, here measured in terms of frequency of cultivation, diminishes away from the homestead. Worsley's reassessment (1956) of Fortes' material on the Tallensi shows how the manured ground around homesteads gains in value over the unmanured integument. It begins to become clear that the economic assessment of any technique applied to the manipulation of a given ecosystem, discussed above, will be greatly influenced by the situation of the plot in relation to the place of residence of the operator and to all the other plots under his control.

Viewed from the farm level, the operator's residence is thus the first point of integration in an agricultural system, and where the great bulk of farm produce is consumed on the farm, it is also the most important point of integration. The study of settlement pattern and location is thus intimately linked with the study of the agricultural system. But settlement pattern inquiries had been at a standstill for many years before the revival of interest in Thünen's analysis. It was recognized that there is often a relationship between nucleated settlement and dispersed and fragmented holdings, and between dispersed or homestead settlements and compact holdings, as in much of North America; but while case material has accumulated, successive contributions were left stranded for want of any flowing mainstream of theory which they might join. As Chisholm ably demonstrates, the study of the distance separating field from settlement provides us with a new source for such a mainstream.

But while we may thus regard the settlement as the central point for its distribution of fields, casual observation shows that many settlements are in fact quite eccentric in respect of this distribution. Before this phenomenon can be analyzed and explained, it is necessary first that it be measured. A "central point of a distribution of fields" can be obtained by any one of a variety of measures of which the most meaningful is perhaps the Point of Minimum Aggregate Travel (Hart, 1954). However, this is cumbersome to obtain and, since the mean and median points both have disadvantages, I have experimented with use of the point obtained by the simple formula for resolving the force exerted by a body of particles of varying mass, in this case fields of varying area, into a single force acting through a single point.[2] It is easy to compute, and has the advantage that the fields making up the distribution can readily be weighted according to some such variable as the labor input required under different systems of cultivation. A simple illustration is provided in Figure 1. Application of the method to an interesting case is provided by use of Ward's data on the Fijian wet-zone village of Saliadrau (Ward, 1965, p. 271–77). This small and remote village depends today largely on the growing of *yaqona* (kava) as a cash crop, but also grows taro, cassava, bananas, coconuts, and some yams. Figure 2 provides a visual impression of zonation of crops around the village, with cassava and taro closest, then bananas, and yaqona occupying the most distant gardens. Soils around the village have been heavily used, and cassava is the only root crop that can give satisfactory yields, since no manuring is practiced. Taro and cassava gardens need to be visited frequently; yaqona, which takes five or more years to mature after planting, needs little attention once the crop is sufficiently grown to shade out weeds. Activity has recently moved southward onto the accessible lands of an adjacent village territory, the owning village being remote. The "central point" (C) thus lies about a quarter of a mile south of the village, having probably moved away from the village only recently as a result of the southward migration of cultivation; were this movement to persist, it would become advantageous to relocate the village. Figure 3 shows that the distribution of acreage under different crops (excluding coconuts, three yam gardens, and a few other gardens for which area data are not given) is as a whole closer to the village than to C, but nowadays presents a more regular zonation when viewed from C, the central point, than when viewed from the village itself which is somewhat separated from its main food gardens. This is especially evident when Figure 2 is studied in conjunction with Figure 3, for most of the taro and cassava gardens are now to one side of the village, but around C.

---

2. For a body of particles of mass m_1, m_2 . . . situated at points x_1, y_1 . . . x_2, y_2 . . . with regard to any horizontal and vertical axes, the resultant force always passes $\bar{x}\,\bar{y}$, where $\bar{x} = \dfrac{m_1x_1 + m_2x_2 \ldots}{m_1 + m_2 \ldots}$, and similarly for $\bar{y}$. (From A. H. Short, *Elementary Statics*, Oxford, 1955.)

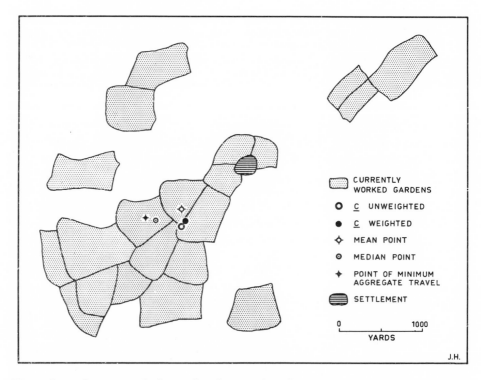

Fig. 1. Central points applied to a distribution of gardens. Data from year One in Figure 4. *C* is the "central point of garden distribution."

The movement of the central point of a field distribution over time in a land-rotational system, or of the central point of fields weighted according to labor in-put, yield, and gross or net returns under any system, is clearly a useful parameter. In Figure 4 is a hypothetical example, inspired perhaps from Africa·rather than Melanesia, in which a village is in the center of a territory divided into permanent plots which, however, are used in rotation over an eleven–twelve year cycle, being cultivated normally for only one or two years. The central point was calculated as above for each date, first treating all gardens as equal (outer ring of points), then giving double weight to those gardens near the village to which manure is carried, which are used more intensively, and hence demand more labor input (inner ring of points). There being a roughly clockwise rotation of cultivation, *C* moves around in this direction and returns to the initial area in the twelfth year. This is, in fact, an unlikely pattern; examination of most actual data shows that where there is a fixed settlement site, fields are normally located at any date on both sides of the settlement, not on only one side as here, so that the central point remains much closer to the settlement site at all dates. A spiraling movement away could reflect increasing spread of farming, a situation likely to lead to

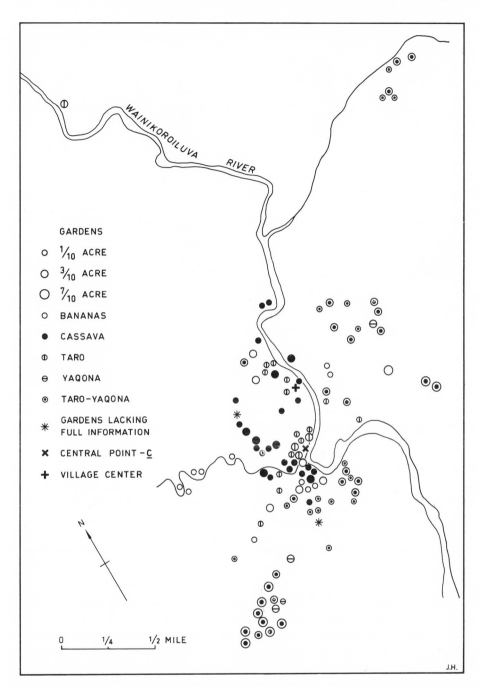

Fig. 2. Gardens by size-class and crop around the village of Saliadrau, Viti Levu, Fiji (data adapted from Ward 1965, p. 271–77).

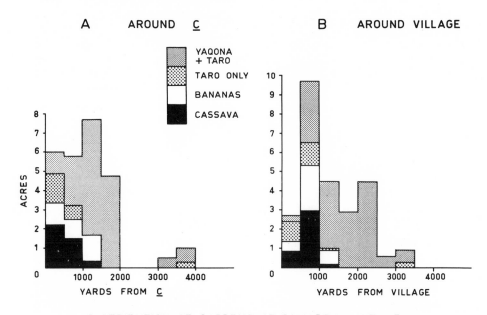

DISTRIBUTION OF GARDENS AT SALIADRAU, VITI LEVU

Fig. 3. Distribution of garden area under different crops around the village center and the central point of garden distribution (C) at Saliadrau, Viti Levu, Fiji (data adapted from Ward, 1965, p. 271–77).

breakup of the settlement, while a spiraling inward could reflect, as here, an increase in the area of intensively used home fields.

Freeman's material (1955) on the Iban of Sarawak is relevant here. When the forest within about a half-mile radius of the longhouse becomes exhausted under a system of rudimentary swidden cultivation, the community breaks up into groups which form temporary settlements farther out, each group farming in a different part of the longhouse territory. After a few years of such dispersal, during which groups frequently migrate, they return to the longhouse for another period of cultivation in the nearby forest. Chisholm, who has examined Freeman's data along with others, notes that the Iban conform to a general pattern; here as elsewhere, when new cultivable land cannot be found within a limiting radius normally between 1 and 2 kilometers, new settlements are normally founded away from the parent village (Chisholm, 1962, p. 146–47).

The problem that faced me in this connection was peculiarly complex. The Chimbu have both dispersed settlement and dispersed landholdings; furthermore, men live in communal houses, while women live in individual houses at a median distance of 220 yards from their husbands, and at a further median distance of 290 yards from their pigs, though in many instances the latter are still to be found in the same house as the women. As noted earlier, the agricultural system is a

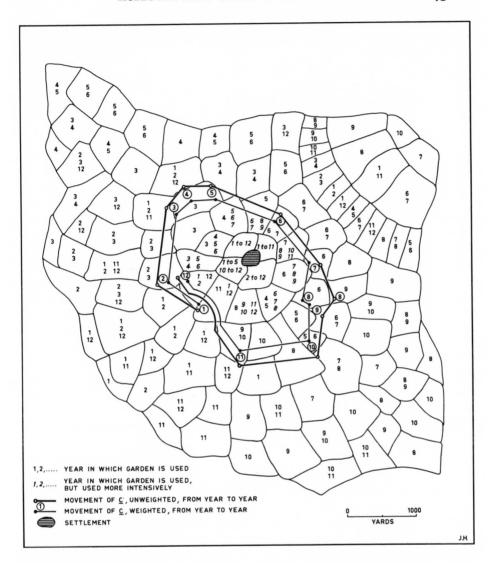

Fig. 4. A hypothetical village and its lands, used under crop–fallow rotation over an 11–12 year cycle, showing the movement of the central point of garden distribution (C) from year to year.

mixed one, but everywhere it includes tillage and field drainage; fallow vegetation is managed on some plots but not on others, and the cultivation–fallow time ratio shows little or no regularity. Settlement shifts; the mean life of a Chimbu house at construction is just under 47 months, but people move more frequently than this. In 1958, among a sample of twenty-six families, 86 per cent of all garden area lay within 1,500 yards of the men, 80 per cent within 1,500 yards of the women. By 1965, perennial coffee had largely replaced food crops in the central area, and gardening had spread more widely; the 1,500-yard values for 1965 corresponding to those for 1958 were only 80 per cent for men and 75 per cent for women. The scatter of Chimbu gardens is very wide, and the plots used by any one cultivator during the eight-year period, covered by surveys at five dates, might often cover a linear distance of more than 5,000 yards.

Central points were calculated for the gardens of a sample of families at each survey date, and residences used by family members at each date were then linked to the relevant positions of C. Figure 5 illustrates the result for four families. I decided at this stage against weighting gardens other than by area, since our surveys have not been designed to provide data on labor input for different garden types and stages. Although in three of these examples the movement of C does recurve back toward the original point near the end of the period, there is little evidence of a clear cycle. In part this may be explained by the shortness of the period, for such elements of land rotation as may be discerned in the Chimbu agricultural system are of very slow movement. More than this, however, the pattern reflects the rather rapid establishment of a coffee belt in the area between 500 yards above and about 1,500 yards below the main road, thus stabilizing a growing portion of the total agricultural activity of each family in this central area.

The central point C rarely lies close to the residence of either husband or wife. Sometimes it falls between them, but more often lies wholly to one side of both. In 1965 the men of the whole sample lived a mean 484 yards (standard deviation 305) from C, while their wives and attached women lived a mean 704 yards (s.d. 356) from C. This reflects the very wide dispersal of gardens. It is, however, apparent that residence does in some instances move in sympathy with movements of C, though over a wider range. By regression analysis, I found in correlating movement of C between dates with movement of residence in the same directional axis that, above 1,440 yards of its movement, C moves approximately 70 yards in the same direction with each 100 yards of residential movement. This regression is significant at the 1 per cent level. The failure to find any correlation between shorter movements corroborates Chisholm's general observation (1962, p. 148):

> Any distance up to about a kilometre from the dwelling is of such little moment for any but specialized farming . . . that little adjustment is called for in either pattern of settlement or land use. Beyond about 1 kilometre, the costs of movement become sufficiently great to warrant some kind of response; at a distance of 3–4 kilometres the costs of cultivation necessitate a radical modification of the system of cultivation or settlement . . . though adjustments are apparent before this point is reached.

Conklin (1957, p. 34) likewise reports from the Hanunóo that "rarely are sites [for swiddens] selected further than a kilometer . . . in 1953 the walking distance from settlement to swidden site ranged from less than 100 to almost

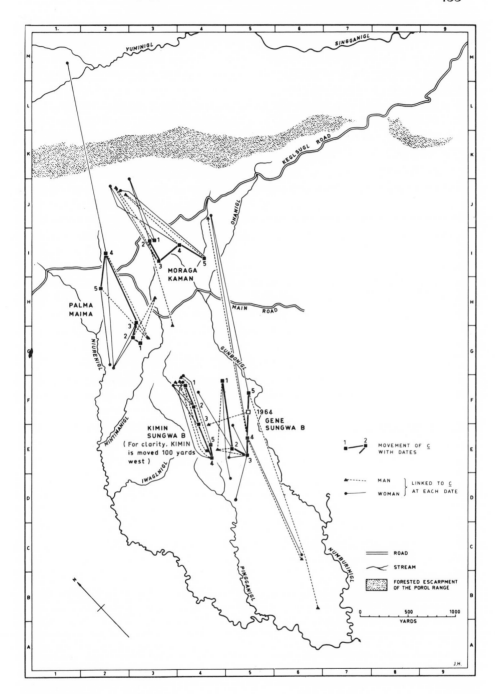

Fig. 5. Movement of the central point of garden distribution (C) in relation to shifts of residence among four families of a sample in central Chimbu, New Guinea, in 1958 (1), 1959 (2), 1962 (3), 1963 (4), and 1965 (5) (data from field survey).

1,200 metres; but in more than 80 per cent of the cases noted, including 1954 and 1955 data, such distances were less than 500 metres." Among the Hanunóo, shifts in residence are on a bilocal system, between the locality of wife's parents and husband's parents; there is nothing like the free-ranging system of the Chimbu, within and among group territories.

In Chimbu, then, we inevitably find ourselves drawn outside the agricultural system to explain shifting residence. In a paper in which the work outlined above is to be briefly reported, Brown and I have suggested ways in which analysis of the total pattern of movements of Chimbu men and women, not only on productive work but also on social and ceremonial activities, might better fit the observed distribution (Brown and Brookfield, forthcoming).

The emphasis on measurements of how time is spent thus becomes more and more dominant. Time is the only valid common measure by which we can quantify labor inputs, traveling distance, leisure time, social and ceremonial intercourse, and political discussion. In viewing the interconnections of the ecological system and the social system, in assessing the impact of changes in social, economic, and natural factors, we are often only making inspired guesses without data on the allocation of time. Yet solid data on this aspect are scanty and inadequate, even from work studies carried out in Europe.

From the tropics two inquiries among several come to mind; particularly interesting is that of Kay, in a Zambian village. Kay provides data (1964, p. 35–75) on the distance of every garden from the village among thirteen households, then analyzes carefully the total working time spent on all activities by the adults of these households over a twelve-month period, including but not distinguishing the travel time. Conklin (1957, p. 149–52) has broken down the work requirements in the rather elaborate swidden system of the Hanunóo according to the various stages, noting variations among the three wild ecosystems in which swiddens may be made, but he does not include traveling time and provides only estimates of the large additional time spent on food preparation and treatment. Few other inquirers have provided so much. A major inquiry recently completed by Waddell and Krinks, however, reports the allocation of time over a period of twenty-six weeks by sampled residents of two villages in the Orokaiva area of Papua. Though agricultural methods are not intensive here, between 25 and 35 hours a week are spent on productive activity, traveling time included but separately recorded (Waddell and Krinks, 1968). Waddell is currently going on to study the ecology of an intensive agricultural system in the western New Guinea Highlands, with careful measurement of time for a small sample of families on all forms of activity, and finds relationships between intensity of input and distance from operator's house. He finds a dispersed settlement pattern with much closer proximity of residence to the intensively cultivated mound fields than we encountered in Chimbu, and he argues that there may be a positive correlation between intensiveness of farming and the field-to-settlement distance, and hence with the dispersal of settlement (E. Waddell, personal communication).

A PROBLEM, A HYPOTHESIS, AND A CONCLUSION

Work at this level by agrarian geographers brings us up against a methodological difficulty. Geographers have been accustomed to working on a wider scale, and we experience some alarm at the increasing restriction in the size of the framework which is imposed by the growing demand for additional data in depth. Chisholm argues that the fallacy of composition applies to the assemblage of detailed studies to build up an increasingly accurate picture of the geography of wider regions, and hence of the whole world. Writing specifically of studies aimed at the classification of farming types, but with wider implications, he maintains: "The smaller the area studied, the more painstaking the research has to be and the less useful the results for wider generalization. There seems to be a rapid progression along the curve of diminishing returns" (Chisholm, 1964, p. 101). In reply I would argue that he and the many others of like mind are completely missing the point. If we adopt the view that our problem is the analysis of systems, it is inescapable that we will formulate hypotheses on how these systems operate, and equally inescapable that they must then be tested in carefully chosen laboratory locations in the field where they must then be explored in as much depth as is necessary.

Such considerations apply to an important hypothesis advanced by Geertz, who draws a sharp distinction between the two extreme contrasts in manipulated ecosystems found in Indonesia. Swidden, or shifting cultivation *sensu stricto,* is in very precarious ecological equilibrium, while *sawah,* the wet-rice *padi* ecosystem, is extraordinarily stable. This characteristic gives the latter an enormously inflatable capacity to support rising population on the same land area. Population pressure "can reach a height limited only by the capacity of those who exploit it to subsist on steadily diminishing per capita returns for their labour. Where swidden 'overpopulation' results in a deterioration of the habitat, in a wet-rice regime it results in the support of an ever-increasing number of people within an undamaged habitat" (Geertz, 1963, p. 33). Geertz is offering us a lesson from simple economics: if we can draw up productivity schedules for swidden and *sawah,* we will find for a constant unit of land that both average and marginal physical productivity of labor will decline very steeply to and beyond zero under swidden, but only very gradually indeed toward zero under *sawah.* His argument would suggest that in the densely peopled areas of east-central Javà, both average and marginal productivity have long since passed their peak, but that while marginal productivity may now be very low, average productivity is still sufficient to support the population depending on any given area at a near-minimal level of subsistence. That is to say, the economy still retains a small measure of elasticity in its demand for labor, and he further seems to argue that demand for land in all but extreme cases is even now less elastic than the demand for labor. Agriculturalists using the fragile swidden ecosystem, on the other hand, will soon obtain only negative increments of product in return for additional inputs of labor, and for them an increase in the supply of land is the only means within the system by which production can keep pace with rising demand.

Geertz is undoubtedly simplifying, but he seems to be inviting us to draw up productivity schedules from the accumulating field evidence with which to test his hypothesis. It may then be proper to extend the hypothesis and to ask whether agricultural systems cannot first be ranked according to some scale of ecosystem stability, then examined to see how average and marginal productivity of labor decline with increasing labor input in systems of varying stability, and what are the relative elasticities of the demand curves for labor and for land with variations in output. This too is gross oversimplification, and some economists, Higgins (1959) for example, have been exploring the concept of the margin in less developed societies for some years. Data have not been collected in the form most suited for such inquiry nor have agricultural systems been broken down descriptively in a form suitable for this kind of analysis, but Geertz' hypothesis seems to provide us with the opening toward a more meaningful study of the interrelationship of resources, their use, and population than has been possible in the past.

A final consequence of adopting systems analysis in agrarian studies is the fuller realization that change in any one part of the whole system brings about changes throughout the system. In the case of major transformations this is strikingly obvious. Sauer's recent study of the first twenty-seven years of the Spanish irruption in to the Caribbean demonstrates, *inter alia,* the manner in which the well-adapted pre-1492 agricultural ecosystems were so disrupted by a few years of Spanish depredations and demands for tribute and forced labor that the people vanished and their land was repossessed by a wild growth of tropical vegetation (Sauer, 1966). Less dramatic, and dependent rather more on *a priori* reasoning than on solid evidence, is Watson's speculative paper (1965) on the demographic, social, and cultural consequences of the still undated introduction of the sweet potato into the agriculture of the New Guinea Highlands. But it can also be shown that such lesser changes as the enforced adoption of a new settlement pattern, the crystallization by law of a formerly fluid and adaptable system of land tenure, and the introduction of a higher-yielding variety of an existing crop and of new and improved tools can have effects that spread through the whole ecosystem from the soil to social customs. Such is the manner in which we might study the effects of introducing a cash economy in its several aspects—wage labor, changes in diet, new cash crops, new agricultural techniques, marketing, and the development of a network of routes and central places through which local economies are integrated into wider economies. Work in this field, by economists as well as by anthropologists and geographers, has so far been concerned mainly with aspects of the problem; analysis of changes in the whole system, at whatever scale of inquiry, is only now really beginning.

I thus return to where I began, to Simmons' demand for a union of economics with ecology in land-use studies, to my appeal for an orderly description of agricultural systems under categories that are capable of cross-cultural comparison and quantification in terms of units of input of the factors of production, to the theoretical advantages flowing from an adoption of systems analysis as the overriding problem, and to the convergence of thinking among workers from different disciplines. The problem is challenging, for the analysis of any system may take us across a whole disciplinary spectrum from botany to economics, but this is being faced up to by a growing number of workers. This convergence is the most exciting aspect of the ecological and quantitative revolutions that are going on in some of the social sciences; by means of it, enormous new fields are being opened up to investigation.

Acknowledgments. Grateful thanks are due to Mr. J. Heyward who drew the figures, to Mrs. D. Hart who carried out much of the data analysis used and referred to, to Dr. Paula Glick (formerly Brown) who shared with me much of the data collection and organization in Chimbu, to my wife who nudged me toward the quantitative revolution, and last but not least to present and former students from whose work and conversation flowed many ideas here expressed. Responsibility for the use and misuse of these, however, remains my own.

ADDENDUM

Since this paper was completed an important new work has been added to the literature on tropical agricultural systems (Spencer, 1966). While it is not now possible to amend the body of the paper to take account of this publication, particular mention should be made of the discussion of technologies, tools, and typologies (p. 136–65) and of the list of diagnostic criteria significant to an analysis of shifting cultivation (p. 181–86) where Spencer's argument is not dissimilar from that of my briefer presentation here. Though I would disagree with Spencer on some matters of definition and interpretation, the whole tenor of his book comes closer to what I am here seeking than anything in the previous literature.

REFERENCES

Ackerman, E. A., 1963. Where is a research frontier? *Ann. Assoc. Am. Geographers*, 53: 429–40.

Allan, W., 1949. Studies in African land use in Northern Rhodesia. *Rhodes-Livingstone Papers*, 15.

——, 1965. *The African Husbandman*. Oliver & Boyd, Edinburgh.'

Baer, J. G., 1965. Teaching about natural resources and conservation patterns. *Nature and Resources*, 1: 9–14.

Barrau, J., 1956. *L'Agriculture vivrière autochthone de la Nouvelle-Calédonie*. Nouméa. Commission du Pacifique-sud.

——, 1958. Subsistence agriculture in Melanesia. *B. P. Bishop Mus. Bull.*, 219, Honolulu.

Biebuyck, D., 1963. Introduction. In *African Agrarian Systems*, ed. Ɖ. Biebuyck. International African Institute, London, p. 1–64.

Blaut, J. M., 1959. The ecology of tropical farming systems. In *Plantation Systems of the New World*: Papers and discussion summaries of the seminar held in San Juan, Puerto Rico. Pan-American Union, Washington, p. 83–103.

Bowers, N., 1965. "Agricultural practices and successional vegetation in the upper Kaugel valley, Western Highlands, Australian New Guinea." (Mimeo.).

Brinkmann, T., 1935. Theodor Brinkmann's economics of the farm business. *From* Die Oekonomik des Landwirtschaftlichen Betriebes, in v. 7 of *Grundriss der Sozialoekonomik*, Tübingen, 1922. (Trans. by E. T. Benedict, Univ. of California, Berkeley).

Brookfield, H. C., 1962. Local study and comparative method: An example from central New Guinea, *Ann. Assoc. Am. Geographers, 52*: 242–54.

——, 1964. Questions on the human frontiers of geography. *Econ. Geog., 40*: 283–303.

Brookfield, H. C., and P. Brown, 1963. *Struggle for Land: Agriculture and Group Territories among the Chimbu of the New Guinea highlands.* Oxford Univ. Press, Melbourne.

Brown, P. and H. C. Brookfield, 1967. *Chimbu Residence and Settlement: A Study of Cycles, Trends and Idiosyncracies. Pacific Viewpoint, 8:* 119–51.

Bureau of Statistics, Papua and New Guinea, 1963. Survey of Indigenous Agriculture and Ancillary Surveys. Gov. print., Konedobu.

Chisholm, M., 1962. *Rural Settlement and Land Use: An Essay in Location.* Hutchinson, London.

——, 1964. Problems in the classification of farming-type regions. *Institute of Brit. Geographers, Transactions, 35:* 91–104.

Colson, E., 1966. Land law and land holdings among the valley Tonga of Zambia. *Southwestern J. Anthropol., 22:* 1–8.

Conklin, H. C., 1954. An ethnoecological approach to shifting cultivation. *Trans. N.Y. Acad. Sci., 17:* 133–42.

——, 1957. Hanunóo Agriculture: A report on an Integral System of Shifting Cultivation in the Philippines. FAO, Forestry Development Paper, 12.

——, 1961. The study of shifting cultivation. *Curr. Anthropol. 1:* 27–61.

Crocombe, R. G., 1964. *Land tenure in the Cook Islands.* Oxford Univ. Press, Melbourne.

DeSchlippe, P., 1956. *Shifting Cultivation in Africa: The Zande System of Agriculture.* Routledge & Kegan Paul, London.

Fosberg, F. R., 1963. The island ecosystem. In *Man's Place in the Island Ecosystem,* F. R. Fosberg, ed. Bishop Mus. Press, Honolulu, p. 1–6.

Frake, C. O., 1962. Cultural ecology and ethnography. *Am. Anthropologist, 64:* 53–59.

Freeman, J. D., 1955. *Iban Agriculture: A Report on Shifting Cultivation of Hill Rice by the Iban of Sarawak.* Colonial Office, United Kingdom. Colonial Research Studies, 18.

Geertz, C., 1963. *Agricultural Involution: The Process of Ecological Change in Indonesia.* Univ. of California Press, Berkeley and Los Angeles.

Geiger, R., 1965. *The Climate Near the Ground,* revised ed. Harvard Univ. Press, Cambridge.

Gluckman, M., 1941. *Economy of the Central Barotse Plain.* Rhodes-Livingstone Papers, 7.

Hall, P., 1966. Von Thünen's Isolated State. English ed. of *Der isolierte Staat,* (with an introduction). Pergamon Press, Oxford.

Hart, J. F., 1954. Central tendency in areal distribution. *Econ. Geog., 30:* 48–59.

Higgins, B., 1959. *Economic Development: Principles, Problems and Policies.* Constable, London.

International Geographical Union: Commission for Agricultural Typology, 1966. "Principles, basic notions and criteria of agricultural typology: Discussion of the Commission questionnaire No. 1. Warsaw (mimeo.).

Kay, G., 1964. *Chief Kalaba's Village: A Preliminary Survey of Economic Life in an Ushi Village, Northern Rhodesia*. Rhodès—Livingstone Papers, 35.

Kostrowicki, J., 1965. Land utilization; Case studies; origins, aims, methods, techniques. In *Land Utilization in East-Central Europe: Case Studies*, J. Kostrowicki, ed. Geographia Polonica, 5. Wydawnictwa Geologiczne. Warsaw.

Lea, D. A. M., 1964. "Abelam land and sustenance: Swidden horticulture in an area of high population density, Maprik, New Guinea." Ph.D. thesis, Australian National Univ., Canberra.

——, 1965. The Abelam: A case study in local differentiation. *Pacific Viewpoint, 6:* 191–214.

——, 1966. "A Report on the Wosera Resettlement Scheme." (Mimeo.).

Leach, E. R., 1961. *Pul Eliya: A village in Ceylon*. Univ. Press, Cambridge.

Meggitt, M. J., 1958. The Enga of New Guinea: Some preliminary considerations. *Oceania, 28:* 253–330.

——, 1965. *The Lineage System of the Mae-Enga of New Guinea*. Oliver & Boyd, Edinburgh and London.

Nye, P. H., and D. J. Greenland, 1960. *The Soil under Shifting Cultivation*. Commonwealth Bureau of Soils. Harpenden. Tech. Comm., 51.

Ormeling, F. J., 1956. *The Timor Problem*. Wolters, Djakarta and The Hague.

Popenoe, H., 1959. The influence of the shifting cultivation cycle on soil properties in Central America. *Proc. Ninth Pacific Science Congress 7 (Conservation)*, p. 72–77.

Sauer, C. O., 1966. *The Early Spanish Main*. Univ. California Press, Berkeley and Los Angeles.

Scudder, T., 1962. *The Ecology of the Gwembe Tonga*. Kariba Studies, 2. Univ. Press, Manchester.

Simmons, I. G., 1966. Ecology and land use. *Institute of Brit. Geographers. Transac., 38:* 59–72.

Spate, O. H. K., 1953. "The compass of geography: An inaugural lecture." Australian National Univ., Canberra.

Spencer, J. E., 1966. Shifting cultivation in southeastern Asia. *Univ. Calif. Publ. in Geogr., 19*, Berkeley and Los Angeles.

Steward, J., 1955. *Theory of Culture Change*. Univ. Illinois Press, Urbana.

Stoddart, D. R., 1965. Geography and the ecological approach: The ecosystem as a geographical principle and method. *Geography* [U.K.], *50:* 242–51.

Veldkamp, F., 1958, MS. "Nota over de Baliem-Vallei." Hollandia [Sukarnopura].

Waddell, E. W., and P. A. Krinks, 1968. The organization of production and distribution among the Orokaiva. *New Guinea Research Bulletin, 21.*

Ward, R. G., 1965. *Land Use and Population in Fiji: A Geographical Study*. United Kingdom Dept. of Technical Co-operation. Overseas Research Publication, 9.

Watson, J. B., 1965. The significance of a recent ecological change in the central highlands of New Guinea. *J. Polynes. Soc., 74:* 438–50.

West, R. C., 1957. *The Pacific Lowlands of Colombia*. Louisiana State University Studies. Social Science Series, 8.

Worsley, P. M., 1956. The kinship system of the Tallensi: A revaluation. *J. Roy. Anthropol. Inst., 86:* 37–76.

Index

New York State, Lower Devonian of, 246, 247, 250

New Zealand, 391; Ordovician faunas of, 154

Newell, N. D., 232, 233, 234, 235, 236, 237, 248, 258

Newland limestone, 16, 31

Niche: definition of, 325–26; evolutionary theory of, 325–40; fundamental and realized, 325; optimal, 331

Niche breadth, 325; of *Drosophila* species, 326–27; and environmental uncertainty, 328; and environmental variability, 330; and habitat selection, 334, 336; and intrapopulation selection, 334; limits to, 338; measurement of, 327; and polymorphism, 332

Niche overlap, 181, 325

Nicolaysen, L. O., 14, 68

Niel, C. B. van, 10, 11, 16; with Stanier, R. Y., 71

Nier, A. O., with Goldich, S. S., et al., 12, 65

Nijenhuis, L. E., 366, 368

Nikitin, P. A., 106

Nipa, 127; sp., 130

Nipissing Diabase, 11

Nirenberg, M. W., 6, 68

Nishiyama, I., 388, 389, 411

Noakes, L. C., 33, 68

Noble gases, 4

Nomoto, M., with Yanagisawa, K., et al., 300, 306, 319, 324

Noncircadian rhythms, 290, 292

Norris, K. S., 297, 299, 300, 301, 305, 315, 321, 323

North America: diversity of mammals in, 178–79; Ordovician faunas of, 150–51, 152

North-south gradient in diversity distribution, 186–87

Northcutt, R. G., 269, 270, 273, 275, 277

Nothia, 79

Nuclear membrane, 11, 16

Nucleic acids, 6, 7, 58, 59

Nucleotides, 6, 59, 60

Nucleus, 60

Nursall, J. R., 17, 47, 51, 69

Nutrient control, 418

Nye, P. H., 420, 439

Obolella, 27, 31, 52, 53

Obolus sp., 31

Obrhel, J., 75, 102, 106

Ocean currents, 193

Oceanic swells, 243

Odontocete acoustic mechanisms, evolution of, 297–321

Odontocetes: air sacs, 301; bulla, 313, 317; click noises, 321; forehead, 300, 320; fossil record of, 297; head structures, 298; loss of sense of smell, 320; lower jaw of, 300, 308–13; the mesorostral cartilage and canal, 319, 320; origin of, 302–04; the premaxillary and maxillary bones, 319; sound generation, 299; surface angles of, 316; telescoping of skull, 306. *See also* Cetacean

Ogishke conglomerate, 10

Ogygopsis-like trilobite, 23

Okulitch, V. J., 146, 162

Olds, W. E., Jr., 219

Olenellids, 23, 37

Olenellus, 37

Olfaction, 269

Olfactory sense in odontocetes, loss of, 320

Olson, E. C., 252, 255, 256, 258, 270, 277

Ontario: Huronian rocks in, 31; iron ores, 14

Onverwacht Series, 10

Oosthuizen, M. J., 262, 277

Ooststroom, S. J. van, 388, 389, 411

Oparin, A. I., 6, 69

Ophidia. *See* Snakes

Optimal niche, 331

Optimum level of expression, 341

Orcinus orca, 299

Ord Group, 29

Ordovician: Antarctica faunas, 158–59; biogeography of seas, 139–62; climatic belts, 143; distribution of faunas, 142; earth axis, 143; equator, 143; faunal provinces, 141; interpretation of biogeography, 144; paleoecology of seas, 139–62; regional biogeography, 150–62; regional faunas of marine provinces, 150–62; sea salinity, 150; sea temperatures, 149

Organelles, 11, 16, 43

Organic abundance, 236

Organic materials, nonvital production, 8

Organic reworking of sediments, 243

Organisms as environmental modifiers, 239–41

Origin of life, polyphyletic vs. monophyletic, 9. *See also* Life on earth

Oriskany sandstone, 246

Ormeling, F. J., 416, 439